A HANDBOOK OF
SOCIAL PSYCHOLOGY

A HANDBOOK OF
SOCIAL PSYCHOLOGY

By

W. C. Allee

Gordon W. Allport

Friedrich Alverdes

R. E. Buchanan

Frederic E. Clements

J. F. Dashiell

Erwin A. Esper

Herbert Friedmann

Edwin Deeks Harvey

Melville J. Herskovits

Catharine Cox Miles

Walter R. Miles

Gardner Murphy

Lois Barclay Murphy

O. E. Plath

Thorleif Schjelderup-Ebbe

Victor E. Shelford

Warren S. Thompson

W. D. Wallis

F. L. Wells

Raymond Royce Willoughby

Clark Wissler

Ada W. Yerkes

Robert M. Yerkes

Edited by

CARL MURCHISON

VOLUME ONE

NEW YORK / RUSSELL & RUSSELL

PRINTED IN THE UNITED STATES OF AMERICA

PREFACE

This is the initial attempt to organize a representative cross-section of serious methods of investigating social mechanisms. It is not for us to say which ones of these methods gain in dignity and effectiveness through this contrast and which ones droop by comparison. The critics will point those things out, for which blessing we are already truly grateful.

The social sciences at the present moment stand naked and feeble in the midst of the political uncertainty of the world. The physical sciences seem so brilliant, so clothed with power by contrast. Either something has gone all wrong in the evolution of the social sciences, or their great day in court has not yet arrived. It is with something akin to despair that one contemplates the piffling, trivial, superficial, damnably unimportant topics that some social scientists investigate with agony and sweat. And at the end of all these centuries, no one knows what is wrong with the world or what is likely to happen to the world.

It is to be hoped that this book may be useful in helping serious students to reflect concerning the problems of social mechanics that are basic enough to require identification and analysis before progress can even begin in this field. Whatever those mechanisms may be, they are certain to be essential components of all social behavior in all social bodies in all social situations whatever. The social scientist must discover those mechanisms, or there will never be a social law and the assurance will not be great that human society is permanent.

It is to be regretted that the interesting work in the Clark laboratories on the experimental measurement of social hierarchies in animals is not developed far enough for inclusion in this book.

I acknowledge with gratitude the important work done by Dr. Luberta Harden in preparing these manuscripts for the printer and in making the indices.

CARL MURCHISON

CLARK UNIVERSITY
WORCESTER, MASSACHUSETTS
January 17, 1935

[IX]

TABLE OF CONTENTS

[XI]

PART I

SOCIAL PHENOMENA IN SELECTED POPULATIONS

CHAPTER 1

POPULATION BEHAVIOR OF BACTERIA

R. E. BUCHANAN

Iowa State College

A review of the behavior of populations of bacteria must perforce combine consideration of bacterial genetics and of bacterial physiology. The hereditary complex of a cell determines the possible responses to environmental stimuli; in fact, heredity may be defined as the ability transmitted from parent to offspring to respond in a particular manner to a fixed set of environmental conditions. Physiology is the study of all of the interreactions between living cells on the one hand and the cell environment on the other. It includes the interrelationships between component cell parts and their intracellular environment, the interrelationships between the cell and the extracellular environment, and the interrelationships between masses or colonies of cells (including tissues of multicellular forms) and their intercellular and extracellular environment. It must constantly be borne in mind that the cell response is conditioned not only by the immediate environment of the moment, but by previous environments as well. Population behavior (or behavior of any kind) among bacteria is determined by the hereditary potentialities, by the past experiences and environments, and by the character of the immediate environment. It is the purpose of this chapter to review briefly the relationships of these factors to behavior of bacteria, emphasizing as far as possible their behavior en masse rather than as individual cells.

It is obvious, however, that any behavior of a population of bacteria must be dependent upon the behavior of the individual units of which it is composed. It is necessary therefore in this case to study the responses and behavior of the single bacterial cell, then to note the resulting behavior of populations of such cells. Furthermore, it is desirable to delimit the group bacteria, and to characterize the bacterial cell.

The *bacteria* constitute a group of ubiquitous minute unicellular plants, some forms showing certain resemblances to the protozoa and perhaps intergrading with them. It is not improbable that the bacteria are polyphyletic, for there are certain groups which show marked resemblances to the blue-green algae, others intergrade with the true algae, others with the yeasts, and still others with the filamentous fungi, particularly the Hyphomycetes.

A "typical" bacterial cell is one which is minute, perhaps one-half to two microns in diameter, spherical or elongate; if the latter, from one to five microns in length. There may, of course, be considerable departures from these sizes. The protoplasm of the cell is surrounded by a cell wall which is usually relatively firm, though in some forms the cell may be flexuous. The cell membrane is usually thin, though occasionally greatly

[3]

thickened by an external layer of gummy or mucinous material constituting a *capsule*. The cell may be either non-motile or motile. The motile bacterial cells usually swim by means of slender protoplasmic protrusions termed flagella. These may be single or numerous. If single or few in number, the flagella are usually situated at one end of the cell; if numerous, they may be distributed over the entire cell surface. In one group (the spirochetes) the entire cell is flexuous, there are no flagella and the cells swim about by rapid flexing movements of the entire cell which is usually quite elongate and relatively slender. In still a third group (the myxobacteria) the cell exhibits a gliding motion; apparently the cell excretes a slime asymmetrically in such fashion that the cell is pushed along. The protoplasm of the bacterial cell may appear homogeneous when viewed under the microscope, or it may be vacuolate or granular. In general it is not possible to make out a distinct nucleus, though in some forms (as the myxobacteria) one has béen described. It is probable that nucleoplasm is present, however, and there is no reason to predicate a cell structure different in any marked degree from that found in many of the simple thread fungi. The cells may be entirely free, or they may be united into groups or colonies, bound together usually by a capsular material. The bacterial cell is among the most simple cells of the plant or animal kingdom, but this by no means indicates a necessarily simple chemical constitution or a simple type of metabolism. Chemically bacteria seem to be as complex as the cells of the higher plants and animals, and the metabolic changes which they can produce are of the most varied and complex nature. It is not to be anticipated, therefore, that because the bacteria are frequently referred to as "primitive" and "simple" their reactions and relationships are *a priori* simpler than those of cells of "higher" forms of plants and animals. Chemically they are complex, containing proteins, fats, lipoids, waxes, nucleic acids, carbohydrates, chitin, nucleoproteins. Bacteria have powers of synthesis quite beyond that of cells of most higher forms. Enzymes of the most varied character are known to be produced. Among the bacteria may be found those which are capable of synthesis of carbon compounds from carbon dioxide through energy secured from light (true photosynthesis) or from the oxidation of inorganic substances (chemosynthesis, as by oxidation of free sulphur to sulphuric acid). It is evident that "population behavior" of bacteria is determined by a great variety of hereditary potentialities, and the responses likewise by a great variety of environmental conditions. Notwithstanding this complexity, there are certain types of cell behavior (and population behavior) that can be best studied perhaps by use of the bacterial cell.

RATES OF CHANGE IN BACTERIAL POPULATIONS AS RELATED TO ENVIRONMENT

Bacterial populations are constantly changing in size, sometimes the numbers are increasing, sometimes decreasing. The rates at which these increases and decreases take place are markedly influenced by environment and constitute one of the best of criteria of effect of environment. It is understood that methods are at hand for making sufficiently accurate estimates of bacterial population from time to time. It will be convenient to consider first the interrelationships of environment and rates of increase, to be followed by similar discussion of rates of decrease.

RATES OF INCREASE OF BACTERIAL POPULATIONS

Bacteria may multiply in several different ways, most frequently, however, by an increase in the cell size followed by a simple splitting or fission (hence the class name of the bacteria, Schizomycetes, or fission fungi). For preliminary discussion it may be assumed that one has for experimental study a pure genetic strain (pure culture) of the organisms in an environment suitable to the growth and multiplication of the cells. The population changes may be profitably considered under three headings: (*a*) rates of increase in a uniform environment; (*b*) rates of increase in modified controlled environments; and (*c*) rates of increase in an environment modified progressively as a result of the growth and increase in the cells.

RATES OF INCREASE IN A UNIFORM ENVIRONMENT

Two criteria of rates of increase are commonly used in studies of rates of increase of bacteria, namely, the *generation time* and the *rate of increase per cell* (velocity coefficient of the rate of growth).

The generation time in a bacterial culture is the average time which elapses between the completion of one fission to the completion of a second, that is, the time required by a cell to grow to its full size and divide to form two daughter cells. The following symbols will be used:

t = Time
B = No. of bacterial cells at zero time
b = No. of bacterial cells after time t
g = Length of a generation period (expressed in same units as t)
n = No. of generations in time t.

It is evident that if the initial seeding of the medium (substrate) is with a single cell, after the lapse of one generation period there will be two cells, each of these will divide in the next generation, giving rise to four, these in turn to eight, etc. The following tabulation gives the results for several generations:

No. of bacteria

Initial seeding	1st generation period $n=1$	2nd generation period $n=2$	3rd $n=3$	4th $n=4$	n $n=n$
$1=2^0$	$2=2^1$	$4=2^2$	$8=2^3$	$16=2^4$	$=2^n$
$b=B2^0$	$B2^1$	$B2^2$	$B2^3$	$B2^4$	$B2^n$

or

$$b = B2^n \qquad [1]$$

However, since $n = \dfrac{t}{g}$, the expression may be written

$$b = B2^{t/g}$$

Solving for generation time (g)

$$g = \dfrac{t \log 2}{\log b - \log B} \qquad [2]$$

The fundamental assumptions must be borne in mind, that the cells are being maintained in an unchanging environment, and that they divide with clock-like regularity. There is a very close approximation to these conditions in young cultures of bacteria, but the rate of multiplication is frequently so rapid that the environment of the cells does not remain sufficiently constant for more than a few hours. A determination of the constancy of the generation time may be made readily by use of a characteristic of equation 2. This may be written

$$\log b = \dfrac{\log 2}{g} t + \log B = \dfrac{0.3t}{g} + \log B \qquad [3]$$

Equation 3 is in the form of an equation of a straight line, hence a graph of the logarithms of the numbers of bacteria against time is a straight line, with slope $\dfrac{0.3}{g}$ and with the intercept on the y axis at $\log B$. It is evident that this relationship holds whenever in a culture the value of g is constant. An organism showing this constancy of g is said to be in its *logarithmic phase* of growth.

It was noted above that in addition to g (generation time) a second criterion of rate of change in bacterial population is frequently used, the rate of increase per cell (velocity coefficient of the rate of increase). From the preceding discussion it is clear that the rate at which a bacterial population in the logarithmic growth phase increases is proportional to the number of cells present, hence

$$\dfrac{db}{dt} \propto b \text{ and } \dfrac{db}{dt} = kb \qquad [4]$$

in which k is the proportionality constant. It may be defined by rearranging equation 4

$$k = \dfrac{\dfrac{db}{dt}}{b}$$

that is, k is the rate of change in numbers of cells per unit (cell), or rate of increase per cell (velocity constant).

Integration of 4 gives

$$b = B^{kt} \qquad [5]$$

or

$$k = \frac{\ln b - \ln B}{t} = \frac{1}{t} \ln \frac{b}{B} = \frac{2.3}{t} \log \frac{b}{B} \qquad [6]$$

also

$$\ln b = kt + \ln b \qquad [7]$$

Here it is evident that a graph of the natural logarithms of the numbers of bacteria against time gives a straight line of which the slope is k, the rate of growth per cell.

Whenever two counts are made at suitable intervals during logarithmic increase in a population of bacteria one may readily secure values for either g (generation time) or k (velocity constant). These values may be used for determining differences in the hereditary potentialities of different strains or species of bacteria kept under the same conditions, or of the effect of varying the environment upon the rates of change in bacterial population of a particular strain or species.

RATES OF INCREASE IN MODIFIED CONTROLLED ENVIRONMENTS

Numerous environmental factors have been studied in an effort to determine the effect of each upon rates of increase in bacterial population. In general these can be classified under the headings of "physical" and "chemical" stimuli. Of particular importance among the physical environmental factors are temperature and radiant energy.

In general an increase in temperature increases the rate of chemical reactions. The growth and multiplication of cells, the increase in a bacterial population, are the resultant of a chain of chemical reactions, each of which is speeded up by an increase in temperature. Within certain well-defined limits an increase in temperature will increase the rate of growth in a bacterial population.

A criterion frequently used for measuring temperature effects is the ratio between rates of increase per cell (velocity constants) or between generation times determined at suitable temperature intervals. This ratio is termed the temperature quotient ($Q_{\Delta t}$). Most commonly the temperature interval of 10° C is chosen ($Q_{10°}$). Inasmuch as the velocity coefficient of the rate of increase is inversely proportional to the generation time

$$\frac{k_2}{k_1} = Q_{\Delta t} \text{ and } \frac{g_1}{g_2} = Q_{\Delta t}$$

where k_2 and k_1 and g_1 and g_2 represent velocity coefficients and generation times at the higher temperature and lower temperatures respectively.

It is a common experience in chemistry when working with reactions in temperature ranges suitable for life processes in organisms to find that a temperature increase of 10° C is accompanied by a two- to three-fold increase in the velocity constant of the rate of the reaction. A similar effect is commonly to be noted on increase of bacterial populations. In certain temperature ranges the generation time is decreased from one-half to one-third by the ten-degree rise in temperature. This rule has many exceptions, but has so frequently been observed that there are numerous references in the biological literature to the so-called R.G.T. rule.[1]

Experience likewise teaches that this rule can have but limited application to living things, for if applicable in all temperature ranges it would mean that as the temperature of a bacterial culture is increased the rate of increase in number of cells produced in a unit of time would increase geometrically. We know as a matter of observation that for bacteria such a temperature relation may occur over a limited temperature range, but undue increase leads to a decreased acceleration, and at higher temperatures to decreased growth rates and finally to cessation of growth. That temperature which gives the minimum generation time (highest velocity constant of growth) is often termed the "optimum temperature."[2] Temperatures higher than this show decreasing growth rates, and finally at some rather definite temperature for a particular environment the cells cease multiplying. The highest temperature at which growth occurs is termed the "maximum growth temperature."

It is quite evident therefore that temperature quotients for bacterial increases must decrease as the temperature approaches the optimum, become fractional at supra-optimal temperatures, and zero at the maximum growth temperature. Nevertheless in certain sub-optimal temperature ranges the R.G.T. rule holds reasonably closely.

The chemist has shown that for chemical reactions in temperature ranges through which the so-called heat of activation remains constant the temperature quotient decreases with rise in temperature. The law governing the change in rate of reaction with change in temperature has been formulated into the van't Hoff–Arrhenius equation, which states that the rate of change in the logarithm of the velocity coefficient with change in temperature is inversely proportional to the square of the absolute temperature. For each type of reaction, therefore, there may be deter-

---

[1] R.G.T. = from *Reaktionsgeschwindigkeit Temperatur.*

[2] It should be noted that the term "optimum temperature" may be defined in a variety of ways, depending upon the criterion used. As here defined the criterion is rate of cell increase. Another frequently used is the crop yield, i.e., the total number or mass of cells produced in a culture medium. In some cases we are interested in rates at which various products of metabolism (such as alcohol or lactic acid) are formed in a culture of the organism. It may be shown that the same temperature is not always optimum as measured by these various criteria.

mined a constant which is characteristic of the reaction. In its biological form the relationship may be written

$$k_2 = k_1 \epsilon^{\frac{\mu}{2} \frac{(T_2 - T_1)}{T_1 T_2}}$$

in which μ represents the heat of activation (or thermal increment), k^2 and k_1 the velocity constants at absolute temperatures T_2 and T_1. Inasmuch as velocity constants of rates of bacterial increase have also been shown to decrease with rise in temperature, the applicability of the van't Hoff–Arrhenius equation to this phenomenon has been frequently suggested. That it should be applicable has been particularly urged by Crozier and his school on the basis that a phenomenon such as growth (resulting in cell increase) must be due to an ordered catenary sequence of chemical reactions, each reaction in the chain using as substrate the products of the preceding reaction and supplying in turn the substrate for the succeeding reaction. As pointed out by Blackman and others, the rate of the final reaction in the chain will be controlled by the rate of the slowest reaction in the chain. Applied specifically to rates of increase in bacterial populations, one might assume that such rates would be governed by the slowest rates in the chain determining the growth of the individual cells. Further, changes in temperature would change a rate of increase primarily by changing the rate of this slowest component. The assumption may be tested by taking advantage of a characteristic of the relationship between the values of the velocity coefficients of the growth rates and absolute temperature. The van't Hoff–Arrhenius equation indicates that the logarithms of the velocity coefficients graphed against the reciprocals of the absolute temperatures should yield a straight line the slope of which is proportional to the value of μ. Studies of increases of bacterial populations by this means show that in many cases and over suitable temperature ranges the straight-line relationship holds.

It is self-evident, however, that such a simple relationship cannot hold over wide ranges of temperatures. The existence of an optimum temperature range requires that over such a range the value of the temperature quotient shall be unity and the value of μ shall be 0. Crozier and others have suggested that in different temperature ranges different fundamental reactions may step into position as controlling factors in the catenary series of reactions. In other words, through one temperature range one reaction with its characteristic value of μ may dominate, through another range a different reaction may be the slowest and in turn dominate the final result. It is argued that if this is the case the log k–temperature reciprocal graph should show a series of straight lines, the positions of the intersections indicating the temperatures (so-called critical temperatures) at which one dominating reaction gives way to another. It has been suggested by some authors that the slope of these lines (values of μ) give one an insight into the fundamental character of the reaction on the assumption that certain values of μ indicate perhaps an oxidative change, another value an hydrolysis, etc. In some cases such abrupt changes in the direction of the lines have been demonstrated, and this technique heralded as giving an unusual opportunity to delve deeply into the fundamental reactions underlying rates of increase or of growth. In other cases the determined values of log k will be found to lie on a smooth curve, which obviously would require a different hypothesis for explanation than the one outlined above. The whole problem is one which demands further study.

The existence of an optimum temperature for population increase demands, moreover, that the value of μ over a definite (usually narrow) temperature range be 0. No chemical reaction is known for which such a relationship is true. If we extend the hypothesis outlined above (one controlling or dominant reaction in a sequence) to this region some modifications are evidently essential. Apparently at temperatures above the optimum any increase in temperatures slows down the rates of cell multiplication and of population increase. The following interpretation of the existence of a temperature optimum may be useful. Chemical changes in biological systems are usually catalyzed, most commonly by enzymes. The rate of any chemical change is therefore dependent not only on the concentrations of the reactants and resultants, but on the concentration of the necessary enzyme. The latter is produced by the cell, the rate of production determined by many factors, among them temperature. Enzymes are in most cases relatively unstable compounds in that they are markedly thermo-labile, i.e., the temperature quotients for their rates of destruction are high. The rate at which a given chemical reaction will take place is determined by the rate of production of the catalyst, the rate of destruction of the catalyst, the rate of the catalyzed reaction, the rate at which reactants are supplied by the preceding reaction in the series, and the rate at which the resultants are removed by the succeeding reaction. It seems reasonably clear, therefore, that the optimum temperature is that at which for the slowest reaction in the catenary series the balance among the various controlling factors is such as to give a maximum rate. Obviously a temperature at which the rate of destruction of the enzyme is greater than its rate of production must be higher than the optimum temperature.

One additional point relating to temperature optima requires emphasis. The rates of the various reactions controlling increase in bacterial populations are determined by many environmental factors other than temperature. The effects of such other environmental factors are not uniform on the various reactions. In consequence a change in environment may and will *change* the optimum temperature for population increase under the new environment. In other words, there is no fixed optimum temperature for bacterial population increase, but instead a series of optima, one for each set of environmental conditions.

In summary, it may be emphasized that bacteria react to temperature by showing marked differences in rates of population increase, by the existence of an optimum temperature for each set of environments, likewise a maximum and a minimum growth temperature, and a growth temperature range. The hereditary characteristics of the species determine the responses secured in each case. There are bacteria with persistently high optima (thermophiles), others with low optima (psychrophiles) and those with optima at "moderate" temperatures (mesophiles). In some species the growth temperature range (distance from minimum to maximum) is relatively narrow, in others relatively wide.

Another physical factor of the bacterial environment is radiant energy. Most studied are the portions of the spectrum which include visible light and the ultraviolet. Radiant energy undoubtedly affects rates of change in bacterial population by affecting rates of chemical reactions. Furthermore, only such rays as are absorbed by the bacteria or by the medium (substrate) in which they are growing can be effective in producing changes. In general, bacterial protoplasm shows its maximum absorption in the blue, violet, or ultraviolet. Pigmented bacteria of course show varied absorption bands depending upon the color of the pigment produced. The energy of the absorbed light may produce any one of several types of changes in the cell. The radiant energy may be transformed directly into heat. The bacterial cells are so small and the rate of heat diffusion in the medium so great that probably little effective change in temperature in the cell is produced. In other cases the absorbed energy catalyzes various chemical reactions. Particularly when absorbed by protoplasm, the changes produced may be injurious to the cell. Apparently it is such absorption and activity that explains the high germicidal efficiency of the short waves of light, particularly ultraviolet light, in the destruction of bacteria. There are, however, many species of sulphur bacteria which produce pigments that are useful in photosynthesis. The absorption of light by these pigments catalyzes the reduction of carbon dioxide and the activation usually of sulphur and in the presence of water the production of carbonaceous compounds which may serve as cell nutrients. It is to be noted, therefore, that light in general has a tendency markedly to decrease or even to inhibit multiplication of bacteria, but in a few cases light increases rates of multiplication due to the photosynthetic activity of the pigments. In other words, the chemical changes induced by light absorption may be useful in some kinds of cells and harmful in others. Rates of increase of bacterial populations are also influenced by several other physical characteristics of their environment. The more important, however, may be listed as viscosity, surface tension, agitation, sound waves, mechanical pressure, and osmotic pressure.

The *chemical* characteristics of the environment are perhaps even more potent than the physical characteristics in determining rates of bacterial increase. The chemical environment may influence micro-organisms in a variety of ways.

The chemical elements or compounds may be significant as *cell nutrients*. The rates of increase of bacterial populations are quite directly dependent upon concentration of food stuffs. The elements and compounds which are taken into the cell serve two relatively distinct functions.

In some cases, directly or after some modification, they are incorporated into the cell structures in such forms as protoplasm, cell walls, reserve food materials, granules, and capsules. In other cases they serve directly as hydrogen donators in the oxidative metabolism of the cell. The chemical reactions in which they are involved yield the energy necessary for cell motion, cell growth, and synthesis of many chemical compounds which are built up by the cell. For example, bacteria are known which take up hydrogen sulphide, oxidizing this compound to sulphuric acid, which compound is then excreted. The energy secured as a result of this transformation is in part at least utilized for the reduction of carbon dioxide and the building-up of carbon compounds useful to the cell (chemosynthesis). It is evident that a supply of nutrients suitable both for building cell structures and for securing an adequate supply of energy must have a profound influence upon the rates of increase of bacterial populations. In some cases chemical compounds and their ions may be of major environmental significance in that they largely determine by their concentration the permeability of cell membranes and the ability of the protoplasm of the cell to absorb water and the various nutrients.

Not only may the chemical environments accelerate the increase of bacterial populations but they may also prove inhibitory and induce a negative acceleration. A substance in very low concentration may be without apparent effect; in somewhat higher concentrations it may prove stimulating; in higher concentrations it may retard growth and prove inhibitive, and in still higher concentrations it may be so toxic as not only to stop increase altogether but to kill the bacterial cells. Enough has been said to indicate that changes in rates of increase of bacterial populations may be easily induced by modifications in the chemical environment.

RATES OF INCREASE IN AN ENVIRONMENT MODIFIED BY THE GROWTH OF BACTERIA

In the discussion to this point it has been assumed that bacteria under a given sort of environmental conditions favorable to growth will continue to grow indefinitely in a logarithmic fashion. It is apparent, however, that it is difficult to maintain for any long period of time such uniform conditions for bacterial growth and increase. If a small number of bacterial cells, particularly resting cells, are planted in a medium such as a nutrient broth favorable for growth, observation will show that for a time there usually is no increase in the number of cells, and frequently even after the cells have shown evidence of growth a little time must elapse before the maximum rate of growth or increase per cell is reached. This period of time during which the organism is becoming again vegetatively active and adapted to its environment and is reaching its maximum rate of reproduction is frequently spoken of as the *lag* period in the development of a bacterial population. After the close of the lag period, unless the bacteria are crowded, there is usually a period during which there is a maximum rate of increase per cell, that is, the velocity coefficient of the rate of increase is at a maximum.   During this period the generation time is at a minimum.   It is the logarithmic growth phase.   As the bacteria increase in number the environment gradually changes.   The concentration of food materials present in the medium is gradually decreased as a result of utilization by the bacterial cells.   Waste products of metabolism are excreted and tend to accumulate in the medium.   As the food supply decreases, diffusion of the dissolved food material into the bacterial cell occurs at a decreasing rate and the rate of increase per cell tends to decrease, that is, the generation time becomes longer.   Eventually, the available food may be completely utilized, when, of course, all increase in bacterial population ceases.

Coincidentally with this decrease in available food is an increase in the concentration of the waste products of the cell metabolism.   In some cases these may tend to stimulate and accelerate cell growth.   For example, most cells excrete carbon dioxide.   A certain concentration of this gas in solution in the environment of certain bacteria tends to accelerate their rates of division.   This stimulation of rates of increase in the presence of other cells of the same type has been termed autocatakinesis.   On the other hand, many of the products of metabolism may prove to be distinctly inhibitory to the cells excreting them, and to other cells as well.   For example, many bacteria growing in the presence of sugar produce acids such as lactic acid.   The accumulation of this acid changes the hydrogen ion concentration of the medium and this in turn may prove to be distinctly inhibitory to the cells.   The toxic material may accumulate eventually to a point that all cell growth ceases.   It is evident, therefore, that in the growth of a bacterial population the rates at any time are dependent upon food supply and concentration of substances producing positive acceleration on the one hand and on the concentration of inhibitory substances producing negative acceleration on the other.   It is further evident that due to the exhaustion of available food or to the inhibitory influences of products of metabolism the bacteria in a culture may cease multiplication altogether.

In a closed bacterial culture, then, the so-called growth phases usually appear in the following sequence: There is first manifest the lag phase of growth or phase of positive growth acceleration.   This is followed by a shorter or longer period of maximum rate of increase per cell or logarithmic growth.   The third phase is that during which the rate of growth per cell is decreased (that is, the average generation time is increased), the phase of negative growth acceleration.   Finally, the bacterial population reaches the fourth or stationary phase in which numbers are maintained and the tendencies to increase and to decrease are balanced.   It is evident that a population-time graph will rise more and more rapidly until a point of inflection is reached and then more and more slowly to the maximum or stationary phase.   The slope of such a line is constantly proportional to the true rate of increase of the population. These facts may be shown even better by a graph of the logarithms of the numbers of bacteria against time.   In such a graph the slope of the line is constantly proportional to the rate of increase per cell and inversely proportional to the generation time. The line rises more and more rapidly until it reaches the phase of logarithmic growth where it is straight. It merges eventually into a curve convex to the X axis, and finally into a line parallel to the X axis.

There has been much discussion of the equation which might most adequately represent this entire growth curve. Quite evidently the growth curve is sigmoid in character and resembles in many respects the growth curves which have been studied for many animals and plants. In a few instances the curve has been found to be symmetrical, but usually it is asymmetrical. Discussions of the equations which have been derived to fit such curves may be found elsewhere.

POPULATION DECREASES

In general, it may be emphasized that when bacteria are not growing or increasing in number they are dying. In some cases the rates of death may be extraordinarily slow and cells are said to be dormant or in a resting condition. Under other conditions the destruction of large populations may be so rapid as to appear almost instantaneous. In studies of population decreases it is obviously necessary to differentiate between surviving and dead cells. There are several criteria which have been suggested for this differentiation. Usually a bacterial cell is said to be dead if it fails to multiply when it is transferred to favorable conditions for growth. In some cases, however, there may be evidences of life such as excretion of products of metabolism from cells which do not meet this criterion and are unable to multiply. The ability to take up certain dyes such as methylene blue is highly correlated with cell death in certain organisms as yeasts and the reaction may be used as a quick method for identification of live cells. It is evident that rates of population decrease may be somewhat dependent on the criterion of cell death adopted.

It is a matter of common observation that when a population of bacteria is placed under unfavorable conditions the cells do not all die at the same instant. Apparently there are various gradations in resistance among the cells. The form which is assumed by the survivors' curve (secured by graphing numbers of surviving bacteria against time) has been a matter of discussion and controversy among bacteriologists for many years. In many cases the bacteria apparently die in such a manner that a definite fixed proportion of those which are alive at the beginning of any definite period of time will die during this period. Another way of stating it is that the rate of death is constantly proportional to the number of survivors. This hypothesis has been regarded by many bacteriologists as having all the finality of a law, and as being generally applicable. There are other students of the question who contend that while there may be a superficial resemblance to logarithmic death such resemblance is quite fortuitous. For discussion of this problem the student is referred to the numerous treatises on this subject. If one could be sure that bacteria under all adverse conditions do tend to die logarithmically as noted above, the problems of evaluation of environmental influences upon death rates would be greatly simplified. If the rate of decrease is constantly proportional to the surviving bacteria then

$$- \frac{db}{dt} = kb$$

in which k (the proportionality constant) is the velocity constant of the rate of death, that is, the rate of death per cell. When integrated this becomes

$$k = \frac{1}{t} \ln \frac{B}{b}$$

or

$$b = B \epsilon^{-kt}$$

When this relationship holds it is evident that one may evaluate the effects of various environments upon rate of decrease in bacterial populations by comparing the values of the velocity coefficients under the several conditions. For example, the usefulness of various disinfectants could thus be directly compared.

Bacterial populations may decrease under the adverse influences of either physical or chemical environment. Among the physical environments most frequently injurious to bacterial cultures are temperature and radiant energy (usually in the form of light).

Populations of different species of bacteria show wide variations in their ability to resist high temperature. In general, any temperature above the maximum growth temperature will prove to be lethal. The higher the temperature the more rapid will be the death rate. Many studies have been made in an effort to determine the value of $Q_{10°}$ for death rates of bacteria. In general with the more resistant types of cells such as bacterial spores the rates of death per cell will be multiplied by 5 to 10 for each 10° rise in temperature. This explains the extraordinary increase in efficiency of sterilization by heat with increased temperatures. It is suggested that the student guard against a fallacious connotation of a term frequently found in bacterial literature—*thermal-death point.* The term would seem to indicate that a particular kind of bacterium may be killed by a particular temperature. This concept is erroneous. It is much better to use the term *thermal-death rate,* which indicates that the bacteria do not die simultaneously under the influence of high temperatures.

As noted previously, light may have a decidedly destructive effect upon many kinds of bacteria. Apparently certain of the short, particularly the ultraviolet rays which may be absorbed by protoplasm, especially by nucleoplasm, are very destructive.

Several different names have been applied to groups of chemicals which prove to be destructive or injurious to micro-organisms. Antiseptics are sometimes defined as substances which inhibit bacterial growth, germicides as substances which kill bacteria, and disinfectants as substances which kill pathogenic bacteria. Inasmuch as the efficiency of any killing agent decreases with decrease in concentration, and inasmuch as any substance which inhibits the growth of pathogenic micro-organisms also kills other cells, there can be no very strict differentiation between these terms.

The literature on effects of various chemicals upon bacterial populations and death rates is very voluminous, and cannot be reviewed here.

RELATIONSHIPS OF ENVIRONMENT TO MORPHOLOGY

The shape, size, and appearance of bacterial cells may show marked variations depending upon the environment in which they have been grown. When these cells are associated in large numbers these modifications in cellular morphology modify in turn the appearance or morphology of the mass of cells as a whole. If a bacterial cell is placed in a suitable environment which is sufficiently viscous to prevent movement, its continued multiplication will give rise to a mass of cells termed a colony. Modifications in an environment, both physical and chemical, will show marked variations in the appearance of colonies which are developed.

The cells of an organism which under one set of conditions may appear as a small isolated rod not united in any way to the neighboring cells may under another environment appear as a giant cell, perhaps greatly swollen, sometimes even branched, and it may be united to the neighboring cells, forming chains or packets of various types. When grown in colonies there may be the greatest variation in appearance. Under one set of conditions the colony may resemble a lump of transparent jelly. Under another set of conditions it may appear relatively dry and hard. In one liquid medium cells may be isolated, in another medium they may be joined in long chains.

ENVIRONMENT AND METABOLISM

Species of bacteria are quite as frequently differentiated each from the others on the basis of physiology as upon the basis of morphology. With higher forms of life we ordinarily tell species apart by differences in appearances. With bacteria the differentiation is quite as frequently based on what physical or chemical changes can be produced when the cells are growing together in large numbers. Changes in environment may completely change the products of metabolism. For example, an organism which under one set of conditions produces large quantities of alcohol and carbon dioxide may under another set of conditions produce carbon dioxide only or may produce a large proportion of glycerol. Under one set of conditions an organism may increase the hydrogen ion concentration of its medium by the production of organic acids. Under another set of conditions the same organism may render a medium alkaline by the destruction of the salts of these same acids.

ASSOCIATIVE ACTION OF BACTERIA

Probably among the bacteria we find some of the simplest examples of living things working together to mutual advantage as well as all grades of antagonism and parasitism.

There are numerous instances on record in which two kinds of bacteria living together may bring about chemical changes which neither could produce separately. For example, one of the bacteria found in the alimentary tract of man is capable of producing gas and acid when grown in a medium containing the sugar dextrose. It cannot attack cane sugar (sucrose). Another organism rather closely related is known which is capable of fermenting a solution of sucrose with production of acid but no gas. When cells of both these species are inoculated together into sucrose both acid and gas are produced. It may be inferred that one organism is able to attack sucrose with formation of certain products which the second organism is able to break down further.

Such associations of bacteria are very common in nature. In fertile soil, for example, many species of bacteria grow together and are more or less mutually benefitted. Two organisms which when growing together are mutually beneficial are said to live in a condition of *symbiosis;* if one utilizes the waste products of the other the association is termed *anabiosis*. If one organism antagonizes another, as by the production of deleterious compounds the association is one of *antibiosis*. It should be emphasized that these relationships may exist between bacteria and other species of animals and plants. For example, there are many examples of symbiosis of bacteria with higher forms. The bacteria of the root nodules of legumes are apparently supplied with carbohydrates by the clover and the clover is supplied with combined nitrogen by the bacterium. Numerous sea forms supply food and a suitable growth environment for bacteria which have the ability to luminesce.

It is not a long step from organisms which live in a condition of symbiosis to those which live upon the waste products of others and to those which are definitely parasitic. In some cases this parasitism may not be harmful and the condition is said to be one of commensalism. In another case the bacteria may definitely attack and injure living cells of other species of plants or animals. It should be emphasized that bacterial parasitism and pathogenesis is known for almost every other group in the plant and animal kingdoms. It should be emphasized also that injurious results following bacterial parasitism are induced by the presence of great numbers of organisms.

ENVIRONMENT AND MOVEMENT

As noted above, bacteria may be divided into those which are motile and those which are non-motile. The motile forms in turn may be divided into those which swim about by means of special hair-like swimming organs called flagella, others that move by a snake-like bending of the slender cell, and still others that move by pushing themselves along by the asymmetrical extrusion of a gummy or slimy material.

Many studies have been made upon the influence of environment upon the rates of motion of micro-organisms higher in the evolutionary scale than are the bacteria. Comparatively few studies have been made upon bacteria themselves. There is no reason to suppose but what the studies which have been made upon protozoa and algae would not be equally applicable to the bacteria. One of the most careful studies of the influence of environment on bacterial motion has been on the effect of temperature upon rates of movement of the sulphur bacterium Beggiatoa. This organism exhibits a creeping motion in a drop of water when it is in contact with a glass slide. It is found that within the range of the more favorable growth temperatures the rate of movement increases with increase of temperature. The applicability of the van't Hoff–Arrhenius equation was demonstrated and values of the thermal increment determined. The existence of definite critical temperatures was also shown.

Effects of environment upon direction of movement of bacteria may also be readily demonstrated. One of the classic illustrations of this phenomenon is to fill a capillary pipette with a solution of beef extract, then insert the tip into a drop of water containing a large number of motile bacteria of certain species. The bacteria will be found soon to be thickly clustered about the mouth of the pipette and to enter it in great numbers. This was one of the earlier demonstrations of the phenomenon termed chemotaxis.

The phenomenon of aerotaxis may also be demonstrated by placing a large number of bacteria of several species in a drop of water, and placing this under a cover glass on a suitable slide, making sure that one or more small air bubbles will be included. After the oxygen dissolved in the water becomes reduced in concentration the organisms will be found frequently to arrange themselves in concentric circles about the air bubbles. The oxygen dissolved in the water about the bubble exhibits a regular concentration gradient.

A somewhat analogous phenomenon is frequently manifested by micro-organisms which are pathogenic. Certain types of bacteria when inoculated into the blood stream of animals will tend to localize in a particular tissue, perhaps in the liver or spleen or the joints. Certain of the filterable viruses are said to be neurotropic because they tend to localize in nerve fibers or in nerve tissues. The phenomenon of phototaxis or heliotaxis is manifested by certain of the photosynthetic bacteria. For example, if a liquid culture of certain of the pigmented sulphur bacteria is exposed to light the micro-organisms tend to swim in the direction of the light and come to rest on the side of the container toward the source of the light. Organisms which show this phenomenon are ordinarily chemosynthetic.

Bacteria belonging to the order of myxobacteria exhibit a very interesting series of movements. These bacteria are in the form of rods which multiply by transverse fission. They show marked power of locomotion but are destitute of definite organs of locomotion. They secrete considerable quantities of a jelly-like mucus. Apparently this is secreted at points of contact between the bacterial cell and some more or less solid object. The material is excreted asymmetrically and pushes the organism along as it is formed. The bacteria show, when massed together in the early stages of colony formation, a decided tendency to move away from each other, apparently a manifestation of negative chemotaxis. In consequence they tend to move in the form of an ever widening circle. When conditions are right they develop a more or less definite community organization. The negative chemotactic response apparently disappears and the cells move together into definite clumps. The cells continue to secrete the mucus and produce masses or even branched stalks of semi-solid jelly. The bacteria crawl up the surface of this jelly and congregate in masses at the tips of the branches. Here the cells tend to increase in width and decrease in length. With some species the cells may become spherical or coccus-like. The cell mass then surrounds itself by a more or less firm jelly-like membrane, and constitutes a type of cyst or sporangium. This cyst may then undergo desiccation and may even be broken loose and blown about by air currents. When it falls under conditions favorable for growth the cyst swells and softens under the influence of moisture. It then breaks open at one end usually and the enclosed cells which have again elongated swarm out. The conditions which induce reversal of chemotaxis and induce formation of these complex fruiting bodies are not well known. Among these myxobacteria we may find probably the simplest of community life and organization, one which resembles in many respects that of the slime molds or myxomycetes. A study of the taxes of these forms should prove most profitable.

SELECTED REFERENCES

BROOKS, S. C. 1919. A theory of the mechanism of disinfection, hemolysis and similar processes. *J. Gen. Physiol.*, **1**, 61. Summary in *Physiology and biochemistry of bacteria*, by R. E. Buchanan and E. I. Fulmer. Baltimore, Md.: Williams & Wilkins, 1918. P. 466.

BUCHANAN, R. E. 1918. Life phases in a bacterial culture. *J. Infect. Dis.*, **23**, 109-125.

————. 1926. Nomogram for determination of generation time and velocity coefficients of growth and death. *Ia. State Coll. J. Sci.*, **1**, 63. Summary in *Physiology and biochemistry of bacteria*, by R. E. Buchanan and E. I. Fulmer. Baltimore, Md.: Williams & Wilkins, 1928. P. 467.

————. 1928. Growth curves of bacteria. In *The newer knowledge of bacteriology and immunology*, by E. A. Jordan and I. S. Falk. Chicago: Univ. Chicago Press; Cambridge, England: Univ. Press. Pp. 46-57.

BUCHANAN, R. E., & FULMER, E. I. 1928. Physiology and biochemistry of bacteria. Vol. 1. Baltimore, Md.: Williams & Wilkins, Pp. 517.

CHESNEY, A. M. 1916. The latent period in the growth of bacteria. *J. Exper. Med.*, **24**, 387-418. Summary in *Physiology and biochemistry of bacteria*, by R. E. Buchanan and E. I. Fulmer. Baltimore, Md.: Williams & Wilkins, 1928. P. 468.

CHICK, H. 1908. An investigation of the laws of disinfection. *J. Hygiene*, **8**, 92. Summary in *Physiology and biochemistry of bacteria*, by R. E. Buchanan and E. I. Fulmer. Baltimore, Md.: Williams & Wilkins, 1928. P. 468.

COHEN, B. 1922. Disinfection studies. *J. Bacteriol.*, **7**, 183. Summary in *Physiology and biochemistry of bacteria*, by R. E. Buchanan and E. I. Fulmer. Baltimore, Md.: Williams & Wilkins, 1928. P. 468.

ESTY, J. R. 1928. Determinations of thermal death-time. In *The newer knowledge of bacteriology and immunology*, by E. A. Jordan and I. S. Falk. Chicago: Univ. Chicago Press; Cambridge, England: Univ. Press. Pp. 285-300.

FALK, I. S., & WINSLOW, C.-E. A. 1926. A contribution to the dynamics of toxicity and the theory of disinfection. *J. Bacteriol.*, **11**, 11. Summary in *Physiology and biochemistry of bacteria*, by R. E. Buchanan and E. I. Fulmer. Baltimore, Md.: Williams & Wilkins, 1928. P. 470.

FULMER, E. I., & BUCHANAN, R. E. 1923. Studies on toxicity. *J. Gen. Physiol.*, **6**, 77-89. Summary in *Physiology and biochemistry of bacteria*, by R. E. Buchanan and E. I. Fulmer. Baltimore, Md.: Williams & Wilkins, 1928. P. 472.

HANSEN, M., BREUER, H., & HAAG, F. E. 1934. Ueber die Vermehrung der Spaltpilze nach der Einsaat in flüssige Nährmittel. *Centbl. f. Bakteriol., etc.*, Abt. I, **131**, 469-477.

HOLMAN, W. L. 1928. Bacterial association. In *The newer knowledge of bacteriology and immunology*, by E. A. Jordan and I. S. Falk. Chicago: Univ. Chicago Press; Cambridge, England: Univ. Press. Pp. 102-119.

KRÖNIG, B., & PAUL, T. 1896. Ueber das Verhalten der Bakterien zu chemischen Reagentien. *Zsch. f. physiol. Chem.*, **21**, 414. Summary in *Physiology and biochemistry of bacteria*, by R. E. Buchanan and E. I. Fulmer. Baltimore, Md.: Williams & Wilkins, 1928. P. 477.

LANE-CLAYPON, J. E. 1909. Multiplication of bacteria and the influence of temperature and some other conditions thereon. *J. Hygiene*, **9**, 239-248. Summary in *Physiology and biochemistry of bacteria*, by R. E. Buchanan and E. I. Fulmer. Baltimore, Md.: Williams & Wilkins, 1928. Pp. 478.

LEDINGHAM, J. C. G., & PENFOLD, W. J. 1914. Mathematical analysis of the lag-phase in bacterial growth. *J. Hygiene*, **14**, 242-260. Summary in *Physiology and biochemistry of bacteria*, by R. E. Buchanan and E. I. Fulmer. Baltimore, Md.: Williams & Wilkins, 1928. P. 479.

LEE, R. E., & GILBERT, C. A. 1918. Application of the mass law to the process of disinfection. *J. Phys. Chem.*, **22**, 348. *Summary in Physiology and biochemistry of bacteria*, by R. E. Buchanan and E. I. Fulmer. Baltimore, Md.: Williams & Wilkins, 1928. P. 479.

LOTKA, A. J. 1925. Elements of physical biology. Baltimore: Williams & Wilkins. Pp. xxx+460. Summary in *Physiology and biochemistry of bacteria*, by R. E. Buchanan and E. I. Fulmer. Baltimore, Md.: Williams & Wilkins, 1928. P. 480.

MADSEN, T., & NYMAN, M. 1907. Zur Theorie der Desinfektion: I. *Zsch. f. Hygiene u. Infektionskh.*, **57**, 388. Summary in *Physiology and biochemistry of bacteria*, by R. E. Buchanan and E. I. Fulmer. Baltimore, Md.: Williams & Wilkins, 1928. P. 481.

MOLISCH, H. 1907. Die Purpurbakterien. Jena: Fisher. Pp. vii+95. Summary in *Physiology and biochemistry of bacteria*, by R. E. Buchanan and E. I. Fulmer. Baltimore, Md.: Williams & Wilkins, 1928. P. 482.

PENFOLD, W. J. 1914. On the nature of bacterial lag. *J. Hygiene*, **14**, 215-241. Summary in *Physiology and biochemistry of bacteria*, by R. E. Buchanan and E. I. Fulmer. Baltimore, Md.: Williams & Wilkins, 1928. P. 485.

PFEFFER, W. 1895. Ueber Election organischer Nährstoffe. *Jahrb. f. wiss. Bot.*, **28**, 205-268. Summary in *Physiology and biochemistry of bacteria*, by R. E. Buchanan and E. I. Fulmer. Baltimore, Md.: Williams & Wilkins, 1928. P. 485.

PHELPS, E. B. 1911. The application of certain laws of physical chemistry in the standardization of disinfectants. *J. Infect. Dis.*, **8**, 27. Summary in *Physiology and biochemistry of bacteria*, by R. E. Buchanan and E. I. Fulmer. Baltimore, Md.: Williams & Wilkins, 1928. Pp. 485.

RAHN, O. 1932. Physiology of bacteria. New York: Blakiston. Pp. xiv+438.

REICHENBACH, —. 1922. Die theoretisch Grundlagen der Desinfektion. *Centbl. f. Bakteriol., etc., Abt. I, Orig.*, **89**, 15. Summary in *Physiology and biochemistry of bacteria*, by R. E. Buchanan and E. I. Fulmer. Baltimore, Md.: Williams & Wilkins, 1928. P. 486.

ROBERTSON, T. B. 1908*a*. On the normal rate of growth of an individual, and its biochemical significance. *Arch. f. Entwickmech.*, **25**, 581-614.

————. 1908*b*. Further remarks on the normal rate of growth of an individual, and its biochemical significance. *Arch. f. Entwickmech.*, **26**, 108-118.

————. 1910. Explanatory remarks concerning the normal rate of growth of an individual and its biochemical significance. *Biol. Centbl.*, **30**, 316-320.

————. 1913. On the nature of the autocatalyst of growth. *Arch. f. Entwickmech.*, **37**, 497-508.

————. 1915. The multiplication of isolated infusoria. *Biochem. J.*, **15**, 595-611.

————. 1921. Experimental studies on cellular multiplication: II. The influence of mutual contiguity upon reproductive rate and the part played therein by the "x-substance" in bacterised infusions which stimulate the multiplication of infusoria. *Biochem. J.*, **15**, 612-619.

————. 1922. Reproduction in cell-communities. *J. Physiol.*, **56**, 404-412.

————. 1924. The nature of the factors which determine the duration of the period of lag in cultures of infusoria. *Australian J. Exper. Biol. & Med. Sci.*, **1**, 105. [Summary of Robertson articles in *Physiology and biochemistry of bacteria*, by R. E. Buchanan and E. I. Fulmer. Baltimore, Md.: Williams & Wilkins, 1928. Pp. 486-487.]

SLATOR, A. 1917. A note on the lag-phase in the growth of microorganisms. *J. Hygiene*, **16**, 100-108.

————. 1921. Yeast crops and the factors which determine them. *J. Chem. Soc.*, **119**, 115-131. [Summary of Slator articles in *Physiology and biochemistry of bacteria*, by R. E. Buchanan and E. I. Fulmer. Baltimore, Md.: Williams & Wilkins, 1928. P. 489.]

WINSLOW, C.-E. A. 1928. The rise and fall of bacterial populations. In *The newer knowledge of bacteriology and immunology*, by E. A. Jordan and I. S. Falk. Chicago: Univ. Chicago Press; Cambridge, England: Univ. Press. Pp. 58-83.

CHAPTER 2

SOCIAL ORIGINS AND PROCESSES AMONG PLANTS

FREDERIC E. CLEMENTS

Carnegie Institution of Washington

Concepts and Terms. In a comprehensive survey of the dynamics of plant societies, it will aid to consider at the outset such terms and concepts as have attained a certain sanction. This is all the more essential in view of the fact that social groups have so far been studied from separate approaches, and the general unity that underlies them has often been obscured as a consequence. The very immensity of the field of social relations affords a ready explanation of partial viewpoints as well as their justification up to a certain stage, but it is now increasingly manifest that refinement and correlation must rest in a large measure upon synthesis. Apart from a static attitude, probably no other barrier is so great as that of terminology, involving as it does the ease and certainty with which concepts may be handled. The use of different terms for the same concept and of the same word for different things appears to be an unavoidable overcharge for individuality, and one to be compensated only by the process of definition and re-definition. However, no considerable improvement in this respect is possible until investigators recognize the need for a wider perspective over related fields.

Vernacular terms in constant use are susceptible of the greatest variation, and in this respect no others equal *society, community,* and *association.* As an example, the first of these not only possesses a different significance in sociology so called, in animal and in plant ecology, but it also has varied applications in each of these. The extent of the dilemma can best be appreciated by the shift in the meaning of society from Espinas (1878) to Deegener (1918), Park and Burgess (1921), and Alverdes (1927), though by all these society is regarded as a primary and association as a secondary distinction. With no need to employ and hence to define instinct, and perhaps with too little knowledge of other usages, plant ecologists have reversed the relation, association usually including societies as secondary units, which are less definite and stable. The distinctions drawn by Wheeler (1930) and somewhat modified by Allee (1931) are more or less usable with animals, especially invertebrates, but apply less well to human societies and not at all to plant groupings. Even in the first instance, the difficulties have been clearly pointed out by Allee (*loc. cit.,* p. 35), who finds a practical solution in the use of the word *aggregation,* employed much earlier by plant ecologists for the process and not the product of it (Clements, 1905, 1916).

As is shown later in some detail, a logical analysis of the process of coming together or aggregation among plants led to the designation of the nascent units as the family and colony respectively (Clements, *loc cit.*). It was later recognized that these fitted the facts equally well among animals and that with slight modification they were also applicable to man (Clements and Shelford, 1935). At the same time, it became evident that colonies among animals, and in particular protozoans and insects, were actually families and that this was true likewise of societies based upon instinct, as in the social hymenoptera. The sole issue from such confusion appears to be to extend the general usage of dynamic ecology to all three fields, with the material gain that the two terms maintain the same meaning throughout. This has the further advantage of freeing the term *society* to be employed in a general sense, as is at present the case with human groups and to some extent with plant units, a function that it would share with *community,* which has generally been employed with this significance by plant ecologists.

NATURE OF SOCIAL PROCESSES

From the dynamic viewpoint, it is axiomatic that social groups are to be considered merely as the end result of the forces that produce them and that the explanation of their nature and significance must be sought in these. In other words, they are distinguished by their inherent processes or functions, just as in the case of the individual, and their essential relationships are to be determined only upon this basis. This applies in particular to their evolution, which is primarily a matter of group physiology, even though the visible evidence be recorded in structure. Hence, the characteristics of societies and communities are to be derived from what they do, and this must furnish the interpretation of what they are.

Characteristics. Every grouping of organisms is the outcome of two basic cycles of behavior, one governed by the physical factors of the environment, the other by the mutual relations of the component individuals. Either of these may be paramount in any particular case, and the whole epic of social evolution is to be seen in the gradual shifting of emphasis from one to the other. The two cycles are marked by one significant difference, inasmuch as the control of physical factors is exerted through the response of the individual, while mutual relations involve two organisms as the minimum, as is illustrated by the reproduction of unisexual plants or animals. However, the two basic processes, i.e., the action of the habitat or ece[1] upon the individual and the interaction between two or more individuals are bound together by a third, which is the reaction of organisms upon the physical habitat. Such an effect is actually or potentially present with every organism, but it becomes significant only when the aggregation of individuals permits it to accumulate to the point of becoming directive. Thus, the proper integration of ece and society hinges upon three rather than two primary processes, namely, the action of the habitat, the reaction of the group, and the coaction between the members of the latter. The linking rôle of reaction is a critical

---

[1]From *oikos,* home.

one in all groups, since it determines the entrance of social response in the comprehensive meaning of the word.

The general tendency to restrict the term *social* to specialized group-ings, best exemplified by ants, termites, and man, is readily understood as due to their striking nature and to the fondness of mankind for in-terpreting in its own terms. However, this usage is hardly justified by a comprehensive survey of the entire field of related phenomena, which suggests instead that the word is better applied to the range of processes in which reaction and coaction are concerned. The outstanding fact is the continuity of the process, which permits no sharp distinctions to be drawn, though it does allow the recognition of changing emphasis. Such a conclusion finds further warrant in the original meanings of the word and the root from which it is derived. Thus, the primary adjective, *socius,* is formed on the root *sec-, soc,* with the primitive sense of *follow,* and exhibits a gradation of meaning from *following* through *kindred, united,* and *sharing.* *Socialis* is a secondary form with similar connota-tions and is thus well adapted to cover the range of interactions in which space and time are paramount. There would seem to be no valid ob-jection to employing the word *social* in both a general and a special sense, as at present, though such terms as *subsocial* and *supersocial* may well find a place.

A significant consequence of the use of *social* in the inclusive sense is the assumption of an objective and somewhat skeptical attitude toward the rôle of instinct in social groupings, which has been well expressed by Allee (1931, p. 11):

> Insofar as is possible, we shall avoid dwelling upon the aspects of behavior usually called "instinctive," except in reference to the litera-ture. This is not due to a disbelief in the reality of instinctive social behavior, but rather to a conviction that progress lies in a field where the elements of behavior can be more exactly ascertained. The drive which leads an animal to exhibit such behavior as is usually classified as being due to the operation of social instinct I prefer to regard, as does Wheeler (1928), as an expression of appetite. Wheeler says in this connection: "It thus takes its place with the other appetites like hunger and sex, though it is feebler and more continuous, i.e., less spasmodic and therefore less obvious."

Allee further emphasizes the fact that the term *instinct* has deservedly fallen into disfavor because of loose usage. To the several causes for this may be added the tendency to make it a synonym of mystery or of ignorance, and hence to justify a negative attitude toward its analysis through research. It has become increasingly clear that the line between experience and instinct is a shadowy one, and that the latter is probably nothing more than sublimated learning, always more or less subject to individual error. Nearly forty years ago, the Peckhams concluded that the prevailing view that the acts of ants, bees, and wasps were merely varying forms of instinct was untenable, and that to instinctive responses must be added acts of intelligence and probably of imitation also (1898). They also showed conclusively that the homing of wasps was based upon learning, in a fashion not unlike that of carrier pigeons. In spite of such facts, there is still a tendency to regard the migration and pathway of birds as determined by instinct, and the appeal to mystery in this phenomenon is yielding but slowly to the experimental attack upon the problem (cf. Rowan, 1931, 1932; Kendeigh, 1934; Clements and Shelford, 1935). The latter is especially significant in the present connection, since migration regularly involves a recurrence of aggregation into flocks, exemplifying a type of temporary social response.

Kinds of Societies. It was inevitable that static concepts should take precedence in the organization and classification of social groups, and to much the same extent in the three related fields of plant, animal, and human ecology. They do sometimes serve the purpose of giving a preliminary organization to a wide range of facts, but they tend to outlive their usefulness and to stereotype ideas in procrustean fashion. Such a system is that of Deegener with its numerous subdivisions and its multitude of relatively unimportant details. In sharp contrast stands the dynamic viewpoint in which process and development are paramount, with structure

FIGURE 1

FAMILY OF AN ANNUAL, *Cleome serrulata*, INTEGRATED BY EXTENSIVE SEEDING AND SURFACE WASH

or form merely an end-product of these. To such a viewpoint, classification is not a matter of immediate importance and when employed must be cast in a mold sufficiently flexible to adjust itself to the demands of development. In short, classification gains value only as it reflects the increasing knowledge of dynamic processes, and hence must follow this rather than anticipate it. It should consequently be simple and adaptable in form, with a large capacity for assimilating new concepts and units without obscuring primary divisions.

The basic social grouping in the ecologic and to a large degree in the primitive human sense is the family (Clements, 1907, 1916). As has been previously indicated, this corresponds to the society and colony of the zoologists in so far as their general usage is concerned. Below man, the family is considered to consist always of individuals of a single species, which naturally may often be represented by a subspecies. It may contain the offspring alone or the parents and young of one to several generations, in which case it bears a certain resemblance to the patriarchal type of human families. Number in itself is not significant, since the essential interactions are the same within or without the family whether it consists of a few or of thousands of individuals. Much the same statement may be made with regard to origin. In the narrow sense, the family consists of those members descended from a single parent or pair, but the patriarchal or matriarchal type again renders it evident that several generations may be present in a single family. Moreover, the latter may be dispersed and under modern conditions with man usually is so scattered that it exists only in a genetic and not a spatial relation. The family may be materially modified in genesis and numbers by adoption, without significant effect upon its relations to the community and to the physical environment. It may break up and reassemble for periods of varying length and in the process may be reconstituted by individuals of different genetic source. This justifies the extension of the term to a group of diverse parental origin, since practically all the dynamic processes involved remain unchanged. In the light of these facts, there would appear to be abundant warrant for extending the concept of plant ecology to cover all similar groupings, as has already been done in bio-ecology (Clements and Shelford, loc. cit.).

In the study of plant succession, it was found that two or more pioneer families sooner or later began to mingle with each other by means of propagative devices or by the dispersion of spores or seeds. The outcome was the development of a mixed grouping, for which community was first regarded as the appropriate designation, but this was later replaced by colony. This change was made primarily to permit emphasis upon the process of invasion, but partly also to release the word community as a general term for all kinds of social groups among plants, a practice that has likewise been brought over into bio-ecology. While the idea of migration and settlement by a number of families is uppermost in the term, it is obvious that, in the case of the plant matrix at least, seeds or spores may remain dormant in an area denuded by fire or clearing and later give rise to one or more colonies that initiate succession. In general, this unit will consist of two or more species of plants or of animals, but until the interactions of organisms are much better known, it may well include similar groupings of plants and animals. However, the social relations of attached or internal parasites are rather to be sought among themselves, so that a host with such parasites is not to be regarded as a colony.

The further expansion of families and colonies in an area marked by succession results in a mosaic-like cover that is more or less continuous over the surface of the ground. Competition for raw materials and energy on the part of the plants is greatly magnified, and out of this arises a new social relation of dominance and subordination, which is henceforth the chief feature of the successive communities and of the climax vegetation in which they terminate. At the same time, the animal groupings increase in number and complexity, with the struggle for food correspondingly enhanced in terms of the degree of coaction upon plants as well as each other, the final outcome being a dynamic balance in the form of coordination and subordination. The major details of the processes involved in the social integration from pioneer to climax communities are considered in the later sections on community functions and on climax and succession.

ORIGIN AND DEVELOPMENT OF COMMUNITIES

Number and Space. Axiomatically, families arise in consequence of an increase in number of individuals, but by itself this may be ineffective. It is only when supplemented by some physiological or mechanical bond that multiplication results in certain simple social groupings. This is the essence of the basic social process known as aggregation, in which the primary groupings are due to continuing attachment or to factor response, and the secondary ones to a coming-together of individuals that have been dispersed. In such secondary families, the process of migration takes a positive rôle, but in general its action is to carry young out of the family and hence to produce colonies. Those in which the individuals are aggregated by the action of wind or water constitute the most primitive of social assemblages, in which the bond is of the feeblest. But where actual motility is concerned, as with cenobic algae and many protozoans, there may be discerned the beginning of a definite social force. In certain instances, this simulates the sex attraction exhibited in conjugation, and in essence the two processes may be merely variations of a basic response.

While sex is recognized as a primal urge in social groupings, its importance is naturally far less in plants than among animals, since it can operate in this respect only in the relatively few genera with motile sex spores or at least with antherozoids. The formation of families through attachment, or rather through lack of detachment, is a much more frequent phenomenon among the simpler algae, and in quite a different form it is a regular feature of perennial herbs among flowering plants. Not only are the large majority of the latter bisexual, but even in the unisexual trees and shrubs the immotile sperm is the passive beneficiary of the wind.

Hence, reproduction by seed is not primarily a social process and can become so only as the forces of aggregation operate. On the other hand, propagation by fission or by offshoots in various form leads to direct aggregation and consequent family groups when separation and dispersion are absent or relatively at a minimum. Such families obviously owe their unity to morphological features in contrast to the physiological response exhibited by the aggregation of motile cells, or the accidental nature of groups brought together by means of currents of water or air.

Types of Plant Families. These fall into several major divisions, in accordance with the ruling process, which may be attachment, aggregation not attended by migration in any considerable amount, or re-aggregation as an outcome of motility or the physical factors of the habitat. In all of these, there is interaction in some form or degree among the members of the family, depending chiefly upon the nature and permanence of the spatial relations. Identical or similar social groupings are found among the lower classes of animals, principally protozoa, hydroids, coral polyps, and bryozoa, all of which serve to demonstrate the existence of common social forces for plants and animals.

The first definite families among the unicellular algae arise as a result of multiplication by fission, accompanied by sufficient pressure to prevent separation or by the production of a mucilage that serves a similar purpose. These may take the form of threads, plates, or cubes, and are to be found not only in the blue-green and yellow-green algae, but among bacteria as well. The degree of cohesion between the cell individuals varies much, and in many desmids and diatoms the thread-like family is merely temporary. In certain specialized genera, division takes place within the mother-cell to give a definite form to the 4-8-celled family. The evolution of filamentous families is directed in accordance with division of labor, so that special cells develop for the respective tasks of dividing the thread, of apical growth, and of spore production. This denotes the passing of the family into a multicellular individual, and these in turn may constitute the units of a new family, as in the mucilaginous thallus of *Nostoc*. Among the protozoa, some heliozoans and radiolarians produce families kept together by protoplasmic threads or jelly, while with flagellates and ciliates stalked groups are more or less frequent, especially among the relatives of *Vorticella*.

The formation of families by union or fusion of motile cells is characteristic of such cenobic algae as the water-net and allied genera, in which the zoospores arrange themselves in definite symmetrical patterns of much beauty. Even more striking and beautiful are such forms as *Pandorina* and *Volvox*, in which the family itself is motile. In *Volvox*, the original form is a whirling hollow sphere within which are developed new families; each mature family exhibits a distinct division of labor in connection with reproduction. Among the protozoa, families of unique character are produced by the coming-together of ameboid or flagellate cells to form a motile plasmodium that creeps over moist soil or decaying plant parts. Such slime-molds, as they are still termed, were long thought to be plants belonging among the fungi, because of the high differentiation of the fruiting bodies in response to aerial conditions, leading them to resemble tiny puffballs.

Families due to the aggregation and attachment of motile larvae occur in some of the higher classes of invertebrates, notably the mollusks and such crustacea as the barnacles. The best-known examples of this habit in the first class are provided by the oysters, which are regularly attached, and the ship-worms, which bore into wood.

In connection with the process of budding, cohesion or mutual attachment may give rise to families in the case of yeasts, certain molds and other fungi, and comparable behavior is found with some lichens and liverworts. In much more highly differentiated form, it is a universal feature of perennial herbs throughout the groups of ferns and flowering plants. Here the buds are borne on shoots specialized for propagation by food-storage and more or less extensibility; familiar examples are the runners of the strawberry, the rootstocks of Solomon's seal, and the bulbs of lilies. Such offshoots represent various combinations of enlargement

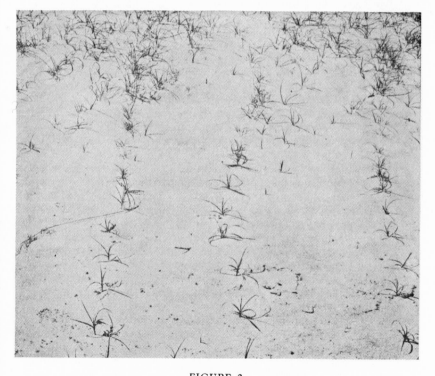

FIGURE 2

FAMILY OF A PERENNIAL SEDGE, *Carex arenaria*, INTEGRATED BY ROOTSTOCKS AND MIGRATING RADIALLY FROM THE PARENT GROUP

for storage and of extension through actual growth, the two features being necessarily opposed. In social terms, they may be said to embody varying compromises between aggregation, which is paramount in the lily and crocus, and migration, emphasized in the strawberry and various grasses with runners.

The nature of the bud as a potential individual is clearly disclosed in the stolon of shrubs in which an ordinary leafy shoot bends down and strikes root at the tip, and is shown even more graphically in certain viviparous ferns and flowering plants where buds grow into new individuals on the parent. In other words, each shrub or tree may be regarded in some measure as a family, an interpretation that obtains further support from the branching forms of the hydroid and coral polyps, as well as the polyzoa or "zoophytes." These, as well as the massive corals, may constitute families that run into thousands or millions of attached individuals derived from budding. The actual and potential nature of such complex groupings is considered later under the discussion of the organism.

The looser families originating from free adults, spores, or seeds represent two types, one arising from aggregation as an immediate outcome of multiplication, the other developed by re-aggregation as a result of swimming, floating, the action of wind or other agent of migration. In the case of aquatic organisms, especially those of the plankton, such families are essentially identical for plants and animals, though they pass more quickly into colonies with the motile forms of the latter. These communities may contain an incredible number of individuals and cover many square miles, as is true of water-bloom and duckweed on the surface of lakes and stagnant streams, or the water-hyacinth in the rivers of Florida. Smaller families of similar nature are represented by the green coating of minute algae on the north side of trees and fences in humid regions. In the case of terrestrial plants, the direct fall of seeds or spores about the parents produces families of various extent. For annuals, these comprise but a single generation, while with perennials, there may be several, as well as members derived from offshoots. In dry regions with winter rainfall, a family formed by a single annual species may color the landscape for a hundred square miles or more.

Types of Colonies. As indicated earlier, colonies are initial communities composed of two or more species and hence regularly follow families in the succession of populations in bare areas. In water, families readily mingle to form colonies as a consequence of motility or the action of currents, while on land the same result may be effected by the migration of offshoots or the dissemination of fruits, seeds, or spores. However, colonies may arise directly on areas denuded by fire especially, when the burning is not sufficiently intense to destroy the seeds buried in the soil. Plants are usually the visible pioneers in new soil, but with them, or even before, insects and soil animals may enter to produce a biotic colony from the outset. As additional species invade, the grouping becomes more complex, competition sorts the members into different ranks, and the colony is transformed into a society of higher degree. Much the same process occurs with the miniature colonies to be found on leafy shoots, decaying logs, and humus, and composed of parasitic and saprophytic organisms. These are derived primarily from plant families, largely fungi and bacteria, but the terrestrial slime-molds become frequent members, as well as a variety of minute soil animals.

Similar in character but more definitely integrated are the groupings that have a fair claim to the designation *symbiotic*. The term *symbiosis* has sometimes been rendered meaningless or at least superfluous by being extended to include practically all the phenomena of association, but is here employed in its proper sense of a specialized coaction, involving some degree of mutuality. The latter may fluctuate greatly from type to type, and in our present knowledge no hard and fast limits can be set. Thus, one of the best known of symbiotic colonies is the lichen, in which the integration of the producing alga and consuming fungus is so complete that lichens long passed for simple organisms. In certain species such as

FIGURE 3

COLONY OF CRUSTOSE AND FOLIOSE LICHENS, EACH OF WHICH IS ALSO A SYMBIOTIC COMMUNITY, INITIATING SUCCESSION ON A ROCK

Peltigera aphthosa, the colony consists of three different organisms, a second alga growing on the communal thallus, while in other instances another fungus may be present as a parasite on or in the community. The general relation between the primary algal host and the fungus is one of parasitism, but there is no question that the alga as a species profits by the symbiotic relation, in spite of the fate of the individuals. Apart from protection and other favorable conditions, evidence of this is drawn from the fact that migration and propagation regularly take place by means of small "buds" that contain both elements.

Symbiosis naturally leads to the production of colonies only when both members are present in some number. In the large majority of instances, one or both of the partners is represented by a single individual, and the social relation is merely that of a family of one species or a rudimentary colony comprising but one individual of each. The former is the situation between many plant symbionts, as with the nitrogen-fixing bacteria and clovers, while the latter obtains with a considerable number of marine animals, represented by the partnership of crab and mollusk. Apart from the lichens, there are few cases of definite symbiotic colonies among plants, but there are a number of such interactions between plants and animals. These may occur between the bud families of some hydrozoans or bryozoans and unicellular algae. Very different in nature but still constituting a biotic colony is the coaction between fungus-growing insect cultivators, such as certain ants and termites, and the particular species of fungus that each grows. Nutritive relations are also the bond in the various types of colonies formed by ants and their slaves, guests, or parasites (Wheeler, 1923).

Social Bonds in Plant Communities

Primary Bonds. As has been previously suggested, all organisms manifest three basic and interrelated processes, in which the habitat or ece appears first as cause and then as effect. For the clearest analysis of these interactions, it is necessary to emphasize the distinction between ece and environment, since the latter is employed in both general and special meanings. It has been the practice to speak of the physical and biotic factors of the habitat, but in the strict ecological sense, the physical-chemical conditions are alone to be termed factors. The organisms present belong to the community and, while they may exert profound effects upon each other, these pertain to quite a different category. As a consequence, the directive process for each free-living organism is response to the action of the physical factors, in which is almost immediately involved the beginning of its reaction upon the ece and the coactions between aggregating individuals.

Reaction becomes cumulative and significant only with the development of family and colony, and coaction grows progressively complex as more species enter the community. The social value of response to physical factors is more or less rudimentary, but it does represent a general bond to the extent that only those individuals or species that require or tolerate a particular set of conditions can become or remain aggregated. In reaction, the social influence is much more evident, inasmuch as this process becomes significant only as individuals approach each other and thus begin to cooperate in enhancing or preserving the effect of each. This in itself involves a simple type of coaction, and the latter is steadily developed to constitute the chief bond of all biotic communities. Since animals are typically motile and heterotrophic, they assume the active rôles in coaction as a rule. Many of these interactions, as in the mutual relations of flowers and insects, are definitely social, while others such as the destructive food-coactions may be either asocial or antisocial. However this may be, the need for food has definite if elementary social value for the communities of animals or of animals and plants, and this marks a control that is an advance upon the requirement of plants for favorable physical conditions merely.

Cooperation and Disoperation. The values of reaction and coaction in initiating or maintaining the social group depend primarily upon the

FIGURE 4

BIOTIC COLONY COMPOSED OF A FAMILY OF ANTS AND A CIRCULAR ONE OF ANNUAL WEEDS, EXHIBITING A LOOSE TYPE OF COOPERATION

advantages accruing to individual and species. In the development of a family, the gain derived from reaction upon the habitat is offset in some degree by the disadvantages arising from competition, and these may easily become paramount in cases of crowding. In consequence, the strength of the social bond can best be expressed in terms of the forces that promote integration by contrast with those that hinder or diminish it. The first may be summed up in general under the term *cooperation,* the second under *disoperation.* Both are at work in every community, no matter how simple, and the major task of analysis is to determine the ratio between them. Not only may one be an outcome of the other, but cooperation between certain members of a community may lead to disoperation among others, or the one process may pass more or less completely into the other. At the extreme, disoperation is destruction, but, while this may affect individuals adversely, it may not be without advantage to the species or the social group. In another form, it assumes the guise of competition and may then exercise a definite control upon the equilibrium of the community. This is well exemplified by the structure of a forest, where the social layers are the result of a competition by which the trees come to dominate the canopy and the other species assume subordinate positions in accordance with their competitive equipment.

In conformity with well-known general principles, cooperation in family and colony is regularly expressed in terms of division of labor, increased parental care, or both. Examples of the first are seen in the differentiation of units in the filaments of *Nostoc* and the more highly specialized spheres of *Volvox,* as well as in the peculiar mimicry of the fruiting thallus of the slime-molds. Among plant colonies, it is strikingly exhibited in the lichen thallus, where the rôles of fungus and alga are so nicely adjusted as to give the illusion of a simple organism. Much less integrated but with a unique allotment of tasks are the colonies of flowering plants and anthophiles, a few of which exhibit an obligatory relation between flower and bee, though as a rule a number of species of plant and pollinator are concerned. In the case of many animal families and colonies, both integration and specialization may be carried much further, though in practically all instances increased parental care or at least nutricism is involved.

Increased concern for the protection, nutrition, or general welfare of certain members of the community in itself leads to division of labor. This is usually expressed in terms of parental care of offspring, but it may be directed also to parents, guests, parasites, or symbionts. Naturally, this process is rudimentary in plant societies, though it may be seen in the juvenile families enclosed within the adult *Volvox,* and it is likewise exhibited by the soredia or propagules of many lichens. As a function of the individual parents, it characterizes the formation of families by means of stolons, runners, rootstocks, etc., where the young remain attached to the parent until they are able to support themselves. Division of labor also enters the process when those individuals of a certain type or age alone produce offshoots. Parental care likewise operates with those plants in which buds grow into plantlets on the adult, as it does in a variety of fashions in species where some part of the parent is modified to protect, disseminate, or sow the embryos contained in the seed. This is true of practically all fleshy fruits, but it is most effective in genera like *Stipa* and *Erodium,* in which the awn provided by the parent serves not merely for distribution but also for effective planting. In connection with reproduction, division of labor assumes a great variety of forms, of which the unisexual or dioecious habit is one of the most significant. Increased care is further a regular feature of the symbiosis of plants and animals, as in the cultivation of fungi by ants especially, but it reaches its height in the social insects characterized by nutricism and in particular by trophallaxis (Wheeler, 1923).

In the large and complex communities, such as forest or prairie, as well as in the successional stages that reproduce them, cooperation is present not only in the multitude of component families and colonies, but it is likewise typical of the varied reactions upon climate and soil by which the climax maintains its place. Side by side with cooperative processes of all kinds and degree in the biotic groupings, as well as in the plant matrix, are disoperative ones that tend to change or restrict the expression of social forces. Obviously, these are secondary as long as climax and the controlling climate remain essentially in balance, but they are freed to a larger degree when climate or man brings about profound disturbance. This is what occurs when succession is initiated in bare or denuded areas, as discussed in a later section. The building-up of a particular community is primarily a matter of cooperation in effecting favorable reactions, but after a longer or shorter period of occupation the reactions become disoperative, and the community is gradually displaced through the competition of one better adapted to the changing habitat. This alternation of communities, of cooperation and disoperation, continues until the climax is reached, when it ceases for the lack of successful competitors under the existing climate.

The Community as a Complex Organism. The view that the plant community constitutes an organism of a new order was first advanced in 1901 (cf. Clements, 1904, 1905). With the full recognition of the social bonds between plants and animals, the concept was broadened to apply to the entire biotic grouping, which was regarded as including man, under natural conditions at least (Clements, 1916; Clements and Shelford, 1935). It was later recognized that this view had been foreshadowed in part by Comte (1830), by J. S. Mill (1843), and more particularly by Spencer (1858, 1864), who emphasized certain striking similarities between simple organisms and societies. Essentially the same concept in terms of animal and human societies with higher integration has been actively elaborated during the past decade by the "emergent evolutionists," notably Child (1924), Morgan (1926), Smuts (1926), Sumner and Keller (1927), and Wheeler (1928). In all of these, the basic principle that the whole is greater than the sum of its parts was explicit or implied, but the logical synthesis of all the organisms of a community into a complex one of a new category was not perceived. This theme has been discussed at some length by Clements and Shelford (*loc. cit.*) as the basis for the organization of the field of bio-ecology, which in its primary aspects is regarded as comprising sociology.

In terms of developmental synthesis, this concept of the community has been expressed as follows:

> The plant formation or climax is an organic unit. It exhibits activities or changes which result in development, structure, and reproduction. These changes are progressive or periodic, and in some cases rhythmic, and there can be no objection to regarding them as functions of vegetation. According to this point of view, the formation is a complex organism, which possesses functions and structure, and passes through a cycle of development similar to that of the plant. As an organism, the formation arises, grows, matures, and dies. Its response to the habitat is shown in processes or functions and in structures which are the record as well as the result of these functions. Furthermore, each climax formation is able to reproduce itself, repeating with essential fidelity the stages of its development. The life-history of a formation is a complex but definite process, comparable in its chief features with the life-history of the individual plant. (Clements, 1905, p. 199; 1916, p. 3)

The recognition of the fact that plant and animal communities in reality constituted a biotic unit or biome led to a corresponding modification of the concept of the complex organism. In this, plants formed the matrix of dominants and producents in all terrestrial climaxes, while the animals as consuments and hence as influents of great importance were bound to the matrix by a wide range of coactions. Thus, the inclusion of the animals increased the number and complexity of the social bonds in the community, but affected in no essential fashion the basic features of development, structure, and relationship. Man was likewise regarded as a member of the biome and subject to much the same interactions and controls under primitive conditions, and it was further emphasized that his freedom from the influence of climate and vegetation under modern conditions is more apparent than real, the rural stages of culture marking the long transition. His ability to shift his home, to control his environment to an all but unlimited degree, to expand and transport his food supplies to meet every need, and incidentally to produce profound disturbances in the biotic community, stamp him as a super-dominant, with reactions and coactions peculiar to himself in intensity if not in kind.

By virtue of their simplicity and small or even minute size, families and colonies furnish examples of the complex organism that are most easily appreciated. This is especially true of those with unicellular members, in which increasing integration through division of labor leads to the production of multicellular organisms. In the lichens, the alga may be either one- or many-celled, while the fungus is always the latter. The colonies of fungus-growing ants represent the next general stage in which the fungus has become a producent instead of consument, and the bond is an obligatory food-coaction rather than attachment. In other ant-colonies with guest or parasitoid species, the integration remains definite in spite of the fact that all the members are more or less motile.

As indicated earlier, rooted plants with runners or rootstocks constitute fully integrated families until the connection with the parent is broken, sometimes only after two or three generations. However, the general relations within such families remain essentially the same, except for the gradual detachment of the offspring. The transition to the situation found in the matrix of grassland, for example, may be followed in its major features through the life-history of *Buchloe,* the buffalo-grass of the western plains. This is a bisexual or monoecious species, each plant provided with numerous runners that strike root at each joint. A single individual produces a dense mat-like family, often several yards in extent, in which the new plants exhibit every possible degree of connection with the parent. As these are freed, they often if not regularly become unisexual, i.e., staminate or pistillate, and may then invade the parental mass to form a colony-like group containing three different types of individuals. In short, while the aggregation in multi-individual societies is spatially looser than in the multicellular families and the simple organisms derived from unicellular plants and animals, the processes present many striking similarities, while the differences seem adequately expressed in the term "complex organism."

Community Functions

These embrace the activities or processes that characterize communities of all kinds and degrees. They grow out of the functions and behavior of individuals, but in most if not all cases they represent a response "whole" that is greater than the sum of its parts. Such composite functions are best exemplified in the biotic community, but they inhere also in the smaller societies of plants or animals, or the two combined. Taken together, they not only bring about the growth or development of the climax, but they constitute the entire group of social bonds that integrate the communities in varying degree. Their operation may be traced in nature by appropriate methods, and it may also be reproduced and studied under experimental control. Their final effect is crystallized in terms of structure, as is true of the functions of individual plants, and the respective structures serve as an index to the dynamics of the community, even in the apparently stable climax.

Most of the community functions have been considered in certain of their relations in the preceding pages. A detailed account of them is impossible in the present place, and it must suffice to enumerate them and to emphasize their rôle in the development and behavior of the climax or biome. They fall into more or less natural groupings in the growth sequence, such as aggregation, migration and ecesis, cooperation, reaction and co-action, disoperation and competition. These are combined into complex functions, such as invasion and succession, resembling the growth of the individual in this respect, and they are reflected in the fluctuations of dynamic balance in the more or less stable climax, as shown in aspection, annuation, diurnation, and hibernation, all of which are expressions of seasonal or annual cycles.

Aggregation, Migration, and Ecesis.   Aggregation is the initial process in the formation of all social groups.   It may be immediate, as in the case of budding or the persistence of young about the parent, owing to attachment or the lack of migration, or delayed when seeds, spores, or larvae are first set free and then come together later.   It may be termed simple when individuals of one species are concerned, and mixed when those of two or more are involved.   Aggregation operates in essentially the same fashion with plants and animals, or the two together, though the effect varies with the organisms that are brought into social relation.   It plays a major rôle in succession, integrating the offspring of pioneers into groups capable of cooperation and reaction, and conversely subject to competition and other disoperations.   This process continues to operate in the climax, reflecting the annual variations in climate and filling the gaps as individuals or groups disappear under competition or destructive coaction.   It further bears a constant and reciprocal relation to migration, inasmuch as either may precede or follow the other, and may be aided or hindered by it.

By migration is understood the movement of an organism or group away

FIGURE 5
COLONY OF DUNE-FORMING PERENNIALS, ARISING FROM MIGRATION BY ROOTSTOCKS
AND CAPTURING A WANDERING COASTAL DUNE

from its point of origin or its home. This may be a few inches or thousands of miles; it may be temporary, recurrent, or permanent, and may concern adult, young, or resting stage, such as egg, seed, or spore. Though motile forms move independently, non-motile ones have undergone high specialization for effective transport, as is seen in many seeds and fruits. However, even with seed-plants, a certain type of motility is exhibited by the various types of propagules, such as runners, rootstocks, etc. These serve to maintain something of the group integration, since the movement radiates for a relatively short distance about the parent plant, but this is usually lacking when disseminules are carried to considerable distances by wind, water, or man.

The annual migration of birds and other animals is distinctly a social process, though the aggregation into a huge family or more rarely a colony is temporary and recurrent in the case of most migratory species, including many fishes. In contrast to this process, which is a cyclic re-migration, are the permanent movements or emigrations, which are often social phenomena of great magnitude likewise, but attended with very different consequences. Classical examples of this process are the cyclic migrations of the lemming in the north of Europe, and periodic invasions of hordes of locusts or dragon-flies, all of them probably due to hunger aggregation. Less striking and frequent but much more significant are the mass migrations of great climax communities under the compulsion of climatic changes. In these the basic social bonds of response, reaction, and coaction are maintained more or less intact, and the community moves slowly but irresistibly as a unit, the animals adjusting their advance to that of the much less mobile plant matrix. The outstanding instances of this type are associated with the glacial period, but climatic migration has recurred at every great climatic shift in the past, as is attested by the structure of the biotic mantle of the globe today.

Since the early observations of Darwin and others on carriage by ocean currents, attention has been focused on migration to the exclusion of the crucial rôle of establishment or ecesis, i.e., the making of a home. It is now known that the vast majority of seeds and fruits do not withstand immersion in sea-water, that carriage by birds either through swallowing or attachment is almost wholly ineffective, and that transportation by wind is regularly local in extent. The assumption, still more or less current, that the presence of the same species on isolated mountain peaks in the West is to be explained on the basis of transport by birds or wind is no longer tenable, as the occurrence of many of these in Sweden and the Alps has long indicated. Not only is carriage over such distances impossible, but even more critical is the improbability of reaching places in which ecesis can take place. The primary reason for this is the intense competition offered to newcomers by the community in possession, quite apart from the handicap constituted by different physical factors. Even when plants have been transported to new situations in the same climate and climax, and given more or less care and protection from competition, they have usually succumbed after a few years (Clements and Weaver, 1924). In short, the significance of all migration on land is determined by the test of ecesis, and climatic mass migration furnishes only an apparent exception, in view of the fact that the climax moves only as the climate advances, thus affording the proper conditions for survival.

While ecesis is somewhat less critical in the migration of animals, it still operates more or less decisively. The migration of birds is an annual movement away from changing seasonal conditions in which normal metabolism or survival is increasingly difficult or impossible, and it is also influenced by intensified competition with the young. Though the adjustment brought about seems temporary, it is probably a permanent one, inasmuch as the winter home possesses much the same climatic features as that of the breeding season. Similar movements to maintain themselves within a proper range of conditions are made by other animals, and in all cases there is clear evidence of the integrating action of preferred habitats.

Cooperation, Reaction, and Coaction. It has already been emphasized that simple aggregation leads to both cooperation and competition, and that the former finds one expression in reaction or modification of the home or habitat. Such an outcome is a universal feature of the plant matrix, in which the animals have a certain though much smaller share, except in the communities of deep water. This difference between the two rôles is denoted by terming the controlling plants of a community the *dominants* by virtue of their reactions, while the animals are known as *influents,* in consequence of exerting their chief effects through the plants. Reactions exist in the greatest variety, every factor of the habitat coming under their sway. In the case of aerial conditions, their magnitude may be seen in the sharp contrast between the interior of a forest and a sunny meadow. The light intensity is the factor most modified by the leafy canopy, but accompanying this are significant modifications of temperature, humidity, effective rainfall, etc. Similarly, the soil is not only greatly changed by the decay of plant parts and the activities of roots, but it also owes its formation and characteristic properties chiefly to the reactions of plants, with the cooperation of burrowing rodents, ants, earthworms, etc. In consequence, reaction is considered the primary social bond in the plant matrix, existing in its simplest form with pioneer families and colonies, becoming more complex with the entrance of animal reactors and bringing about a high degree of integration in the climax biome.

In their rôle as influents, animals exert their effect either by means of interactions among themselves or with plants. Such coactions may be cooperative in varying degrees, or they may be disoperative; in many instances the two are combined in some measure. Since they comprise all the relations between associated organisms, their number is beyond practical reckoning, but they may be summarized under a few general types. By virtue of their motility and manner of nutrition, animals are for the most part the active agents or coactors in the interactions with plants, which thus serve as food, material, or shelter. The food relation in particular binds the herbivores to the plant matrix of the community, while carnivores are similarly linked directly to the herbivores and indirectly to the plants. In rare cases, the situation may be reversed and plants become coactors, as in insectivorous species, but these are too few to be of community significance.   Heterotrophic plants, such as bacteria and fungi, universally assume the rôle of coactor and then resemble animals in being influents of greater or less importance.   In symbiotic communities, the relations are more evenly balanced, though one organism takes the lead or secures the larger share of benefits as a rule.

Disoperation and Competition.   Disoperation includes the entire range of unfavorable coactions from complete destruction at one extreme to competitions of minor intensity and slight disadvantage at the other.   It may even be mutual in certain cases, such as the grazing of poisonous plants by sheep, or the dependence of a single species of flower and pollinator upon each other.   Moreover, in the more complex communities, disoperation involving two species often results in a beneficial effect upon others articulated in a series of coactions, or at least in a reduction of the amount of harm done.   A much-discussed instance of this is found on the ranges of the West, where the interactions of coyotes, sheep, rodents, grasses and other herbs bring certain benefits out of what appears on the surface to be a sequence of destructions.   Out of such complex relations comes the apparent paradox of disoperation often producing what are essentially cooperative values and hence serving in some measure to integrate the community rather than loosening the bonds within it. This is more or less regularly exemplified in the case of competition, in which two species or more may handicap each other but in so doing bring a certain advantage to some of their associates.   Such an outcome is readily seen to have its parallel in the interactions of human groups, even to the extent of enacting legislation to promote competition.

In aquatic communities, competition may exist between plants and animals, as in the presence of a limited supply of oxygen, but on land this type of coaction is practically confined to animals on the one hand and plants on the other.   The essence of competition is a joint demand in excess of the immediate supply of food, materials, energy sources, working conditions, space, mates, superior ranking, and so forth.   In plant communities, as in the plant matrix, the chief demands are for raw materials in food-making and for supplies of radiant energy, and hence the keenest competition is for water and minerals in the soil and for incoming light in the air.   The resulting struggle is most severe between species with similar demands, which are usually indicated in the life-form, such as tree, shrub, grass, herb, etc.   Out of this comes the sorting of the constituent species into dominants, subdominants, and subordinates, which form strata or layers of diminishing rank, and this process is accompanied by the suppression or elimination of the weaker individuals or species.   The nature and outcome of competition and the weapons that plants employ have been studied both in experimental cultures and in garden and field, with the result that the community significance of the process is fairly well understood in certain climaxes, such as the prairie especially (Clements, Weaver, and Hanson, 1929).

Our knowledge of competition among animals is still general in character, in the absence of definite quantitative and experimental investigations. Although based upon the same relation between demand and a limited supply, this process in animal groups is centered about elaborated food rather than raw materials and radiant energy. The motility of land animals in general introduces another difference that finds expression in spatial relations, or what has been termed "territory." This is exhibited especially by birds, but occurs likewise with some mammals, insects, and other animals. In birds, it represents an area sufficiently large to furnish the food necessary to rear a family, and is thus an outcome of the needs of a social group. The limits of territories are apparently drawn with considerable definiteness and are maintained vigorously against trespass, calling forth coactions of attack and defense. Not only is the need for food, the "hunger drive," a more or less regular force in social integration, but it also brings about other social responses. These are seen especially in the development of the herd among grazing animals as a means of protection, and a similar phenomenon is found in the formation of packs among carnivores for hunting and offense. In all such societies, whether temporary or permanent, competition is a constant feature, but one necessarily subordinated to the primary motive for aggregation. Offense and defense also frequently enter into the competition for mates, while "courting" is another type of sex response with distinct social value.

Invasion and Succession. Among plants, invasion comprises not merely the migration into a bare area or an existing community, but also the ecesis of the invaders so that they actually take possession and hold the ground for some time. This statement applies equally to animals as members of a community, though their motility also permits drifting or temporary raids. Bare areas naturally afford the best opportunity for invasion because of the absence of competitors, and open communities permit it to a larger or smaller degree. It is increasingly difficult as they become more fully integrated, and almost impossible in the climax biome on account of the thoroughness with which the dominant and subdominant plants maintain possession. As has been stated previously, the influent animals exert a different and secondary control through coaction, but nevertheless the balance of numbers permits only a certain degree of fluctuation, so that competition at times of maxima is a regular stimulus for emigration. The resulting hordes can establish themselves only as they enter territory unoccupied by that particular life-form, and in the instances most studied, namely, the lemming, springbuck, locust, and dragonfly, migration leads to destruction.

Succession is a series of invasions, passing over the same area in more or less definite sequence. It is initiated only in bare soils that have been newly formed, recently exposed or denuded, though in this connection shallow water and rock are to be regarded as soils, since they permit invasion. The pioneers may be either plants or animals, or both, but plants constitute the chief reactors and hence direct the course of succession. This begins with families of submerged plants in pond and lakelet, and of lichens on rock surfaces, and by aggregation and extension these develop into colonies.   In both types of habitat, the dominants cooperate to produce soil; in water this is accomplished by the deposition of silt and the accumulation of organic remains, on rock it is brought about by corrosion and the much slower deposition of humus.   As the water is shallowed in the one case and the layer of soil deepened in the other, species of greater requirements invade and through their competition gradually displace the occupants.   In ponds the submerged pioneers are dispossessed by floating pondweeds and water-lilies, while on rock the crust-like lichens yield to larger foliose ones and these in turn to mosses. In the case of both, successive communities of higher demands appear and disappear by virtue of continuing migration, aggregation, reaction, and competition, until the final stage or climax is reached.   This is in essential equilibrium with the climate and can be displaced by no other population without an effective change of climate, unless fire or other destructive agencies intervene.

FIGURE 6

PRIMARY SUCCESSION FROM OPEN WATER, REPRESENTED BY AN AMPHIBIOUS COMMUNITY OF RUSHES AND BULRUSHES IN DEATH VALLEY

While succession of this type is frequent and universal, occurring wherever primary soils are to be found, the shorter and simpler process typical of soils denuded by various agencies is far more common. Though natural causes do operate in producing such soils, the activities of man in terms of fire, clearing, lumbering, cultivating, and construction are vastly more important, with the consequence that countries long settled are a mosaic of secondary successions, with the virgin climax reduced to a relatively few fragments. The drive and the course of such successions are the same essentially as in the primary ones, but their duration is much abridged by the existence of a soil already formed and often also the presence of seeds or propagules for immediate colonization. Annual herbs usually appear the first year, accompanied by various insects, and are replaced in a few seasons by perennials, which in their turn are dispossessed by grasses. In prairie, these constitute the climax organism, but in a forest climate the sequence continues through stages of shrubs and trees to a permanent community of the latter. In all of these, co-operation in terms of reaction is naturally confined chiefly to the air factors, especially light, but competition plays an even larger rôle. The animals of the original climax are either destroyed or driven out by most of the denuding agencies, and by fire in particular, but in regions not too intensively cultivated they gradually re-enter the stages indicated by their food and other coactions.

In harmony with the concept of the complex organism, succession is regarded as the growth or development of the adult or climax and the various stages as embryonic and juvenile forms of it. In other words, it is a complex function of the community, much as growth is a correlation of the several functions of the individual plant. In each stage are represented the chief social bonds that bring about the integration of the successive adolescent communities, but from the standpoint of the adult organism there is a further major bond involved in the fact that each population prepares the way more or less directly for the succeeding one. In consequence, succession is considered to possess a twofold social value, expressed by bonds within as well as between communities, and thus to give to the climax a degree of integration that marks a new category of organisms.

Nature and Structure of the Climax. The climax as a complex organism naturally possesses certain of the attributes of the simple organism as seen in ordinary plants and animals. Chief among these is the fact that it consists not merely of the adult community, but likewise comprises all the developmental stages that lead up to it. Under natural conditions, the climax occupies by far the larger portion of its climatic area, but this is interspersed with primary successions on new soils and secondary ones on denuded soils. The first represent growth processes through which the climax adds to its mass, while the second is the method by which destroyed parts are regenerated. Both have their counterparts in perennial plants and especially in shrubs, where normal buds and offshoots produce new parts and adventitious ones bring about regeneration when stem or shoot is injured. The other significant parallel between plant and climax lies in the fact that both are activated by the habitat, which controls the expression of the inherent nature of each in terms of development that leads to a characteristic structure. Furthermore, much as new forms of plants are produced by changes in the directing physical factors, so are climaxes differentiated into two or more derived ones by shifting climates. In short, the climax has attained a degree of social integration in which it exhibits a proper development, structure, and evolution, resembling the multicellular individual in these three respects, but differing in the details by virtue of its multi-individual nature.

Within itself, each climax formation or biome exhibits not only juvenile and adult stages or communities, but in addition more or less definite divisions or structures of the adult matrix or actual climax. These are primarily responses to regional variations in the controlling climate, though the past experience of the component dominants and influents is involved also. For example, in the prairie and plains of North America can be recognized three groups of dominant grasses derived respectively from

FIGURE 7

CLIMAX COMMUNITY OF ARCTIC-ALPINE TUNDRA ON THE SUMMIT OF PIKES PEAK, THE THISTLES INDICATING REACTION AND COACTION BY POCKET GOPHERS

mass migration operating from the circumpolar area, from the montane
Southwest and the subtropical Southeast. In their advance and mingling,
these have been sorted out by the subclimates of the grassland climate to
produce a number of corresponding communities or *associations,* each occupying a distinct geographic region. Such are the true prairie of the
Missouri Valley, the mixed prairie of the Great Plains, the desert savan-
nahs of the Southwest, and the bunch-grass prairie of California (Clements, 1920). These are bound together not only by their common response
to a grassland climate, but especially by certain wide-ranging dominants
and influents. A similar structure is displayed by the deciduous forest
of the East, which comprises three associations, namely, the beech-maple,
oak-chestnut, and oak-hickory. Associations are themselves differentiated
into other communities, such as *consociations* characterized by the more
or less exclusive control of a single grass or tree dominant, and *faciations,*
which mark regional responses of the association, as the latter does of the
climax or formation.

The social complexity of the climax is further displayed in the numerous
smaller groupings contained within it, such as societies and clans in the
adult matrix, and socies, colonies, and families in the various successions.
From the standpoint of structure, the most important and extensive of
these are the societies, though the socies may sometimes approach them in
large developmental communities, such as subclimax forests or reed swamps.
Clans are essentially small societies, probably due to the fragmentation
resulting from competition, while families and colonies owe their abundance to the widespread operation of succession, especially as an aftermath
of disturbance. The most conspicuous societies are those of subdominant
perennials, denoted by the fact that in consequence of competition they
assume a rank subordinate to that of the dominant trees or grasses. In
the further action of cooperation and competition, these may be grouped
in layer societies, in forest especially, or they may be arranged in a sequence determined by the seasons. This ensues from the fact that the
greatest demands of each society are made at the time of flowering, and
competition is evaded in large measure by seasonal grouping into spring,
summer, and autumn societies. Here again the plants form the matrix
of such communities, but animals also contribute to the social bond, particularly in the case of pollinating insects and such highly integrated
colonies as those of bees and ants (Clements and Long, 1923).

Concrete examples of succession are known as *seres,* and these are designated as *priseres* or *subseres* in accordance with their primary or secondary
character, the one arising on new soils, the other on denuded ones. Both
consist of a series of stages or communities, of which all but the initial
ones possess a complex social structure. In this respect they resemble the
divisions of the climax and in accordance are termed *associes.* This suffix
is employed to designate developmental or seral communities in contrast
with the adult ones, and is further utilized in such subdivisions as the
consocies and *socies,* corresponding to consociation and society in the climax. As succession advances, the later associes increase in degree of

integration and hence in relative permanence. This is particularly true of the last one, which precedes the climax and is consequently termed the *subclimax*. Because of its relation to initial disturbance and of its duration, the subclimax is the prevailing type of community where the coactions of man are controlling, illustrated by the "piney woods" of the Coastal Plain and the "short-grass plains" of the West.

In conclusion, it appears hardly necessary to emphasize the manifold nature of social integration in the climax biome. This is exemplified in varying degree by the several types of subordinate communities within both climax and sere, from its most tangible expression in the innumerable families and colonies to the much more intricate pattern in climax and subclimax. It assumes the form of a developmental or ontogenetic bond between associes in each sere, and these are further articulated by their convergence as they approach the climax and by their final transformation into it. Behind these lies the great phylogenetic bond between climaxes, which has arisen out of the evolution of an earlier "eoclimax" through climatic differentiation and subsequent mass migration. This is strikingly exemplified by the close relationships of the great grassland, deciduous, coniferous, and arctic climaxes of North America and Eurasia, and by the even closer connection between the arctic and alpine tundras, and the boreal and montane coniferous forests of our own continent. How intimate the bond may be within and between climax communities is most graphically demonstrated by relict fragments left behind during the great migrations of the past (Clements, 1934). Such relicts of the pine-hemlock or the beech-maple climax still persist today, hundreds of miles from the main body and after thousands of years of competition pressure from an encircling climax favored by the general climate.

SELECTED REFERENCES

ALLEE, W. C. 1931. Animal aggregations: a study in general sociology. Chicago: Univ. Chicago Press. Pp. 440.

ALVERDES, F. 1927. Social life in the animal world. New York: Harcourt, Brace. (Trans. by K. C. Creasy.) Pp. 225.

CHILD, C. M. 1924. Physiological foundations of behavior. New York: Holt. Pp. xii+330.

CLEMENTS, F. E. 1901. The fundamental principles of vegetation. (Abstract.) *Amer. Asso. Adv. Sci.*, Denver, 1901.

————. 1904. The development and structure of vegetation. *Rep. Bot. Survey Nebr.*, No. 7. Pp. 175.

————. 1905. Research methods in ecology. Lincoln, Nebr.: Univ. Publ. Co. Pp. viii+334.

————. 1907. Plant physiology and ecology. New York: Holt. Pp. xv+315.

————. 1916. Plant succession. An analysis of the development of vegetation. *Carnegie Instit. Washington Publ.* 242. Pp. xiii+512.

————. 1920. Plant indicators. The relation of plant communities to process and practice. *Carnegie Instit. Washington Publ.* 290. Pp. xvi+388.

————. 1929. Plant succession and indicators. New York: Wilson. Pp. xvi+453.

————. 1934. The relict method in dynamic ecology. *J. Ecol.*, **22**, 39-68.

CLEMENTS, F. E., & LONG, F. L. 1923. Experimental pollination. An outline of the ecology of flowers and insects. *Carnegie Instit. Washington Publ.* 336. Pp. vii+274.

CLEMENTS, F. E., & SHELFORD, V. E. 1935. Bio-ecology. (In press.)

CLEMENTS, F. E., & WEAVER, J. E. 1924. Experimental vegetation. The relation of climaxes to climate. *Carnegie Instit. Washington Publ.* 355. Pp. vii+172.

CLEMENTS, F. E., WEAVER, J. E., & HANSON, H. C. 1929. Plant competition. An analysis of community functions. *Carnegie Instit. Washington Publ.* 398. Pp. xvi+340.

COMTE, A. 1830. Cours de philosophie positive.

DEEGENER, P. 1918. Die Formen der Vergesellschaftung im Tierreiche. Ein systematisch-soziologischer Versuch. Leipzig: Veit. Pp. xii+420.

ESPINAS, A. S. 1878. Des sociétés animales. Paris: Baillière. Pp. 588.

MILL, J. S. 1843. A system of logic ratiocinative and inductive. London & New York: Longmans. Pp. xv+662.

MORGAN, C. L. 1926. Emergent evolution. London: Williams & Norgate; New York: Holt. Pp. xi+313.

PARK, R. E., & BURGESS, E. W. 1921. Introduction to the science of sociology. Chicago: Univ. Chicago Press. Pp. xxiii+1040.

PECKHAM, G. W., & PECKHAM, E. G. 1898. On the instincts and habits of the solitary wasps. *Wis. Geol. Nat. Hist. Survey Bull.* 2. Pp. iv+245.

ROWAN, W. 1931. The riddle of migration. Baltimore, Md.: Williams & Wilkins. Pp. xiv+151.

————. 1932. Experiments in bird migration. *Proc. Nat. Acad. Sci.*, **18**, 639-654.

SMUTS, J. C. 1926. Holism and evolution. New York: Macmillan. Pp. vii+362.

SPENCER, H. 1858. Essays.

————. 1864. Principles of biology.

SUMNER, W. G., & KELLER, J. C. 1927. The science of society. (4 vols.) New Haven, Conn.: Yale Univ. Press. Pp. xxxii+1-754; xxii+735-1481; xxi+1482-2251, xxi+1-1331.

WEAVER, J. E., & CLEMENTS, F. E. 1929. Plant ecology. New York: McGraw-Hill. Pp. xx+520.

WHEELER, W. M. 1923. Social life among the insects. New York: Harcourt, Brace. Pp. vii+375.

————. 1928. Emergent evolution and the development of societies. New York: Norton. Pp. 80.

————. 1930. Societal evolution. In *Human biology and racial welfare*, ed. by E. V. Cowdry. New York: Hoeber. Pp. 139-155.

CHAPTER 3

HUMAN POPULATIONS

WARREN S. THOMPSON

*Scripps Foundation for Research
in Population Problems*

I. THE PATTERN OF POPULATION GROWTH

In spite of the fact that almost nothing is known regarding the growth of human populations in past ages it is quite commonly assumed that there has always been a more or less steady growth in man's numbers. It is not difficult to understand why this should be so when modern census data are studied. Every country for which reliable census data are available has shown a fairly large and in most cases a fairly steady growth from the very beginning of its census taking. Sweden, which has the longest series of actual census data, grew from 1,780,678 in 1750 to 6,190,364 in 1932. Even France, the slowest-growing European country during the nineteenth century, increased from 27,394,003 inhabitants in 1801 to 39,790,000 in 1913, while the United States now has over 30 times as many people as it had in 1790. It is not surprising, then, if increase in numbers seems to many people the normal condition for a human population. It is quite certain, however, as will be shown presently, that throughout vastly the greater part of man's life on the earth this cannot have been the case.

Table 1 gives the best data on China's population at different periods that the author has been able to find. The movement of numbers as indicated in these data has been very erratic, so erratic that one is disposed to give them little credence until after 1792, even when the varying area of the country at different times is taken into account. However, considerable reading in Chinese history and a careful study of all the discussions of China's population growth in past times which he can read have convinced the author that, even though the figures given cannot be relied upon, they probably do present a fair picture of the general character of population movements in China in past ages. It is highly probable that there has been no continuous movement either of increase or decrease in the numbers of the Chinese over any considerable period of time. Rather there appear to have been irregular movements of growth and decline depending chiefly upon whether the social and economic conditions of the period were conducive to a low or a high death rate.

II. BIOLOGICAL AND SOCIAL THEORIES OF POPULATION GROWTH

Estimates of the population in Greece and Rome, like those for China, are very unsatisfactory. But, like similar discussions of China's population movements, they tend to confirm the belief that considerable fluctuations in numbers were by no means unusual. Assuming, then, that

[49]

TABLE 1
ESTIMATES OF CHINA'S POPULATION*

Ninth Century B. C.	21,753,528	North of Yang-tze River
At time of Christ	80,000,000	North of Nan-ling Mountains
280 A. D.	23,180,000	
606 A. D.	46,019,956	North of Nan-ling Mountains
754	70,000,000	
976	16,000,000	Taxable persons
1021	43,388,380	
1102	100,095,250	
1381	59,850,000	
1412	65,377,000	
1580	60,692,000	
1662	21,068,600	
1668	25,386,209	
1710	23,312,200	
"	27,241,129	
1711	28,241,129	
1736	125,046,245	
1743	157,343,975	
"	149,332,730	
"	150,265,475	
1753	103,050,600	
1760	143,125,225	
"	203,916,477	
1761	205,293,053	
1790	155,249,897	
1792	307,467,200	
"	333,000,000	
1812	362,467,183	
"	360,440,000	
1842	413,021,000	
1868	404,946,514	
1881	380,000,000	
1882	381,309,000	
1885	377,636,000	
1895	421,000,000	
1902	439,947,271	
1910	438,373,680	
"	372,563,495	
1923	436,094,953	
1926	485.508 838	Does not include Sinkiang and Tibet

*These data, except the second figure for 1910, were taken from S. Wells Williams: *The Middle Kingdom,* vol. 1, pp. 258-273, and from *The China Year Book,* 1932, pp. 1 and 2. The smaller figure for 1910 is taken from a letter to the author in which Mr. Shih-ta Wang, who has made a special study of the Minchengpu census (1910-1911), discusses the results of his work.

fluctuations in numbers have been more or less characteristic of man's life in any given area, two possible explanations of them may be advanced. They may be due either to the environing conditions of the population or to changes in its inherited traits. The former explanation, to which the author is inclined, holds that fluctuations in numbers are to be explained by the particular social and economic conditions existing at a given time and place. According to this theory wars, famines, pestilences, particular modes of living (city life), particular attitudes of mind (generally associated, of course, with particular modes of living), and the physiological effects of particular modes of living would be regarded as the chief causes of fluctuations in population growth. Hence, if a population were to decline the explanation would first be sought in the events or conditions which in some way led to a maladjustment of the population to its environment or to a change in environment which necessitated a downward adjustment in its numbers.

On the other hand, the biological explanation holds that there are basic changes going on in man's hereditary nature which operate to increase or decrease his numbers. Such changes are regarded by the proponents of this view as of vastly greater importance, in the long run, than the environmental factors mentioned above. Pearl and Gini may be regarded as the most important advocates of this view at the present time. Its support seems naturally to lead to the belief that a life-cycle of some kind is, in the last analysis, responsible for the fluctuations in population growth which have been observed in human history. It is maintained that the capacity of man to reproduce passes through a cycle. At certain points in the cycle the urge to reproduce is very great and at this period population growth is large. At another point this urge declines and with it population growth declines until there may be an actual decline in numbers.

In Pearl's work there is a definite attempt to establish a law of population growth similar to the law of growth of the *Drosophila* (fruit-fly), which he found took the form of a logistic curve. Pearl recognizes, however, that for man the social and economic conditions of his life modify the biological law governing the growth of animal populations. But, even so, he places the emphasis upon the biological factors in population growth, and the cause of fluctuations in the size of populations is sought in a biological law rather than in the external circumstances of human life.

The theory of population growth as developed by Gini goes much beyond that of Pearl in several respects. There is something almost mystical in the fluctuations of the urge to growth as envisaged by Gini. This urge to reproduce is perhaps somewhat analogous to the *élan vital* in the philosophy of Bergson. It seems to be something which is a part of man and yet to have an existence quite apart from him. The growth of the race is, therefore, little affected by the particular conditions of his environment. This biological principle governing man's growth in numbers is also supposed to be closely related to, if not the source of, the energy he displays in developing his civilization. The general character of the population movements induced by this principle of life is cyclical as is also the movement of civilization, since the latter in fact derives its vitality from the former. The movement of human life on the earth may, therefore, be likened to the life of an individual. There is a period of very rapid growth accompanied by an accumulation of strength—a period of youth; this is followed by a period of maturity in which achievement takes the place of growth; and lastly there is a period of senescence—a period of growing old and weak, to be followed, perhaps, by "the dark ages" before a new dawn and the commencement of a new cycle.

As was said above there is something rather mystical about Gini's treatment of population growth. Perhaps this is because the biological principle invoked as cause is yet obscure. But it seems more scientific not to invoke an unknown principle to explain population growth when the effects of man's social and economic conditions upon his numbers are so obvious and when they are as yet but little explored. It appears to the author more reasonable to assume that population growth varies according to the actual environing conditions of life rather than according to some internal quality of life itself. These external circumstances may at times repress growth through a high death rate as is the case in China and India today, as well as in many other parts of the world; or they may operate through a low birth rate brought about by sexual tabus and abortion, or, as in our own days, by voluntary control of conception. It is also possible that a low birth rate may result from some physiological derangement of the bodily functions arising from a given manner of life, e.g., the sedentary habits of many urban dwellers. Besides there are numerous environmental circumstances which create attitudes of mind either favorable to population growth, as, for example, pioneering, ease of securing a living, low standards of household care, and public approval of large families; or unfavorable to population growth, as the difficulty of finding work, public condemnation of large families, increasing freedom of women, and rising standards of living.

All these factors must be studied carefully and their influence on population growth in any given community must be evaluated with precision if we are to understand this growth as a natural phenomenon. If such study shows that there are still unexplained factors in population growth, then, and not until then, will it be necessary to assume fundamental changes in man's hereditary reproductive capacity, or some vital and immanent, though unknown, principle governing population movements; also whether these movements conform to any regular pattern, e.g., the cyclical, a straight-line trend, or can be expressed by some other formula which may be looked upon as a definite law of growth from which future numbers can be predicted. However, until such a biological law of human reproduction is clearly proved it will be better to confine our explanations of fluctuations in population growth to those social, personal, and economic factors which affect the reproductive life of individuals.

It is highly probable that the biological theory of population growth has had a considerable vogue in recent years because of the very rapid decline in the birth rate which has been taking place. In the very nature of the case it is impossible to prove beyond question that this decline is solely or even chiefly the result of the voluntary prevention of conception, of an increase in abortion, of a growing maladjustment between the individual organism and its environment, or of any combination of these together with other environing factors. Since this is the case it is not especially surprising that many persons have felt inclined to attribute the decline in the birth rate to some biological principle controlling fluctuations in the reproduction of living organisms. It is scarcely scientific, however, because of this lack of proof of the part played by particular social factors, to discard them altogether and to proceed as Gini has done to erect a comprehensive theory of social evolution—growth, maturity, senescence—upon a biological theory of population growth of which there is even less proof. It savors of the search for the philosopher's stone. It would be fine if such a simple explanation of the ups and downs in the lives of nations and peoples could be found, for it would enormously lighten the task of students of social science. What is needed, however, is not a simple explanation but a true one—one which illuminates the processes of population growth, enabling us to understand them and, in the end, to control them for the greater welfare of mankind. To achieve this end the adjustments of man to his surroundings must be studied far more carefully than has been done hitherto.

III. MAN'S REPRODUCTIVE POWER

As long as procreation is largely uncontrolled and survival, in large measure, depends upon the natural rigors of life it would be expected that man's numbers would be influenced greatly by natural events. Under conditions where procreation is uncontrolled as was largely the case during our pioneering days the average woman could easily give birth to five or six children between her seventeenth and twenty-seventh years. If four of these children lived to their twenty-seventh year and reproduced at the same rate, the population would double each 27 years even if every one died upon reaching that age. It is therefore well within the limits of possibility that population should double in about 25 years as Malthus assumed, and there is good reason to believe that such a rate of growth has actually taken place at certain periods, for example, during the days when the agricultural lands of the United States were being settled. But doubling in 25 years by no means represents the highest possible rate of human growth, for just as a woman may easily bear five or six children by the time she is 27 so she may have eight or nine by the time she is 35. If six of these survive to reproduce in like manner it is obvious that 35 years would see the tripling of the population even allowing for the death of the parents at this age. But, if it seems that a 25-per-cent allowance for wastage by death is too little, a still further allowance can be made by assuming that all children born to women over 35 fail to survive to reproduce.

Let us see what such rates of increase would actually mean in the growth of population. In 540 years a single couple would have 2,097,000 descendants if the numbers doubled each 27 years and 45,956,000 descendants if they tripled every 35 years. In 1080 years the figures would be 2,199 billions and 1,056,000 billions, respectively. Similar calculations have frequently been made since the days of Malthus. Their only usefulness is to show, as Malthus did, that very seldom in human history has man actually increased in numbers at anything like his maximum capacity. Obviously an explanation of why he has not so increased will throw much light on the processes of population growth.

Another way to indicate how little of man's reproductive power has ever been actualized in population growth is to take a given population, let us say the estimated 22,000,000 of China in the ninth century B.C., and see what rate of increase would give the 400,000,000 so commonly claimed today. If a population starting at 22,000,000 were to grow steadily for 2800 years and amounted to 400,000,000 at' the end of that time the yearly rate of increase would be but one per 1000 per year. The average period of doubling would be 669 years. At any given moment a population growing no faster than this would be considered stationary by most people. Certainly unless we possessed longer records than are now in existence we could not with safety speak of a trend of population in a country growing at this rate. This is well illustrated by the situation in France during these last decades when one can speak of a trend only with certain reservations. Indeed, most students have been disposed to think of the French population as stationary since the Franco-Prussian war, although there have been only a few years since then, except during the World War, when births have not exceeded deaths by more than 1 per 1000.

IV. FACTORS LIMITING POPULATION GROWTH

Calculations of growth such as those made above are of academic interest only, yet they do raise the question which worried Mathus and which still concerns all those who, like him, are anxious to understand the relations between population growth and human welfare, namely, why it is that there is such a vast discrepancy between man's reproductive power and his actual growth. The answer Malthus first gave was that population, because of man's natural reproductive urge, always tended to grow faster than subsistence or food (he seemed at times to use these terms interchangeably), hence man was doomed to perpetual poverty unless in some way he could curb this urge. Later he recognized many factors other than lack of food as limiting man's growth in numbers. But, even though we now recognize many shortcomings in Malthus' theories, yet we cannot fail to acknowledge that this work was basic in helping to lay the foundations for the scientific study of population growth which has since developed. It was not until man was ready to study his own growth as an ecological problem, i.e., as a problem of his adjustment to his environment, both physical and social, that he could make any substantial progress in understanding the why and wherefore of his numbers. It would be a great mistake, however, to suppose that man's growth in numbers has ever been solely a problem of his adjustment to his physical environment. No doubt there have been many times when population growth was largely determined by the relations between man and his physical surroundings; when a scanty or an abundant food supply determined his numbers, when endemic and epidemic diseases took a heavy and fairly regular toll of human lives, thus keeping numbers down, and when climate has been decisive in population growth both through the rigors of life it introduced and the limits it placed to the food supply in such areas as the Far North.

A. Social Checks. But even though the physical environment is very potent in determining man's growth there has never been a time in human history when there were not many social, that is man-made, checks to the growth of human populations. In the light of what is known today about such checks among primitive peoples as well as among civilized peoples before modern birth control, Malthus' assumptions that births were determined solely, or almost solely, by the capacity of women to conceive and bear children and that the growth of population was limited in large part by the means of subsistence appears rather naïve. He seems never to have recognized the full importance of the social checks to the birth rate or the economic significance of the industrial revolution, in the midst of which he was living. His blindness in these matters is probably due to the fact that he lived at a time when many of the older social checks to population growth were being loosened to such an extent that he was not even aware of their existence, and that he did not appreciate how the industrial revolution was increasing the productivity of human labor, thus making possible a release of population pressure such as the world had never known previously.

In order to make clear the effects of the social checks to population growth which have existed from time immemorial it will be well to describe rather briefly some of these checks and to indicate how they affect man's numbers. Sexual tabus of various kinds have been almost universal in past times. The net effect of all such tabus is to reduce the birth rate by withdrawing women from the exposure to conception for longer or shorter periods. Sometimes for as much as half of the childbearing period primitive woman is thus rendered sterile. These sexual tabus are also frequently associated with a prolonged period of nursing children which of itself has a somewhat depressing effect on the birth rate. As a result of these customs among many primitive peoples the average number of children born to a woman surviving the childbearing period often does not exceed four or five. This is certainly fewer than most of our grandmothers bore.

No doubt the small number of births per woman among many peoples who know almost nothing of the control of conception is frequently the result of abortion rather than of few conceptions; for abortion appears to have been almost universally practiced from the earliest times. The methods used to induce abortion are legion and where the practice has been more or less sanctioned by the community, as has very frequently been the case in the past, it alone may account for a relatively low birth rate. There is no need to dwell long upon the effect of abortion on population growth. That it is widespread is generally acknowledged, even though it is now illegal in most of the Western World. It is, in fact, so common that many physicians believe as many conceptions are terminated in this manner as by live births. In the very nature of the case no clear proof of such a statement can be adduced. There is not the least doubt, however, that throughout human history abortion has been one of the very important checks man has used to keep down his birth rate.

But man did not limit his purposeful control over numbers to reducing the birth rate. After children have been born he has quite commonly practiced infanticide. In Western lands the open practice of infanticide was well established among the Greeks and early Romans and although it gradually came under the ban of both the church and state it is not entirely wiped out yet although in this part of the world it is of comparatively little consequence as a check to population growth at the present time. This is not true, however, in the East. There infanticide is still of some importance as a check of population. Also it is of more importance than its absolute amount would indicate because it is practiced largely on female infants. Where men outnumber women by as much as 10 per cent to 50 per cent, as appears to be the case in most Chinese communities, it needs no argument to prove that population growth is affected by such a deficit of women. It may be maintained, of course, that this disparity of the sexes is not due to infanticide but rather to a high proportion of male births. As yet, however, there is no very convincing evidence that such a great disparity between the sexes at time of birth is a natural phenomenon.

There are still other of man's customs and institutions which directly affect his growth in numbers, for example, late marriages and concubinage, but on the whole they are probably of less importance in recent times than those customs and institutions which engender individual attitudes of mind favorable or unfavorable to fertility; for these latter largely determine whether the individual will or will not make use of the generally known methods of controlling the number of his or her offspring. At the present time these attitudes of mind are probably of greater importance than all other factors combined and thus merit as detailed discussion as space will allow. But before pursuing further this matter of the effects of social attitudes on population growth in the industrialized West, it may be well to turn attention to those physical events which have exercised great and direct effects upon population growth in all past ages and which are still of prime importance in the greater part of the world.

B. *Catastrophic Factors in Population Growth.* The life of man has been a continuous effort at adaptation to his surroundings. Man not only attempted to adjust his life to his physical surroundings but also to alter these surroundings so that they would yield him more comfort and leisure. His population policies have been developed merely as one phase of his efforts to make life more tolerable. Sometimes these population policies have been quite successful in the sense that numbers have been rather nicely adjusted to the means available for their support. At such times life has been relatively easy and a high degree of social stability has ensued. At other times, and they probably include much of the greater part of man's history, the struggle for life has been bitter and numbers have fluctuated in accordance with his ability to wrest the necessities of life from his environment or to resist the onslaughts of disease and to ward off his enemies. There is much truth, therefore, in Malthus' contention that man's life has been a constant struggle to provide the necessities of life to a population larger than he could adequately support at the given moment with the resources and techniques at his disposal.

History is full of facts which warrant the belief that by and large man has not been very successful in adjusting his numbers to his productive capacity. Chinese history, for example, is replete with tales of wars and famines and floods and pestilences which swept away people by the millions. The aggregate of the losses from these disasters which were of sufficient importance to attract the attention of the historians of the time cannot even be guessed at but that it amounted to many hundreds of millions, perhaps to thousands of millions, during the last 3000 years seems highly probable. How prevalent famine has been in China is well attested by the following quotation:

> . . . a study recently completed by the Student Agricultural Society of the University of Nanking brought to light the surprising and significant fact that between the years 108 B.C. and 1911 A.D. there were 1,828 famines, or one nearly every year in some one of the provinces. (Mallory, 1926, p. 1)

Prevalent as famine is shown to be by such a study, it undoubtedly understates the facts, for in almost all countries lacking modern transportation facilities local famines are of almost yearly occurrence. They are so common that they are not regarded as of sufficient importance to record. Walford, from a study of the history of the British Isles, a region highly equable climatically, found that 201 famines had occurred between 10 A.D. and 1846 A.D.; one about every nine years. Walford is also authority for the statement that 34 famines occurred in India from 1769 to 1878. Here, too, it is more than probable that many local famines never came under the historian's eye.

Most of those who read this will have no difficulty in recalling the great Russian famine of 1918-1922 and several famines of almost equal extent in China since 1920. These very recent famines alone are variously estimated to have cost between 10,000,000 and 15,000,000 lives directly through loss by hunger and the epidemics of typhus, plague, cholera, etc. which followed them. Besides, untold millions were so weakened by want and disease that they will never be able to carry on as normal members of the community. When it is remembered that until rather recently practically all lands occasionally suffered from famine, while lands with uncertain climates suffered from scarcity very frequently, it is not difficult to believe that throughout the greater part of human history the tendency for numbers to grow about up to man's capacity to produce the necessities of life has been a very important factor in causing the fluctuations in numbers which seem to have characterized his population movements.

But famine arises not only from variations in the weather and the attacks of pests, it also frequently follows such disturbances as war and pestilence and in turn gives rise to them. In fact famine is almost always accompanied with and followed by destructive epidemics so that it is not uncommon in times of famine for more people to die of disease than of starvation. A good example of the way in which famine, disease, and war intertwine is found in the Taiping Rebellion in China. Here the war, which was started by some religious fanatics, came first and was waged with great cruelty. Its victims alone were probably counted by the millions. But, as destructive of human life as the war itself was, it was probably responsible for far fewer deaths than the famine and pestilence which followed in its wake. Some of the most competent observers believe that as many as fifty millions of people perished within five years (1856-1860).

It should be noted also that the effects of such a catastrophe upon population growth are by no means confined to the direct destruction of human life that takes place. The whole structure of life in vast areas is broken up and it is often decades before a social order is again established within which man can live a normal life and population movements can proceed as usual. This fact is attested over and over again by those who have witnessed the awful havoc wrought by famine and its accompanying evils. The author himself has seen the ruins of a number of villages in the vicinity of Nanking, China which were destroyed by the Taipings and there is clear evidence in the rural economy now prevailing there that this region has not yet recovered from the catastrophe it suffered almost eighty years ago. Once all the ecological relations between man and his environment are destroyed, as when a population is wiped out or forced to migrate, it is no easy matter to establish a people on the land again and to develop anew a reasonably satisfactory adjustment of man to his environment. In a very real sense an area once completely devastated constitutes a frontier which must be pioneered anew.

The following quotation from one who studied carefully the social and economic effects of the great Indian famine of 1837-1838 will serve to show how profoundly such a catastrophe disturbs the life of a community. It corresponds not to the passage of an army, nor even to a flood; for both of these, while destroying property, only temporarily drive people away. A great famine and its attendant evils are rather like a tornado passing over a wood. It uproots and twists and breaks the trees so that, although it leaves their roots lying almost in the same spot where they had been growing, it has destroyed that organic connection between tree and soil which made them a woods. So a great famine and pestilence destroy those vital relations between men and their locality which make of them a community, and without a community man is of small account and contributes but little to human welfare. But it will be better to let a vivid description of this process of community disintegration speak for itself.

1837-38.—The famine of 1837-38 was the last of the great desolating famines which characterized this epoch; like the Doji Bara in the Deccan, and the Chalisa in Upper India, it loosened the bonds of society, laid waste large tracts of country, and permanently modified the development of industry. It is the one famine of the old type of which we possess adequate detailed record; the reports of the local officers at various stages of the famine are, in many cases, still extant, and Mr. Girdlestone, in his "Past Famines in the North-West Provinces," has given a history of it which covers twenty-eight pages. The main features of the famine may be clearly traced, and they are unmistakably characteristic of the worst famines of this epoch. There had been a succession of bad harvests since 1832, which had caused considerable distress in various localities.

The summer of 1837 brought a terrible drought which extended over the greater part of the Doab, and into Banda and Gualior on the west, and over Behar, and as far as Calcutta and Cuttack on the east. July and August are described as having been absolutely rainless, and such were the anticipations of dearth that "in Aligarh the *baniyas* would not produce grain even when payment was offered at their own exorbitant prices." With the prospect of inevitable starvation at their homes, the people naturally began to wander; in August Bulandshahr was already being overwhelmed with emigrants from Marwar and Hariana. In September there were a few partial showers towards the south, but in the upper Doab this month was practically rainless. "The utter hopelessness of their case was enough in the minds of the lower classes to justify recourse to violence, and soon in Rohilkhand, Allahabad, Aligarh, Agra, Bulandshar, Gurgaon, Rohtak, and Delhi, neither grain-boats nor storehouses were safe from attack, whilst the public roads were dangerous to travellers, owing to the number of armed men who were roaming about in quest of plunder." On October 20, John Lawrence wrote from Gurgaon: "I have never in my life seen such utter desolation as that which is now spread over the pergunnahs of Horul and Pulwul. The people have been feeding their cattle for the last two months on the leaves of trees, and since this resource has failed, are driving them off." The difficulty of feeding the cattle is often mentioned. From Cawnpore in the beginning of 1838, Mr. Rose wrote: "There was not, I am told, in 1783 that total absence of vegetation which has caused the present dearth of cattle, and in milk the people then possessed a valuable article of food which is now wanting. . . . To those who have not witnessed the melancholy change it will scarcely be credible that an extensively-cultivated and thickly-populated country like the Doab could, by one year's drought, be reduced to its present state of waste and desolation. Flourishing villages, which last year contained from 300 to 400 cultivators, are now occupied by half a dozen starving beggars, and I have travelled for twenty miles in the pergunnahs adjoining the Jumnah, where there are no wells, without seeing a vestige of cultivation." The accounts of distress as given by Mr. Rose are fully corroborated from other sources. So long as the rich zemindars had the means, they fed their poor neighbours, and even went to the length of selling jewels and ornaments in order to raise money for the purchase of food. When their resources were exhausted and the *baniyas* proved inexorable, the poorer classes resorted to the jungle, in the hope of securing a meal from some of the wild trees. The small thorny berry of the Singárbár was in great request, as was also the bark of the wild fig-tree. The people dried and pounded what they gathered, and with a little addition of meal, had the means of making a sort of *chupati* (bread) that was just palatable. Women were ready to sell their children for 2 or 3 seers of wheat, whilst their husbands and brothers waylaid and plundered travellers. Gold and silver were parted with at half their ordinary value, and brass and copper were esteemed worth their weight in grain. Artisans disposed of their tools at a quarter their cost price.

Newspapers at this period come to our assistance as contemporary records of famine, and in the *Englishman* of March 24, there is the following graphic account: "You ask me to tell you all about the famine in Cawnpore; but, indeed, no account nor description of mine could convey to you any adequate idea of the misery of the poor in this place and throughout its vicinity. At the beginning of the cold season the station literally swarmed with starving wretches, and now where are they? I believe I am within bounds when I say that in cantonments alone, but a short time back, from twenty to thirty died daily. The river, owing to the sluggishness of the stream, became studded with dead bodies, and we have ceased to eat of its fish or

drink of its waters. At last it became requisite to hire establishments, not merely for the purpose of taking the starved-to-death
wretches to the ghats for their being flung into the Ganges, but also
to have a river establishment in constant play in order to push down
the corpses below Gajmow. The Relief Society feeds about 1,500
daily; but then, owing to the villainy of those who have to serve
out the food, in spite of the most energetic exertions on the part of
the superintendent, the *attah* (flour) was so adulterated with *chunam*
(lime) and sand, that heaps upon heaps have died from eating it,
and now there is great difficulty in getting the poor to go to the
almshouse. Kungla guards patrol the station all day long, not merely
to give notice where the dead bodies are lying but to drive the living
to the refuge. A great number of poor have lately left the station
to get in the scanty harvest. They will never return. Starvation
will be their lot. Of grain there is abundance in the province, but
there is no labour for the poor, and consequently they have no money
to buy food. The Calcutta people seem to be in earnest, but let them
keep in mind that the famine in and about Cawnpore has been, is,
and must continue, and that every rupee that can be raised should
be sent up as soon as possible. Between Calpee and Agra it is
perfectly dreadful. The dead are seen lying together by fifties. To
add to the misery of the poor starving population, the small-pox is
becoming rife at Cawnpore." (Morison, 1918, pp. 262-266)

The point to remember here is that such catastrophic upheavals will
almost certainly occur where the population has become so great that it
can continue to exist only as long as the entire social and economic organization keeps functioning in its usual manner. Throughout human
history there probably have been untold instances in which man's numbers
have grown so close to the subsistence level that any slight disturbance
of the equilibrium attained was practically certain to result in almost
incredible calamity. This was especially common in fairly well-settled
agricultural lands before the advent of steam transport. In such lands
the entire social organization, including the numbers of people that could
be supported, is predicated upon the ability of the community to keep the
goods on which it is dependent flowing in about the same amount as they
have been. When this normal flow is interfered with famine is not long
delayed and suffering is terrible, for the community has no reserve on
which it can call.

C. *Adaptation of Population to Resources.* The vast amount of hardship man has undergone because of the pressure of population on the
means of livelihood should not blind us to the fact noted above that there
have been peoples that achieved a fairly successful adjustment of numbers
to available resources. Probably this usually occurs when the settlement
of new lands is undertaken and before the population becomes dense.
No doubt it has occasionally happened that such an adjustment of numbers to resources has endured for some time, but this seems to be the
exception rather than the rule. Oddly enough, it seems that such a stable
adjustment has more often been achieved among primitive or tribal peoples
than among civilized peoples. One reason for this is that they have more
often resorted to drastic methods to keep population in step with their
available resources. They have seldom hesitated to practice infanticide
and the killing of the old. Besides, the murders committed by, or at the

behest of, the chiefs and witch-doctors are often so numerous that they must be reckoned among the tribe's measures making for a satisfactory adjustment of population to resources. Other practices such as head-hunting and scalping also contribute much to this adjustment, although they probably do not have their origin directly in the urge to control population growth. Such methods of restricting population are, of course, immediately effective and it requires no argument to convince anyone that a shortage in the tribal food supply can frequently be avoided by making away with the older members of the group, or by otherwise reducing the number of useless mouths to be fed.

Another reason why tribal peoples suffer a smaller diminution of numbers from catastrophic events than civilized peoples may be because the daily hazards of tribal life are so much greater that the thinning of the population by violence and accident is a more continuous process among the former, hence drastic reductions in numbers are less needful at any given moment.

Then, too, in the very nature of the case, the catastrophes of tribal peoples go almost unrecorded, while among civilized peoples records telling of them are frequently preserved. Thus we know that civilized peoples have often suffered heavily from war, famine, or pestilence; but when a tribal people suffers proportionally or even is entirely wiped out, as has no doubt happened many times, the event will generally pass unnoticed. As an illustration of this point one may cite the situation on some of the South Sea Islands where tuberculosis, syphilis, measles, and whisky have practically exterminated some groups and are even now wreaking havoc among many others. In prior ages when there was no communication with such distant places a similar catastrophe among a small isolated people could have taken place without its being known outside the local community.

Finally it should be remembered that the more highly differentiated and complex any social order becomes the more its people suffer from relatively slight disturbances in the functioning of the system. A tribal people having almost no trade relations with its neighbors does not suffer any hardships from variations in the volume of foreign trade, or from the discovery of new and cheaper methods of producing certain types of goods by its trade rivals, or from the tariffs set up by its neighbors to encourage home industry. In a word, civilized man by the very fact of his civilization becomes part of an intricate and delicate system of social relationships the disturbance of any of which issues in contingent disturbances throughout the entire social order. Hence, strange as it may appear, in past ages tribal man has probably been more successful in adjusting population to the means of subsistence than civilized man. Furthermore, he has often been able to understand the causal relations between numbers and resources more easily than civilized man because with him such relationships are more direct since his social organization is more simple. But the Chinese and Indians have left records which at least tell us a little about some of the most catastrophic of the setbacks to the growth of their populations.

D. The Constant Checks to Population Growth. The catastrophic checks to population growth have been dwelt on at some length because they show in striking manner man's failure to adjust his numbers to his physical environment and to his methods of production and distribution. It should be noted, however, that in the long run these horrifying failures have cost him less dearly than his daily failures of which he has seemed quite unconscious. Probably there never has been any people anywhere among whom the daily hardships of life have not cost more lives than all the catastrophic events which attract attention. The proof of such a sweeping assertion is to be found in man's regular death rates. The highest death rate of any large country for which reliable data are available for 1930 is 26.8 per 1000 in British India. The lowest recorded rate for the same year is that of New Zealand—8.6. The difference here is 18.2 per 1000 per year. With this difference in death rates there would be 18,200 more deaths in a million population living in British India than in a millon living in New Zealand. The population of all India is about 350 millions, hence, assuming equal accuracy in the figures for India and New Zealand, which is a rather large assumption, there would be 6,370,000 more deaths in India each year than in a population of like size living in New Zealand. A condition of chronic pressure on subsistence such as exists in India may, therefore, be said to be a far greater destroyer of human life than the terrible catastrophes about which we read so much at the time they happen; and this is true even though only a half, let us say, of the annual excess of deaths in these poverty-stricken lands is directly attributable to the pressure of population on the means of subsistence. The daily hardships of life have been and still are, save in a few Western lands, the most potent natural forces in retarding civilized man's growth in numbers. Possibly even the qualification "civilized" need not be made. (Note the differences in death rates in Table 2.)

Another interesting proof of this position is found in the variation in the death rates of different social classes in modern industrial lands. The best evidence of these variations comes from the office of the Registrar-General of England and Wales. In these countries in 1921-1923 among males 20-65 years of age only 812 belonging to the upper and middle classes died for every 1258 belonging to the unskilled laboring class. That is to say the death rate among males of these ages was over one-half greater among unskilled laborers than among the well-to-do. This differential death rate is largely due to differences in economic status although no doubt there are some selective differences in the physical equipment of men in those two classes, i.e., men of poor physique probably tend to fall into the class of unskilled labor. It is perhaps not generally recognized that a low economic status in a wealthy community is a form of population pressure, but such is really the case and the poor in England and the United States may just as truly be said to suffer from the pressure of population on subsistence as the great mass of people in India, or China, or Java, although not to the same extent. As long as this is the case it can scarcely be said that even the richest countries have achieved a very satisfactory adjustment between their economic system and their control

TABLE 2

BIRTH RATES, DEATH RATES, AND NATURAL INCREASE

	1930	1910	1890	1870	1850
United States					
Birth rate	18.9	27.4	31.5 (white)		
Death rate	11.3	14.6	19.6 (total)		
Natural increase	7.6	12.8	11.9		
England and Wales					
Birth rate	16.3	25.1	30.2	35.2	33.4
Death rate	11.4	13.5	19.5	22.9	20.8
Natural increase	4.9	11.6	10.7	12.3	12.6
France					
Birth rate	18.0	19.6	21.8	25.5	26.8
Death rate	15.6	17.8	22.8	28.4	21.4
Natural increase	2.4	1.8	— 1.0	— 2.9	5.4
Germany					
Birth rate	17.5	29.8	35.7	38.5	37.1
Death rate	11.1	16.2	24.3	27.4	25.6
Natural increase	6.4	13.6	11.4	11.1	11.5
Sweden					
Birth rate	15.4	24.7	28.0	28.8	31.9
Death rate	11.7	14.0	17.1	19.8	19.8
Natural increase	3.7	10.7	10.9	9.0	12.1
Australia					
Birth rate	19.9	26.8	35.0	38.0	
Death rate	8.6	10.4	14.3	13.0	
Natural increase	11.3	16.4	20.7	25.0	
New Zealand					
Birth rate	18.8	26.2	29.4	42.3	
Death rate	8.6	9.7	9.7	11.1	
Natural increase	10.2	16.5	19.7	31.2	
India					
Birth rate	32.9	39.5	36.5		
Death rate	26.8	33.2	30.1		
Natural increase	6.1	6.3	6.4		
Japan					
Birth rate	32.4	33.6	28.8		
Death rate	18.2	20.9	20.4		
Natural increase	14.2	12.7	8.4		
Java (Europeans)					
Birth rate	24.3				
Death rate	10.6				
Natural increase	13.7				
Straits Settlements					
Birth rate	40.6	25.3 (1911)			
Death rate	29.0	46.3			
Natural increase	11.6	—21.0			
Egypt					
Birth rate	45.7	45.2			
Death rate	25.0	27.3			
Natural increase	20.7	17.9			
Union of South Africa (Europeans)					
Birth rate	26.6	32.5			
Death rate	9.7	10.8			
Natural increase	16.9	21.7			

of population growth. No doubt there will often be ample room for argument as to whether, in any particular country, it is lack of resources or a faulty social and economic organization which is chiefly responsible for most of the higher death rate among the poorer people; but in many lands there should be little difficulty in placing the responsibility where it belongs. Thus it seems entirely clear that there are many lands in which any appreciable improvement in the lot of the poor would result in such an instantaneous increase in numbers that this improvement would be but of short duration. In such lands the lack of population control is basic and this is the situation in most of Asia today: witness the growth of population in India and Japan in the last fifty years. There is every reason to believe that the same sort of increase in numbers would take place in China if peace were achieved, agriculture improved, and industry started. In such lands population responds at once to better living-conditions and there is therefore little hope of a consistent improvement in these conditions.

On the other hand, there is probably no thoughtful person who does not believe that poverty can be practically eliminated today in those lands where population control has become possible. Even in the best of social orders certain kinds of personal deficiencies will almost certainly issue in poverty and a high death rate, but in a country like the United States, having vast resources, a highly productive technology, and a large measure of birth control, only a badly functioning social order can be held responsible for a large poverty class. But a situation in which poverty is no longer a decisive factor in population growth is of very recent development. We are only now in process of adjustment to it. It appears, however, that progress is being made and that the Western World is rapidly acquiring the technique of a thoroughgoing control of population growth that will enable it to eliminate excess population as a source of high death rates. This prospect opens up for discussion the whole matter of the operation of birth control and the motives, or attitudes of mind, leading to its general adoption.

V. FACTORS MAKING DESIRABLE THE CONTROL OF POPULATION GROWTH IN THE WEST

In the discussion which ensues birth control will be understood in the sense of control of conception, abortion being left out of account, not because it is unimportant but because it is believed that the motives are much the same as those leading to control of conception; also because as control of conception becomes more simple abortion is likely to disappear as an important factor in determining population growth.

As was pointed out above, birth control, even with abortion out of the picture, was not unknown in past ages. Onanism is a very ancient practice as is also sexual abstinence arising from sexual tabus, while it is not unlikely that the effects of acid douches on spermatozoa have long been known among wine-using peoples. But in spite of the knowledge of these ancient methods, the preventing of conception on a vast scale is essentially a modern phenomenon and the discussion here will be confined to this modern phase.

The development of civilization has rendered the cruder methods of population control—infanticide, the killing or neglect of the aged, abortion, etc.—more and more repugnant to man but it has also rendered the control of numbers more imperative; for, as was shown above, there is a vast difference in the death rates of peoples living under the conditions which prevail in New Zealand, or any other Western land, and the death rates of those who live under a less efficient social order such as exists in China and India. (Table 2.) The first effects of the lowering of the death rate which has accompanied industrialization and the removal of the older restraints on the birth rate are clearly shown in the growth of Europe's population during the last century and a half; also in the present growth of population in Japan, Russia, Korea, the Philippines, Java, and other lands where some measure of modern sanitation is now becoming effective. Naturally it was in the West, where an unprecedented growth of population was taking place, that man became interested in new and more humane methods of controlling that growth. It was also in the West, where an increasing productiveness of human labor was taking place, that the taste for the decencies, comforts, and luxuries of life developed in strata of the population which had hitherto known only the barest necessities of existence.

The present birth-control movement is, therefore, to be regarded as just another of man's efforts to make an adjustment between his numbers and his production which will enable him to live the *good life*. In its present stage it represents almost solely the efforts of the individual to work out his own economic and personal problems; it has almost no relation to the population needs of the nation, nor does it even reflect the mature judgment of the individual as to the size of family that would be best from the standpoint of personal development.

The most significant fact about the birth-control movement is that it is becoming• tremendously effective all over the Western World, as the table given above abundantly proves. This would seem to indicate that in the not-distant future the growth or decline of population in this part of the world will be determined largely by the attitudes of individuals towards the effect of the number of their children upon their welfare as individuals and as members of a community. Voluntary control of the size of the family will soon be the rule rather than the exception in this part of the world. How fast it will spread to other parts of the world cannot be told, but it seems fairly safe to say that it will spread as fast as communications improve and an urban industrial development brings into operation motives similar to those leading to restriction among the industrialized peoples of the West at the present time. If this is rather vague as to time, it is necessarily so because of the uncertainty involved in the course of development of machine industry in those parts of the world where its introduction is only now getting under way. In what follows an attempt will be made to elucidate briefly the factors which

are operative in leading people to practice birth control in the industrialized countries of the West.

This statement of the problem makes an assumption which some persons will be unwilling to accept. It is that the slowing-up of population
growth is primarily a matter of voluntary control. Those who hold to
the biological view of population growth outlined above will deny that
this assumption is justified. However, the weight of evidence seems to
the author to be in its favor and it will be accepted here; for the writer
holds that the rather marked decline in the birth rate which has followed
upon the spread of the knowledge and the means of conception control
is not a mere coincidence. On the other hand, the knowledge of the
means of preventing conception should not be regarded as a cause of the
decline in the birth rate in any true sense; it is merely the means used
to accomplish a desired end. The causes in which we are interested are
the conditions which lead people to want to remain childless or to restrict
their families to small size. The author does not pretend to any very
extended or exact knowledge on this point but out of a long-sustained
study of the matter will discuss rather briefly those conditions which seem
to him to be of particular significance in leading to the voluntary control
of the size of the family.

A. *The Falling Death Rate.* The first point to notice is that the
death rate has fallen so greatly in the Western World during the last
century that biological survival is assured with a far smaller number of
births per woman now than at any preceding period in human history.
(See Table 2.) Death rates of 30-40 per 1000 per year were not uncommon a century ago in most European countries and are still common
in the Orient. Even in Sweden in the latter half of the eighteenth century a death rate of 25 was a rather low rate, and in one bad year it
reached the appalling height of 52. Manifestly, when rates of 11 and
12 have become common, as has happened since the World War, fewer
births are needed to maintain or even to increase population growth than
was formerly the case. Thus it is not uncommon today to find Chinese
women who have borne eight or ten children yet who at the time of the
last birth have but one or two living. This figure is not given as an
average since there are no data on which an average can be based; but
certainly to find a Chinese mother who had given birth to ten children
with five or six living at the time of the last birth would be rather unusual among the vast mass of farmers and laborers. In the United States,
on the other hand, of all the women giving birth to their tenth child in
1930, 89.0 per cent had seven still living, 78.1 per cent still had eight
living, and 57.7 per cent still had nine living. Now it is quite clear that
the United States can have a very considerably lower birth rate than
China and yet increase in numbers much faster. It is the situation arising
from a rapidly declining death rate in a growing industrial community
which has made the great mass of people aware of the need to restrict
the size of their families. A couple today is faced with an altogether
different family problem from that confronting their grandparents when
it is probable that they will raise almost twice as high a proportion of

the children born to them as their grandparents did or even if out of six or seven born they will raise one or two more than their parents.

B. *Basic Changes in Economic Organization.* But this decline in the death rate is only one factor in the new situation in which parents find themselves. The very economic development out of which conditions favorable to declining death rates have grown also tends to render children an increasing economic burden to their parents. In all backward industrial countries one is impressed constantly with the youth of the workers. Not only is this the case among unskilled workers but among skilled workers and clerical workers as well. Even more than among our pioneering ancestors the Chinese or Javanese child is expected to begin to "earn his keep" at a very tender age. There is probably no school for him to attend in any event so he helps about the farm or shop almost as soon as he can get about. For the vast majority of the population the tasks of life are fairly simple, hence young children can learn them easily. With increasing industrialization along modern lines this situation undergoes a rather rapid change as anyone who has studied the industrial history of Western Europe will readily realize.

In the early days of the Industrial Revolution in any country child labor in its worst forms is found in almost all industries—spinning, weaving, mining, stores, factories, and personal service. Gradually it is realized that the conditions of labor are different in the city, in machine industry, and in the office from those which prevailed at home and on the farm. Then begins a long fight to give the children a chance to go to school, to play, to grow strong and healthy, and in general to share the increased welfare made possible by the enhanced productivity of the community. The steps in this struggle are too well known to need detailing, but, briefly, they consist in excluding children of tender years from certain heavy and dangerous occupations, in restricting their hours of labor, in requiring more and more attendance at a school, and in a variety of other ways rendering them useless to the family from an economic standpoint. In general this is all to the good but it must not be forgotten that it means a longer and longer period of dependence upon the parents and a progressively increasing expense for maintenance and education.

As parents find that they must be wholly responsible for their children for 16, 18, 20, or even more years they realize that they cannot raise as large families as were customary in grandmother's day if they are to live according to the customary standards of their group. They must begin to plan for smaller families in order not to be swamped by their increasing parental obligations. Furthermore, city living more and more removes from the home almost all the small tasks and chores which have been the boy's from time immemorial and also modifies greatly the household tasks of the girl, although it does not leave her so completely without regular duties as the boy.

At the same time that industrialism has been complicating the problems of the non-agricultural family the passing of the frontier and the increasing need of education has added to the responsibilities of raising large families among the farmers. No longer can the country boy make a start for himself as a farmer with a plentiful supply of grit, a wagon, a team, a plow, and a wife. Land prices are high and modern farming requires stock and tools in considerable amounts. To be successful the modern farm boy also needs more than the three "R's" which constituted almost the entire education of his father. Furthermore, the farmer, too, must forego the help of his children for a relatively long period although he is not so completely deprived of their assistance while attending school as is the townsman.

All this may be summed up by saying that the increasing complexity of our economic and social life is more and more making parents feel the difficulties and responsibilities of large families and is thus supplying them with many additional motives for the restriction of the numbers of their children. Since modern industry and modes of living at the same time make it possible to give effect to these motives it is not surprising that the birth rate is declining at a very rapid rate in practically all the countries of the Western World. It seems only reasonable to believe that these motives will become universal as the conditions which produced them arise in other lands.

It must be recognized, however, that even though the basic urge to fewer births derives from fundamental differences between the social situation of today and that of past generations, yet the actual motives in the lives of individuals which induce them to have fewer births arise more immediately in the special conditions surrounding the particular couple. Quite naturally, therefore, the desire to limit one's family never has the same immediate motive in any two cases; but this does not mean that motives are so utterly different in different people that they cannot be discussed in rather general terms with profit to those who would have a better understanding of the factors governing population growth today.

C. Factors Operative in Different Social Groups. One of the most important differences in the size of family now observable between groups is that between urban and rural populations. Assuming, then, as the author does, that the major portion of the decline in the birth rate is due to voluntary control, it appears that everywhere in the Western World urban people have been more ready to restrict the number of their children than rural people. So far as the author knows there are no exceptions to this rule. Why is this the case?

Certainly no categorical answer can be given to this question, but it would appear that the differences between rural and urban dwellers in mode of life have much to do with their different attitudes towards a desirable size of family. In the city the complexities of living have become so great and the ability of the individual to control his own destiny has become so uncertain that one is not surprised that city life has so greatly disturbed the traditional reproductive processes that most large cities are now producing fewer children than are needed to keep up their numbers when the age composition of their populations has become stabilized. Therefore, it may truthfully be said that modern urban life is in some way inimical to reproduction. But it is not sufficient to know that the city discourages reproduction, we must press farther to find out whether the city is a homogeneous whole in this respect. A little inquiry suffices to show that it is not. Within the city itself there are very marked differences between social classes in the number of children born to the average family. Briefly, the higher the economic and social status the smaller the family, and, *vice versa,* the poorer and more lowly the status of the family the more children there are. Clearly, here are differences which if explained will throw much light on the motives controlling population growth; also the situation arising from this differential growth of classes is of interest to all who are concerned about the quality of our future population.

This latter point will be discussed in due course, our immediate concern, however, will be with an attempt at the explanation of the differences between social groups in the size of their families.

Perhaps the first point to make in explaining the differential birth rate as it has existed for several decades is that the knowledge of birth control and the possession of the means to practice it have been very unevenly distributed throughout the community hitherto. It is only natural that people with fairly good education and of moderate and better economic means would be the first to learn of the better methods by which they could control the size of their families. It is also evident from facts already cited that it is just in this group that the death rate is lowest; hence, it is not surprising that this group should be the first to become keenly interested in the means of keeping the size of their families at a level that will not interfere too seriously with their plans for life.

In very much the greater part of this group the struggle to attain a better standard of living, or to maintain the high standard already achieved, is felt keenly, probably more keenly than in any other part of the community even though actual need is not present. Hence, it was to be expected that the decline in the birth rate would first manifest itself in the middle class and that in most countries the poorer-paid of the white-collar group would rapidly come to have the lowest birth rate of any considerable group in the community. Paradoxical as it may seem, therefore, it was in the relatively well-to-do part of the community that the handicap of large families was first felt and that birth control first came into use as a means of reducing their size. This explains the very general differential in size of family between the relatively well-to-do and the poor.

As indicated above, however, the motives to birth control are legion and although the absolute hardships of large families are felt very keenly in most quarters they are by no means the only factor making for smaller families. In addition to desiring to avoid the real hardships of too many children, many people in moderate circumstances have found that they can enjoy a considerable amount of luxury if they have few or no children, whereas they are doomed to a perpetual and severe struggle to maintain very modest standards if they have large families. The desire for luxury and ease of living may, therefore, be added to the desire to avoid poverty as an important factor in leading the more favored classes to reduce their birth rate both early and drastically. This is, of course, largely another facet of the economic motive.

It is quite impossible to assign any definite share of influence in lowering the birth rate to the emancipation of women. But that the increasing control of women over their own lives has been a factor of the greatest importance cannot be doubted. There are probably very few women who would choose of their own free will to spend all the best years of their lives bearing and nursing children. As long as no other "sphere" of activity was open to them they accepted the inevitable. However, when women began to have rights as well as duties, to exercise the right of living their lives as they chose, they naturally did not choose to be merely breeding animals; they wanted some freedom from the burdens of almost continuous childbearing. In general, the husbands were also anxious for freedom from the hampering social and economic burdens of too large families. Since the most obvious way in which a woman could prove that she was emancipated was to have a small family, no family at all, or even to remain unmarried, it is not surprising that the birth rate declined as the emancipation of women increased. The proof of this relationship is to be found in the fact that women of superior educational and economic status who are also most emancipated from the life routine traditional among women have the smallest families of any group in the population.

At the opposite end of the economic and social scale the poorer women have been slowest to throw off their traditional attitudes towards husband and family and to claim the right to live in their own way. They still live more after the traditional manner of women and they also have larger families than women in the more favored classes. They do not yet yearn so for higher standards of living that they are unwilling to bear and rear fair-sized families. Possibly this is simply because they have been slower than their economically more fortunate sisters to learn of the possibilities of birth control and to adjust themselves to the changed economic conditions making it possible for women to support themselves outside the home.

At present it is, therefore, impossible to tell how much of this difference in birth rates between economic classes is due to differences in the spread of the knowledge of conception control and how much is due to differences in social attitudes which would persist even if such knowledge were uniformly spread throughout the population. It is, for instance, important to know whether the necessity of working hard and even then living close to the margin, as is the case with a considerable part of the population at all times, issues in mental attitudes which are more favorable to a fairly high birth rate than the attitudes developed under less arduous conditions of life; also whether and how far the fact that in the poorer parts of the population the children generally do go to work as soon as the law allows them to influences the willingness of the poorer people to raise larger families. Then, too, the desire for ease and luxury in living which is very important in the more comfortable economic groups in determining the number of children born is of considerably less importance in those groups which have never known much ease or luxury. It is not hard to understand that people who have never known any mode of life but a fairly hard one do not feel so keenly that they are being deprived of some very desirable opportunity when another baby arrives as do those who have already become accustomed to certain advantages and not only are anxious to retain them but are also desirous of adding others. In other words, hardship is not an absolute condition but rather a matter of feeling, an attitude of mind, at least for the greater part of the population, hence those who have known some of the good things of life are more likely to consider the effects of another child or two on their ability to maintain their standards than those who have not enjoyed such advantages. It seems reasonable to suppose, however, that it is only a matter of time until the desire for ease and luxury will penetrate all classes.

Another element in the differential birth rate as between the higher and lower economic classes is the fact that children very definitely tie people to a given place of residence. Travel is much more difficult for all classes where children are involved and becomes practically impossible even for those who are quite comfortable if there are several children. Hence it comes about that many couples in the more comfortable classes so plan their families that the children will not be so numerous as to interfere seriously with their freedom of movement. The desire to travel lies at the root of many a decision to postpone the starting of a family and also to limit it to one or two children. The mere statement of this motive is sufficient to indicate where its incidence falls.

Whether the present differential birth rates will continue cannot, of course, be foretold. However, there is some evidence now being gathered in Sweden and in Germany which seems to indicate that the higher birth rate of the lower economic groups is of a temporary character only. Edin (1929, p. 259) has found that in Stockholm in 1927 the number of births per 1000 women aged 15-45 was the same (36) in the wealthier districts of the city as in the poorer districts although up to that time it had been higher in the latter. Among married women, however, the number of births per 1000 women (15-45) was 84 in the wealthier districts as compared with 74 in the poorer districts. In 1911 the figures were 143 and 154, respectively. Thus, although the conditions of Edin's investigation are not such as to prove definitely that in Stockholm there is now a direct correlation between larger incomes and larger families, yet the care with which the work was carried out and the number of cases investigated are such as to make it appear highly probable that this is the case.

Furthermore, Burgdörfer (1932, p. 59) has found that in the cities of Germany the number of children increases as the income increases in so far as the income-tax statistics are reliable in showing the size of the family.

If these findings are typical of what may be expected as the knowledge and practice of birth control spread to all groups in the community it means that the desire for more complex and higher standards of living is rapidly spreading into all groups in the modern city. To many this will seem a perfectly natural development. But in this connection it should be noted that if such a differential in birth rates (the more comfortable

TABLE 3

AVERAGE NUMBER OF CHILDREN ACCORDING TO THE STATISTICS OF THE
INCOME TAXES ASSESSED, 1925

| Income group | Average number of children per 100 married persons in so far as children are taken into consideration for family deductions | | | | | |
	Empire	Large cities	Berlin	Munich	Medium-sized cities	Other communities
Under 1500 RM	160	96	75	98	129	176
1500-3000 RM	174	110	87	110	147	199
3000-5000 RM	164	116	91	107	145	189
5000-8000 RM	152	119	94	107	150	176
8000-12,000 RM	144	125	109	108	148	166
12,000-16,000 RM	142	124	106	115	145	162
16,000-25,000 RM	141	129	110	120	150	160
25,000-50,000 RM	142	131	120	114	154	160
Over 50,000 RM	148	140	130	121	157	164
Total	162	109	88	105	140	181

having the larger families) becomes general the present eugenics movement would have to be very considerably modified.

Returning now to the discussion of differences between urban and rural birth rates it will be seen that the above discussion throws considerable light on the general factors needing investigation. Reasoning by analogy, it seems fair to assume that these differences inhere in the different modes of life of country and city people. In many respects rural living, particularly on the farm, is greatly different from city living.

In the first place country children at relatively young ages become of some economic value to their parents. They are helpful in doing chores of many kinds and can early contribute a little to their own keep even while they are yet attending school regularly. From the age of 12 or 13 country children can contribute materially to the family welfare. Furthermore such work as they can do is done at home directly under the control of their parents. Therefore, contributing to the economic welfare of the family does not involve such a complete separation of parents and children as is usually the case in the city. Farming is still primarily a family function, while in the city every person is employed as an individual worker and his family relations have almost nothing to do with his economic function in the community, nor with his economic reward. This economic difference between farm and city families undoubtedly has something to do with the differences in the size of family in these two communities. Here again, however, it must be remembered that the knowledge of birth control is much more general in the cities than in the country.

Another difference between country and city which probably is and will likely remain of great importance in maintaining a differential birth rate is found in the character of farm work as contrasted with city work. In the very nature of the case general farming involves being on the job every day and nearly all of the day. This point need not be greatly elaborated. It is obvious that cattle and hogs must be tended regularly. It is also clear the field work has to be done when the time is right or large losses will ensue. Since the farm family has to be at home regularly because its living depends upon its steady attention to the job in hand it does not feel the presence of another child or two as a hindrance to its mobility as the city family does. Most city people have definite hours of work and are responsible to their employers during those hours only; besides most city jobs are readily interchangeable and frequently they provide a vacation period so that if one can afford it it is not difficult to get away occasionally from the routine of daily tasks.

The above facts only need statement to show how very different the urban situation is from that in the rural districts where it is very difficult for the farm family to get away even over night, to say nothing of taking longer vacations. The important point here is that, since farm work is such that it keeps the family quite closely at home in any event, another child, or two, or three, does not make any great difference in the plans of the family. Besides, since the cost of farm children until they are through the common school is largely a matter of a little more work, it seems highly probable that farm people will be less anxious to keep their families small than city people who live almost entirely on a money basis.

There is, however, another aspect of this matter which should be mentioned here although little is known about it as yet. For two or three generations now American farmers have seen their children grow up only to move to the cities taking with them a considerable part of the accumulated wealth of rural communities. They have seen the cities grow wealthy and increase in luxury and ease, in part, at least, at their expense. Are the farmers going to be willing to furnish a supply of adult workers having considerable amounts of capital to the cities in the future as they have in the past? No answer to this question will be attempted. But it does not seem improbable that if the farmer finds the urban dweller unwilling to help in the education of his children through state or federal aid to rural districts, in the maintenance of his roads, in the building of electric lines, and in the upkeep of certain other services needful for good living on the farm, he may come to ask himself why he should raise children to go to the city to increase its numbers, to raise its real estate values, to add to its wealth-gathering capacity, and, in general, to aid the city to secure greater dominance over the economic and social life of the rural community. Such an attitude of mind is not wholly fantastic in the face of the increasing hostility of the farmer towards the city which he believes is exploiting him in an unconscionable manner.

D. *The Changing Functions of Children.* It must also be recognized that in the economy which has prevailed in rural communities in most parts of the civilized world until quite recently the chief insurance of an endurable old age lay in the having of children to look after one when no longer able to work. With the development of a capitalistic industrial system in which it was increasingly possible to substitute a claim on the community's future income, through the ownership of property, for a claim on children, the need of children as old age insurance has greatly diminished. The higher economic classes in the cities found quite early that they were able to dispense with children as a support of their old age. They also found that with the growth of corporations the carrying-on of family business by sons was less and less likely. It is not improbable that this diminishing reliance upon children for economic safety as age increased is another reason why the birth rate has fallen first and farthest in the class which has profited most by the capitalistic system.

Also along with the development of a capitalism which assured a claim on the future production of the community, to those who did not currently use up all their incomes, has gone the development of an increasing measure of paternalism on the part of the state towards those unable to care for themselves whatever their age may be—organized health service and poor relief, mothers' pensions, old-age pensions, etc. Thus another of the traditional economic functions of the family, viz., the care of blood relations, is being taken from it. This change is particularly noticeable in the cities. In fact the economic development which has gone along with increasing industrialization has badly disrupted the family both as a social and as an economic organism and has rendered of no importance many of the relations between its members which have subsisted heretofore. Naturally such a disruption affects profoundly all the social relations of those who are intimately involved in the system. This is unquestionably another reason for the lessened interest in children which is so clearly manifested in the West, particularly in its industrialized communities.

The statement that there is a lessened interest in children today will probably be challenged by many. Unfortunately this matter cannot be discussed here at any length; but it is the conviction of the author that in spite of this being called the "age of the child" there is really very little provision being made for him in the modern community. It is true that our schools are better than in times past, that the ailments of children are being cared for as never before, that less and less labor is being required of them at tender years, and that in many other ways they are being given larger opportunity than has been customary in the past. But, on the other hand, there has never been a time when so little provision has been made for children in the general life of the community. In our cities play facilities are so inadequate for the poorer people that we have a vast amount of social and economic degeneracy fostered by the crowded conditions under which they live and the unsuitable character of the places where they must spend their leisure. Furthermore, economic organization takes almost no account of the father's or mother's obligations to the family in planning for its use of them; hours of labor, times of work, and place of work are seldom adjusted to the needs of the family or of the children. Besides, the general scheme of social life in urban communities has almost no place for those who have children young enough to need almost constant care. Urban social life is planned for those having a minimum of family obligations. Even among commercialized amusements only the movie welcomes children. In fact the whole of our social and economic life in modern industrialized communities is built up around the vigorous adult and makes almost no provision for the family as a unit or for children. Modern society scarcely takes the family into consideration in fixing modes of payment for labor, in planning the use of its labor force, in selecting its location, or indeed in any kind of planning it undertakes. While, as for business, children simply do not exist for it until they are old enough to be used as workers. It is because of this total ignoring of the family and children by the modern industrialized community that one can truthfully say children have no place in its daily calculations. The effect of this failure to adjust the conditions of life to the presence of children, to organize our community life so that the family, as a family, will be assigned a definite rôle, can but discourage men and women in the raising of children.

Briefly these are the reasons why the author believes that this is not the age of the child but rather the age of the young adult. It is only the worker in whom the modern business community is interested. Once he is here, the physical well-being of the child is cared for quite assiduously for several years, but basically the community is not making a place for the child in its social and economic structure. The child is becoming more and more an incubus to the economic welfare of both community and parents. It is shortsighted of both individuals and the community to allow this burdensomeness of children to result in a semi-sterile population, provided we really believe in the essential soundness of our social order. But perhaps it is just the lack of abiding faith in the worthwhileness of our civilization that lies at the root of race suicide; perhaps a dying-out of population is inevitable in a social order where an increasing part of the people are being withdrawn from contact with the basic biological and economic processes involved in dealing directly with nature. It is very doubtful whether any city people has for long kept up its own numbers, and it may be that an urban civilization such as we are now developing will soon lack the reproductive vitality to perpetuate itself. It would be interesting to speculate upon the future of a civilization three-fourths to seven-eighths urban in which the death rate regularly exceeded the birth rate, but space does not permit. Suffice it to say that any civilization depending upon immigration for its very existence is bound to be changed very rapidly in form and texture because the immigrants must necessarily lack the outlook and traditions which the children of the natives would have. Whether the civilization the immigrants will build will be better or worse than that the sons of natives would have built, only history can say, but that it will be different is as certain as anything in human life can be.

VI. Conclusion and Reflections

But to return to the main line of argument, it must be recognized that in a period like the present when practically all the traditional social values are being questioned it is quite impossible to foretell with any assurance what will happen to the birth rate of a community as a whole, or to that of any social class within it. At such a time all men are becoming more delicately attuned to make rapid adjustments to the conditions of the moment and since we do not know in advance what adjustments may be required we cannot be at all certain of the extent to which population growth may be affected by them. It seems, however, that the great instability and uncertainty of life in the modern urbanized and industrialized world where most people live by some kind of barter (a money economy) are rather important factors in leading men to reduce the size of their families, inasmuch as they feel that the rather drastic reorganization of their lives which may at any time be required of them will be easier and simpler if they have not given too many hostages to fortune. That they are correct in such a judgment seems incontestable, but that the reduction in number of children thus brought about may be greater than is good for the community is not improbable. If, then, birth control is to be used for the control of population growth in the interests of the community rather than merely as a means to make individual adjustments easier, it seems highly probable that the community will have to bring about a greater stability of life for its members. Uncertainty and instability of social and economic position are proving, under present conditions, enemies to a rational control of population growth by throwing the whole responsibility for growth upon confused and uncertain individuals—individuals who are not sure of their own status and who see no object in bringing children into the world when they cannot assure them reasonably good opportunities. It would seem natural that reproduction would follow no predictable course when the meaning of life is being so generally questioned and when it is relatively easy to avoid parenthood. No one will pretend that parenthood does not involve manifold obligations an over-abundance of which most people would willingly avoid and which they probably will avoid more and more if they do not feel that in parenthood, and in the continuance of the race, and in the carrying-on of the civilization of which they are a part is to be found the fundamental meaning of life. Once social and biological values become confused and uncertain and rest largely upon individual rather than social judgments, it is not in the least surprising that many people see no reason for sacrificing present enjoyment for the individually dubious recompense of sharing in the life of the race both socially and biologically.

In view of what is happening to the birth rate in the Western World it appears rather doubtful whether it is correct to speak of the urge to *reproduction* as though it alone were sufficient to guarantee the future of any given people, or of any particular civilization. What has commonly been called the urge to reproduction begins to appear more as a mere sexual urge which assures reproduction only when man's customs, desires, and social organization do not interfere too greatly with the normal consequence of sexual relations. In the light of what is happening in the Western World but one prophecy regarding man's future growth seems justified and that is that man is certain to bring population growth more and more under definite control. It also seems rather likely that in the process of doing this he will make many mistakes in determining the proper numbers. For such mistakes nature has adequate penalties: for having too large a population she condemns him to poverty and suffering and for having too few she decrees his gradual elimination by race suicide or his subjugation by outsiders, and with this the extinction of his distinctive civilization.

BIBLIOGRAPHY

BONAR, J. 1924. Malthus and his work. New York: Macmillan. Pp. vi+438.

————. 1931. Theories of population from Raleigh to Arthur Young. London: Allen. Pp. iii+253.

BUER, M. C. 1926. Health, wealth and population in the early days of the industrial revolution (1760-1815). London: Routledge. Pp. xi+290.

BURGDÖRFER, F. 1932. Volk ohne Jugend. Berlin: Kurt Vowinckel Verlag, G. M. B. H. Pp. xv+448.

CARR-SAUNDERS, A. M. 1922. The population problem: a study in human evolution. Oxford: Clarendon Press. Pp. 516.

DOUBLEDAY, T. 1847. The true law of population shewn to be connected with the food of the people. (2nd ed.) London: Pierce. Pp. xvi+278+vii.

DUBLIN, L. I. 1928. Health and wealth, a survey of the economics of world health. New York: Harper. Pp. xiv+361.

DUBLIN, L. I. [Ed.] 1926. Population problems in the U. S. and Canada. Boston: Houghton Mifflin. Pp. xii+318.

DUBLIN, L. I., & LOTKA, A. J. 1930. On the true rate of natural increase. *Metron,* **8,** 107-119.

DURAND, E. D. 1916. Some problems of population growth. *Publs. Amer. Statis. Asso.,* **15,** N. S. No. 114, 129-148.

EAST, E. M. 1923. Mankind at the crossroads. New York: Scribner's. Pp. viii+360.

————. 1927. Heredity and human affairs. New York: Scribner's. Pp. vii+325.

EDIN, K. A. 1929. The birth rate changes; Stockholm's 'upper' classes more fertile than the 'lower.' *Eug. Rev.,* **20,** 258-266.

FAIRCHILD, H. P. 1926. The melting pot mistake. Boston: Little, Brown. Pp. vi+266.

FIELD, J. A. 1931. Essays on population and other subjects. Chicago: Univ. Chicago Press. Pp. xxix+440.

GILLETTE, G. M. 1926. Immigration and the increase of population in the United States. *Soc. Forces,* **5,** 37-51.

GINI, C. 1926. Decline in the birth rate and the "fecundability" of women. *Eug. Rev.,* **17,** 258-274.

GINI, C., NASU, S., KUCZYNSKI, R. R., & BAKER, O. E. 1930. Population. (*Lectures on the Harris Foundation,* 1929.) Chicago: Univ. Chicago Press. Pp. ix+311.

GODWIN, W. 1820. Of population; an enquiry concerning the power of increase in the numbers of mankind, being an answer to Mr. Malthus' essay on the subject. London: Longman. Pp. 626.

GONNER, E. C. K. 1913. The population of England in the eighteenth century. *J. Roy. Statis. Soc.,* **76,** Pt. 3, 261-296.

GOSNEY, E. S., & POPENOE, P. B. 1929. Sterilization for human betterment. A study of results of 6,000 operations in California, 1909-1929. New York: Macmillan. Pp. xviii+202.

GRIFFITH, G. T. 1926. Population problems of the age of Malthus. Cambridge, England: Cambridge Univ. Press; New York: Macmillan. Pp. 276.

HOLMES, S. J. 1933. The eugenics predicament. New York: Harcourt, Brace. Pp. xi+232.

INTERNATIONAL UNION FOR THE SCIENTIFIC INVESTIGATION OF POPULATION PROBLEMS. 1932. Problems of population; being a report of the proceedings of the second general assembly of the Union, held at London. June 1931. (Ed. by G. H. L. F. Pitt-Rivers.) London: Allen. Pp. 378.

KNIBBS, G. H. 1928. The shadow of the world's future; or the earth's population possibilities and the consequences of the present rate of increase of the earth's inhabitants. London: Benn. Pp. 131.

KUCZYNSKI, R. R. 1928 & 1931. The balance of births and deaths. (2 vols.) New York: Macmillan. Pp. xi+140; 170.

KULKA, E. 1931. The cause of declining birth rate. Cold Spring Harbor, N. Y.: Eug. Res. Asso. Pp. iv+29.

MALLORY, W. H. 1926. China: land of famine. New York: Amer. Geog. Soc. Pp. xvi+199.

MALTHUS, T. R. (n.d.) An essay on population. (2 vols.) (Everyman's library.) New York: Dutton. Pp. xviii+315; viii+285.

MONTGOMERY, E. G. 1925. Adjustments in standards of living as population increases. Amer. Soc. Agronomy J., 17, 245-252.

MORISON, T. 1918. The industrial organization of an Indian province. London: Murray. Pp. vii+327.

NATIONAL BIRTH RATE COMMISSION, GREAT BRITAIN. 1917. The declining birth rate; its causes and effects. London: Chapman & Hall. Pp. xiv+450.

NEWSHOLME, A. 1923. The elements of vital statistics in their bearing on social and public health problems. London: Allen. Pp. 623.

PEARL, R. 1925. The biology of population growth. New York: Knopf. Pp. xiv+260.

PLACE, F. 1930. Illustration and proofs of the principle of population; being the first work on population in the English language recommending birth control. (With an introduction and critical and textual notes by N. E. Himes.) Boston: Houghton Mifflin. Pp. xv+354.

REUTER, E. B. 1923. Population problems. Philadelphia: Lippincott. Pp. xvii+338.

———. 1927. The American race problem. New York: Crowell. Pp. xii+448.

ROBBINS, L. 1927. The optimum theory of population. In London essays in economics in honor of Edwin Cannan, ed. by T. E. Gregory and H. Dalton. London: Routledge. Pp. 103-134.

ROSS, E. A. 1927. Standing room only. New York: Century. Pp. xiv+368.

SANDERS, J. 1929. Comparative birth rate movements among European nations. Cold Spring Harbor, N. Y.: Eug. Res. Asso. Pp. viii+126.

SANGER, M. [Ed.] 1927. Proceedings of the World Population Conferences, Geneva, 1927. London: Arnold. Pp. xiv+285.

SPENGLER, J. J. 1930. The fecundity of native and foreign born women in New England. Washington, D. C.: Brookings Instit. Pp. 63.

THOMPSON, W. S. 1929. Danger spots in world population. New York: Knopf. Pp. xi+343.

———. 1930a. The eugenics bugaboo. Amer. Mercury, 19, No. 73, 33-37.

———. 1930b. Population problems. New York: McGraw-Hill. Pp. xi+462.

THOMPSON, W. S., & WHELPTON, P. K. 1930. A nation of elders in the making. Amer. Mercury, 19, No. 76, 385-397.

————. 1933. Population trends in the U. S. New York: McGraw-Hill. Pp. x+415.

UNGERN-STERNBERG, R. V. 1931. The causes of the decline in birth rate within the European sphere of civilization. Cold Spring Harbor, N. Y.: Eug. Res. Asso. Pp. vi+202.

WILLCOX, W. F. 1933. Introduction to vital statistics of the United States (1900-1930). Washington, D. C.: Govt. Print. Office (U. S. Bur. Census). Pp. v+138.

WILLIAMS, S. W. 1883. The middle kingdom. Vol. I. New York: Scribner's. Pp. xxv+836.

WOLFE, A. B. 1928-29. The population problem since the World War. *J. Pol. Econ.*, **36**, 529-559, 662-685; **37**, 87-120.

————. 1934. On the criterion of optimum population. *Amer. J. Sociol.*, **39**, 585-599.

WOLFE, A. B., & KUCZYNSKI, R. R. 1934. Population. In Vol. 12 of *Encyclopaedia of the social sciences,* ed. by E. R. A. Seligman and A. Johnson. New York: Macmillan. Pp. 240-254.

WOOFTER, T. J. 1933. Races and ethnic groups in American life. New York: McGraw-Hill. Pp. xii+247.

PART II

SOCIAL PHENOMENA IN INFRAHUMAN SOCIETIES

CHAPTER 4

INSECT SOCIETIES

O. E. PLATH

Boston University

When we see these intelligent insects dwelling together in orderly communities of many thousands of individuals, their social instincts developed to a high degree of perfection, making their marches with the regularity of disciplined troops, showing ingenuity in the crossing of difficult places, assisting each other in danger, defending their nests at the risk of their own lives, communicating information rapidly to a great distance, making a regular division of work, the whole community taking charge of the rearing of the young, and all imbued with the stronger sense of industry, each individual labouring not for itself alone but for all its fellows—we may imagine that Sir Thomas More's description of Utopia might have been applied with greater justice to such a community than to any human society. "But in Utopia, where every man has a right to everything, they do all know that if care is taken to keep the public stores full, no private man can want anything; for among them there is no unequal distribution, so that no man is poor, nor in any necessity, and though no man has anything, yet they are all rich; for what can make a man so rich as to lead a serene and cheerful life, free from anxieties, neither apprehending want himself, nor vexed with the endless complaints of his wife? He is not afraid of the misery of his children, nor is he contriving how to raise a portion for his daughters, but is secure in this, that both he and his wife, his children and grandchildren, to as many generations as he can fancy, will all live both plentifully and happily."—Thomas Belt, *The Naturalist in Nicaragua* (1874).

I. INTRODUCTION

At the present time, when the social order of the human race seems to be afflicted with an exceptionally severe attack of growing pains, some of the more complex infrahuman societies take on a greater significance. Nowhere in the animal world has social organization reached such a high degree of perfection as in the social insects, the Isoptera (termites) and the Social Hymenoptera (ants, bees, and wasps). The societies of some of these insects, as Wheeler (1923) has pointed out recently, are very ancient in comparison with human social organization, having been fully perfected at least 65,000,000 years ago, since which time they have undergone little or no change. Although the social life of insects differs in many important respects from that of man, it nevertheless shows a large number of striking similarities. Like our own complicated social order, it apparently had very simple beginnings, and passed through various stages of evolution which in some instances we can still trace with a considerable degree of certainty.

Of the approximately 500,000 insect species which have been described up to the present time, by far the vast majority are solitary, while the social and the subsocial species probably amount to less than 3 per cent. In a few of the solitary species, for example, the walking sticks, the female simply lets her eggs drop to the ground, while those of many other species merely deposit their eggs or larvae on or near a suitable food supply. In still other species, e.g., the Acrididae, the female lays her eggs in a cavity which she has dug for this purpose and then lets the resulting progeny work out their own salvation. Some more provident insect mothers collect food, put it in a safe place, or in a nest which they have prepared for this purpose (mass provisioning), carefully close the nest, and then pay no further attention to their young. A considerably higher degree of parental care is found in the subsocial insects, for here the mother guards her eggs and young and in some cases even feeds them from day to day (progressive provisioning) until they are ready to pupate, whereupon she closes the burrow and shows no further solicitude for her progeny. A still higher degree of affiliation between parents and young is found in the social species (cf. Emery, 1894a). Here the insect mother—in the termites the father as well—does not leave the young,[1] and at least some of the latter remain with their parents and assist them in various ways, including the rearing of additional offspring. However, before giving a more detailed account of the social and subsocial insects, it seems desirable to consider briefly what is usually referred to as the gregarious "instinct."

II. GREGARIOUSNESS

Gregariousness, which is a familiar characteristic of many vertebrates including our close relatives, the monkeys and apes, is also a common phenomenon in the insect world, even among the so-called solitary species. While in most of the solitary insects neither the male nor the female ordinarily pays any attention to others of the same kind, some solitary species congregate in large numbers during the mating season. Here belong the familiar dancing swarms of midges (Chironomidae) and other Diptera. Strangely enough, these swarms are sometimes made up almost entirely of males (cf. Allee, 1931). Similar temporary, but much more compact aggregations are regularly formed by some species during protracted periods of inclement weather. During the rainy season on the Pacific Coast, the writer has on several occasions found large clusters of hibernating ladybird beetles (*Hippodamia convergens*) in low, dense evergreens. Some of these clusters were about the size of a coconut and must have contained several thousand beetles. Other insects, for example, some of the grasshoppers, form immense migratory swarms, which, according to Whiting (1915), sometimes appear in "such thick clouds as to obscure the sun." Even some of the Lepidoptera show a tendency in this direction, for in our midwestern states the writer has repeatedly seen hundreds of migrating Monarch Butterflies (*Anosia plexippus*) settle down together in some tree for the night. An exceptionally high degree

---

[1]It is rather interesting that parental care in the vertebrates shows an almost identical series of evolutionary stages.

of gregariousness is manifested by some of the aquatic insects, such as the water-striders (*Gerridae*) and whirligigs (*Gyrinidae*), for the latter —at least on the surface of the water—are rarely seen singly.

However, gregariousness is not restricted to the adults. It is also found in the immature stages of quite a number of insect species. According to Uvarov (1928), the gregarious "instinct" is well developed in acridid nymphs and compels the latter "to keep close to each other, and to repeat each other's movements." Even more striking is the persistence with which the larvae of certain moths (Lasiocampidae) try to keep in physical touch with each other, the caterpillars of certain species even going so far as to cooperate in the construction of a communal tent.

Among the solitary insects which show gregarious habits, we apparently must also include certain solitary species, such as *Anthophora*. As is well known (cf. Rau, 1926), the females of this bee nest together in immense numbers. But what is more remarkable, the nesting aggregations of some species of this solitary bee apparently make common cause in driving away intruders, for the well-known German bee student, Friese (1923), reports that he was attacked by "a whole swarm" of *Anthophora parieta* when he tried to catch some of the females with his net near their nesting place. As we shall see when we take up the more primitive social bees, like Halictus, it is probably from such gregarious ancestors as *Anthophora* that some of the social bees were derived (cf. Gutbier, 1914).

III. SUBSOCIAL INSECTS

As was pointed out earlier, the subsocial insects are chiefly characterized by an increasing interest on the part of the mother during the larval development of her young, which, in some species, may even be reared by progressive provisioning as we find it in altricial birds. According to Wheeler (1928a), who has made a very thorough study of this subject, subsocial insects occur in at least seven insect orders, some of which contain quite a number of subsocial families. Since it would be impossible to discuss all of these in the space allotted to the writer, it seems best to consider briefly the social behavior of a few of the more representative members of this group.

Among the more primitive insects which are subsocial in their mode of life, the earwigs (Forficulidae)—order Dermaptera—occupy a prominent place. These insects are very common in Europe and in some of our southern states, and taxonomically were formerly placed among the Orthoptera. The life-history of only a few of the Forficulidae has been carefully studied, and most of these have been found to lead a rudimentary social life. Maidl (1933-) has recently reported some interesting observations made by Stäger on *Anechura bipunctata*. The female of this earwig makes a flat cavity under a stone and lays 50 to 60 ivory-white eggs in a small heap. These she covers with her body, every now and then licking one egg after the other until the young larvae emerge. Some of these are lost as a result of failing to free themselves completely from the egg shells, the mother making no attempt to assist them; she is, to use Stäger's words, a specialist in protection and defense, but does not choose to serve as midwife. Stäger describes the behavior of the earwig family upon being disturbed as follows:

> Whenever I turned over a stone of a certain size on an expansive Alpine terrace, I found the mother among a brood of about 50 to 60 young larvae. Before my eyes the slender, graceful creatures squirmed as they tried to hide themselves in the small cavity, which the mother had dug in the earth for her brood. And she, herself, did not flee, but, on the contrary, sheltered her young with her own body and with her pincers snapped at the fingers of the intruder, who attempted to seize her. If I resorted to force and separated the mother from her brood, then she hastened back immediately to the cavity and continued to defend her young. However, when I pushed one of the small larvae aside, the mother followed shortly afterwards, seized her kidnapped offspring with her mandibles and carried it back into the nest.

This earwig mother, however, does even more than protect and defend; she provides nourishment for her young as well, and does not permit them to seek their own food outside the nest even when they are half grown. She alone goes outside in order to bring the necessary provisions, piles up supplies and renews them when they have vanished before the mandibles of her young. In certain other species of earwigs, the mother leads her progeny to places where suitable food is available in much the same manner as a hen does her chicks.

Subsocial propensities, as has been recently shown by Wheeler (1923), are also exhibited by at least six families of beetles. The habits of several species of these subsocial beetles have been studied by Fabre (1911). According to this famous naturalist, the female of the Sacred Scarabaeus (*Scarabaeus sacer*) makes elaborate preparation for the hatching of her eggs. Under a molehill of the rubbish which she has cleared out of the excavation she made for her nest, in a chamber the size of a man's fist, lies a pear-shaped pellet of dung, containing in its narrow end the hatching chamber and a single egg. The outer rind of the pear has been made hard by means of pressure by the mother beetle, while the inner part, which is to serve as food for the developing larva, remains soft and moist. The loose particles about the hatching-chamber are admirably suited to the food requirements of the earliest larval stage, for, according to Fabre, "the recess is plastered with greenish-brown matter, shiny, half-fluid, a real cream destined to form the first mouthfuls of the grub." Fabre believes that this is "a broth elaborated in the maternal stomach" and compares it with the "milk" in the crop of pigeons, which the latter feed to their young. The mother Scarab does, therefore, supply her offspring with food sufficient for its development to maturity. After this is accomplished, the mother beetle leaves the chamber, digs another burrow, and provisions it in the same manner.

Fabre discovered a considerable degree of cooperation between the male and female of *Minotaurus typhoeus*, another scarabaeid beetle. These beetles, after mating in March, proceed to dig a tunnel preparatory to the building of their nest, which is generally five feet below the surface of the ground. In forming the tubular burrow, the female does all the digging, while the male carries away the rubbish. The female lays her eggs at the base of the gallery and the male collects sheep-dung, powders it, and moulds it into pellets, which he then lowers into the tunnel to the waiting female. She, in turn, kneads the pellets into finger-length cylinders, arranging the layers, and furnishing each egg with its loaf of dung. The male, after having for a month or more carried rubbish up the long gallery and brought food down, leaves the completed birthplace of his prospective children and dies outside. The mother, who since mating has not left the nest-site, lives long enough to watch for the emergence of her young and to escort them to the surface of the ground.

As the Peckhams (1905), Hudson (1912), and the Raus (1918) have shown, subsocial species also occur among the wasps. The Raus have made a very detailed study of the life-history and habits of *Bembix* (=Bembex) *nubilipennis,* one of the digger-wasps. The females of this wasp are semi-gregarious for they generally build their nests in the same locality, each wasp digging its own burrow in the ground and forming a separate nest-cell at the terminus of the five- or six-inch tunnel. Unlike other species of the solitary Hymenoptera, the *Bembix* female constantly supplies her larva with food until the latter is ready to pupate, not laying any additional eggs until the first larva has spun itself into a cocoon. Due to this concentrated maternal care, each mother rears only five to six young during the ten to twelve weeks of summer. The Raus found that the diet varied with the stage of the development of the larva: a tiny waspling was discovered feeding on a delicate, yellow-winged dipteran, while coarser flies, such as houseflies and stableflies, were brought to the older larvae. The mother not only varies the food according to the needs of her infant, but also allots sufficient space to the cavity wherein the larva develops to permit its growth in size. She is, of necessity, an industrious worker, for the developing larva possesses an almost insatiable appetite. According to the Peckhams (1905), Fabre fed 82 flies to a *Bembix* larva in the eight days that preceded the spinning of its cocoon, while the Raus record 79 flies as the diet of a waspling which they reared before it began spinning its cocoon; and even after the spinning had begun, the larva devoured 26 additional flies.

IV. The Social Wasps

Up to the present time about 10,000 species of wasps (Vespidae) have been described, of which less than 10 per cent are social. Bequaert (1918) divides the Vespidae into nine subfamilies, four of which (the Ropalidiinae, Polistinae, Vespinae, and Polybiinae) are completely social, while two others, the Zethinae and the Stenogastrinae, apparently also contain a few very primitive social species (cf. Wheeler, 1928a). Although the Ropalidiinae and the Polistinae differ in structure, their habits are so similar that a brief discussion of the rather cosmopolitan genus

FIGURE 1
NEST AND COLONY OF *Polistes versicolor* UNDER A SHELTERING LEAF
Considerably reduced.
(Photograph by Mr. Phil Rau)

Polistes will suffice to illustrate the chief social characteristics of these two subfamilies. The nest of *Polistes* (Figure 1) consists of a single, naked, paper comb which is usually suspended by a pedicel from the underside of some shelter. The cells are hexagonal and usually open downward. In temperate regions, the nest is almost invariably started by one queen (monometrosis or monogyny), but in the tropics (cf. Roepke, 1919, and Rau, 1933) new colonies are apparently normally founded by more than one female (pleometrosis or polygyny). Upon hatching, the young females assist their mother in rearing additional offspring until the colony breaks up. A *Polistes* colony very rarely consists of more than several dozen adults, and it is difficult, if not impossible, to find any structural differences between the females (cf. Bequaert, 1918), although some of these apparently do not mate, and hence represent a worker caste. As in other social wasps, the females feed their larvae almost exclusively with malaxated insects, and in return receive a sweet secretion from the larvae, a mutual exchange of food to which Wheeler (1923) has given the name *trophallaxis*. *Polistes* also feeds partly on nectar which it sometimes stores in small quantities (cf. Rau, 1928). The females, as Rau (1931) has recently shown, have the interesting habit of drenching their nests with water in extremely hot weather, obviously for the purpose of protecting the larvae; but, as the experiments of Rau (1933, p. 45) show, they also do the reverse and systematically remove water from the nest, when the latter is excessively drenched.

The subfamily Vespinae, to which our yellow-jackets belong, has representatives in all parts of the world, except in South America and the southern part of Africa. The nest, which may be aerial or subterranean, at first resembles that of *Polistes,* but the *Vespa* queen soon begins to build a paper envelope, which gradually surrounds the comb, except for a small flight hole near the bottom. During the greater part of the summer only workers are produced. These are much smaller than their mother and do not mate, but assist her in rearing additional offspring. As the colony grows, additional combs are built beneath the first one, each somewhat larger than the preceding and suspended from the comb directly above by one or more tough paper pedicels. In late summer or early fall the males and queens are produced. After mating, the young queens find a suitable place in which to hibernate, each one starting a new nest the following spring. The colonies of the Vespinae are much larger than those of the preceding subfamilies (cf. Bequaert, 1932).

The Polybiinae are primarily a neotropical subfamily, but they also have a few representatives in Africa and the southern and far western parts of the United States, the range of one species (*flavitarsus*) even extending into Western Canada. This subfamily of social wasps consists of a large number of genera (23), and exhibits such great diversity in structure and habits that Bequaert (1933) has recently raised the question "whether they are not a composite, or polyphyletic, group." Although we find great differences in temperament and in the feeding habits among the Polybiinae, this diversity is even more marked in the size of the colonies and the architecture of the nest. Some of the more primitive genera, such as *Belonogaster* and *Mischocyttarus,* build a single, naked comb closely resembling that of *Polistes.* A somewhat higher type of architecture is that of *Gymnopolybia,* which constructs a nest very similar to that of the Vespinae, but the combs are always placed vertically, instead of horizontally, and are never covered with a paper envelope.

Quite a different type of architecture is used by the genus *Polybia,* as the following description by Rau (1933) shows:

> As in all species of *Polybia,* the combs are supported entirely by the circular walls; there are no props or columns from one comb to the next to lend support. The opening to the nest is at or near the bottom, and above this a passage way extends from the bottom to the top of the nest, near one side, perforating all the combs, thus giving a ladder-like effect from comb to comb on the interior.

The genesis of one of these nests—in this case one of clay (Figure 2)— is described as follows by the same author:

> The cells forming the first layer are attached directly (not on pedicels) to the inside of the roof of the nest. When this has attained a diameter of two and one-half or three inches, the cylindrical wall of the nest is extended around the edges of this comb like a curtain, and a thin sheet of clay is spread across horizontally, enclosing but not touching the shallow-celled comb above. It seems almost unbelievable that clay could be manipulated so artistically by these little builders. But the next step is more astonishing; the wasps, using this new cover as a foundation, build another layer of cells on the

FIGURE 2

A SMALL CLAY NEST OF *Polybia fasciata* BROKEN OPEN TO SHOW COMB. THE
ENTRANCE IS AT THE LOWER RIGHT
Considerably reduced.
(Photograph by Mr. Phil Rau)

bottom (now the outside) of this covering. Thus each successive
comb is built on each successive bottom of the nest. They are not
connected by stems or props, but are supported only by their attachment to the outer shell. There is sometimes heavy reinforcement at
the junction of the comb and wall.

Although several other genera, e.g., *Synoeca* and *Metapolybia,* never
construct more than one comb, the back of which is always attached
directly to its supporting base, they always protect the exposed side with
a paper cover. Rau has found that these single combs are sometimes
more than two feet in length, and the paper cover of some species, for
example, those of *Metapolybia pediculata,* have translucent patches, comparable to windows, while the nest cover of other species, e.g., *Synoeca
surinama,* is distinctly corrugated (Figure 3). During his stay on Barro
Colorado Island, Rau discovered that *Synoeca surinama* has an ingenious
way of frightening away intruders by beating the wings against the inner
surface of the nest cover, the latter serving as a sort of sounding board,
and he suggests that the peculiar structure of the cover probably adds to
its strength and increases the resilient qualities of the "music box."

The highest type of nest is that constructed by some of the species of
the African genus *Polybioides.* According to Bequaert (1918) "these
wasps have acquired the habit of utilizing both sides of their combs,
thus securing a notable saving of building material and space. This
architecture, which is well known for the honeybee, is quite excep-

FIGURE 3
NEST OF *Synoeca surinama* SHOWING CORRUGATED COVER. THE ENTRANCE
IS AT THE TOP
Greatly reduced.
(Photograph by Mr. Phil Rau)

tional among the Vespidae. The only record of a similar case is, so far as I was able to make out, a nest of the South American *Synoeca irina* Spinola,[2] described by A. Ducke, in which a supplementary comb showed cells on both sides." *Polybioides melaina,* which apparently builds similar combs, surrounds the latter with a cover consisting of several layers of paper. The whole structure resembles an inverted bee skep, but may be much larger, for the nests sometimes reach a length of three feet. According to Bequaert, *Polybioides melaina* is often seen on flowers, and hence it seems probable that this species may also store honey, as do some of our American Polybiinae.[3]

As already mentioned, the Polybiinae are also very diverse in temperament, feeding habits, and the size of their colonies. In some of the more primitive species, e.g., *Mischocyttarus,* the colonies are usually even smaller than those of *Polistes,* and the females of some species, according to Bequaert (1933), do not make any attempt whatsoever to defend the

---

[2] This is of considerable interest, since Pellett (1931) and Rau (1933) have recently discovered that some of the Polybiinae (*Nectarina lecheguana* and *Synoeca surinama*) also have a barbed sting.
[3] As Bequaert (1933) has recently shown, the first reports of this habit were questioned by some of the earlier entomologists, among them F. Smith, who contended that carton cells do not make suitable honey containers, not realizing, of course, that the human race would some day use similar receptacles for liquids.

nest. As we turn to the less primitive genera, we gradually get larger colonies, but also a greater degree of pugnacity (cf. Rau, 1933), which apparently reaches its climax in *Polybioides melaina,* for, according to Bequaert (1918), this species is exceedingly aggressive so that it is greatly dreaded by both natives and Europeans. Some of the colonies of the Polybiinae become very large indeed. Rau (1933) found 1,965 adults and 12,610 immature individuals in a nest of *Gymnopolybia pallidipes* in addition to about 30 adults which escaped, while a *Chartergus* nest examined by Möbius (cf. Bequaert, 1933) contained about 60,000 cells. How great a population one of the mammoth nests of *Polybioides melaina* contains we can only guess, but since this wasp is comparatively small (cf. Bequaert, 1918) the number of individuals in some of the larger colonies must equal, or even surpass, the largest colonies of the honeybee.

Although the females of some of the less primitive Polybiinae are said to be differentiated into queens and workers, the difference between these two castes is much less pronounced than in the Vespinae (cf. H. von Ihering, 1896). As in the honeybees, the colonies of the higher Polybiinae are perennial and new ones are started by swarming. Some species, e.g., *Polybia occidentalis,* have the habit of storing large numbers of male ants, and male and female termites, during the dispersal flights of these insects and in some cases even considerable quantities of honey[4] (cf. Bequaert, 1933, and Rau, 1933). What is even more strange is the fact, recently discovered by Pellett (1931) and Rau (1933), that some of these wasps have a barbed sting, and that they lose their life when they make use of this weapon. Like the ants, certain species have also learned how to secure honeydew from other insects, for Belt (1874), the famous naturalist, reports that he saw *Nectarina* obtain this liquid from young frog-hoppers by stroking them. Whenever an ant intruded while one of these wasps was thus engaged, the latter, instead of grappling with its rival, would fly into the air, hover over the ant, and then pounce on it and strike it to the ground.

That the Polybiinae have at least a rudimentary division of labor is indicated by some interesting observations recently made by Schwartz (1931), who believes that the workers of a colony of *Polybia occidentalis* which he studied were at least roughly divided into water-carriers, foragers, nurses, artisans, and hod-carriers. The behavior of some of the "hod-carriers" is described as follows by Schwartz:

> The laden wasp arrived at the nest with her burden held not merely by her mandibles but enfolded like a bundle by her front pair of legs. Without releasing this hold, she walked about the nest on her middle and hind legs, seeking a worker with whom to share the pulp. Sometimes the entire load was handed over to an accommodating individual, and the foraging wasp was then free to set forth

[4] Wasp honey is said to be very highly regarded by the natives of Central and South America (cf. Bequaert, 1933) and is often sold in the market in certain parts of Mexico, where some of the Indians engage in a sort of primitive "wasp-keeping."

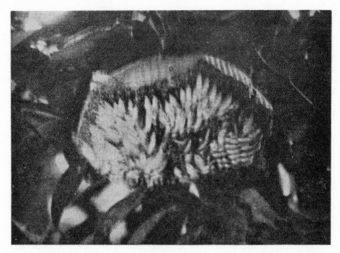

FIGURE 4

Nest and Colony of *Apoica pallida* Seen from Below
About one-half natural size.
(Photograph by Mr. Phil Rau)

at once.   More often, however, the receiving wasp took over only
half the burden, holding it in like manner with mandibles and fore-
legs, and thereupon both wasps moved about over the nest, dividing
their respective loads with other wasps, which in turn sought out
additional members of the colony with whom to share, until finally
the material was fractioned so finely that it could be used for building
purposes.

Schwartz has also made the interesting discovery that the females of
this species systematically bail water from their nest when the latter
becomes too wet from natural causes or is artificially drenched by means
of a medicine dropper.   However, the following incident—observed by
the same author—is even more remarkable.   A leaf over the nest sloped
in such a way that it acted as a conduit which flooded the roof of the nest
with rain water.   This difficulty the workers solved very effectively by
removing the leaf itself.   Like the bumblebees—to be discussed later—
these wasps have also learned to ventilate their nests by making living
"electric fans" of themselves.

However, the most remarkable thing about the Polybiinae is the fact
that some species, e.g., *Apoica pallida,* have become nocturnal in habit.
Apoica pallida, as well as its nest, is light yellow in color, and Rau (1933),
who has recently made some observations on the habits of this wasp, believes that the light color and the nocturnal activities of this insect are
closely interrelated.   Several other unique habits of *Apoica pallida* are
very interestingly described by Rau, as follows:

> The inhabitants when viewed during the daytime were quietly at
> rest on the under side of the nest, their bodies parallel and their

heads always turned away from the center of the nest, whereas
wasps usually rest on the nest in any haphazard arrangement. These
were so crowded that in places they were piled one atop the other,
five or six deep, but still they were in the orderly rows [Figure 4].
This position, with heads lined all along the edges of the nest, made
it possible for them to see an oncoming enemy from any direction.
In the center of this mass of life was a small gangway to the open
cells, where occasionally one went in or came out. . . . The organized arrangement and the aggressive position which they assume for
their sleep during the daytime would indicate that perhaps they have
more enemies during the day than at night, and that this habit, not
seen in other wasps, was evolved after these wasps had changed from
day- to night-workers.

V. The Social Bees

The "honeywasps" which were discussed in the preceding paragraphs
form a sort of connecting link between their more carnivorous relatives
and the bees, for the latter, as Wheeler (1923) very aptly puts it, may
quite properly be "regarded merely as a group of wasps, which have
become strictly vegetarian." As is well known, bees feed almost exclusively on the pollen and nectar of flowers, and for this reason they are
frequently called *Blumenwespen* (flowerwasps) by German entomologists.
So far, more than 12,000 species of bees (*Apidae*) have been described,
of which probably less than 10 per cent are social. The latter occur only
in five of the fifteen or more subfamilies into which the family Apidae
is usually divided. Three of these five subfamilies—the Bombinae, Meliponinae, and Apinae—are completely social, while the remaining two—
the Ceratinae and Halictinae—consist of both solitary and social species.

Like the Little Carpenter Bee, one of our American representatives of
this group, apparently almost all of the Ceratinae are solitary with the
exception of a few South African species of the genus *Allodape*. According to Brauns, who has recently studied certain species of this interesting
genus (cf. Wheeler, 1928*a*), the *Allodape* female excavates a tunnel in
some plant with soft pith, as do our American Ceratinae. In some
species of *Allodape,* according to Brauns, the female provides food for
her larvae but once, as do nearly all the solitary bees and wasps, while in
other species she feeds them from day to day, as do most of the social
insects. Upon hatching, the young *Allodape* females remain with their
mother—at least for a time—and help her rear some of the remaining
brood. Brauns believes that the young females, after mating, later leave
the maternal burrow and found colonies of their own. If further investigations confirm the observations of Brauns, the Ceratinae will have to be
regarded as representing the most primitive level among the social bees.

A. The Halictinae

The subfamily Halictinae comprises about 1000 described species of
small burrowing bees which are very common in most parts of the world.
Although the life-history and habits of the European *Halicti* had been
studied for almost a century (cf. Wheeler, 1928*a*), the representatives of

this subfamily were, until quite recently, believed to be solitary or, at most, semi-social. However, the epoch-making observations of Stöckhert (1923) show that this is by no means the case. This author, after seven years of thorough study, has clearly demonstrated that almost all of the German *Halicti* which he studied are social and that in many cases the workers and queens of certain *Halicti* have been described as two distinct species. Since Stöckhert's observations were made chiefly on *Halictus malachurus,* it seems best to give a rather detailed account of the social life of this species, since it is, with the exception of a few minor details, identical with that of the next subfamily, the Bombinae. Like *Anthophora, Halictus malachurus* often nests in immense numbers in rather hard, clayey soil, into which the queen burrows almost perpendicularly to a depth of eight to fifteen inches. In Upper Bavaria, where Stöckhert did most of his work, the young *malachurus* queens begin to leave the maternal burrow about the latter part of March, and soon afterwards start nest-building, either by cleaning out the old burrow or by digging a new one. Although several queens usually hibernate in the maternal nest, one nevertheless, according to Stöckhert, almost always finds only one queen in each burrow. However, sometimes two and occasionally even three queens—probably sisters— may use the same tunnel. In trying to explain why each burrow at the beginning of the breeding season normally contains only one queen, Stöckhert suggests that some of the queens either leave the maternal nest of their own accord, or, what is more probable, that they are ousted by a more vigorous sister, for he frequently noticed considerable discord between the queens making use of the same tunnel. Stöckhert considers it probable that each queen—whenever the tunnel is used by more than one—builds and provisions her own cells and pays no attention to those not constructed by her. During the latter half of June, the brood begins to appear, and this at first consists exclusively of females. These are invariably considerably smaller and differently sculptured than their mother and belong to a form which taxonomists have described as *Halictus longulus.* Although a few males begin to emerge in July, they pay no attention to these small females. The latter stay with their mother and begin to construct and provision new brood cells, as do the workers of other social bees; these *"longulus"* females are, in fact, as has been definitely proved by Stöckhert, nothing else but the worker caste of *Halictus malachurus.* As additional workers emerge, the *malachurus* queen gradually lets her daughters do most of the foraging and assumes the important duty of guarding the nest entrance against various intruders, among them *Sphecodes,* a close relative, but deadly foe, which will be discussed later. As the summer progresses, additional workers emerge, supplanting those which have died, or have been lost in some other way, so that a colony examined in August may consist of a dozen or more workers, a few males, and the old queen, and in some cases even a few young queens. Instead of foraging, as do the workers, these latter seem to be in a sort of stupor and remain in the nest, but in clear weather they occasionally come out to sun themselves. As soon as one of these young queens appears in the open, she is immediately pounced upon by a large number of males which swarm about the nesting place. In this way, the males—with loud buzzing—sometimes form a regular ball about the young queen, as each one endeavors to mate with her, but, as already pointed out, they pay no attention to the workers, including those which have but recently hatched. The young which are produced in August and September are almost exclusively males and young queens. In late summer the old queen usually loses her power of flight and is then —on clear days—not infrequently seen crawling about near the entrance to her nest. Although some of the old queens sometimes live until October, most of them die earlier. As the weather becomes more inclement in September, the workers and males gradually die off, and this finally leads to the dissolution of the colonies, the young queens having previously retreated into the lower parts of the maternal nest where they hibernate, after they have carefully closed the entrance to the burrow with earth. This resemblance between the social organization of certain *Halictus* species and *Bombus* becomes still more striking if we take some of the other social *Halicti* into consideration. For example, the young queens of *Halictus scabiosae* apparently never hibernate in the maternal burrow, nor do they nest in large communities, like those of *malachurus* and other species, and each colony is founded by only one queen. Still other species, for example, *quadricinctus* and *calceatus,* do not place their cells singly along the main tunnel, as does *malachurus,* but rear their brood in a clay comb around which they excavate a cavity, an arrangement which is similar to that found in subterranean nests of *Bombus,* and in another species (*scabiosae*), according to Fahringer (1914), some of the brood cells may even be used for storing pollen, as in the higher social bees.

B. The Bumblebees

Although the members of the three remaining subfamilies, the Bombinae, Meliponinae, and Apinae, are similar in that they have very highly perfected pollen-baskets (corbiculae) and secrete wax which they employ in building their combs and brood cells, they differ fundamentally in their habits, and it can therefore be assumed with a considerable degree of certainty that they represent a convergent group with two or—what seems more likely—three distinct lines of ancestry. The most primitive of these three subfamilies are the bumblebees (Bombinae), but, since their social organization is very similar to that of *Halictus malachurus,* it will not be necessary to discuss it in detail.

Most of the approximately 200 known bumblebee species inhabit the colder regions of the North Temperate Zone, a considerable number of species being found even as far north as Alaska (16 species), Siberia, and Greenland. In the colder parts of the world, the young *Bombus* queen, after mating, digs a small hole in the soil and hibernates until the following spring, when she proceeds to establish her own colony. But instead of digging her own nest cavity, as does the *Halictus* queen, she almost invariably establishes herself in the unoccupied nest of some rodent, where she builds a waxen honey-pot and an egg-cell, in which she deposits her first

FIGURE 5
QUEEN OF *Bombus impatiens* INCUBATING HER BROOD
Natural size.
(From O. E. Plath's *Bumblebees and Their Ways*, by permission of
The Macmillan Company, publishers)

clutch of eggs, usually eight in number. She then incubates (Figure 5) the latter and the resulting larvae and pupae.[5]

Unlike the *Halictus* queen, she feeds her larvae from day to day and assists her young in emerging from their cocoons. From this point, the development of the bumblebee colony is almost identical with that of *Halictus malachurus,* except that the *Bombus* queen does not assist her daughters in foraging or in guarding the entrance to the nest. She also is much more prolific than the *Halictus* queen, with the result that her family, under favorable conditions, may sometimes consist of from 500 to 1000 individuals. While in our latitudes (northern United States) bumblebee colonies are annual growths which normally last from about three to six months, depending upon the species, the colonies in the tropics, according to R. von Ihering (1903*a*), are perennial, while those of arctic species probably last only a month or two. It has even been suggested by Sparre-Schneider (1909) that certain *Bombus* species are solitary in the Far North. Though interesting, this hypothesis still lacks confirmation.

Very questionable is von Ihering's assertion that in the tropics new bumblebee colonies are founded by swarming. This assertion is not based on von Ihering's own observations, but, as he himself states, on newspaper reports and on information obtained from a lumber-jack (*Waldarbeiter*), and hence need not be taken too seriously. The correctness of von Ihering's statement becomes still more doubtful in view of the fact that

---

[5]Huber (1802), who observed some bumblebee workers incubating cocoons, believed that they were trying to keep the latter in an upright position.

FIGURE 6
INCIPIENT COLONY OF *Bombus impatiens*
Two workers—one at the right and one at the left—ventilating the nest.
Natural size.
(From O. E. Plath's *Bumblebees and Their Ways*, by permission of
The Macmillan Company, publishers)

even in the warmer parts of California new bumblebee colonies are
founded in the same manner as in the colder parts of the world. It is
quite probable, however, that the young *Bombus* queens of tropical regions
start their colonies shortly after leaving the maternal nest, for, as the
writer has pointed out recently (1934), *Bombus* queens—like those of
Apis—are physiologically ready to breed shortly after hatching.

As Huber (1802), Hoffer (1882-83), Wagner (1907), Lindhard
(1912), Sladen (1912), the writer (1934), and others have observed,
a very curious phenomenon may be witnessed in bumblebee nests in late
summer. While the queen is ovipositing, some of the workers crowd
about her and attempt to snatch and devour the newly laid eggs. She
repels the bolder individuals with legs and mandibles, and sometimes even
makes effective use of her sting. Somewhat similar quarrels occur between
laying workers and queenless colonies. While one of them is engaged in
ovipositing, another worker may push her from the cell and immediately
begin to lay her own egg in the latter. During these quarrels, the workers
frequently chase each other over the comb, but these encounters rarely prove
fatal. Huber, Lindhard, and Sladen have attempted to explain this
curious race-suicidal habit, but none of these explanations seems very
plausible, the correct solution having apparently not yet been reached.

Bumblebees have several interesting ways of protecting their nest and
brood. As the comb grows, the workers add to the nesting-material by
collecting dry grass or moss near the home. This work is usually done in
the evening and sometimes as many as thirty workers may be thus engaged.
Facing away from the nest-entrance, each worker seizes a bit of dry
grass with her mandibles and, after placing it on the ground, pushes it

farther back with her legs. Here the fragment is seized by another worker, which treats it the same way, until it reaches the nest. Many species also construct a waxen dome between the comb and the nesting-material and thus prevent the brood from becoming drenched.

If the air in the nest becomes stale or too warm, one or more workers begin to ventilate the nest by rapidly vibrating their wings (Figure 6). Some of the earlier observers, e.g., Goedart (1700) and Hoffer (1882-83), interpreted this activity in a very anthropomorphic manner, for they believed that the bumblebee "trumpeter" was calling the members of the colony to work.

As the writer discovered some years ago (1922), one of our American bumblebee species (*Bombus fervidus*) has a very unique method of expelling certain intruders from its nest. Instead of attacking the latter with their stings and mandibles, the *fervidus* workers cautiously approach and daub the intruder with honey, until the unwelcome guest—"tarred" if not feathered—considers it advisable to leave.

C. The "Stingless" Bees

The Meliponinae, or "stingless" bees, comprise some 250 species, of which about four-fifths occur in Central and South America and the rest in the tropics of the Old World. They are less hairy and much smaller than bumblebees, some of the smaller species measuring barely 3 mm. in length. The name "stingless bees" is really a misnomer, for these insects do possess a sting, but the latter is vestigial and is no longer used for defense. However, judging from the experience of Wheeler (1913) and Rau (1933), some species are anything but harmless, and it is probably for this reason that some of the Latin-Americans facetiously call them *Angelitos,* "little angels" (cf. Jardine, 1840).

In the construction of their combs and the use of wax, as Rau (1933) has recently pointed out, the Meliponinae are very similar to the bumble-bees, and this has led him to surmise "a very near kinship" between these two subfamilies. In other respects, they are more primitive than the bumblebees, since they still rear their young by mass provisioning. They also have certain characteristics which are found only in the honeybees, for example, the degeneration of the *corbiculae* and wax glands of the queen. Instead of being secreted on both the dorsal and the ventral sides of the abdomen, as in bumblebees, wax is produced only on the dorsal side, and not only by the workers, but also by the males. What is still more strange, however, is the fact, recently discovered by Rau (1933), that the males, at least those of *Trigona cupira,* use "the same methods of defense as the workers," something unique indeed in the behavior of hymenopterous males.

The colonies of the Meliponinae become much larger than those of the Bombinae. A nest taken by Rau contained about 4800 pupae, and the total population of some species, according to H. von Ihering (1904), may sometimes reach 80,000. As in the Bombinae, there is only one queen, but unfertilized young queens are apparently also tolerated in the nest. In

some of the more primitive Meliponinae there is no difference between
worker and queen cells, but in the higher forms, e.g., *Trigona dorsalis,*
as Rau (1933) has recently shown, each queen cell occupies about the
space of six male or worker cells.   New colonies are founded by swarming,
but since the old queen apparently does not retain her power of flight,
the swarms must be accompanied by young queens.   While the Meliponinae, like other bees, feed chiefly on honey and pollen, they also make
use of other substances, but, as Wheeler (1913) and Rau (1933) have
found, they are not very particular in regard to the nature of the latter.

The nests—usually situated in hollow trees—are made of "cerumen,"
a conglomeration of wax and other substances, which is generally brownish-
black in appearance.   The entrance to the nest may be a simple opening,
but often it consists of a spout or funnel (Figure 7), made of cerumen.

FIGURE 7
FUNNEL-LIKE ENTRANCE OF THE NEST OF *Lestrimellita limao*
About one-fourth natural size.
(Photograph by Mr. Phil Rau)

The interior of the nest of *Trigona cupira* is partly described as follows by
Rau (1933):

> The brood cells . . . occupy the central and most important portion
> of the nest cavity. . . . There are occasionally small props or pedicels
> between the horizontal combs, but the main reinforcement is a
> series of vertical pillars, one-eighth of an inch thick, going from
> the floor to the top of the nest, passing directly up through the many
> combs. . . Each comb comprises a mass of brood cells.   These are
> made of a finer quality of wax than are either the honey-pots or the
> tunnelled walls.   A series of such combs examined in September
> revealed that as one went progressively downward the combs con-
> tained more and more fully developed organisms.   The lowermost

layer contained young adults almost ready to emerge, while the top-most layer contained an egg in each cell, attached to the inside of the lid. The smaller larvae, each in its own tiny cell, floated on a gummy concoction of pollen and nectar. This was seen in several nests with surprising regularity. No one comb in any of the half-dozen nests examined had organisms of different sizes or stages in its cells.

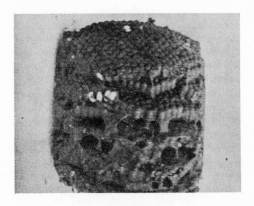

FIGURE 8
SEVERAL COMBS FROM A NEST OF *Trigona dorsalis*
Considerably reduced.
(Photograph by Mr. Phil Rau)

A large nest of *Trigona dorsalis* (Figure 8), containing thirteen tiers of combs, the same author describes as follows:

> Immediately under the wax ceiling was a set of honey-pots. These . . . were of various shapes and widths, but all were about one inch high. Below there was a brood chamber, six inches high, 3½ inches wide and 2¾ inches from front to back. . . . To the left of the brood chamber and behind it were more honey-vats, extending in a vertical column, one on top of the other, from the floor to the ceiling of the entire nest, a length of 8 inches. These were enormous vats, vary-ing in size from 1½ to 2½ inches high and an inch or more wide. One, which was two inches in diameter, had two necks. . . . These honey-vats, as stated, were on the left side of the brood-chamber. On the right of it and behind the entrance tube and partly behind the combs were the big pots of pollen. . . . The brood-chamber was filled to capacity with the mass of dormant life.

Rau found that the entrance to the nest was always carefully guarded.

D. The Honeybees

The Apinae, or honeybees, are represented by only four species, of which the common hivebee (*Apis mellifica*) is best known. The latter is often referred to as the "domesticated bee," but this term is incorrect, for *Apis mellifica* is no more domesticated today than it was thousands of years ago, when some enterprising member of our race first conceived the idea of placing its colonies into artificial domiciles. Although *Apis mellifica* has been carried to every continent on the globe by man, it is probably a native of Asia and may originally have been derived from *Apis indica,* with which it readily hybridizes. The largest and most primitive of the honeybees is *Apis dorsata,* which—although common in other parts of Asia—is usually referred to as the giant bee of India (cf. von Buttel-Reepen, 1915). It builds a large, single comb, which is usually suspended from a branch, and sometimes, according to Schneider (1908), as many as sixty-five colonies may be found nesting in one tree. As in some of the more primitive *Meliponinae,* all three castes of *Apis dorsata* are reared in cells of the same size. The colonies of this species have the unique habit of forsaking their old home and migrating to more promising pastures whenever nectar and pollen become scarce.[6] The workers of *Apis dorsata* apparently have a method of communicating with each other very similar to that of *Apis mellifica,* for Dathe reports (cf. Friese, 1923) that, if honey is placed out-of-doors, swarms of *Apis dorsata* are attracted to the place from a considerable distance, whereupon they start building combs on neighboring trees. It seems probable, therefore, that the workers of *Apis dorsata*—like those of *Apis mellifica*—are constantly on the lookout for a new food supply and that they lead the whole colony to the latter in the same manner as that employed by the scouts of *mellifica* in guiding the swarm to the new home which they have discovered.

Apis florea has a geographical distribution very similar to that of its giant relative, *dorsata,* but its workers are less than half as large as those of the latter, and for this reason *Apis florea* is often called the pigmy bee of India. Like *dorsata, florea* builds a single, pendent comb, but it uses three different kinds of cells for rearing its brood, as does *Apis mellifica.* According to Friese (1923), the full-sized comb of *Apis florea* is only about 10 inches long and 8 inches wide, and is usually attached to the smaller branches of shrubs and trees. The comb shows an arrangement very similar to that of *Apis mellifica.* The top of the comb is used for the storage of honey. Directly below this area is a larger one which consists entirely of worker cells, and below these are the drone cells. The queen cells are nipple-shaped, as in *mellifica,* and—as is often the case with those of the latter—are suspended from the lower edge of the comb.

Apis indica has even a wider geographical distribution than *dorsata* and *florea* and is commonly kept in the Orient for the production of honey and wax. *Apis mellifica* and *Apis indica* are so similar in structure and habits that Friese (1923) considers it quite possible that *indica* merely represents the ancestral stock of *mellifica.* *Apis indica* and *Apis mellifica* differ from

---

[6]Since the worker of *Apis dorsata* has a somewhat longer tongue than that of *Apis mellifica,* several attempts have been made to introduce *Apis dorsata* into other parts of the world, with the hope that this species would make the nectar of red clover (*Trifolium pratense*) available for human consumption, but, owing to the nomadic habits of *Apis dorsata,* all of these attempts have come to naught (cf. von Buttel-Reepen, 1906).

 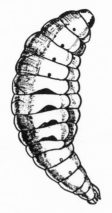 

FIGURE 9
IMMATURE FORMS OF *Apis Mellifica*
Left, egg; center, full-grown larva; right, pupa. Greatly enlarged.
(Courtesy of Dr. J. F. Payne)

dorsata and *florea* in that they usually nest in hollow trees or similar cavities and construct several combs side by side instead of only one. As in some of the Meliponinae, a honeybee colony sometimes consists of as many as 70,000 individuals, of which by far the vast majority are workers. In addition to the queen, the colony, as a rule, also contains a considerable number of males (drones). The honeybee male is no longer able to forage for himself, as are his more primitive cousins. His only purpose in life is to fecundate the queen, a function which invariably results in death. Unlike the worker, the honeybee queen has retained and greatly developed her sexual function, but she has degenerated in other respects, having completely lost her pollen-collecting apparatus, as well as her pharyngeal glands. Although larger than the worker, she has a smaller brain and a shorter tongue, and is unable to secrete wax. Yet both the worker and queen result from the same kind of egg, the difference between the two being entirely due to larval feeding, a fact which has been proved by transferring eggs, or very young larvae, from worker to queen cells and *vice versa*. The larvae of the three castes are fed with food of a different chemical composition, and this, as Table 1 shows, influences the duration of the various larval stages (Figure 9).

TABLE 1
NORMAL LENGTH OF LARVAL DEVELOPMENT OF *Apis mellifica*
(Modified from Payne)

Stages	Queen	Worker	Drone
Egg	3 days	3 days	3 days
Larva	6 "	6 "	6 "
Pupa	7 "	12 "	15 "
Total	16 "	21 "	24 "

From Table 1 it will be seen that the queen, although the largest of the three castes (Figure 10), reaches her maturity in a considerably shorter

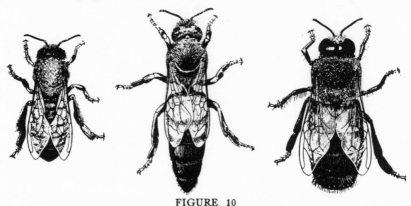

FIGURE 10
ADULT FORMS OF *Apis mellifica*
Left, worker; center, queen; right, drone. Considerably enlarged.
(Courtesy U. S. Bureau of Entomology)

time than the workers and males. This, as well as the enormous development of her ovaries, is chiefly due to the fact that she is fed on a richer food ("royal jelly") than are the two other castes. The queen mates but once and stores the protozoa—at least 200,000,000 according to von Buttel-Reepen—in her spermatheca where they are kept alive during the

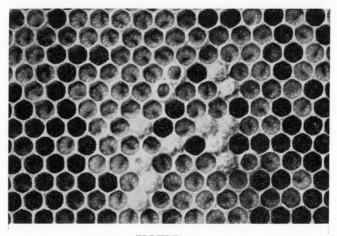

FIGURE 11
COMB OF *Apis mellifica* SHOWING WORKER LARVAE IN VARIOUS
STAGES OF DEVELOPMENT
About natural size.
(Courtesy of Mr. F. C. Pellett)

five or six years of her life. Her sole duty is the production of eggs, which she lays in large quantities, sometimes as many. as 2000 per day for weeks at a time (cf. von Buttel-Reepen, 1915).

As in the other Social Hymenoptera, honeybee workers are females with stunted reproductive organs, and, while they—without mating—sometimes lay eggs, which invariably produce males, they are chiefly concerned with other matters. It is their duty to collect pollen and nectar, to take care of the queen and the males, as well as the brood (Figure 11), to secrete wax and keep the hive clean, to regulate the temperature of the nest, and to defend the latter in case of danger. With all these duties to perform it is not at all surprising that the life of the worker bee—at least during the summer—averages only about a month, and that these remarkable communities have a well-regulated division of labor. As Rösch (1925) has recently shown, each of the various duties enumerated above is normally performed by workers of a certain age. He divides the life of a worker bee into three chief periods. During the first two or three days of her life, the young worker bee cleans and prepares the brood cells from which she and other bees have recently emerged and assists in keeping the brood sufficiently warm. Beginning about the third day, she becomes a nurse, feeding the older larvae until she is about six days old. At this time her pharyngeal glands begin to function, and she now devotes herself chiefly to the care of the younger larvae, which need comparatively large quantities of pharyngeal secretion for their development. After serving about a week as "nurse-maid," the worker, now about ten days old, begins her second period of activity in the hive. As a rule, the young worker takes her first orientation flight during her activity as nurse-maid, but if she has been prevented from doing so by inclement weather, or in some other way, she attends to this important matter during the second period of activity in the hive. During this second period, which usually lasts for about ten days, the worker assumes a variety of duties. She distributes or stores the nectar which her older sisters bring in, and "stamps" down the pollen which the latter have deposited in empty cells. She also assists the young to emerge from their cocoons and finally performs guard duty near the entrance to the hive. During the third period, which commences about the twentieth day, she devotes herself entirely to foraging until she dies.

This division of labor apparently does not apply to the "retinue" of the queen. It has been known for a long time that the honeybee queen is constantly surrounded by a circle of workers (Figure 12) which are much interested in her and are always ready to groom and feed her. Some of the earlier observers thought that these workers were doing homage before the queen (cf. Rösch), while others, e.g., Wildman (1768), believed that they form "a kind of retinue, and follow her wherever she goes." During his work on the division of labor, Rösch discovered that this "retinue" of workers is not made up of certain individuals but that these circles break up and are constantly reformed by other workers, as the queen moves slowly over the comb. Nor does the

FIGURE 12

CIRCLE OF WORKERS OF *Apis mellifica* SURROUNDING THE QUEEN (RIGHT CENTER)
About natural size.
(Courtesy of F. C. Pellett)

"retinue" represent bees of any particular age, for Rösch found that these "ladies in waiting" were anywhere from one to twenty-eight days of age.

The honeybee queen, as was pointed out earlier, has become so specialized that she is no longer able to found a colony by herself, as are the queens of the more primitive Social Hymenoptera; hence new colonies—under natural conditions—are always started by swarming. In our latitudes, the first swarm of the season is always accomplished by the old queen, while after-swarms invariably contain at least one virgin queen. As already mentioned, the swarm apparently sends out scouts (cf. von Buttel-Reepen, 1900) which locate a suitable nesting place and then guide the swarm to it. It has also been known for some time (cf. von Buttel-Reepen, 1915, p. 194) that the worker honeybee has a method of informing her sisters that she has discovered an exceptionally abundant food supply, but how this was done remained a mystery until the latter was cleared up by the ingenious experiments of von Frisch (1923). This author has shown that the honeybee worker which has discovered an exceptionally abundant supply of nectar performs a dance (*Rundtanz*) on some crowded comb. This causes considerable excitement among her sisters, some of which follow her and place their antennae against the abdomen of their laden sister, whereupon they leave the hive and search for the source of the particular kind of nectar which caused their sister to dance. A somewhat different type of dance (*Schwänzeltanz*) is performed by workers which have discovered an abundant supply of pollen, and this "tail-dance" apparently has the same object as the "round-dance"—to apprise the colony of the existence of an abundant food supply.

In addition to ventilating and cooling the hive, honeybees have also developed a method of surviving a fairly rigorous winter, provided the colony is well sheltered and has a sufficient supply of honey. This is done by crowding closely together and forming a compact cluster whenever the temperature falls below 57° Fahrenheit. One of the first steps in getting ready for the winter is the elimination of the drones from the colony, a curious phenomenon which is frequently referred to as the "slaughter" of the drones. All summer long, the latter are cared for by the workers and are permitted to come and go as they please, but as soon as the first frost cuts down the food supply—sometimes even earlier —they receive an entirely different sort of treatment. They are not only refused food by the workers, but the latter do not rest until all of them have been "ridden" out of the hive. This phase in the life of the honey-bee colony is very interestingly described as follows by Pellett (1931):

> During the warm days the males have led a lazy life, flying about in the sun and visiting from hive to hive as fancy dictated. Everywhere they were welcome and everywhere they were fed freely by the busy workers. Now, alas, they are wanted nowhere, and when they alight at the hive entrance the guards seize them and drag them away. They are worried and dragged about until they leave the hive and gather in little groups outside, getting such comfort as they can from each other's company. Usually the workers do not kill them outright, but drive them out to perish from their own inability to hustle for themselves. All summer they have depended upon the liberality of their sisters for food, and when this fails they are unfortunate indeed.
>
> Sorry is the lot of these poor fellows as they huddle together in an effort to warm themselves. When the skies are overcast and chill winds blow, the warmth of the hive is most inviting, but they are not permitted to enter. When days were fine they played about while their sisters worked feverishly storing up the harvest. Now that the sisters have time to rest they will no longer share their wealth with those who have not helped to earn it. . . . How sad to die of cold and hunger at the very door where food is stored in abundance and where grateful warmth is not lacking! With what solicitude does nature nourish the young and immature and how relentlessly does she cast them aside when they have reached the time when they are no longer of use to her!

To this vivid account the writer would like to add from his own obser-vations that during this "massacre" of the males, as Maeterlinck (1924) calls it, one or more workers usually seize one after another of these help-less fellows at the base of the wings and make motions as if they are going to sting, and in this way drive the bewildered males in front of the hive, where hundreds of these exiles sometimes remain closely huddled together for days. Strangely enough, queenless colonies, according to von Buttel-Reepen (1915), do not molest their males. Although the expulsion of the males was known even to the Romans (cf. Wildman, 1768), so far we have no satisfactory explanation of this curious habit, unless we assume that the bees realize—or did so once—that the drones have become useless for the time being and, like cold-blooded Spartans, turn them out to die.

FIGURE 13
NEST OF CARTON ANT, *Azteca* PROBABLY *trigona*
Greatly reduced.
(Photograph by Mr. Phil Rau)

However, as the writer has frequently observed, apparently the workers sometimes make mistakes in expelling "cripples" from the hive. During the month of July, when milkweed (*Asclepias*) is in bloom, a very amusing phenomenon may be observed in front of every hive in the vicinity of Boston. While gathering nectar from *Asclepias,* the tarsi of the workers sometimes become so thickly coated with the pollinia of this plant that the workers look as if they have six wooden shoes on. Curiously enough, such individuals are dragged from the hive in a very similar manner as the drones, but being much lighter than the latter, they are usually taken up into the air by the workers which are trying to eject them. As soon as this happens, the "ejectee" also begins to use her wings and both bees come whirling to the ground. At this time the "ejector" releases her hold, and both bees fly back to the hive. But as soon as the "pollinia-shod" worker tries to enter, she is at once seized by some other self-appointed "guardian" of the commonwealth and treated in the same manner as before.

VI. ANTS

Unlike the two preceding subdivisions of the Hymenoptera, all of the approximately 3500 known species of ants are social. Nowhere in the animal world do we find a greater degree of plasticity than in these insects, especially in the higher species, the colonies of which show an interesting similarity to human society in their elaborate social organization, their domestication of other insects, and their organized warfare and possession of slaves. Wheeler (1910) believes that the dominant position of the ants is partly due to their freedom from a restricted diet and dependence upon one fertilized queen, and that, as a result of their adaptability to almost any environment, ants are found everywhere—in deserts and rain forests, in arctic regions, and in the tropics.

A brief consideration of the principal types of nests of these insects will serve to illustrate their plastic habits. Some of the nests penetrate the soil for a considerable distance, while others are shallow excavations under stones and logs. There are the domed nests of mound-building ants, and nests made in the cavities of living plants and in decaying wood. In the tropics, some species construct paper nests and fasten them to trees, as do some tropical wasps (Figure 13), while the weaver-ants of Asia and Africa build their nests in trees among the leaves, which they sew together with silk produced by the larvae. Doflein (1905) and Hingston (1929) have seen the workers of *Oecophylla smaragdina* in the process of repairing their nests by sewing leaves together. Hingston observed that the workers of this species stretch across the gap between two leaves, gripping one edge with their jaws and the other with their hind legs (Figure 14).

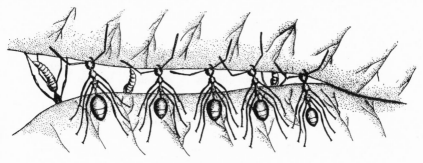

FIGURE 14
WORKERS OF *Oecophylla smaragdina* IN THE PROCESS OF REPAIRING THEIR NEST
Considerably enlarged.
(After Doflein. Courtesy of Professor W. M. Wheeler.)

If the gap between the leaves is too wide for one ant to span, they form a chain of as many ants as are necessary, one ant grasping the other by the waist. If the gap happens to be of varying width, single workers operate at the narrow apertures, and chains of ants at the wider gaps. With remarkable precision, the ants pull the leaves together, changing their positions as is necessary until the gap is completely closed. The leaves now need to be fastened together, and this is done in a most interesting manner. Since the adults do not produce silk, several workers fetch larvae (Figure 15), each worker gently applying the head of its larva alternatingly to the edge of the two leaves, thus attaching a thread of silk each time the larva touches a leaf. The larva cooperates by bending its head whenever it is lowered by the ant, and this sewing continues sometimes for a day or more, a new larva being substituted for the one exhausted.

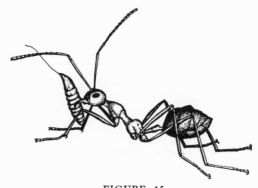

FIGURE 15
WORKER OF *Oecophylla smaragdina* USING A LARVA IN MENDING THE NEST
Greatly enlarged.
(After Doflein. Courtesy of Professor W. M. Wheeler.)

In the ant colony there are three types of individuals, winged males and queens, and wingless workers, the latter being divided into numerous castes in the higher species. In these higher forms, the workers are polymorphic and range in size from the tiniest ants up to workers which are almost as large as the queen (cf. Emery, 1894*b*, and Buckingham, 1911). Other species contain only workers of two sizes, while the more primitive ants, for example, the Ponerinae, are monomorphic.

According to Wheeler (1933), the behavior pattern of colony-founding queens, with few exceptions, is very uniform. After she has taken her nuptial flight and mated, the queen descends and rids herself of her wings. She then either finds a small cavity under a stone or log suitable for her nest or prepares one in the soil. She closes her small nest and remains imprisoned for several months, during which time she lays a clutch of eggs, later feeding and tending the developing larvae until pupation takes place and her young emerge as small workers. During all this time the queen has no access to food, but feeds her larvae with her saliva and lives on her original abdominal fat supply, as well as the degenerating tissues of her now useless wing-muscles. Sometimes the queen even resorts to feeding upon a few of her eggs or larvae in order that she and the remaining brood may survive. As soon as the first workers leave the nest and forage for themselves and their mother, the queen devotes her entire attention to egg-laying. As in the case of the honeybee, the queen ant is fecundated but once, and has been known to live as long as seventeen years.

Some striking variations in colony-founding have recently been recorded by the same author. One of the most interesting is that of the females of certain African species of the genus *Carebara*. The queen is so much larger than the workers that, even though she has a supply of abdominal fat and wing-muscles, she is unable to feed her minute larvae. The

Carebara queen, however, does not start her colony independently, for when she leaves the maternal nest she carries with her—attached to her tarsal hairs—a number of tiny workers, which, like those of the honeybee, assist the queen in bringing up her first brood.

The habits of *Myrmecia regularis* in caring for her initial progeny also differ from the behavior of the higher ants and resemble those of the queen bumblebee, for the female of *Myrmecia regularis* leaves her underground nest in order to forage for herself and her brood, making an opening in the outermost wall of the nest and closing it again when she returns with provisions.

While all ants are social, many of the species show varying degrees of social development, and we find that the colonies of primitive ants are small and that the females and workers are very similar to each other in structure and size. The Ponerinae represent the lowest social organization among the ants. The colonies are usually very small, sometimes consisting of only a few dozen individuals, which is due either to low fertility of the queen or to her short life-span. As the monomorphic workers are often fertile, there is little to distinguish them from the queen, and the latter does not receive from the workers the special attentions that are given to the queens of the higher ants (cf. Wheeler, 1910).

Most of the nests of the Ponerinae are situated in the soil or in old logs and lack the smoothly finished chambers and galleries found in the nests of the higher ants. The pupae, so far as known, are always enclosed in cocoons, and, according to Wheeler (1910), this is probably the primitive, ancestral condition from which the absence of a cocoon in the Myrmicinae, Dolichoderinae, Dorylinae, and many Camponotinae has been derived, either by a suppression of the spinning habit of the larvae, or, as in *Oecophylla,* by use of the silk for other purposes, for example, the building of nests and aphid-tents.

The larvae, as well as the adults of the Ponerinae, are carnivorous, and Wheeler has observed workers feeding the young with pieces of insects by turning the larva on its back and placing the insect food on its ventral surfaces within reach of its mouthparts. The callows hatch unaided, and the young males and females emerge from their cocoons with their wings already spread. Wheeler believes that such peculiar habits of the Ponerinae as feeding pieces of insects to the larvae, the retaining of the cocoon and the unaided hatching of the callows, as well as the small size of the colonies, and the low fertility of the queens of many species, in addition to morphological similarities, suggest wasp ancestry.

A. The Driver and Legionary Ants

The Dorylinae, or driver and legionary ants, represent, as Wheeler (1910) puts it, "the Huns and Tartars of the insect world." The two main groups of this subfamily are the drivers (Dorylii) of tropical Africa and Asia, and the legionary ants (Ecitonii) of the American tropics. These ants, being carnivorous and forming huge polymorphic colonies, must necessarily forage over a vast territory in order to obtain a sufficient amount of food. Although the workers are almost totally blind—some have no eyes at all—and have to depend entirely on their contact-odor sense, they orient themselves quickly and move with great rapidity. An excellent photograph showing an immense army of *Dorylus nigricans* has been recently published by Hegh (1922) and clearly illustrates the manner in which these columns of marchers travel; soldiers—flanking the outer sides of the file—form two living walls between which the workers carry the larvae and pupae. The driver ants have been found so efficient in clearing human habitation of vermin that some of the people in Africa find it advisable to vacate their homes while hordes of these ants rid the houses of undesirable tenants. These ants have been known to kill even large domestic animals while the latter were tethered and unable to escape. Hingston (1932) describes the activities of the Ecitons as follows:

> The driver ants of Tropical America are well known to go about in large armies. They search every cranny of the forest, blackening the whole surface of the ground, sending out columns in all directions which flush cockroaches, crickets, grasshoppers, spiders and destroy every living thing they meet with.

Rau (1933) has recently made similar observations on *Eciton burchelli*, which he very interestingly describes as follows:

> Here in these two pockets of a tree millions of ants were packed, and the moving line was pouring more into the mass every minute. They clung to one another in a rounded mass like swarming bees. On the outside of the group walked many heavy-jawed soldiers, as though they were directing the traffic. I could make no estimate of the number of ants here, but you may base your calculations—or imaginings—on the following measurements: one mass was eighteen inches long, ten wide and five and one-half inches deep!

This same author, after following the line of a traveling colony of *Eciton hamatum* to its source, found a large mass of ants the behavior of which he describes as follows:

> On a broad leaf was a large pile of immature ants. At the point where I had first discovered this exodus, none of the ants were carrying young, but at this point many were now taking them up and falling into line with them. Others were emerging from under the brush pile and depositing young and pausing, as though this were either a loading point or a relay station.

The Ecitons have even been observed to make temporary bridges of themselves. The genesis of such a bridge is described as follows by Belt (1874):

> Another time they [the Ecitons] were crossing a water-course along a small branch, not thicker than a goose-quill. They widened this natural bridge to three times its width by a number of ants clinging to it and to each other, over which the column passed.

An excellent photograph of such a bridge, made by *Dorilus nigricans,* has recently been published by Hegh (1922). *Eciton burchelli* even goes a step further than *Dorilus nigricans* by actually bridging gaps. Hingston (1932) observed a large column of *Eciton burchelli* in the act of passing from a tree-trunk to a contiguous sapling, and drew the latter an inch from the tree-trunk, thus creating a gap too wide for the ants to cross, and then tied the sapling in that position. Within three minutes the ants had completely bridged the gap, about thirty ants linking themselves together and forming a tangled mass, over which their comrades marched in thousands.

B. The Harvesting Ants

Due to scarcity of food, many Formicidae inhabiting desert regions have forsaken their carnivorous habits and have adapted themselves to a vegetarian diet. These ants, comprising a dozen or more genera, all belong to the subfamily Myrmicinae, and build complicated nests containing granaries in which they store seeds. They not only collect seeds, but husk them, dry them when they become wet, and cart away the seed-pods. In some species of harvesting ants, the mandibles have even become blunted, the soldiers, or major workers, according to Wheeler (1910), functioning as official seed-crushers. Some of the American harvesting ants belonging to the genus *Pheidole* are unable to keep their seeds from germinating in the nest during the wet weather, and from this Wheeler has inferred that these ants do not bite off the radicle as has been asserted by Moggridge (1873) in regard to some of the European harvesters.

While large-headed soldiers of the carnivorous species of *Pheidole* dissect insects brought in by the smaller workers, the soldiers of the harvesting species of this genus crush the hard-coated seeds, and other workers feed crushed pieces directly to the larvae.

Wheeler has also studied *Messor pergandei*, a moderate-sized black ant, which is very common in the deserts of southern Arizona and the Mojave Desert of California. The workers of this ant resemble the Mediterranean *Messor barbarus* in that they, too, vary greatly in the size of the body and the head. He describes the nest as having a single crater "much flattened, with rounded slopes, 50 cm. or more in diameter, and with one to three large and very irregular central openings. Sometimes these are slit-shaped and as much as 5 or 6 cm. long. The rough galleries and granaries are excavated to a depth of at least 60 cm. in the hardest and most sunbaked portions of the desert." He found long files of the workers busily harvesting late in the afternoon and saw that they eagerly seized all the mature seeds they could find in the sparse vegetation. The ants then carried the seeds to the nest, removed the husks, and stored the kernels in the granaries, afterwards carrying out the chaff and seed-pods and dumping them on the outer edge of the craters. When sound seeds are thrown out with the chaff, they later germinate and the old nests are often encircled by the resulting plants, a fact which in the past gave rise to the myth that the harvesting ants not only collected and stored grain but also planted and cultivated it.

According to Wheeler, the workers of *Messor pergandei*, when foraging, keep in files for a distance of about 70 feet from the nest before they disperse, while the workers of another species, *Ischnomyrmex cockerelli,* forage singly despite the fact that the colonies are large. Hingston (1929) observed how *Holcomyrmex scabriceps,* one of the Old World harvesting ants, cleared a path from the source of food to the nest. After the workers had made a rough track, they freed it from pebbles and debris, cut down stalks of grass, and finally made a smooth pathway along which they traveled when they carried the seeds to the nest.

Like the driver ants, certain harvesters, e.g., *Solenopsis geminata,* which often nest along streams, have the interesting habit of massing themselves into a ball around their eggs and larvae whenever their nest is inundated and of floating on the water until the ball reaches dry land.

C. The Fungus-Growing Ants

The fungus-growing ants belong to the Myrmicine tribe Attiini, of which about 100 species are known. These ants are found in tropical and subtropical America, and the fungi which they grow in their nests form the only food of these insects. Each species cultivates its own particular fungus, and no other kind is permitted to grow in the nest. In the United States, the comparatively primitive genus *Cyphomyrmex* is represented by two species, *rimosus* and *wheeleri.* The latter, according to Wheeler (1910), collects small slivers of plants upon which it cultivates its fungi, while *rimosus* uses caterpillar excrement for this purpose. The gardens of both species, in addition to being small and irregular in shape, are never suspended, but lie on the floor of the galleries.

Mycetosorites hartmani, another fungus-growing ant which occurs in the United States, builds small craters, the openings of which run vertically into the sand for a distance of about 24 to 79 cm., expanding at large intervals into several subspherical chambers. When excavating these chambers, the workers of this ant leave plant rootlets dangling into them, and upon these pendent rootlets the fungus gardens are built. The material used for these gardens consists of flower anthers, which have been made into a spongy paste, the whole mass being held together by the snow-white mycelium of the fungus. The species of three other genera (*Apterostigma, Sericomyrmex,* and *Trachymyrmex*) construct nests similar to those of *Mycetorsoritis,* building pendent fungus gardens (Figure 16) of insect excrement and vegetable debris.

Atta texana, the powerful leaf-cutting or "parasol" ant, is the only species of the genus *Atta* that occurs in the United States. According to Wheeler (1910), the nest appears externally as a large, flat mound, sometimes covering an area of 100 sq. m., and is made up of a number of more or less fused craters, 10 to 100 cm. in diameter, with large openings leading into galleries. These often extend to a depth of from 2 to 5 m., entering chambers which occasionally are 50 to 100 cm. long and 30 cm. broad and high. In the center of the floor, each chamber has a large fungus garden made of triturated leaves.

The manner in which the fungus spawn for each colony is obtained is

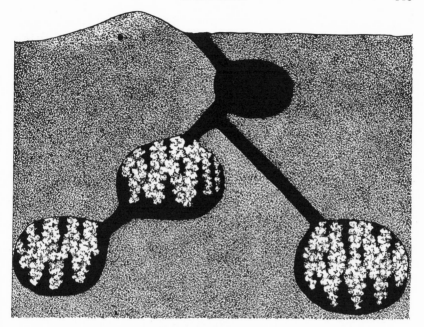

FIGURE 16

DIAGRAM OF A NEST OF *Trachymyrmex septentrionalis* SHOWING THE ORIGINAL
CHAMBER OF THE QUEEN AND THREE PENDENT FUNGUS GARDENS
Slightly reduced.
(Courtesy of Professor W. M. Wheeler)

extremely interesting. Before leaving her maternal nest, the unmated
queen eats heartily of the fungus, and the hyphae of the latter get into
her infrabuccal cavity along with other extraneous material to be expelled
later in the form of a pellet. After mating and ridding herself of her
wings, the queen prepares her nest in the soil, casting the pellet on the
floor. The hyphae begin to proliferate in the moist air, and the queen
aids their growth by manuring them with her feces. After she has begun to
lay eggs, she breaks some of them, adding them to the garden. The ant
larvae feed on the mycelium, and later emerge as workers, which break
through the soil and bring the proper material to increase the fungus
garden (cf. Huber, 1905).

Detailed observations on a colony of *Atta cephalotes polita* have recently
been made by Lutz (1929) in the Panama Canal Zone. The trail between the nest and the tree from which the ants were cutting leaves was
only 15 meters long and led along a network of lianas, so that the ants
could be readily observed. The workers carried loads averaging more than
twice the weight of each carrier, and the number of burdens deposited in
the nest during a day's work was estimated to be about 2400 pieces.

Among the leaf-cutting ants there are workers of several sizes, and the tiniest ones, called subminims, often go "hitch-hiking" on the leaves carried by the larger workers. This interesting habit Lutz describes as follows:

> They are among the first out in the morning and among the last in at night, lingering around the entrance to the nest, but they seem to do little that is very useful. When a carrier is in trouble with its burden, these subminims, if anywhere near, rush in and pull with the rest. In such a case the piece of leaf when finally balanced over a carrier's back will almost certainly have at least one of these subminims resting calmly on it and riding back toward the nest. However, these subminims do not always wait for trouble but often on their own initiative stop an incoming carrier and get on its leaf for a ride. Sometimes, when another carrier's leaf touches the one a rider is on, the rider will change conveyances and continue its journey on the other leaf.

Wheeler (1923) believes that the fungus-growing habit must have originated in the more humid portions of the tropics, as nearly all the primitive species of the fungus-growing ants are still to be found in the rain forests. However, by sinking their galleries and chambers to a greater depth in the soil, certain species of these ants found that they could carry on their fungus farming even in arid regions, and, as he aptly expresses it, "They have attained to a control of their environment and food-supply, which even the human inhabitants of those regions might envy."

D. The Honeydew Ants

A great number of Myrmicine, Formicine, and Dolichoderine ants live principally on the sap of plants. This "honeydew," as it is generally termed, is imbibed by the ants in two ways. Some species of *Leptothorax* lick the honeydew directly from the leaves and stems where it is excreted by the plants through small glands, while other ants receive a bountiful supply of this coveted saccharine liquid from a large group of insects, the Phytophthora, which includes the plant-lice, mealy-bugs, scale-insects, and leaf-hoppers. By stroking these insects with their antennae, the ants induce them to void the honeydew, which they eagerly lap up. As has been pointed out by Wheeler (1910), the adaptations of these ants in relation to the honeydew-producing insects are—with one exception—behavioristic rather than structural. For example, the ants do not seize and kill the aphids, as they do when they encounter other sedentary and defenseless insects, but protect them, and, in a few instances, even carry them to a place of safety. Some species, which keep root-aphids and root-coccids, clear the earth from the surfaces of roots and place their charges there, and in some cases even construct "sheds" for their "cattle."

Webster has made some interesting observations on the relations of ants to the corn-root-aphis (*Aphis maidiradicis*), which does much damage to Indian corn in our midwestern states (cf. Wheeler, 1910). In the fall, the eggs of this aphid are found only in the nests of the common garden ant, *Lasius americanus*. The workers of this ant carefully

FIGURE 17

REPLETE OF *Myrmecocystus horti-deorum* REGURGITATING FOOD TO WORKERS
OF THE ORDINARY FORM
Considerably enlarged.
(After McCook. Courtesy of Professor W. M. Wheeler.)

protect the eggs of this aphid all winter, shifting them from place to place within the nest according to changes in temperature and moisture. In spring, when the young aphids have hatched, they are transferred by the ants to the roots of young plants, such as fox-tail grass, smart-weed, and rag-weed, which grow early in places where corn has been raised the previous year. As soon as the corn appears above the soil, the ants transfer the young aphids to the roots of the young plants. All of these aphids are females, and within a few days they give birth to a new female generation, which is also cared for by the ants and placed on the most tender rootlets. As this procedure continues throughout the spring and summer, the multiplication of the aphids is enormous.

As long as the aphids find an abundance of tender nourishment on the roots, they remain wingless, but when the roots become tough, the females of *Aphis maidiradicis* give birth to a generation of both winged and wingless individuals. The winged aphids usually fly to other areas affording a larger food supply. However, Webster also observed some ants making burrows at the base of corn plants and domiciling winged aphids there, and, when these aphids gave birth to young, the ants immediately removed the latter to another part of the root, or to a root near by, and carefully tended them.

The one structural adaptation which has developed as a result of the relation between ants and honeydew-producing insects is found in a group of ants commonly known as the "honeyants." At least six different genera (*Prenolepis, Melophorus, Plagiolepis, Leptomyrmex, Camponotus,* and *Myrmecocystus*) store honeydew and nectar in the crops of certain workers known as "repletes." The abdomen of these ants is capable of being distended to such an extent that when it is filled with honey the sclerites separate and look like dark patches on the taut, intersegmental membrane. The habit of using some of the workers as repletes was probably developed by the ants as an adaptation to arid climates, where the periodic scarcity of food makes it necessary for them to use some method of storage during those seasons when supplies are more plentiful. Whenever a member of a colony becomes hungry, it strokes one of the repletes, and the latter regurgitates droplets of honey (Figure 17).

The first comprehensive observations on the habits of these ants were made by McCook (1882), who studied *Myrmecocystus mexicanus* var. *horti-deorum* in Colorado. McCook discovered nests with hundreds of repletes hanging close to each other in rows from the vaulted ceilings of the nest-chambers (Figure 18). He found no structural differences

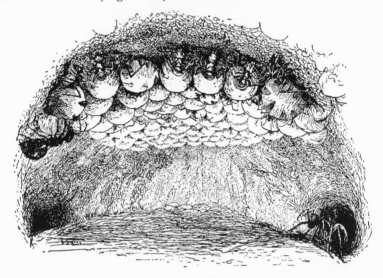

FIGURE 18
REPLETES OF *Myrmecocystus horti-decorum* SUSPENDED FROM THE CEILING
OF THE HONEY CHAMBER
Somewhat enlarged.
(After McCook. Courtesy of Professor W. M. Wheeler.)

between ordinary workers and repletes and thought it probable that any of the former could develop into the latter, a surmise which has been confirmed by Wheeler (1910), as the following account of this author shows:

> In the nests which I excavated during July there were many callow workers, males and females. While keeping several colonies in artificial nests, it occurred to me that the change from the ordinary to the replete worker must begin during the callow stage, while

the integument of the gaster is still very soft and distensible. I accordingly isolated a number of young callows in two of my nests and fed them with maple syrup and cane sugar water. They partook of these substances greedily, and a few of the workers in each nest gradually began to assume the replete condition. During the course of four to six weeks several of them became what I have called semirepletes (McCook's semirotunds), and four, three in one nest and one in the other, actually attained the dimensions of the perfect replete. Most of the workers, however, showed no inclination to assume this form.

Wheeler very interestingly reflects on the life of the replete as follows:

> Those who, in anthropomorphic mood, are wont to extol the fervid industry and extraordinary feats of muscular endurance in ants, should not overlook the beatific patience and self-sacrifice displayed by the replete *Myrmecocystus* as it hangs from the rafters of its nest, month in month out—for years, perhaps—a reservoir of temperamental as well as liquid sweetness.

E. The Slave-Making Ants

All the known slave-making ants belong to the genera *Formica, Polyergus, Strongylognathus,* and *Harpagoxenus.* The last three of these genera are known as obligatory slave-makers, that is, they can no longer exist without slaves, while the slave-making species of *Formica* comprise the facultative slave-makers, since they sometimes live without slaves. One of the best-known facultative slave-makers is *Formica sanguinea* (cf. Donisthorpe, 1915), which is common throughout temperate Europe. This species usually lives under stones, or in logs and stumps, and is one of the most belligerent, as well as versatile, of ants, attacking intruders instantly with its mandibles, simultaneously turning the tip of its gaster forward and injecting formic acid into the wound. The workers of *sanguinea* excavate the nest, forage, and care for the young, even when slaves are present in the nest. During a slave raid, the army of workers moves directly to the nest to be plundered, the colony having apparently received information from the scouts in regard to the position of the nest which is to be pillaged. The raiding workers then pour into the entrance of the nest, seize the larvae and pupae, but do not kill the adults unless these offer resistance, and then start for home.

The amazons, or obligatory slave-makers, belonging to the genus *Polyergus,* are represented by one species in Europe and at least four in North America. These ants have mandibles highly adapted for piercing the armor of adult ants, but they are entirely dependent upon their slaves, being completely unable to excavate their nests, care for their young, or to forage. They, therefore, enslave other species, in whose nests they establish their colonies. Wheeler (1910) describes some inconsistencies in the behavior of these slave-makers as follows:

> While in the home nest they sit about in stolid idleness or pass the long hours begging the slaves for food or cleaning themselves and burnishing their ruddy armor, but when outside the nest on one of their predatory expeditions they display a dazzling courage and

capacity for concerted action compared with which the raids of the *sanguinea* resemble the clumsy efforts of a lot of untrained militia.

Even more vivid is the following description by the same author of a slave-raid of *Polyergus breviceps,* one of the American amazons:

> After waiting nearly an hour (at 1.55 P.M.) I saw the beautiful red ants boil up, so to speak, in the opening. In a few moments they came rushing out in great numbers and kept running about just outside the entrance till 2.15, when they started in a compact army up the embankment and obliquely in a southwesterly direction. Soon, however, they returned to the nest as if changing their minds and again started out due south and straight up the bank. The procession formed with great alacrity and then pushed ahead at the rate of one m. in forty seconds, over smooth ground, but requiring about one minute to make the same distance over the dead oak leaves. There was no leader, the army being headed by a few workers which were continually being passed by workers overtaking them from the rear. They neither hesitated nor stopped till they reached a large *subsericea* nest about 25 m. from their own, on the top of the embankment. This nest was under and around a couple of large, flat stones, and had two entrances a short distance apart. There were a few *subsericea* sauntering about the entrance, but as soon as they scented the approaching army they scampered into their nest. The amazons arrived at 2.40 P.M. and at once poured into the two entrances in a mass like wine being poured into a couple of funnels. Two minutes later the first *breviceps* emerged with a cocoon in her jaws and was at once followed by a file of others similarly laden. They started for home in great precipitation. One that was timed made the entire distance of 25 m. in a little more than four minutes. As the army must have comprised fully 1,000 workers, there was soon a long file, each carrying a larva, nude pupa or cocoon. I returned to the *subsericea* nest in time to see a few workers of this species rush out of the opening with larvae, run the gauntlet of the amazons and make off to the open ground beyond. From time to time a *breviceps* would emerge from the nest carrying a *subsericea* worker, take it a few centimeters from the opening and put it down. To my surprise the black ant scrambled to her feet and ran away uninjured. I saw this performance repeated more than a dozen times by different amazons. Not a single *subsericea* was killed or even maimed. The plundering of the nest continued, the *breviceps* returning repeatedly from their own nest to get more pupae. By 2.55 the number of these brought out of the nest had dwindled considerably and at 3.06 the supply ceased altogether. Nevertheless the *breviceps* kept entering the nest and coming out with empty jaws till 3.15 when they began to straggle home. The last ones left the pillaged formicary at 3.30 and moved away slowly or sauntered about as if reluctant to return home without booty. The feverish excitement so apparent in these insects a few moments before had suddenly subsided. At the entrance of their own formicary the slaves were running about in considerable numbers and seemed to be greatly excited over the quantities of booty that were being brought in. Soon, however, both slaves and *breviceps* entered their nest and all was quiet. I again went back and found the *subsericea* cautiously returning to their pillaged nest. On raising the stones I found a great many unharmed workers in the galleries but not a single larva or pupa. These ants must have remained in their nest during the whole time that the rape of their brood was in progress! The foray was remarkable on account of the behavior of

both species, for the *subsericea,* though abundant, had made no attempt to protect the young which they had for weeks been rearing with infinite solicitude, and the *breviceps* had been more courteous and considerate than their vocation of professional kidnappers would seem to permit.

While *Strongylognathus* and *Harpagoxenus* resemble *Polyergus* in the degree of dependency upon their slaves, they differ in that they permit the queens of the host species to live and reproduce in the mixed colonies, and for this reason they are called "degenerate slave-makers." *Harpagoxenus sublevis,* one of the degenerate slave-makers, has become so utterly dependent upon its slaves that the latter actually have to carry their masters whenever the colony moves to a new nest. The desultory fashion in which *Harpagoxenus americanus* makes its slave-raids contrasts interestingly with the high degree of organization demonstrated by pillaging workers of *Polyergus,* as is illustrated by the following description by Creighton (1924):

> During the progress of a raid the *Harpagoxenus* workers and their slaves cluster about the entrance of their nest in a manner suggestive of *Polyergus,* but with this the similarity ends. There is no rapid moving phalanx of raiders, no concentration about the entrance of the raided nest, no frantic activity to enlarge the entrance. The *Harpagoxenus* leave their nest singly and amble awkwardly and uncertainly to the nest of their victims. Only once did I see more than one *Harpagoxenus* leave the nest at the same time. On one occasion a column of three departed at once for the *Leptothorax* nest. However, this column broke up almost at once and was, I believe, purely fortuitous. On arriving at the *Leptothorax* nest the *Harpagoxenus* wastes no time in preliminaries but enters at once. Having secured a larva or pupa it emerges as quietly as it entered and returns with its burden to its own nest. Quite often they lose their way and I have seen a number of them captured by small spiders while raiding.

VII. TERMITES

Although the termites (Isoptera) are very primitive insects as compared with ants, bees, and wasps, they nevertheless resemble the first of these three subdivisions of the Social Hymenoptera in such a high degree that they are sometimes erroneously called "white ants." However, most of these resemblances between ants and termites are merely superficial and represent parallel developments during the social evolution of these two groups of insects. Moreover, even the workers of a few of the higher termites are not white, but have a pigmented exoskeleton and well-developed eyes, as do most ants and the winged reproductive forms of termites. Like the ants, all of the approximately 1500 known species of termites are social and live together in well-organized communities. The latter are often much larger than those of ants, sometimes consisting of as many as several hundred thousands, or even millions of individuals, all of which have directly or indirectly originated from one pair of adults. Termites also exhibit a remarkable degree of polymorphism, which in some cases is even more pronounced than that of the ants. Like the latter, they have a winged reproductive class of both sexes which at certain times leave the parental colony in large numbers, mount into the air for a short flight, and then shed their wings. Strangely enough, some of the higher termites also resemble the ants in certain other habits, since some species forage for food, store seeds, or grow fungi which, as in the case of the ants, serve as food for both young and adults.

However, there are also many fundamental differences between ants and termites and the social organization of their colonies. There is no larval and pupal stage which requires special care, the young termite nymph being able to move about as soon as it emerges from the egg, whereupon it assists with the various duties connected with the social life of the colony. Unlike the ants, in whose colonies all of the labor is performed by females, the worker and soldier caste of termites is made up of both sexes, and the colonies are normally started and maintained by two parents (king and queen). Instead of being related to the Solitary Hymenoptera, as the ants, bees, and wasps, termites have probably evolved from roaches, with which they have quite a number of characteristics in common (cf. Snyder, 1924, 1926).

While termites are fairly well represented in the warmer parts of the Temperate Zone,[7] they have reached their greatest development in the tropical parts of the world, where they occur in such abundance that large areas are sometimes so dotted with termite mounds that the latter suggest large villages or cities of miniature adobe huts (cf. Snyder, 1925). Equally abundant are the number of species in many parts of the tropics, Emerson (1929) having recently taken over 100 within an area of about a square mile in British Guinea.

A well-established colony of the higher termites normally contains at least one king and one queen, from one to two types of workers, all of which are sterile, and one to three types of structurally differentiated soldiers. Each of these castes has a special function. As already mentioned, almost all new colonies are started by a king and a queen, the latter confining themselves entirely to reproduction as soon as their descendants are old enough to take over the various labors which the complicated social life of the colony requires. It is the duty of the workers to collect food, take care of the eggs and nymphs, as well as the reproductive forms and the soldiers, and to construct and repair the nest. In these labors, the workers are assisted by the nymphs of their own, as well as those of the other castes. In fact, in some of the lower termites there is no worker caste, all of the various duties of such colonies being performed solely by the immature forms.

After the new colony has been founded, the king continues to live with the queen, sometimes for as long as a quarter of a century or more (cf. Snyder, 1926). If an accident befalls one of these primary (macropterous) reproductives after the colony is established, the latter can produce two

---

[7]Termites have been reported from almost all of our states, New England having but one native species (*Reticulitermes flavipes*), while Arizona, with its semi-tropical climate, has at least 25 (cf. Light, 1934*b*).

supplementary types (brachypterous and apterous) of reproductives which differ from each other and from the two macropterous parents. These latter are normally monogamous. However, if the macropterous queen dies, the old king apparently always becomes polygamous, associating himself with several supplementary queens. These secondary and tertiary sexual forms are less prolific than the primary queen, but they make up in numbers what they lack in egg-laying capacity. If—as sometimes happens—both of the primary reproductives are lost after the colony has become established, a number of secondary or tertiary kings are usually also produced. These promiscuously fecundate the supplementary queens by whom they are, as a rule, greatly outnumbered.

After the new colony has been founded by the king and queen, it grows very slowly at first, so that in some species, even after a year or two, the population of the colony may amount to only 100 individuals or less (cf. Harvey, 1934). As in many of the Social Aculeates, the first brood of an incipient colony of most termite species consists of sterile individuals which are smaller in size than those of the later broods. As the new colony grows, highly modified soldiers are also produced, but these always constitute a smaller percentage of the total population than the workers. How the strange modifications of the soldiers come about is as yet not definitely known. The soldiers of the more primitive species, for example, those of *Zootermopsis angusticollis,* are provided with powerful mandibles, while those of some of the higher termites have a syringelike frontal gland in the head, from which they can squirt a volatile liquid which acts as a repellant or toxic gas. In some species this snout-like frontal gland secretes a sticky substance, with which the soldiers can easily disconcert ants and other marauders by "gumming them up." Some of these unique creatures, known as *nasuti,* have become so highly specialized that their mandibles have completely disappeared, while in others they have become vestigial. But there are also certain species of termites (*Armitermes*) in which both the mandibles and the frontal glands of the soldiers can be employed in protecting the colony. In a few genera, the soldiers have queer, twisted, asymmetrical mandibles which no longer serve for biting, but are used instead for "flipping or snapping particles of earth at invaders . . . or flipping themselves away from danger" (cf. Snyder, 1924, 1926).

As the following vivid description by Froggatt (1895) indicates, the soldiers of the less primitive termites are usually very alert and protect the colony to the best of their ability. When this author broke open one of the galleries of a nest of *Eutermes,*

> the soldiers rushed out in a small body, scattering on either side of the damaged roadway; after hunting about on the surface of the rocks, they then retreated to the breach, which they all entered and formed a rank along either side, standing just far enough apart to touch the tips of each other's antennae. While they stood in this regular line with their heads up and their antennae moving backwards and forwards, the workers appeared, each carrying in its mouth a bit of wood or fragment from the wall, and, passing between

the soldiers who were standing guard, deposited its burden upon the edge of the wall and turning round evacuated a small drop of dark brown liquid from its anus upon the top of its brick and then disappeared, the next one taking his place and going through exactly the same performance, an endless gang of workers following each other and rapidly reducing the size of the hole; a gap about an inch long and half an inch deep was rebuilt in half an hour. Unlike the two-jawed termites, which never rebuild their nests in the daytime, the *Eutermes* do not seem to dislike the light, but will expose themselves in the hottest sunlight when mending their nests.

But it is apparently also the duty of the soldiers—at least in some species—to warn the colony of impending danger, for, according to Snyder (1926), the soldiers of certain species bang their heads against the surrounding wood when danger threatens, while those of other species make a noise by clicking their mandibles. When alarmed, the soldiers, as well as the workers, of some species make peculiar, jerky movements, which—Snyder believes—probably serve as a means of communication.

The last of the various castes which are produced by the termite colony are the kings and queens. These primary reproductive forms, as already mentioned, appear in immense numbers at certain seasons of the year during the so-called colonizing flights. If occurring on a large scale, these colonizing or dispersal flights furnish a sight which is not readily forgotten. On several occasions, the writer has witnessed this interesting phenomenon at Berkeley, California, in the case of the Western Subterranean Termite, *Reticulitermes hesperus.* Swarming in this species usually occurs on a clear forenoon following the first drenching autumnal rain. As soon as the temperature becomes sufficiently warm, myriads of young kings and queens of this species issue from their parental nests over large areas, through holes made by the workers, and eagerly mount into the air until millions of wings glitter in the morning sunshine. After all of the young "colonists" have emerged from the nest, a process which sometimes takes several hours, the workers again close the exit holes from within. Being poor flyers, the feeble efforts of the young kings and queens are quickly over. They descend, or fall, to the ground, where they pry off their cumbersome wings, and the young queens now proceed to entice the males. This is accomplished by raising the abdomen and presumably emitting some volatile substance which is attractive to the latter. Having succeeded in enticing one of the young kings, the queen lowers her abdomen and begins a restless, often winding march, followed at every step by her companion, with his head usually touching the tip of her abdomen. Hundreds of such wandering couples can frequently be seen within an area of a few square yards. Sometimes, according to Pickens (1934), it even happens that such a wandering pair is "joined by a third and even a fourth insect, the whole moving along like a train of cars. At times, in turning, the leader curves so far to the right or left that she finds herself behind the last one of the train and the group revolves for some time in a circle."
Similar observations have been made by Castle (1934) after the coloniz-

ing flight of the Damp-Wood Termite, *Zootermopsis angusticollis,* which he described as follows:

> The female stops, elevates the posterior portion of the abdomen, and awaits the arrival of a mate. Evidently an odor attractive to the male is given off which enables it to find the female. The male sets about at once grooming the female by means of the jointed feelers of the mouth parts, also using the mandibles. The female lowers her abdomen, allows the male to groom her for a few seconds, and then starts a search for a colony site. The male follows, but in contrast to male behavior in the mating of other species, he seems rather ʲnattentive, often straying away from the female. If the male wanders too far from the female she stops, raises the tip of her abdomen again, and attracts either the wayward male or another. Having again obtained a mate, she continues the search for a home, and, on finding a suitable place, begins excavating. Most of the work falls to her lot, the male acting as a guard to prevent the intrusion of other males. The male occasionally goes into the opening to assist, but is more hindrance than help. When the opening is large enough to accommodate the pair, the male enters, and the opening to the outside is then closed with pellets and chips of wood.

Before discussing what happens after the young termite king and queen enter their new home, it seems advisable to consider briefly the classification and nesting habits of these interesting social insects. Light (1934*a*) separates the order Isoptera into the five families. The most primitive of these are the Mastotermitidae. This family is represented by only one living species, which is found in Australia and is chiefly of interest because it is by far the most primitive termite known. According to Snyder (1926), the *Mastotermes* queen extrudes her eggs in a mass, in a manner similar to that of the females of certain cockroaches, instead of laying them singly, as do the queens of other termites.

The second family (Hodotermitidae) consists of about fifteen species belonging to the genus *Hodotermes* and is confined to Africa and Central Asia. According to Light (1934*a*), this family represents "large termites of subterranean habit which feed largely on grass, being among the few termites which forage abroad for their food. While primitive in many respects, the termites of this family show a higher social development than those of the next family (Kalotermitidae) in that they have a worker caste."

The third family (Kalotermitidae) is a rather heterogeneous assemblage of about 240 known species belonging to some twenty genera and subgenera, some of which, e.g., *Zootermopsis,* are rather primitive. The members of this family live in wood, and, unlike other termites, manage to get along without having contact with the ground. The Kalotermitidae have no worker caste, the nymphs of the sexual forms performing all the necessary duties required by the social life of the colony. Unlike those of the higher termites, the queens of this family do not become very much distended and hence are able to move about quite freely within the nest.

The fourth family (Rhinotermitidae) comprises about 140 known species, almost all of which are subterranean in habit. To this family belongs our common eastern species *Reticulitermes flavipes,* concerning which considerable is known. As in other termites, the growth of the *flavipes* colony is at first exceedingly slow.   The queen protects the eggs and young larvae, sometimes carrying them about in her mouth when the colony is disturbed.   Later the eggs are taken care of by the workers, which carry them away as soon as they are laid. Emerson (1929) once observed a worker of this, or some other species, taking hold of an egg only half laid, pulling it out, and then carrying it away. According to Snyder (1926), the colonies of *Reticulitermes* in temperate regions readily leave their nests at the onset of winter and burrow into the ground below the frost line, where they remain until the return of warmer weather. A similar method is resorted to in prairie and desert regions, where during periods of drought in the summer, the entire colony retreats to deeper subterranean galleries, if necessary.

All of the preceding termite families, including the Rhinotermitidae, feed primarily on the cellulose found in wood, which is broken down by vast numbers of symbiotic protozoa which are found in the greatly distended intestine of these termites (cf. Imms, 1919, and Kirby, 1934). As Cleveland (1924) has recently shown, these termites cannot digest cellulose themselves and die shortly after the protozoa have been removed from their intestines.   Another characteristic which the preceding four termite families have in common is that they do not build conspicuous termitaria, as do most of the species belonging to Termitidae, the last of the five termite families.

The Termitidae comprise the vast majority (about 1200 species) of termites and are almost entirely confined to tropical regions.   Probably the most fundamental difference between the Termitidae and the other four termite families is the absence of intestinal protozoa in the former. This fundamental difference between the Termitidae, on the one hand, and the remaining four families, on the other, Light (1934a) believes, is closely correlated with the feeding habits of these two groups of termites.   Instead of subsisting chiefly on sound wood, as do the more primitive termites, the Termitidae, according to Light, "utilize largely decayed or weathered wood, fungus, dead and partly decayed leaves, grass, organic detritus, leaf mold," and similar substances.   The Termitidae also exhibit a great diversity in the architecture of their termitaria.   While a few species nest in wood, others live in the ground and construct large earthen mounds (Figure 19).   In some parts of the Old World tropics, these mounds reach enormous proportions, sometimes attaining a height of twenty feet. While the termitaria of some species are rather irregular in shape, those of others show a uniformity and beauty in architecture which is really amazing.   Some species of termites build slender, steeple-like termitaria which often cover the entire landscape as so many huge stalagmites or inverted icicles, while others, e.g., *Eutermes fungifaber,* construct termitaria which resemble gigantic mushrooms.   Still other termitaria closely resemble straw beehives, while those of certain African species have umbrella-shaped or ledge-like processes which serve as "shin-

FIGURE 19
MOUNDS OF *Armitermes medius* IN THE SAVANNAH REGION OF PANAMA
Termite mounds sometimes attain the height of 20 ft.
(After Snyder)

gles" during the torrential rains, so common in that part of the world
(cf. Hegh, 1922, and Light, 1934a). Some Australian termite species
build peculiar wedge-shaped structures, which are called compass-, or
meridional termitaria, since the two long surfaces of the latter always face
east and west, and the narrow ends north and south. Some mound-like
termitaria, as Escherich (1909, 1911) and others have shown, are venti-
lated by a system of air shafts.

Other species of the Termitidae, like some of the ants, build ellipsoidal
carton nests in trees. Such nests are always connected with the soil
below by means of covered runways which in some cases may be over
100 ft. long. Similar shelter tubes are often constructed over metal,
brick, and other hard substances which the termites cannot penetrate.
Some of the South American species, according to Emerson (1929), like
some of their African cousins, also have the habit of building "projections
out from the nests which shed the water and keep the nest comparatively
dry."

Perhaps the most interesting thing about these large termitaria, however, is the fact that many of them have been built by the immediate offspring of a single pair of termites. While the queens of the more primitive termites, as has already been pointed out, increase comparatively little
in size after they have shed their wings, those of some of the Termitidae
reach almost unbelievable proportions (Figure 20) as compared with
the remaining members of the colony. Apparently nowhere in the animal
kingdom is fecundity so well personified as in the queen of some of the
higher termites. For example, the queen of *Termes natalensis* measures
only about 2 cm. in length and .5 cm. in width after she has shed her
wings. But shortly after establishing herself with her spouse in their

FIGURE 20

A GLIMPSE INTO THE ROYAL CHAMBER OF *Termes bellicosus*, SHOWING THE KING
AND HIS PHYSOGASTRIC QUEEN AND MANY SOLDIERS AND WORKERS
Diagrammatic.
(After Escherich)

new home, her ovaries begin to grow, finally causing her abdomen—
originally only 1 cm. in length and .5 cm. in width—to grow to 2.5 cm.
in width and 9 cm. in length. The queen thus becomes a mere egg-
laying machine, fed and tended by the workers. In the following account,
Dr. Uichanco (1919) gives an excellent description of the rather monotonous life of such a physogastric queen:

> In a well-established nest the royal chamber is located a little
> below the level of the surface of the ground. It is a hollow, plano-
> convex chamber, with thick, irregular, clay walls and numerous
> passageways connecting with the adjoining parts of the nest. Within
> the chamber are the king and the queen, attended by a large body-
> guard of soldiers and workers. Occasionally, two queens are found
> occupying the same chamber in a nest; but in all cases not more than
> one male is present. The king has not changed his appearance since
> he first came down from the nuptial flight; he is still very lively
> and is likely to slip away and escape detection unless some care is
> exercised in removing the royal chamber from the nest. On the other
> hand, the queen has changed considerably. Her abdomen is much
> engorged with eggs; and the abdominal tergites and sternites, once
> closely connected, are now situated far apart, with their connecting
> membranes greatly distended. The insect at this time presents a
> characteristic sausagelike appearance. Her activity is restricted in
> so far as locomotion is concerned; and she is now entirely helpless—
> actually a prisoner in her own cell. The workers feed her, clean her

body, and look after her personal comfort. Her abdomen exhibits a succession of peristaltic movements, attended by a continuous discharge of more or less elliptical eggs. A full-grown queen lays eggs at the rate of thirty to sixty a minute. The workers remove the eggs immediately after they are extruded and carry them away to be taken care of in the nurseries.

The preceding passage refers to one of the fungus-growing species of the Philippine Islands. The fungus-growing termites are confined to the Ethiopian and Indomalayan regions and represent the most highly specialized genera of the Isoptera. The "fungus gardens," which sometimes reach the size of a coconut, occupy the greater part of the inner cavity of the mound, each garden having the general appearance of sea coral or cauliflower. The "buttons" or conidia of these fungus growths are eaten by the young termite nymphs and are also fed to the reproductive forms. During the rainy months, according to Uichanco, these mushrooms not infrequently break through the outer wall of the termitaria and develop into full-grown plants.

While most termite species normally shun the light, there are several exceptions, such as the black termite (*Eutermes monoceros*) of Ceylon, a few species of the African genus *Hodotermes,* and *Nasutitermes cavifrons* of South America (cf. Escherich, 1909, 1911; Hegh, 1922; and Hingston, 1932). Both the workers and soldiers of these termites are pigmented, have well-developed eyes, and the workers often forage in large columns in broad daylight. The columns of these diurnal or "wander" termites are usually guarded by large numbers of soldiers which are lined up on both sides, facing outward (cf. Hegh, 1922). In addition to the well-developed eyes and the pigmentation of the exoskeleton, the workers and soldiers of these termites have also retained several other primitive characters, for example, longer legs and antennae, the latter having more segments than those of the "light-shunning" species.

VIII. Symphiles, Synoeketes, and Synechthrans

Besides being afflicted with various external and internal parasites, as are the solitary species, the social insects also harbor a large number of intruders in their nests. Some of these intruders, or inquilines, act merely as scavengers, while others steal the food of their hosts, and in some cases even destroy their brood. These inquilines, or guests, as they are sometimes called, may be divided into two groups. One of these consists of intruders which are phylogenetically far removed from the species in whose nests they are found, while the second group of inquilines consists of very close relatives of the species afflicted. The guests of the second group are usually referred to as social parasites and will be discussed under a separate heading. The first group of guests is usually divided into Symphiles, Synoeketes, and Synechthrans. The Symphiles live in complete harmony with their hosts, are fed and fondled by the latter, which even rear and feed the progeny of these guests, while the Synoeketes are ignored by their hosts and act as scavengers in the nests of the latter. The Synechthrans, on the other hand, are abhorred by their hosts, who attempt in various ways to get rid of these unwelcome guests. While this classification is a convenient one, there are some inquilines which have overlapping characteristics, so that it is sometimes difficult to know to which one of these three subdivisions they really belong. The number of these guests is astounding, when one considers that—despite our limited knowledge of this subject—several thousand species have already been described, Donisthorpe (1927) estimating that the number of ant guests (myrmecophiles) alone will probably amount to about 5000, when they are all known. Since the space allotted the writer would make it impossible to discuss this interesting group of insects in detail, it seems best to describe a few outstanding examples.

An interesting guest, the adults and larvae of which occur in practically every bumblebee nest, is the beetle *Antherophagus.* According to Wagner (1907), the larvae of this beetle cause enormous devastation, but the writer (1934) has never found any evidence of this, although he has repeatedly seen several hundred larvae in all stages of development in a single nest. All of these nests were in a flourishing condition and showed not the slightest indication of destruction. The larvae, as well as the adults, were invariably found on or beneath the old comb at the bottom of the nest and not on that which was being used by the bees (cf. Frison, 1921). Scott (1920), who recently reared some larvae of *Antherophagus pallens,* found that they excavated cells for pupation early in August, pupated the following April, and emerged as adults late in May.

Antherophagus has a novel way of gaining admittance to the nest of his host. The adults frequent flowers such as hydrangea, fox-glove, and hollyhock, where they lie in wait with wide-open mandibles. When a bumblebee approaches, the beetle seizes it by the tongue, or by one of its legs or antennae, and in this fashion is carried into the nest. The mandibles and the peculiarly notched clypeus of the beetle seem to be specially adapted for grasping the more or less cylindrical joints of the appendages of the bee. On several occasions, the writer has seen an adult *Antherophagus*—in one case even two—attached to a bumblebee worker. How long these beetles sometimes cling to their porters is shown by the following observations. While taking a surface nest of *Bombus fervidus,* the writer noticed an *Antherophagus* attached to one of the hind legs of a worker. About fifteen minutes elapsed before the latter was captured, and during all this time the beetle retained its grip. As the accompanying illustration shows (Figure 21), these beetles sometimes cling so tenaciously to their host that they do not release their hold even after being placed in a cyanide jar.

The phenomenon of phoresy is by no means restricted to *Antherophagus,* for there are many examples of it in the insect world. As early as 1899, Forel (1930) discovered that *Thorictus,* a small beetle, attaches itself to the antennal scape of its ant host (*Cataglyphis*) and is thus transported into the ant colony, where, according to Banck (1927) it feeds on insect cadavers and the refuse of the nest. Another comparatively harmless

FIGURE 21

Antherophagus Clinging to the Tongue of a Worker of *Bombus vagans*
Greatly enlarged.
(After Wheeler)

myrmecophile is *Oxysoma,* one of the rove beetles (Staphylinidae), which, according to Escherich (1906), licks its ant host, feeding on the coating of saliva with which ants cover one another. Other species of rove beetles cause real destruction within the ant colony. *Atemeles,* one of these staphylinid beetles, has been studied in great detail by Wasmann (1890). This author found that the adult beetles are readily adopted by the ants, for the latter enjoy the aromatic secretion which *Atemeles* exudes through its trichomes. Another reason why this guest is given an amicable reception by its host is that it begs for food in the same manner as that employed by the ants themselves, namely, by stroking the cheeks of the ant with its forefeet as well as its antennae (Figure 22). The beetle larvae closely resemble those of their host, and, although they possess legs and can crawl about, they generally remain quiet in the spot where the ants have placed them and move only the front part of their bodies to and fro in the same manner as do the ant larvae when inducing the workers to feed them. Thus the ants carefully feed and tend their enemy, for the beetle larvae, as well as the adults, are carnivorous and devour enormous numbers of the ant brood.

Atemeles changes its host twice during the year, spending its period

FIGURE 22
Atemeles SOLICITING FOOD FROM AN ANT WORKER
Greatly enlarged.
(After Wasmann)

of hibernation in the nest of *Myrmica,* and then, after mating, enters a colony of some species of *Formica* where a new generation of *Atemeles* is produced, the *Formica* brood diminishing in proportion to the number of *Atemeles* which the nest contains. There is, however, a natural check upon an undue increase in the population of this guest which aids the survival of *Formica.* The *Atemeles* larva, before becoming a nymph, surrounds itself with earth and spins a delicate cocoon. In order to hatch successfully, the beetle larva must remain in the earth until it is ready to emerge from its cocoon. However, as the ants have the habit of digging up and cleaning their own cocoons, they often do the same with those of *Atemeles,* and this causes considerable destruction to the brood of the beetle.

It was formerly believed that the ants try to remedy the ravages which are caused by *Atemeles* and its young among their offspring by attempting to change queen larvae into workers—or *vice versa*—and as a result producing many individuals (pseudogynes) which are intermediate between queens and workers, but this has been shown not to be true by Donisthorpe (1927), who found populous colonies free from *Atemeles* containing pseudogynes in large numbers.

The harboring of such guests as *Atemeles* by the ants is explained by Wheeler (1923) as follows:

> Any insect possessed of the glandular attractions . . . can induce the ants to adopt, feed and care for it and thus become a member of the colony, just as an attractive and apparently well-behaved foreigner can secure naturalization and nourishment in any human community. But the procedure among the ants is more striking, because the foreigners are so very foreign. . . . Were we to behave in an analogous manner we should live in a truly Alice-in-Wonderland society. We should delight in keeping porcupines, alligators, lobsters, etc., in our homes, insist on their sitting down to table with us and feed them so solicitously . . . that our children would either perish of neglect or grow up as hopeless rhachitics.

Comparatively little is known concerning the guests (termitophiles) which are associated with termites, only about 700 species having thus far been described. As has been pointed out by Snyder (1924), comparatively few termitophiles occur in the nests of the more primitive termites, while the termitaria of the higher termites harbor larger numbers of inquilines, many of which have become physogastric like the termite queen. In some species, this physogastry, or extreme enlargement of the abdomen, is accompanied by the presence of finger-shaped exudate organs and the huge abdomen is turned upward and forward over the head, showing from above the inverted ventral side of the abdomen. As these inquilines produce fatty exudates which are eagerly sought by the termites, they are fed by their hosts in much the same manner as the ants feed the myrmecophiles. The development of physogastry in the guests, as has been suggested by Escherich (1911) in the case of beetle larvae, may be due to the fact that these intruders feed upon the plentiful supply of termites, in addition to being fed the same kind of food as the queen.

However, some of the termitophiles are not welcome guests and therefore must be classed as typical Synechtrans. Emerson (1929) describes the behavior of such a guest as follows:

> I found one beetle which habitually rode on the head of a worker termite, being transported around the nest, periodically changing from one worker to another. If two workers approached and a droplet of food was regurgitated by one for the other, this beetle would steal some for his own nourishment. The termites did not like this beetle and could be seen attempting to scrape it off their heads, but they never seemed able to either remove the parasite or to damage it.

A few years ago, while taking a colony of *Zootermopsis angusticollis* from a pine stump at Berkeley, California, the present writer secured two specimens of an hemipterous termitophile. These were found in the inner galleries of the nest and measured about 1 cm. in length and 0.5 cm. in width. They were blackish-brown in color and were peculiarly flattened, the latter condition, no doubt, being an adaptation to their mode of life in the narrow galleries of the nest of their host.

Snyder (1926) has made the interesting observation that the workers and soldiers of certain species of termites "exhibit peculiar more or less synchronous, convulsive or jerky movements of the whole body when they are alarmed at a disturbance of the colony." Strangely enough, these movements are also exhibited by some of the termite guests.

IX. Social Parasitism

Parasitism is one of the commonest phenomena in the insect world. The members of several large families of flies and wasps, for example, the Tachinidae and Ichneumonidae, regularly parasitize other insects upon whose tissues they feed during their larval development, a habit which almost invariably results in the death of their host. Social parasitism, as is indicated by the name, occurs only in connection with species which are social and represents the temporary or permanent enslavement of the members of one colony by those of another. Since most insect colonies are essentially families, Imms (1931) has recently employed the term "family parasitism" for this type of enslavement. One form of social parasitism—dulosis—has already been discussed in connection with the slave-making ants. However, there is a second type of social parasitism among insects which closely resembles that of certain birds, in that the parasites lay their eggs in the nests of related species, which then rear the "cuckoo" brood instead of their own. This type of parasitism is a fairly common phenomenon among ants, bees, and wasps. All of the permanent social parasites have lost their worker caste and can no longer found colonies of their own.

Comparatively little is known concerning the habits of the social parasites among wasps, *Vespula* (=*Vespa*) *austriaca* and *Vespula adulterina* being the only parasitic species thus far reported. *Vespula austriaca*, which ranges over the entire Holarctic region, has been found breeding in the nests of *Vespula rufa* in the Old World, but in North America its host is as yet unknown. *Vespula adulterina* apparently also is circumpolar in distribution. In the Old World, this species has been found in the nests of *Vespula norwegica*, while Wheeler and Taylor (1921) and Professor Scullen (cf. Bequaert, 1932) have found this wasp breeding in the nests of *Vespula arenaria* (=*diabolica*) in the United States.

So far as is known, social parasites occur only in two groups of the social bees, the Halictinae and the Bombinae. The development of an *Halictus* colony is sometimes interrupted by the female of *Sphecodes*, a close relative, which enters the nest by force and then lays her eggs in the pollen-primed cells of the *Halictus* colony. Legewie (1925) has observed many battles between *Sphecodes* and its host during the attempts of the former to enter the nest. One of these battles lasted six hours and resulted in victory for the parasite, sixteen *Halictus* females being killed during this encounter. However, according to Legewie, it sometimes also happens that the *Sphecodes* female is stung to death by the rightful owners of the nest during these encounters.

Social parasitism is especially common among the bumblebees, which contain a dozen or more known parasitic species all belonging to the genus *Psithyrus*. The queens of this genus leave their hibernacula about a month later than do the *Bombus* queens, and, since they have lost their polliniferous apparatus, they are no longer able to start colonies of their own. Having secured a meal of nectar from the spring flowers, the *Psithyrus* queen at once sets out in search of a *Bombus* nest. Although she has a powerful sting and a thick integument, which gives her a great advantage over the members of the *Bombus* colony, she is vulnerable in certain places, for example, the neck, and thus it not infrequently happens that she loses her life when she attempts to enter the *Bombus* nest. However, the *Psithyrus* queen sometimes does succeed in gaining admittance to the nest of her host, and it is interesting to watch her establish herself in the *Bombus* colony. In the case of *Psithyrus laboriosus*, which breeds in the nests of *Bombus vagans*, the writer (1934) was able to make the following observations concerning this interesting chapter in the life-history of the *Psithyrus* female: On the first day after the *laboriosus* female entered the nest, she seized nearly every worker with which she came in contact, rolled it toward the ventral side of her abdomen, and made movements as if to sting her victim. After a few seconds, however, the mauling ceased and the worker was released, apparently none the worse for this treatment. On the second and third day, the *Psithyrus* female employed this method of intimidation less frequently, and thereafter no animosity was noticed between the *Psithyrus* female and the *vagans* workers. The attitude of the *laboriosus* female and the *vagans* queen toward each other was somewhat different. From the very beginning, the *laboriosus* female paid little or no attention to the *vagans* queen, but during the first few days the latter turned the tip of her abdomen toward the intruder whenever they met, but these signs of hostility also gradually disappeared, and after the fourth or fifth day the two queens lived together in harmony. To the *vagans* males which were present in the nest when the *laboriosus* female first entered, and to two young *vagans* queens which hatched later, the *Psithyrus* paid no attention whatsoever, nor did any of these young queens and males exhibit the slightest fear or hostility toward the intruder.

Among the ants we find quite a number of parasitic species whose habits are very similar to those of *Psithyrus,* but, since there are no fundamental differences in the behavior of these ants, it will suffice to consider very briefly the life-history and habits of *Wheeleriella santschii,* one of the parasitic species which occurs in Northern Africa and breeds in the nests of *Monomorium salomonis.* After fecundation, the deälated *Wheeleriella* queen roams about in search of a *Monomorium* nest. At the entrance of one of these nests, she is sometimes stopped by a number of *Monomorium* workers, which tug at her legs and antennae and draw her into the nest. The workers show no signs of anger toward their new guest, but feed and tend her, as well as the eggs which she lays shortly afterwards. The much larger *Monomorium* queen is ignored by her rival, and, shortly after the latter has established herself in the colony, the *Monomorium* queen is assassinated by her own workers which adopt the parasitic queen in her stead (cf. Wheeler, 1910).

Just how this permanent social parasitism may have originated is suggested by certain observations on ants and bumblebees. It had been known for a long time that certain of the European ants, e.g., *Formica rufa,* which have a worker caste and normally live in independent colonies, sometimes live together in mixed colonies with closely related species. This was considered as an abnormal state of affairs until Wheeler (1904) discovered that the queens of some of our North American ants, e.g., *Formica consocians,* regularly parasitize colonies of *Formica incerta,* but later become independent colonies, a form of symbiosis which he called temporary social parasitism. It has since been clearly shown that a number of European species which were found living in so-called "abnormal" mixed colonies likewise invariably found their own colonies by temporarily parasitizing other species.

A similar explanation has been offered by Sladen (1912) in regard to the permanent social parasitism of *Psithyrus*. Sladen found that many of the later appearing queens of the more common European *Bombus* species do not take the trouble to start colonies of their own, but enter nests already occupied by their own or other species instead. In the resulting struggle, the foundress of the colony is sometimes killed, and her offspring then assist in bringing up the brood of the intruder. According to Sladen, this occurs rather frequently between the queens of *Bombus terrestris* and its smaller relative *Bombus lucorum,* the latter serving as temporary host. From this temporary social parasitism, as Sladen points out, it is but a step to the permanent social parasitism as we find it in *Psithyrus*.

The present writer (1934) has found that a similar relationship exists between *Bombus affinis* and *Bombus terricola,* two of our common New England bumblebee species. During the past thirteen summers, a number of *Bombus affinis* nests have been taken which contained one or more workers of *B. terricola,* and in several instances even the dead *terricola* queen, showing that these colonies were founded by *terricola*. It may be added, that, as in the case of *B. terrestris* and *B. lucorum,* the temporary host, *B. terricola,* is likewise smaller than its "parasite" and also appears earlier in the spring.

X. CONCLUSION

In conclusion the writer cannot do better than to quote the following apt comparison between human society and social insects by Professor Alfred E. Emerson (1929) of the University of Chicago:

> Human society shows many characteristics pointing to our recent origin from solitary ancestors and we seem to be only in the beginning of our social development. We are all more or less possessed with ideas and tendencies which are antisocial, and each one of us as we grow more mature is combating certain antisocial tendencies and fostering that side of our nature which better fits a social ideal. When some of us are unsuccessful in sublimating our antisocial instincts we find ourselves in jails, reformatories or insane asylums where society deems it best for the noncomformists to be. The human race has set aside groups of individuals whose function it is to adjust, prevent and remedy ills resulting from the dominance of our individualistic tendencies. Lawyers settle disputes according to the social code, ministers persuade us to follow the social path, policemen remove social offenders from the scene, teachers train the young toward ideals of social cooperation.
>
> Social insects need no such machinery of control over antisocial instincts. They simply have no antisocial tendencies. These were thoroughly eliminated many millions of years ago and the insects have progressed along a path of perfect social coordination. They have no need for policemen, lawyers, government officials, preachers or teachers because they are innately social. They have no need

of learning the correct social responses. These are predetermined by
their germinal constitution at the time of birth. . . .
There are many other parallels between our own life and the life
of these insects. The social insects are interesting to study, not
only in order to learn how to control the damage they do to human
possessions, but to discover the principles underlying social life
itself. After all, there are not many social animals on the earth and
it behooves us to learn all we can from the social organizations much
older than our own and perhaps the lessons learned may have application to our own problems.

BIBLIOGRAPHY

ALLEE, W. C. 1931. Animal aggregations: a study in general sociology. Chicago: Univ. Chicago Press. Pp. 440.

BANCK, L. J. 1927. Contributions to myrmecophily: I. An anatomical-histolog-
ical and experimental-biological study of *Thorictus foreli* Wasm. Fribourg:
Imprimerie Saint-Paul. Pp. 83.

BELT, T. 1874. The naturalist in Nicaragua. London: Bumpus. Pp. 311.

BEQUAERT, J. 1918. A revision of the Vespidae of the Belgian Congo. Based on
the collection of the American Museum Congo Expedition, with a list of
Ethiopian diplopterous wasps. (*Bull. Amer. Mus. Nat. Hist.*, Vol. 39.) New
York: Amer. Mus. Nat. Hist. Pp. 384. 4 pls., 267 figs.

————. 1932. A tentative synopsis of the hornets and yellow-jackets (Vespinae; Hymenoptera) of America. *Entomologica Americana, 12*, 71-138.
6 figs.

————. 1933. The nearctic social wasps of the subfamily Polybiinae (Hymenoptera; Vespidae). *Entomologica Americana, 13*, 87-144. 3 pls., 4 figs.

BISCHOFF, H. 1927. Biologie der Hymenopteren: eine Naturgeschichte der Haut-
flügler. Berlin: Springer. Pp. viii+598.

BRUN, R. 1924. Das Leben der Ameisen. Leipzig & Berlin: Teubner. Pp. 211.

BUCKINGHAM, E. N. 1911. Division of labor among ants. *Proc. Amer. Acad.
Arts & Sci., 46*, 425-507. 1 pl., 19 figs.

BUTTEL-REEPEN, H. v. 1900. Sind die Bienen Reflexmaschinen? Leipzig:
Georgi. Pp. vii+82.

————. 1903. Die stammesgeschichtliche Entstehung des Bienenstaates, sowie
Beiträge zur Lebensweise der solitären und sozialen Bienen (Hummeln,
Meliponen, etc.). Leipzig: Thieme. Pp. x+138.

————. 1906. Apistica. Beiträge zur Systematic, Biologie, sowie zur
geschichtlichen und geographischen Verbreitung der Honigbiene (*Apis mellifica* L.), ihrer Varietäten und der übrigen Apis-Arten. *Mitt. Zool. Mus.
Berlin, 3*, 117-201. 8 figs.

————. 1907. Zur Psychobiologie der Hummeln. *Biol. Centbl., 27*, 579-613.

————. 1915. Das Leben und Wesen der Bienen. Braunschweig: Vieweg.
Pp. xiv+300.

CASTLE, G. B. 1934. The damp-wood termites of western United States, genus
Zootermopsis (formerly *Termopsis*). In *Termites and termite control*, ed.
by C. A. KOFOID. Berkeley: Univ. Calif. Press. Pp. 264-282. 7 figs.

CLEVELAND, L. R. 1924. The physiological and symbiotic relationships between
the intestinal protozoa of termites and their host, with special reference to
Reticulitermes flavipes Kollar. *Biol. Bull., 46*, 178-227.

CREIGHTON, W. S. 1927. The slave-raids of *Harpagoxenus americanus. Psyche,
34*, 11-29. 2 figs.

DOFLEIN, F. 1905. Beobachtungen an den Weberameisen (*Oecophylla* smaragdina). *Biol. Centbl.*, **25**, 497-507. 5 figs.

DONISTHORPE, H. ST. J. K. 1915. British ants, their life-history and classification. Plymouth, England: Brendon. Pp. xv+379.

——. 1920. "The phoresy of Antherophagus." *Entomologist's Rec.*, **32**, 181-187.

——. 1927. The guests of British ants, their habits and life-histories. London: Routledge. Pp. xxiv+244.

EMERSON, A. E. 1929. The social life of termites. In *Report on the Symposium on Termite Problems of the Termite Investigations Committee*, September 2-13, 1929. San Francisco: Termite Inves. Com., 215 Market St. Pp. 24-30.

EMERY, C. 1894a. Ueber Entstehung des Soziallebens bei Hymenopteren. *Biol. Centbl.*, **14**, 21-23.

——. 1894b. Die Entstehung und Ausbildung des Arbeiterstandes bei den Ameisen. *Biol. Centbl.*, **14**, 53-59.

——. 1909. Über den Ursprung der dulotischen, parasitischen und myrmekophilen Ameisen. *Biol. Centbl.*, **29**, 352-362.

ESCHERICH, K. 1906. Die Ameise. Schilderung ihrer Lebensweise. Braunschweig: Vieweg. Pp. xx+232.

——. 1909. Die Termiten oder weissen Ameisen. Leipzig: Klinkhardt. Pp. 198.

——. 1911. Termitenleben auf Ceylon. Neue Studien zur Soziologie der Tiere. Jena: Fischer. Pp. xxxii+263.

FABRE, J. H. 1911. The life and love of the insect. (Trans. by A. Teixeira de Mattos.) London: Black. Pp. 262.

FAHRINGER, J. 1914. Ueber den Nestbau zweier Bienen. *Zsch. f. wiss. Insektenbiol.*, **10**, 16-20. 5 figs.

FOREL, A. 1930. The social world of the ants compared with that of man. (Trans. by C. K. Ogden.) New York: Boni. Pp. 996.

FRIESE, H. 1923. Die europäischen Bienen (Apidae). Berlin & Leipzig: de Gruyter. Pp. vii+456.

FRISCH, K. V. 1918. Beitrag zur Kenntnis sozialer Instinkte bei solitären Bienen. *Biol. Zentbl.*, **38**, 183-188. 1 fig.

——. 1923. Über die "Sprache" der Bienen. Eine tierpsychologische Untersuchung. Jena: Fischer. Pp. 186.

FRISON, T. H. 1921. *Antherophagus ochraceus* Mels. in the nests of bumblebees. *Amer. Natur.*, **55**, 188-192.

——. 1927. The development of the castes of bumblebees (Bremidae: Hym.). *Ann. Entom. Soc. Amer.*, **20**, 156-180. 1 pl.

FROGGATT, W. W. 1895. Australian Termitidae. *Proc. Linn. Soc. New South Wales*, **10**, 415-438.

GOEDART, J. 1700. Metamorphosis naturalis sive insectorum historia. Pars secunda. Amstelodami: Gallet. Pp. xxxii+259.

GUTBIER, A. 1914. Ueber einige Hymenopterennester aus Turkestan. *Zsch. f. wiss. Insektenbiol.*, **10**, 339-345. 6 figs.

HARVEY, P. A. 1934. Life history of *Kalotermes minor*. In *Termites and termite control*, ed. by C. A. Kofoid. Berkeley: Univ. Calif. Press. Pp. 208-224. 4 figs.

HEATH, H. 1927. Caste formation in the termite genus *Termopsis*. *J. Morph. & Physiol.*, **43**, 387-425. 3 pls., 3 figs.

HEATH, H., & WILBUR, B. C. 1927. The development of the soldier caste in the termite genus *Termopsis*. *Biol. Bull.*, **53**, 145-154. 2 pls.

HEGH, E. 1922. Les termites. Brussels: Desmet-Verténeuil. Pp. 756.

HINGSTON, R W. G. 1929. Instinct and intelligence. New York: Macmillan. Pp. xvi+296.

————. 1932. A naturalist in the Guiana forest. New York: Longmans, Green. Pp. xiii+384.

HOFFER, E. 1882-83. Die Hummeln Steiermarks, Lebensgeschichte und Beschreibung derselben. Graz: Leuschner & Lubensky. Pp. 98.

————. 1889. Die Schmarotzerhummeln Steiermarks, Lebensgeschichte und Beschreibung derselben. *Mitt. d. naturwiss. Vereins f. Steiermark*, **25**, 82-159. 1 pl.

HUBER, J. 1905. Über die Koloniengründung bei *Atta sexdens*. *Biol. Centbl.*, **25**, 606-619, 625-635. 26 figs.

HUBER, P. 1802. Observations on several species of the genus *Apis*, known by the name of humble-bees, and called bombinatrices by Linnaeus. *Trans. Linn. Soc.*, London, **6**, 214-298. 3 pls.

HUDSON, W. H. 1912. The naturalist in La Plata. London: Dent. Pp. x+394.

IHERING, H v. 1896. Zur Biologie der sozialen Wespen Brasiliens. *Zool. Anz.*, **19**, 449-453.

————. 1904. Biologie der stachellosen Honigbienen Brasiliens. *Zool. Jahrb.*, **19**, 179-287. 13 pls., 8 figs.

IHERING, R. v. 1903*a*. Biologische Beobachtungen an brasilianischen Bombus-Nestern. *Allg. Zsch. f. Entom.*, **8**, 447-453. 5 figs.

————. 1903*b*. Zur Frage nach dem Ursprung der Staatenbildung bei den sozialen Hymenopteren. *Zool. Anz.*, **27**, 113-118.

IMMS, A. D. 1919. On the structure and biology of *Archotermopsis*, together with descriptions of a new species of intestinal protozoa, and general observations on the Isoptera. *Phil. Trans. Roy. Soc. London*, **209B**, 75-180. 8 pls., 12 figs.

————. 1931. Social behaviour in insects. New York: MacVeagh. Pp. ix+117.

JARDINE, W. 1840. Bees. Edinburgh: Lizars. Pp. viii+284.

KIRBY, H., JR. 1934. Protozoa in termites. In *Termites and termite control*, ed. by C. A. Kofoid. Berkeley: Univ. Calif. Press. Pp. 84-93. 4 figs.

KOFOID, C. A. [Ed.] 1934. Termites and termite control. Berkeley: Univ. Calif. Press. Pp. xxviii+734

LEGEWIE, H. 1925. Zum Problem des tierischen Parasitismus: I. Die Lebensweise der Schmarotzerbiene *Sphecodes monilicornis* K. *Zsch. f. Morph. u. Ökol.*, **4**, 430-464.

LIGHT, S. F. 1934*a*. A world view of termites. In *Termites and termite control*, ed. by C. A. Kofoid. Berkeley: Univ. Calif. Press. Pp. 108-117. 8 figs.

————. 1934*b*. The termite fauna of North America with special reference to the United States. In *Termites and termite control*, ed. by C. A. Kofoid. Berkeley: Univ. Calif. Press. Pp. 118-126.

LINDHARD, E. 1912. Humlebien som Husdyr. Spredte Traek af nogle danske Humlebiarters Biologi. *Tidsskr. Landbrugets Planteavl.*, **19**, 335-352. 4 figs.

LUBBOCK, J. 1929. Ants, bees and wasps. A record of observations on the social hymenoptera. (New ed. by J. G. Myers.) New York: Dutton. Pp. 396.

LUTZ, F. E. 1929. Observations on leaf-cutting ants. *Amer. Mus. Novitates*, No. 388. Pp. 21. 4 figs.

MAETERLINCK, M. 1924. The life of the bee. New York: Dodd, Mead. Pp. vi+427.

————. 1927. Das Leben der Termiten. Stuttgart, Berlin, & Leipzig: Dtsch. Verlags-Anstalt. Pp. 196.

MAIDL, F. 1933-. Die Lebensgewohnheiten und Instinkte der staatenbildenden Insekten. Wagner. (In process of publication.)

McCOOK, H. C. 1882. The honey ants of the Garden of the Gods, and the Occident ants of the American plains. Philadelphia: Lippincott. Pp. 188.

MOGGRIDGE, J. T. 1873. Harvesting ants and trap-door spiders. London: Reeve Pp. xi+156.

――――. 1874. Supplement to harvesting ants and trap-door spiders. London Reeve. Pp. ix+304.

ORMEROD, E. L. 1868. British social wasps. London: Longmans, Green, Reader, & Dyer. Pp. xi+270.

PECKHAM, G. W., & PECKHAM, E. G. 1905. Wasps, social and solitary. Boston: Houghton Mifflin. Pp. xvi+311.

PELLETT, F. C. 1931. The romance of the hive. New York, Cincinnati, & Chicago: Abington Press. Pp. ii+203.

PICKENS, A. L. 1934. The biology and economic significance of the western subterranean termite, *Reticulitermes hesperus.* In *Termites and termite control,* ed. by C. A. Kofoid. Berkeley: Univ. Calif. Press. Pp. 148-174. 15 figs.

PLATH, O. E. 1922. A unique method of defense of *Bremus (Bombus) fervidus* Fabricus. *Psyche,* **29,** 180-187.

――――. 1924. Do anesthetized bees lose their memory? *Amer. Natur.,* **58,** 162-166.

――――. 1934. Bumblebees and their ways. New York: Macmillan. Pp. xvii +201.

RAU, P. 1926. The ecology of a sheltered clay bank: a study in insect sociology *Trans. Acad. Sci. St. Louis,* **25,** 157-260. 8 pls.

――――. 1928. The honey-gathering habits of *Polistes* wasps. *Biol. Bull.,* **54** 503-519. 1 fig.

――――. 1930. Animosity and tolerance in several species of *Polistes* wasps. *J. Comp. Psychol.,* **10,** 267-286.

――――. 1931. *Polistes* wasps and their use of water. *Ecology,* **12,** 690-693.

――――. 1933. Jungle bees and wasps of Barro Colorado Island (Panama). Kirkwood, St. Louis Co., Mo.: Author. Pp. xii+324.

RAU, P., & RAU, N. 1918. Wasp studies afield. Princeton, N. J.: Princeton Univ. Press. Pp. xvi+372.

ROEPKE, W. 1919. Zur Lebensweise einiger sozialen Faltenwespen auf Java. *Extrait de Treubia,* **1,** 46-50, 61-67. 3 pls.

RÖSCH, G. A. 1925. Untersuchungen über die Arbeitsteilung im Bienenstaat. *Zsch. f. vergl. Physiol.,* 572-631. 1 pl., 11 figs.

SCHNEIDER, G. 1908. Ueber eine Urwald-Biene (*Apis dorsata* F.). *Zsch. f. wiss. Insektenbiol.,* **4,** 447-453. 2 figs.

SCHWARTZ, H. F. 1931. The nest habits of the diplopterous wasp *Polybia occidentalis* variety *scutellaris* (White) as observed at Barro Colorado, Canal Zone. *Amer. Mus. Novitates.* Pp. 27. 1 fig.

SCOTT, H. 1920. Notes on the biology of some inquilines and parasites in a nest of *Bombus derhamellus* Kirby. *Trans. Entom. Soc. London,* 99-127. 8 figs.

SLADEN, F. W. L. 1912. The humble-bee, its life-history and how to domesticate it. London: Macmillan. Pp. xiv+283.

SNYDER, T. E. 1924. "Adaptations" to social life: the termites (Isoptera). *Smithsonian Misc. Coll.,* **76,** 1-14. 3 pls.

――――. 1925. Communism among insects. *Scient. Mo.,* **21,** 466-477. 14 figs.

――――. 1926. The biology of the termite castes. *Quar. Rev. Biol.,* **1,** 522-552. 15 figs.

SPARRE-SCHNEIDER, J. 1909. Hymenoptera aculeata im arktischen Norwegen. *Tromsø. Mus. Aarsh.,* **29,** 81-160. 1 pl.

STÖCKHERT, E. 1923. Über die Entwicklung und Lebensweise der Bienengattung *Halictus* Latr. und ihrer Schmarotzer (Hym.). Zugleich ein Beitrag zur Stammesgeschichte des Bienenstaates. *Konowia,* **2,** 48-64, 146-165, 216-247.

THOMPSON, C. B. 1919. The development of the castes of nine genera and thirteen species of termites. *Biol. Bull.*, **36**, 379-398. 10 figs.

THOMPSON, C. B., & SNYDER, T. E. 1919. The question of the phylogenetic origin of termite castes. *Biol. Bull.*, **36**, 115-129. 5 figs.

————. 1920. The "third form," the wingless reproductive type of the termites: *Reticulitermes* and *Phorhinotermes*. *J. Morph.*, **34**, 591-627. 3 pls., 20 figs.

UICHANCO, L. B. 1919. General facts in the biology of Philippine mound-building termites. *Philippine J. Sci.*, **15**, 59-65. 4 pls.

UVAROV, B. P. 1928. Locusts and grasshoppers. London: Imp. Bur. Entom. Pp. xiv+352.

WAGNER, W. 1907. Psycho-biologische Untersuchungen an Hummeln mit Bezugnahme auf die Frage der Geselligkeit im Tierreiche. *Zoölogica*, **19**, 1-239. 1 pl., 136 figs.

WASMANN, E. 1890. Vergleichende Studien über Ameisengäste und Termitengäste. *Tijdschr. v. Entomol.*, **33**, 27-100.

————. 1905a. Ursprung und Entwickelung der Sklaverei bei den Ameisen. *Biol. Centbl.*, **25**, 117-127, 129-144, 161-169, 193-216, 256-270, 273-292. 2 figs.

————. 1905b. Nochmals zur Frage über die temporär gemischten Kolonien. und den Ursprung der Sklaverei bei den Ameisen. *Biol. Centbl.*, **25**, 644-653.

————. 1908a. Zur Kastenbildung und Systematik der Termiten. *Biol. Centbl.*, **28**, 68-73.

————. 1908b. Weitere Beiträge zum sozialen Parasitismus und der Sklaverei bei den Ameisen. *Biol. Centbl.*, **28**, 257-271, 289-306, 321-331, 353-382, 417-441, 726-731. 3 figs.

————. 1909. Über den Ursprung des sozialen Parasitismus, der Sklaverei und der Myrmekophilie bei den Ameisen. *Biol. Centbl.*, **29**, 587-604, 619, 637, 651-663, 683-703. 2 figs.

WHEELER, W. M. 1904. A new type of social parasitism among ants. *Bull. Amer. Mus. Nat. Hist.*, **20**, 347-375.

————. 1905. Some remarks on temporary social parasitism and the phylogeny of slavery among ants. *Biol. Centbl.*, **25**, 637-644.

————. 1910. Ants, their structure, development, and behavior. New York: Columbia Univ. Press. Pp. xxv+663.

————. 1913. Notes on the habits of some Central American stingless bees. *Psyche*, **20**, 1-9.

————. 1919. The phoresy of Antherophagus. *Psyche*, **26**, 145-152. 1 fig.

————. 1923. Social life among the insects. New York: Harcourt, Brace. Pp. viii+375.

————. 1928a. The social insects. New York: Harcourt, Brace. Pp. 396.

————. 1928b. Emergent evolution and the development of societies. New York: Norton. Pp. vii+80.

————. 1933. Colony-founding among ants, with an account of some primitive Australian species. Cambridge, Mass.: Harvard Univ. Press. Pp. viii+179.

WHEELER, W. M., & TAYLOR, L. H. 1921. *Vespa arctica* Rohwer, a parasite of *Vespa diabolica* de Saussure. *Psyche*, **28**, 135-144. 3 figs.

WHITING, J. D. 1915. Jerusalem's locust plague. *Nat. Geog. Mag.*, **28**, 511-550. 26 figs.

WILDMAN, T. 1768. A treatise on the management of bees; wherein is contained the natural history of those insects, to which are added the natural history of wasps and hornets, and the means of destroying them. London: Printed for the author and sold by T. Cadell. Pp. xx+176.

CHAPTER 5

BIRD SOCIETIES[1]

HERBERT FRIEDMANN

United States National Museum

By a bird society is meant, in a broad sense, any group of individuals, other than the members of a pair and their immediate offspring, living on such terms that each influences the others collectively or individually for good or bad for an appreciable length of time. Bird societies show all sorts of variation in each of these features; some are large in numbers of individual members, while others are small; some are only mildly mutual in their internal relationships, while others are more closely knit; some persist for long periods covering many months, while others are quite temporary. On the whole, as compared with insects, for example, birds show but little social evolution; we find nothing as extreme as the castes and ultra-specializations found in some ants and bees. The fact that birds have not progressed so far in social organization makes it all the easier to visualize the stages by which their social life, such as it is, has come about. Many species of birds are gregarious at one season or another, or even throughout the year, but not many of these may be said to be truly social. We must distinguish between mere gregariousness and the presence of a harmonious system or society. When suitable breeding sites are restricted to certain localities, they are apt to be very crowded during the nesting season. This is especially true of a great many water birds such as the auks, murres, and puffins that nest on the ledges of rocky islets in the arctic waters; it is also found in some terns and gulls that nest in swamps and around reed-fringed lakes and sloughs. In such cases as these, the sheer force of numbers may serve indirectly as a protection from danger for each of the birds, but there is no collective defense, no concerted behavior, no corporate life in any sense. The birds are closely packed individuals or pairs, not really members of a larger unit. However, this formless gregariousness is the first step towards social growth and as such it is worthy of closer attention in the present connection.

To begin with, we may distinguish several distinct types of aggregations. The most important for our study is the aggregation during the nesting season, that is, a breeding colony or group. Other types are late summer and autumn (post-reproductive) roosts; flock formation for duration of the migratory journeys; and winter feeding flocks of birds that

---

[1]For the use of photographic illustrations I am indebted to Dr. Arthur A. Allen of Cornell University and Dr. R. E. Coker of the University of North Carolina. Dr. A. Wetmore of the Smithsonian Institution has permitted me to use the plate of the palm-chat that first appeared in his work on the birds of Hispaniola.

are solitary during the summer. We may dispose of the less important types first as they are free from complicating factors found in the breeding aggregations.

Roosts, often of very large size, sometimes containing hundreds of thousands of birds, are formed by many totally unrelated species. Among these may be mentioned the European starling, *Sturnus vulgaris,* now so common in eastern United States and a serious pest during the winter in many of the cities; the purple grackle, *Quiscalus quiscula,* the cowbird, *Molothrus ater,* the purple martin, *Progne subis,* the robin, *Turdus migratorius,* and a number of species of American and Eurasian crows. The majority of gregarious nesting species remain in their large groups after nesting, and during this later stage of the duration of the group are quite comparable to the gregarious roosting species that nested in comparative solitude. The striking feature characteristic of these aggregations is that the roosts are sleeping assemblages; during the day the birds scatter and feed over a large area; towards dusk they begin coming in singly or in groups of from a few to a few hundred individuals. When such a roost is disturbed at night after the birds have become quiet and are sleeping, the birds do not react as a whole, but the flock scatters in all directions showing how little coordination of action has been established in the group. In some European crows, notably the rook, *Corvus frugilegus,* and the jackdaw, *Corvus monedula,* it is said on apparently reliable evidence that certain individuals act as sentinels for the roost just as during the breeding season they watch over the nesting colonies. This is already a distinct step forward in social evolution—a division and specialization of labor for a collective purpose.

Roosts may be homogeneous or heterogeneous; that is, they may contain but a single species or they may include individuals of several forms. Thus, in Europe, rooks, whose gregarious habits have given rise to the word "rookery" now often applied to other birds as well, and jackdaws generally seem to form fairly homogeneous roosts; the European starling roosts in our cities, such as Washington, Boston, etc., similarly are practically "pure cultures" as are also those of the chimney swift, *Chaetura pelagica.* On the other hand, the roosts of grackles are seldom homogeneous, but usually contain cowbirds, red-winged blackbirds, robins, and other species. The roosts are ordinarily in the same place year after year and in many cases other apparently equally suitable trees or ledges nearby are not used, but shifting does take place with persecution and change. Kalmbach (1932, p. 72) found in the European starling roosts in Washington, D. C., that once a starling has been driven from a roosting spot and has located itself at some other point there is no urge to return to its earlier roost unless driven from its newer one. Results of banding large numbers of the birds revealed that, unless disturbed, the individuals tend to return nightly to the same roosting spot. This tendency may account for what happens at a roost in the course of a winter, or,

    . . . even a series of winters, if we assume there to be a certain

homing instinct lasting from one season to another. A group of
adult birds, returning to old haunts, might well be expected to decoy
the young of the previous breeding season and in that manner a
winter roost might be maintained at the same location for a series
of years.

The idea of a particular roosting spot for each individual bird is,
I find, at variance with the popular conception of large starling
roosts. To the casual observer these congregations may convey the
impression of a mad scramble to find roosting spots. There is, in
fact, a scramble, but behind it all there exists, I believe, the im-
pelling desire of each bird to find its own particular location. Admittedly there is confusion, especially when there are new arrivals at
the roost or when the roosting birds have been disturbed by man
or other causes. But, all in all, these nightly gatherings may be little
more of a riot than what one sees at any football game when each
of 50,000 or more spectators is attempting to plant himself in his
own reserved seat before the start of the game.

However plausible this may seem, we must remember that for the
present, at least, it is more of an assumed than a definitely established
order. The simile may be more correct for the unreserved but localized
sections of a stadium than for the reserved seats.

Another type of aggregation that seems to be essentially a specialized
form of roosting is the late summer flocking in secluded and hidden places
by many birds for the duration of their post-nuptial molt. This is found
in the red-winged blackbird, *Agelaius phoeniceus,* the yellow-headed blackbird, *Xanthocephalus xanthocephalus,* the cowbird, *Molothrus ater,* and
other species. The birds remain in loose flocks in the cattails and rushes
and are seldom seen or heard during this time. To the casual observer
it would seem as though the birds had migrated to some other place.
Their former haunts seem deserted; the marshes appear empty; yet the
birds are there but live hidden in the tall vegetation. In these molting
assemblages there is no social structure, no collective interests or enterprise; there is merely a crowding-together in a sheltered place during a
trying period.

Very similar to roosting is the swarming of certain birds, particularly
swallows, before the commencement of the fall migration. If one were
to walk along a country road in August, one would be very apt to find
the telegraph wires thronged with swallows, hundreds and thousands of
them together. Day by day these flocks grow in size and then, suddenly,
they depart for the south during the night, and the wires are bare again.
There is but one difference between these premigrational gatherings and
true roosting and that is that, whereas the latter is purely a nocturnal,
sleeping aggregation, the former is diurnal as well; the birds may fly off
to feed but come back to the flock afterwards. The swarm on the telegraph wires presents a scene of activity by day not shown in a roost. As
a rule these aggregations are heterogeneous in their membership; swarms
of chimney swifts are, on the other hand, invariably homogeneous.

In the majority of birds given to roost formation or to premigrational
swarming, migration itself is undertaken in flocks or congregated masses.

FLOCK FORMATION IN MIGRATING CANADA GEESE
(*Branta canadensis*)

PREMIGRATIONAL SWARMING OF SWALLOWS (BARN SWALLOWS,
Hirundo erythrogaster, AND BANK SWALLOWS,
Riparia riparia)

PLATE I

Photographs by A. A. Allen.

Just as the roosts or swarms may be homogeneous or heterogeneous so too the migrant flocks are composed solely of one or of several species. On the whole it appears that these flocks are without any social structure or plan when composed of more than one species of bird, and that, while the majority of homogeneous flocks are also mere formless aggregations, there are some species that do show some social flock organization. In these cases the flocks usually have a characteristic shape or form; the well-known V of migrating Canada geese (*Branta canadensis*) is perhaps the most striking instance of this kind, but other birds have less sharply ordered but yet definitely shaped flock formations. Thus, for example, grackles migrate in long, narrow flocks with the long axis of the flock in the direction of flight while their relatives, the red-winged blackbirds, fly in more compactly outlined groups with the long axis at right angles to the direction of flight. The promptness, the simultaneity with which all the members of a flock of sandpipers turn, wheel, dip, or rise also suggests a group entity of which the individuals are coordinated components. A very careful bird observer in England, Edmund Selous, has been so impressed with this remarkable instantaneous coordination of movement that he has come to the conclusion that birds are capable of what he terms "thought transference (or what?)." We may look askance with justifiable suspicion at the idea of an assumed telepathic mechanism, but we must admit the reality of the facts it was created to explain.

The mode of origin and formation of these journeying flocks is not wholly understood, but the results of bird banding on a large scale has enabled Smith (1926), and Messer (1926), and especially Whittle (1926) to conclude that small land birds, such as sparrows and warblers, migrate in groups, the groups being based on families and their neighbors, and migrating as individual groups within a larger flock and wintering together as well. It seems highly likely that in many of our small passerine birds the groups are composed of families from limited areas of the breeding range, and the flocks of groups, additional groups joining the flocks as they pass by. However, aside from this, we have no reason to suppose a social organization; we have no data indicative of a leader (or even a leading family—the one that formed the nucleus of the group).

There are some birds of large size that are eminently solitary during the breeding season and form large flocks only for the duration of the migratory flight. Because of their size, they constitute even more striking, if not more significant, illustrations of this formless gregariousness. Such a case is that of Swainson's hawk, *Buteo swainsoni,* whose flock formation has been described by Griscom (1932):

> The remarkable flights of Swainson's Hawk on migrations in Central America are one of the sights of the bird world, to the few who have been fortunate enough to see one. I have seen three myself, and Mr. Anthony describes one below at second hand. Apparently the great majority of the individuals in existence pass over Central America in a comparatively few days in a few enormous flocks, which take hours to pass a given point. The birds alight only casually,

and only three specimens have been collected in Central America. "There is a very remarkable flight of hawks, passing to the south in October and returning in April, that has often been described to me in different parts of Guatemala, the species described agreeing quite well with this bird. I was told that this flight was all to be seen in one flock, taking hours to pass and the flock consisting of hundreds of thousands of birds. The only chance that I had of observing this interesting migration was when it passed to the south, October 25, 1925. I happened to be hunting in the heavy growth of the coffee plantation, where it was well nigh out of the question to observe what was passing overhead, and it was only when I returned to the hacienda, at noon, that I learned of the southward flight that took some three hours in passing." (Anthony, MS.)

In many species these migratory flocks are further characterized not so much by internal social organization as by exclusiveness of membership, by segregation not only of species, but of groups within the species as well. After the nesting season, males of the yellow-headed blackbird flock by themselves and remain in bands until autumn. Most of the surface-feeding ducks, in which the males leave their mates as soon as the full complements of eggs have been laid, do likewise, and such groups tend to remain apart until time for autumnal migration, so the sexes travel, at least in part, in different flocks. This type of segregation persists only for the journey as the sexes mingle again freely in the winter quarters. In the case of some of the ducks the birds may even pair in the late winter and migrate north in spring in pairs; in other species the males return apart from the females. In most of our small passerine birds the first flocks to arrive in the spring are composed of males; the females come later in flocks of their own or in mixed flocks.

In some of the shore birds, where the males incubate the eggs and rear the young, the females wander off early in flocks and migrate ahead of the males. Even in flocks composed wholly of one sex there is no apparent social structure. Just as the sexes may form separate flocks, so too may the adults and young be segregated. Young cowbirds form large bands after leaving their foster parents; in Europe the adults of the common cuckoo, *Cuculus canorus,* depart for the south before their young are fully grown, and the latter migrate some time afterwards by themselves. Wetmore (1926) has summarized these and many other data on segregation during migration.

Although it yields nothing to the above cases in the nature of interpretative suggestions, we cannot pass over the subject of gregariousness during migration without at least a brief description of the most outstanding example of its kind. I refer to the now extinct but formerly abundant passenger pigeon, *Ectopistes migratorius.* Mershon (1907) has brought together quoted extracts from all the pertinent literature, from which we may select a quotation from Audubon which gives some idea of the enormous bulk of the flocks of this bird (pp. 29-31).

Before sunset I reached Louisville, distant from Hardensburgh fifty-five miles. The pigeons were still passing in undiminished numbers, and continued to do so for three days in succession. The people were all in arms. The banks of the Ohio were crowded with men and boys, incessantly shooting at the pilgrims, which there flew lower as they passed the river. Multitudes were thus destroyed. For a week or more, the population fed on no other flesh than that of pigeons and talked of nothing but pigeons. The atmosphere, during this time, was strongly impregnated with the peculiar odor which emanates from the species.

It is extremely interesting to see flock after flock performing exactly the same evolutions which had been traced as it were in the air by a preceding flock. Thus, should a hawk have charged on a group at a certain spot, the angles, curves and undulations that have been described by the birds, in their efforts to escape from the dreaded talons of the plunderer, are undeviatingly followed by the next group that comes up. Should the bystander happen to witness one of these affrays, and, struck with the rapidity and elegance of the motions exhibited, feel desirous of seeing them repeated, his wishes will be gratified if he only remain in the place until the next group comes up.

It may not, perhaps, be out of place to attempt an estimate of the number of pigeons contained in one of those mighty flocks, and of the quantity of food daily consumed by its members.

*   *   *   *   *   *

Let us take a column of one mile in breadth, which is far below the average size, and suppose it passing over us without interruption for three hours, at the rate mentioned above of one mile in a minute. This will give a parallelogram of one hundred and eighty by one, covering one hundred and eighty square miles. Allowing two pigeons to the square yard, we have one billion, one hundred and fifty millions, one hundred and thirty-six thousand pigeons in one flock. As every pigeon daily consumes fully half a pint of food, the quantity necessary for supplying this vast multitude must be eight millions, seven hundred and twelve thousand bushels per day.

Lest it be thought that Audubon's figures are incredible, we may mention that Wilson estimated a flock to contain two billion, two hundred and thirty million, two hundred and seventy-two thousand pigeons, making his estimate in a way similar to Audubon's.

Winter flocks are even less organized in a social sense than are migratory aggregations. Butts (1931, p. 11) found that the black-capped chickadee, *Penthestes atricapillus,* remains in flocks during the winter, but that,

. . . while the different flocks . . . seemed to behave as permanent units, if one followed a flock and kept a record of the birds seen as he went along, it would appear as if the personnel of the flock were changing. At one time certain birds would be in evidence. A short time later some of these would have disappeared and other individuals would have taken their places. This change was caused by some individuals getting left behind, straying from the main part of the flock, or staying in the tree tops where they were not observed. As the flock progressed through the woods, new birds, which had previously become separated, would be picked up. A slight change in personnel was also brought about in another way. A few individuals (nos. 65284, 65289, 24793, 24799, and 77211) left the South Side flock and later appeared at Glenside. Two of these . . . later returned to the Sanctuary (South Side). The others became permanent members of the Glenside flock and were seen in the neighborhood of Glenside regularly. While the shifting of the range of some birds during the winter caused some variation in the individuals visiting a certain station, nevertheless in the main the same flock visited the station at the end of the winter as at the beginning. We can conclude from these data that the flocks are semi-permanent units.

Lorenz (1931) studied the colonial nesting jackdaw, *Corvus monedula,* and rook, *Corvus frugilegus,* and concluded that within a flock, be it only a migrant or wandering group, there is something akin to a recognition and awareness of individuals, as the disappearance of a member of a flock is quickly noticed and responded to with apparent anxiety and general restlessness by the rest of the flock; similarly a strange intruder is recognized as such and is pursued and driven off. This pursuit of newcomers weakens during the winter months and it appears probable that new members of the flock, provided they have not been born within the colony (when they automatically join the colony as members), can be incorporated only during the time of least intense flock social-solidarity during the winter months. Lorenz found small groups, probably based on one or only a few families, within the breeding colony. This particularly pronounced group formation within the jackdaw or rook societies appears to persist in the wintering flocks and apparently facilitates this "census" or "book-keeping" of each individual member, whereby losses and additions are so quickly noted. The apparent anxiety of a group upset or perplexed by the loss of a member affects the entire flock. This reaction is not induced, however, by the sickness or death of an individual. Of course, here we have species with a true social structure (their breeding societies are described more fully below) and consequently find behavior not shown by such a species as the black-capped chickadee.

Having thus briefly disposed of non-breeding aggregations, we may turn our attention to the most important type of social behavior found in birds—gregarious, colonial, and true social breeding habits. At the outset we may consider the question of territorialism as it is the one feature most directly affected by non-solitary breeding. The concept of territory is based chiefly on the work of Howard (1907-14, 1920, 1929) and of Mousley (1919, 1921) with supporting evidence from the writings of Burkitt (1924-26), Chance (1922), Hamer (1922), Nice (1931, 1933-34), Pickwell (1931), Verwey (1930), Friedmann (1929, 1930a, 1933), and others. To put the matter very briefly the theory of the function of territory is that it so spaces the breeding pairs of birds as to insure enough food for the young close enough to nest so that, in their search for food, the parents do not have to desert the young long enough for any harm to come to the latter. In the spring the male leaves the flock with which it has spent the winter, isolates itself on an exclusive breeding territory to which area it confines its activities, makes itself conspicuous by display and song, thereby attracting a mate and at the same time warning other males not to trespass. In other words, the onset of the breeding season suddenly changes a bird from being gregarious to being solitary. It is only those species that breed in groups, colonies, or true societies that do not make this abrupt change. Before proceeding any farther, we may briefly review those groups of birds of the world that show some signs of gregarious nesting. In this way we may get a comprehensive picture of social nesting behavior, its frequency of occurrence, and its types of manifestation.

In the ostriches (Struthionidae) we find the adults go about and feed in small loosely knit flocks, usually one old male and several hens or young birds. It has often been stated that the ostrich is polygamous, all the hens laying in one common nest. However, this has been denied by other observers who find the birds to be monogamous, and that when, as does happen at times, other unattached hens lay eggs in the same nest so that numbers of eggs up to sixty or seventy result, few of these eggs hatch.

In the rheas (Rheidae) polgamy is the rule, several hens mated to one cock laying together in one nest. The male does the incubating and defending of the eggs and the nest.

In the penguins (Spheniscidae) we find true a social organization of a very remarkable kind. As Stresemann (1928) has shown, it seems that the large breeding colonies of penguins are more than mere dense massing of "parent families," that is, pairs of adults and their young. The birds reveal habits suggestive of a socially corporate group that regards the offspring as a possession of, and a matter of concern to, the whole colony and not merely of each pair of birds. Stresemann gives the following résumé of Wilson's (1907) observations on the emperor penguin, *Apteno-dytes forsteri.* This species breeds during the middle of the antarctic winter and thus has to care for its eggs and young under the most unfavorable climatic conditions. This goal is reached only through a very remarkable arrangement, amounting to an actual division of labor. Wilson found that in breeding colonies of this species a large percentage of the adults lay no eggs; ten to twelve adult birds to each egg. All the members of the colony, hens as well as cocks, take care of the eggs, and later the young, for the good of the whole community, and literally fight for the chance to incubate the eggs or brood the young. Just as soon as one of them, due to hunger or some other stimulus, leaves the egg it has been covering, those birds standing near by immediately begin to struggle with each other to gain possession of it and put it under the warm cover of the abdominal flap and to incubate it. Apparently this habit is to be explained on the basis of the species' becoming sexually mature very late— their average longevity is estimated at about thirty-four years—and that the parental instinct appears in full strength several years before sexual maturity. In other words, the extra birds are too young to breed, but old enough to have the urge to incubate and brood. Levick (1915) studied the Adelie penguin, *Pygoscelis adeliae,* and found a different but equally remarkable habit. At first each pair takes care of its own eggs and young and the colony seems to be merely a densely massed assemblage of independent pairs with no coordinating social structure. However, when the young are about fourteen days old, a sudden change in the composite life of the group takes place; where previously each pair took an interest in only its own young, the young birds begin to gather in small groups of from twelve to several dozen, and each of these "child groups" is accompanied by a few adults, which appear to keep a watchful eye on them and prevent them from wandering off by themselves and becoming easy prey for the predacious skuas that hover around the penguin colony. The rest of the adults betake themselves to the water, which is often some distance away, as this species, unlike most species of penguins, does not nest close to the shore but quite far inland and on high hills, and there disport themselves and look for food. In this manner it comes about that many more than half of all the adults are free to wander considerable distances to procure the necessary food for the young, whose demands and appetites increase with their bodily growth. The adults return with food only to the particular "child groups" in which their own young are to be found, but there is no discrimination within these groups; the booty is divided among all the young alike.

We may mention a few other peculiar features of the penguin colony. Levick (1914, pp. 63-65) found that it took some time for the birds on one knoll or hill within a large colony to settle down for nesting.

As this family life became established, law and order reigned to some extent, and there was a distinct tendency to preserve it, noticeably on those knolls which had so settled down, and I think the following most surprising incident bears evidence of what I have said. I quote word for word from my notes on November 24, 1911:

"This afternoon I saw two cocks (probably) engaged in a very fierce fight, which lasted a good three minutes. They were fighting with flippers and bills, one of them being particularly clever with the latter, frequently seizing and holding his opponent just behind the right eye whilst he battered him with his flippers.

"After a couple of minutes, during which each had the other down on the ground several times, three or four other penguins ran up and apparently tried to stop the fight. This is the only construction I can put on their behaviour, as time after time they kept running in when the two combatants clinched, pushing their breasts in between them, but making no attempt to fight themselves, whilst their more collected appearance and smooth feathers were in marked contrast to the angry attitudes of the combatants.

"The fight, which had started on the outskirts of a knoll crowded with nests, soon edged away to the space outside, and it was here that I (and Campbell, who was with me) saw the other penguins try to stop it. The last minute was a very fierce and vindictive 'mill,' both fighting with all their might, and ended in one of them trying to toboggan away from his opponent; but he was too exhausted to get any pace on, so that just as he got into the crowd again he was caught, and both fought for a few seconds more, when the apparent victor suddenly stopped and ran away. The other picked himself up and made his way rapidly among the nests, evidently searching for one in particular.

"Following him, I saw him run up to a nest near the place where the fight had begun. There was a solitary penguin waiting by this nest, which was evidently new and not yet completed, and without eggs.

The cock I had followed, ruffled and battered with battle, ran up to the waiting bird, and the usual side-to-side chatter in the ecstatic attitude began and continued for half a minute, after which each became calmer, and I left them apparently reconciled and arranging stones in the nest.

"This incident was after the usual nature of a dispute between two mates for a hen, but the pacific interference of the other birds was quite new to my experience. That it was pacific I am quite convinced, and Campbell agreed with me that there was no doubt about it. All the nests round about had eggs under incubation, and the pair in question must have been newcomers."

On returning home I was glad to find that Mr. Bernacchi, who landed at Cape Adare with the "Southern Cross" expedition, says in his account (p. 131) that he also saw penguins interfering and trying to stop others from fighting.

A few notes as to defense against enemies will have to suffice in so brief a summary of the remarkable social life of the Adelie penguin.

A perpetual feud was carried on between the penguins and the skuas. The latter birds come to the south in the summer, and make their nests close to, and in some cases actually among, those of the penguins, and during the breeding time live almost entirely on the eggs, and later, on the chicks. They never attack the adult penguins, who run at them and drive them away when they light within reach, but as the skuas can take to the wing and the penguins cannot, no pursuit is possible.

The skuas fly about over the rookery, keeping only a few yards from the ground, and should one of them see a nest vacated and the eggs exposed, if only for a few seconds, it swoops at this, and with scarcely a pause in its flight, picks up an egg in its beak and carries it to an open space on the ground, there to devour the contents. Here then was another need for constant vigilance, and so daring did the skuas become, that often when a penguin sat on a nest carelessly, so as to leave one of the eggs protruding from under it, a lightning dash from a skua would result in the egg being borne triumphantly away.

The bitterness of the penguins' hatred of the skuas was well shown in the neighbourhood of our scrap-heap. None of the food thrown out on this heap was of the least use to the penguins, but we noticed after a time that almost always there were one or more penguins there, keeping guard against the skuas, and doing their utmost to prevent them from getting the food, and never allowing them to light on the heap for more than a few seconds at a time. In fact, a constant feature of this heap was the sentry penguin, darting hither and thither, aiming savage pecks at the skuas, which would then rise a yard or two into the air out of reach, the penguin squalling in its anger at being unable to follow its enemy. At this juncture the penguin would imitate the flying motion with its flappers, seeming instinctively to attempt to mount into the air, as its remote ancestors doubtlessly did, before their wings had adapted themselves solely to swimming.

Close to the scrap-heap there was a large knoll crowded with penguins' nests, and it was this knoll that provided the sentries. Very rarely did one of these leave the heap until another came to relieve it as long as there were skuas about, but when the skuas went the penguins left it, too. When the skuas returned, however, and without the lapse of a few seconds, a penguin would be seen to detach itself from the knoll and run to guard the heap. That some primitive understanding on this matter existed among the penguins seems to me probable, because whilst there were generally one or two guarding the heap, there was never a crowd, the rest of the knoll seeming quite satisfied as long as one of their number remained on guard. (Levick, 1914, pp. 54-56)

A rather amusing habit is that of group diving. When a number of penguins get to the rim of the ice, they do not dive into the sea immediately, but each seems to try to give way to the other and to push the other one in first. Stresemann writes that although this may partake of the nature of a game, as Levick thought, it may well be an expression of fear of the sea leopard, *Hydrurga leptonyx,* whose lurking presence under the ice floes on which the birds are assembled can be determined only when one of their number is seized by one. If this be the correct interpretation, we have here what may be considered "social martyrs," but with the distinction that these are not self-motivated as are social martyrs in some of the social insects.

In the albatrosses (Diomedeidae) there appears to be no social structure, but, unlike most colonial nesting birds, there appears to be some ill will or resentment towards neighbors on the part of the young birds. This is usually hidden, however, by the general harmony prevailing in the group as a whole. Fisher (1903, pp. 18-22) describes the state of affairs in the Laysan albatross, *Diomedea immutabilis.*

Matters always seem to go harmoniously among the members of a colony and no ill will was shown between adults. The young birds, however, occasionally had slight misunderstandings, and between the old birds and strange young ones there existed at times of feeding a peculiar animosity . . .

After sunrise the albatrosses begin to feed the young. The old bird, coming in from the sea, alights near her offspring, which immediately takes the initiative by waddling up and pecking or biting gently at her beak. This petitioning always takes place and perhaps acts as some sort of stimulus, for in a few moments the mother stands up, and with head lowered and wings held loosely at the side disgorges a mass of squids and oil. Just as she opens her beak the young inserts its own crosswise and skillfully catches every morsel, which it bolts with evident relish. This operation I saw repeated, with short intermissions, ten times . . . The young bird is not at all modest in its demands, but keeps asking for more. The old bird now pecks back in an annoyed manner, and if the other still urges, she arises and walks off, usually to some neighboring young one, which she viciously mauls about the neck. This exhibition usually takes place just before she feeds her young and likewise between courses, as it were. Why she does this I am at a loss to suggest, unless it is mere ill-will. The old bird does not always confine this ill treatment to one strange young bird, but takes in a circle of those whose parents are absent . . .

In many of the shearwaters and petrels (Procellariidae) we find similar gregarious nesting colonies with no real social life or corporate organization.

The pelicans (Pelecanidae) are gregarious in their nesting, but are not really socially organized although they show one remarkable social trait in their method of fishing. A flock of birds fly out to a likely place and then string out to form a large circle and thus surround a school of fish. They then begin to close in and as the fish swim together in denser and denser masses the birds begin scooping them up from all sides. A variant of this is as follows: Instead of making a complete circle the pelicans form a semicircle and gradually drive the fish shorewards into shallower water where they become an easy prey to the birds. The nesting colonies are remarkably free from quarrels and confusion. Bent (1922, p. 291), in writing of the American white pelican, *Pelecanus erythrorhynchos,* states that it is a gentle bird of wild disposition and never makes any trouble for its neighbors on its breeding grounds. However, in the case of the Peruvian pelican, *Pelecanus thagus,* Coker (1919, p. 488) records that an adult on the nest may sometimes reach over with her long neck and bill and take a fledgling from the uncovered nest of a neighbor and throw it away, perhaps into another nest.

> Once, within a space of two square meters, I saw six little "pichones," almost new born, bandied about in a most merciless way, tossed from one alcatraz[2] to another, each seemingly unwilling to have the little birds in their proximity. Finally three of the fledglings were thrown beyond the margin of the nesting ground and left to die in the sun. I watched a pelican that returned to a nest from which the only fledgling had been transferred by a mischievous neighbor into an adjoining nest. The returning brooder did not appear to notice the loss, but sat composedly on the remaining egg; then, pilfering on her own account, she quietly reached over and stole all of the feathers from the nest in which lay her own offspring (supposedly) among others, to add to the lining of her nest. I questioned if the birds invariably occupied the same nest; on one occasion, at least, a bird was seen to brood on two different nests. The birds near the margin had been frightened away, but, most of them returning, all of the nests were soon reoccupied except the ones nearest to me. An alcatraz, after sitting for 15 minutes on one nest, moved slowly over to another nearer to me, while its place on the first nest was at once taken by a bird that was previously covering an empty nest. The young were trampled dangerously by the old birds as they moved awkwardly about.

This presents quite a different picture from the group or collective interest in the welfare of the young shown by the penguins described above.

The close relatives of the pelicans, the boobies (Sulidae), cormorants (Phalacrocoracidae), and frigate birds (Fregatidae) show similar non-social but gregarious nesting with considerable competition between individuals. Fisher (1903, pp. 30-31) has studied the frigate bird on Laysan Island (*Fregata aquila*) and we may visualize these colonies from the following extracts.

---

[2]Local name of the pelican.

PLATE II

PERUVIAN PELICANS (*Pelecanus thagus*) BREEDING ON LOBOS DE AFUERA ISLAND, PERU, 1907

Photographs by R. E. Coker.

At Laysan the birds live in colonies varying from a few pairs to many, and the nests are always built on the tops of low bushes, sometimes very close together. The species has congregated almost entirely on the eastern half of the island, and their villages are spread over the inner slopes of the old atoll basin. The nests, which are sometimes so old that they have become mere masses of filth, are scarcely more than platforms of sticks, not entirely devoid of leaves, woven together loosely with morning-glory (*Ipomoea insularis*) vines. There is one pure white glossless egg, and we observed a very few newly hatched, almost naked, young. The eggs do not vary nearly so much as those of *Sula,* either in size or shape. A rather blunt ovate is the usual contour, though some are elliptical. In some of the eggs the limy outer covering is made apparent by the egg having been scratched when newly laid; but the inner layer is white, not pale blue as in *Sula.*

Both parents take turns in covering the egg, which is a necessity, for if the nest were left without an occupant other frigate birds would quickly appropriate its material, especially if the nest were new. Consequently, even before the egg is laid, either bird holds down the property, as it were, against marauding neighbors. After the nestling is out this vigilance is all the more necessary, for if left unprotected a young bird would very likely serve as food for some watchful reprobate of the vicinity. Mr. Snyder saw an old frigate bird snatch up and fly away with a young of the same species, whose parents had been frightened off the nest. According to Henry Palmer (Avifauna of Laysan) who visited the island a few weeks later in 1891, this is a very common occurrence, but the young were so scarce we considered the accidental demonstration mentioned above as sufficient evidence of the heartless trait. It is probable that the man-o'-war birds eat the young of other species also, but we did not observe anything to substantiate this. The fact that they chase other sea birds, gannets for instance, and make them disgorge their hard-earned prey is well known, but I was not fortunate enough to see them do this. One bird which I frightened excessively disgorged over the side of its nest a mass of squids, which are the staple of diet among all larger sea birds, *Sula cyanops* perhaps excepted.

The size of some of the cormorant colonies is so enormous as to merit some mention here even though the colonies themselves exhibit no true social structure. Coker (1919, pp. 474-478) describes a colony of the white-breasted cormorant, *Phalacrocorax bougainvillei,* on the Chincha Islands, Peru, as follows:

Sixty thousand square meters of ground, or 15 acres, were closely covered with cormorant nests . . . The nests were very uniformly spaced, about three to the square meter, and not an available meter of ground within the outside limits of the rookery was unoccupied. In one place 39 nests were counted in 12 square meters; in another, 52 nests in 18 square meters; in a third place, 33 nests to 9 square meters . . . One may safely compute the number of breeding adults by multiplying by six the number of square meters covered by the aggregation.

At this time, the close of the breeding season, the immature but grown nestlings were still being fed by the parents from mouth to mouth and occupied the parental nest. Estimating on the basis of two birds to the nest and three nests to the square meter, there would be 360,000 parent birds in the flock, with undoubtedly an

PLATE III

PART OF A BREEDING COLONY OF WHITE-BREASTED CORMORANTS (*Phalacrocorax bougainvillei*) ON SOUTH CHINCHA ISLAND, PERU, 1907

Photographs by R. E. Coker

equal or greater number of immature birds able to fly, about three-quarters of a million birds in all. I had the opportunity to revisit this island briefly in the following month of July to find the flock at least 50 per cent larger . . .

Bent (1922, p. 258) describes a huge breeding colony of the Farallon cormorant, *Phalacrocorax auritus albociliatus,* on San Martin Island, Lower California, containing the amazing number of nearly 350,000 nests or about twice the size of the Peruvian colony described by Coker. It was estimated to contain 1,800,000 birds. Of course, such colonies are not wholly typical as most groups are very much smaller, but they are of interest in showing how extensive aggregations may occur without any social organization to bind and strengthen them.

In the herons (Ardeidae) and their allies, the storks (Ciconiidae), and ibises and spoonbills (Threskiornithidae) we find heterogeneous nesting colonies in many forms, although some species are always solitary in their breeding. No true social structure has been reported in any of these colonies; the aggregations probably are of some benefit to their members in the sense that if a bird is killed the survivor very easily finds a new mate. Verwey (1930) has studied the behavior of the European gray heron, *Ardea cinerea,* in Holland. He had a homogeneous colony nesting in some trees near his home and followed the birds from day to day. Much to the surprise of a number of students of territory and its significance, he found that these herons, although nesting close together, had individual territories or spheres of influence that extended considerably beyond the immediate confines of the nest. The territory is defended only by the male and only against other males; it is first established by the males, who come into breeding condition ahead of the hens. The hens seek out and choose their mates who call from definite posts or branches, which are later used as the actual sites of the nests. Inasmuch as the territories are defended only by males and only against males, in some cases where a male dies a neighboring male may extend its interest over two nests.

Flamingoes (Phoenicopteridae) are also gregarious, but not truly social, nesters. Chapman (1905) studied the American species, *Phoenicopterus ruber,* in the Bahamas. The largest colony contained about 2000 nests, with an average of about 50 nests to each 100 square yards, or two square yards to a nest. No real quarreling between birds was described, although occasionally, when newly settled on its nest after a feeding excursion, a bird might spar with one of nearby birds within reach, and, with bill grasping bill, a short and mild test of strength might ensue.

No true social nesting life is known among ducks (Anatidae) except for the fact that in many cases the males desert the females as soon as the eggs are laid and form flocks by themselves. On migration and during the winter, ducks are decidedly gregarious; in summer they often breed in numbers in restricted sloughs and marshes, but the nests are isolated and are more or less hidden from each other by the vegetation. There is a good deal of carelessness in egg-laying, a female of one species often depositing in a nearby nest of another sort, and vice versa. One South

American duck, *Heteronetta atricapilla,* has completely lost the instincts of nest building and incubation and is socially parasitic on other ducks, coots, and other birds (Friedmann, 1932).

In the hawks, falcons, and their allies (Accipitridae and Falconidae) solitary nesting is the general rule although a few species are given to gregariousness to some extent, but in those cases there is nothing suggestive of a social organization. Ospreys, *Pandion haliaetus,* occasionally nest in loose colonies as on Gardiner's Island, New York; the swallow-tailed kite, *Elanoides forficatus,* is of a gregarious disposition but does not form large colonies; the Mississippi kite, *Ictinia misisippiensis,* likewise forms small colonies, one of which described by Howell (1932, p. 167) contained seven nests from ten to one hundred rods apart. According to Howell (1932, p. 169) the Everglade kite, *Rostrhamus sociabilis plumbeus,* is gregarious to the extent that ". . . generally a number of pairs breed in a scattered colony, the nests being usually located several rods apart within a radius of perhaps half a mile. In some cases, however, the colonies are more scattered and cover a larger area, and doubtless there are instances of single pairs breeding in an isolated marsh. A colony of kites frequently locates not far from a rookery of herons. The habit of these birds associating in numbers is continued more or less throughout the year, scattered flocks of a hundred or more birds frequently being found in a limited area where snails are abundant. At times the birds gather in considerable numbers in roosts at night." This remarkable hawk is entirely restricted in its diet to a peculiar ampullarian snail and, inasmuch as these snails are of local occurrence, the birds flock where their food supply may be. Here we have a case of nesting gregariousness largely if not entirely influenced by food supply.

Among gallinaceous birds we find no social nesting although considerable evidence of polygamy and very much non-breeding gregariousness. In the megapodes (Megapodidae) of the Australasian region the reproductive habits are peculiar in that the birds do not build nests and incubate their eggs but they either bury the eggs in warm sand or make large mounds of compost, decaying leaves, etc., and bury their eggs in them, leaving the matter of incubation to the warmth of the decaying materials of the mound. In the case of the mound-building species often several hens use one mound, but no true social life may be seen here as the adults do not remain with the mound and care for the chicks as they emerge. The fact that more than one hen may be engaged in making the mound (which has not yet been entirely proved) may be looked upon as an incipient social behavior pattern.

In the pheasants and their allies (Phasianidae) we find much flocking, and, within the flocks, much social behavior, as is so abundantly described by Schjelderup-Ebbe in his chapter in this volume, but so far we have no indications of breeding societal behavior in wild birds. However, one of the European species, the blackcock or black grouse, *Lyrurus tetrix,* has a remarkable gregarious courtship habit. All the males from a considerable area congregate in a certain open place and the females gather around it, apparently attracted by the spring call notes of the cocks. The males then display their plumage, ruffling the body feathers, drooping the wings, slightly arching the tail, and strut about until they meet with other males, whereupon a fight ensues. These displays and combats last until all the birds have obtained mates. The exact mode of procuring the mate is still uncertain; Selous and some others cling to literal interpretation of the Darwinian theory of sexual selection, but the matter is far from definitely proved.

The cranes (Gruidae) and bustards (Otididae) are solitary nesters although more or less gregarious at other times. The rails (Rallidae) are eminently solitary birds, but some forms, especially the coots, form loose flocks in the winter.

The shore-birds (Charadriidae, Scolopacidae, Phalaropidae, etc.) show no tendency towards gregarious nesting, but in many species the males take care of the eggs and young and the females go off in flocks by themselves as soon as the eggs are laid. This is especially true of the phalaropes. In one Eurasian shore-bird, the ruff, *Philomachus pugnax,* the males have a gregarious display ground not unlike that of the blackcock described above. Portielje (1930) has described this in detail.

The sheath-bills (Chionididae) spend much time in flocks even during the nesting season, but they nest separately and are said to conceal their nests very well—a trait quite foreign to colonial nesting birds.

Gulls and terns (Laridae) are eminently gregarious in their nesting. Herrick (1909) and Strong (1914) have studied the social or community relationships in the herring gull, *Larus argentatus,* and have reported the existence within the colony of family units and family domains that are guarded very vigilantly. They also report a sign of true collective structure—that of cooperation in the face of danger. Herrick states that these gulls will attack en masse a common enemy with a fair degree of concerted action. However, this is rather a looser observation than may be accepted as proof of a social unity or group, corporate interest.

The closely allied skimmers (Rynchopidae) are essentially similar in their breeding habits, but the flock pattern seems to dominate the individuals a little more rigidly as, when standing on a sand spit, all the birds almost invariably face the same way while gulls show no such uniformity.

The auks, murres, puffins, and their allies (Alcidae) are gregarious in the nesting, but, as far as known, show no signs of community life or social organization. Their colonies are merely densely massed pairs of birds.

Sandgrouse (Pteroclidae) are remarkable in that they remain in flocks, often of enormous size, all through the year, but breed in solitude. They are birds of the open plains and nest on the ground; it seems from this that each flock found in the breeding season must be recruited from a very large area, so scattered are the nests. The flocks are remarkable for their punctuality in coming to water holes to drink, indicating a strong group pattern binding all the members.

Pigeons and doves (Columbidae) are, in most cases, solitary nesting species, but show some exceptions. Of these the best known and the most extreme example of gregarious nesting is the now-extinct passenger pigeon. We have already described the enormous migrating flocks and the huge roosts of this bird and may confine ourselves here to a few notes on the breeding colonies. We may again quote from Mershon's (pp. 12-14) compilation.

> Not far from Shelbyville, in the State of Kentucky about five years ago, there was one of these breeding places, which stretched through the woods in nearly a north and south direction; was several miles in breadth, and was said to be upwards of forty miles in extent! In this tract almost every tree was furnished with nests, wherever the branches could accommodate them. The pigeons made their first appearance there about the 10th of April, and left it altogether, with their young, before the 29th of May . . .
>
> On some single trees upwards of one hundred nests were found, each containing *one* young only; a circumstance in the history of this bird not generally known to naturalists. It was dangerous to walk under these flying and fluttering millions, from the frequent fall of large branches, broken down by the weight of the multitudes above, and which, in their descent, often destroyed numbers of the birds themselves; while the clothes of those engaged in traversing the woods were completely covered with the excrements of the pigeons.
>
> These circumstances were related to me by many of the most respectable part of the community in that quarter, and were confirmed, in part, by what I myself witnessed. I passed for several miles through this same breeding place, where every tree was spotted with nests, the remains of those above described. In many instances I counted upwards of ninety nests on a single tree, but the pigeons had abandoned this place for another, sixty or eighty miles off towards Green River, where they were said at that time to be equally numerous.

The Australian flock pigeon, *Histriophaps histronica,* forms enormous flocks during the winter, rivaling in size those formerly formed by the passenger pigeon, but it is not gregarious in its breeding.

Among the parrots (Psittacidae) we find much evidence of flocking, of mating for life, of mutual care, but with one notable exception, the birds nest in solitary fashion, each pair having a hole in some tree or termite mound, and seldom more than one nest hole in a tree. The exception is the monk parakeet of southern South America, *Myiopsitta monachus,* which builds large colonial nests of twigs, the whole structure attaining dimensions of as much as nine feet in length. "Each pair of parakeets has its own private compartment, but the entire flock seems to be on intimate terms. Not infrequently other species, including the tree-ducks (Dendrocygna), occupy one or more of the nest holes in these structures and occasionally even some mammals such as the opossum take possession. The nest is used as sleeping quarters all the year round and is added to from year to year until at times it breaks the supporting branches by its weight" (Friedmann, 1927, p. 177). Steinmetz (1931) has corroborated these field observations with his studies of a colony that nested in a German zoological garden and adds that during the winter each nest hole is occupied, not by a pair, but by five or six birds, possibly the original pair and their offspring.

In the cuckoos (Cuculidae) we find a great many species that are social parasites on other totally unrelated birds. The parasitic species make no nests of their own and merely lay their eggs in available occupied nests of almost any small bird and leave the eggs and subsequent young to the mercies of the host species which acts as a foster parent. There is one other type of breeding habit in this family of birds that is of more interest from the standpoint of social structure. The ani, *Crotophaga ani,* is a gregarious aberrant cuckoo of the American tropics, that builds communal nests. Several pairs of birds (the birds seem to be monogamous) help to build an open nest in which then all the hens lay their eggs. Both sexes take turns in incubation and brooding, and all the parent birds join in the care and feeding of the nestlings. No other gregarious birds are known to be so free from quarrels among themselves as are the anis; the birds working at a nest work, not as individuals, but as pairs, and all work together with the greatest harmony. In regions where the birds are uncommon but a single pair may be involved in a nest; in other places as many as five or six pairs may join forces. The same is roughly true for the closely related white ani, *Guira guira,* and for the groove-billed ani, *Crotophaga sulcirostris.*

None of the owls (Strigidae and Tytonidae) show any signs of colonial nesting, nor in general do the goatsuckers (Caprimulgidae) and their kin (Podargidae, Nyctibidae, and Aegothelidae), but the oil birds (Steathornithidae) of tropical America, a group fairly similar to the goatsuckers, are definitely gregarious. The birds nest in caves, to the walls of which they attach their ledge-like nests. No social organization is known to occur in their colonies.

Swifts (Micropodi) of certain species are gregarious, but not really social, in their nesting habits. The best known of the colonial swifts are the ones whose nests are esteemed by the Chinese as an article of food— the edible nest swifts, *Collocalia;* others are the palm swifts of the West Indies, *Tachornis phoenicobia,* and of Africa, *Cypsiurus parvus,* to mention but a few.

No sign of gregarious nesting is found in the humming-birds (Trochilidae), colies (Cooliidae), trogons (Trogonidae), kingfishers (Alcedinidae), todies (Todidae), or motmots (Momotidae), but in the bee-eaters (Meropidae) we find it to be the regular thing. These brightly colored birds make tunnels or burrows in a sand bank, each pair having its own tunnel, at the end of which is a nest. The colonies may contain from a few pairs to a few hundred pairs, but no social organization is in evidence regardless of size.

We pass over the rollers (Coraciidae), hoopoes (Upupidae), woodhoopoes (Phoeniculidae), hornbills (Bucerotidae), jacamars (Galbulidae), and puff birds (Bucconidae), none of which nest in groups or colonies, and we come to the barbets (Capitonidae). These birds are solitary nesters, except for a genus of brown species in West Africa, *Gymnobucco,* which forms nesting colonies. About a dozen or even two dozen pairs may have their nest holes in the same tree, and the neighboring trees be wholly devoid of holes. Bates (1930, p. 277) writes of one species, *Gymnobucco bonapartei,* that "dead trees standing in farms, in plain sight, may be full of holes of these barbets." No corporate life, no social organization, is in evidence, however.

In the related family of honey-guides (Indicatoridae) we get social parasitism as in the cuckoos, but no social organization, and the honey-guides themselves are rather solitary birds except for the yearling birds of one species (*Indicator indicator*), which do form loose flocks of from five to twenty individuals.

The toucans (Ramphastidae) are not gregarious breeders; neither are the woodpeckers (Picidae) except for one species found in Hispaniola, *Chryserpes striatus.* Wetmore and Lincoln (1934) found a dozen pairs going in and out of nesting holes in a single dead tree trunk standing in an open space. The holes were three to ten meters from the ground, and, in some cases, less than a meter apart. "There was no question that the woodpeckers were colonizing, as the trunk was a veritable apartment house with the birds clambering actively over its surface . . ." From the little that has been recorded, we cannot assume a social organization here.

We come now to the passerine or perching birds, which great group includes all the families of our familiar (and unfamiliar) small land birds. Of the sixty-seven living families included here in Wetmore's recent (1934) classification, we find gregarious breeding behavior in only nine, the swallows (Hirundinidae), crows and their allies (Corvidae), babbling thrushes (Timeliidae), the thrushes (Turdidae), palm chats (Dulidae), wood-swallows (Artamidae), starlings (Sturnidae), weaver finches (Ploceidae), and troupials and their allies (Icteridae). In two others, the birds of paradise (Paradiseidae) and the wrens (Troglodytidae), we find gregarious courtship (in the former) or multiple nest-building (in the latter) that gives an appearance of gregariousness. Within the nine families exhibiting gregarious nesting habits the habit is by no means true of all the species, except the monotypic family Dulidae.

In the swallows we find some species living in holes in sand banks, all the birds burrowing in one bank and not using other equally suitable sites near by. The size of the usual colony varies with the species; thus those of the bank swallow, *Riparia riparia,* attain to twice or more the size of those of the rough-winged swallow, *Stelgidopteryx serripennis,* which may vary from a few to a couple dozen pairs in content. The cliff swallow, *Petrochelidon lunifrons,* makes retort-shaped nests of mud which are attached to a rock wall or the side of a barn, etc. In this species the nests are so closely packed that they are in direct contact with the neighbors on all sides. No true social life has been observed among swallows although it has been noted frequently in the case of the bank swallow that three adult birds may come out of the same nest hole. Whether this implies a communal life in the sense of a breakdown of the strict individuality of the pairs is not clear.

In the crow family we find one of the highest and best-developed types of social life in the whole class of birds. The colonial habits of the European rook, *Corvus frugilegus,* have been known for so long that the term "rookery" has come into use for any large gathering of birds. Lorenz (1931) has studied the rook and especially the jackdaw, *Corvus monedula;* Yeates (1934) has written extensively on the rook. We have already remarked on the fact that the members of a jackdaw community recognize a strange intruder of their own species as such immediately and drive it away. The great energy with which they pursue it makes it appear probable that new members, provided they have not been born in the same colony, can become incorporated only during the time of the winter wanderings.

The disappearance of a member of the society is immediately noticed and is responded to with great anxiety and general restlessness by the wandering flock. The particularly pronounced development of group formation ("cliques") within the larger society obviously facilitates this "book-keeping" of each individual member. The anxiety of a group perplexed by loss affects the whole flock. This reaction is not brought forth by the sickness or the death of an individual.

The old males, especially, zealously attempt to prevent the flying-away of a member from a jackdaw society, as they fly after the departing bird and call with a peculiar note in an attempt to cause it to return and apparently to help to guide it thereby back to the society. This reaction is especially pronounced when strange wandering flocks entice some members to join them. It is not invoked when the yearling birds, which have never bred as yet, depart from the colony at the start of the breeding season, as is apparently the rule, and which readily tends towards the advantage of the species. The yearling birds remain away until autumn when they are re-incorporated into the colony without friction and with apparently definite individual recognition.

If one of the crows, no matter of what species, as well as the rather distantly related jays, is taken out, seized, and driven off by any rapacious animal, the jackdaws that witness it, but more especially the others of the same species of crow as the victim, react with a direct and furious attack on the robber. Jackdaws give, under such circumstances, a very characteristic call, a metallic, ringing rattle call. It seems that jackdaws, rooks, ravens, and hooded crows have other notes in common as well. Crows and jackdaws, and, to a certain extent, apparently also magpies, seem to have formed, in this way, a defensive and offensive bond for driving away rapacious animals. The rattle call seems designed less to rescue the attacked individual bird than to harass the robber, so that he does not get any satisfaction from his booty, perhaps in the sense of learning, for the future, to beware the beaks of the jackdaws, according to Lorenz.

Within a breeding colony of jackdaws there seems to be a gradation of "rank" between individuals, not so very unlike the "peck order" in flocks of domestic poultry. This works out to the advantage of all the members in the following way, as reported by Lorenz. As long as the birds are not yet definitely paired, the males have a high, very short "zick" call, which they utter only when in or near nesting holes that seem suitable to them. This "at nest" call apparently signifies to the hens their readiness to mate, and also serves as a local expression of defiance towards the other males that this particular nesting hole is already claimed. This is in direct accordance with the theory of territorialism. This call does not, however, prevent a male of "higher rank" from evicting one of "lower rank." However, as soon as the birds are mated, this peculiar call is no longer indulged in, and if a strange male, even if of "higher rank," attempts to usurp the nest hole of a mated pair the male of the latter gives a peculiar "help" call, sounding something like the syllable "yip." Its mate then joins with another "yip," and thereupon all the rest of the colony do likewise and attack the disturber of the peace, the threatened pair doing so with unusual vigor and energy. In case the majority of the birds let the matter of the threat rest, the collective torrent of voices in conjunction with the enraged calls of the pair suffices to smooth out the dispute; and then the original aggressor reveals, in most cases, the purely instinctive nature of the drive behind the whole incident by itself joining in the concert of "yip" notes, as if it had been another bird at the same incident and also has no presentiment of the fact that it was the originator itself. This reaction begins in young birds at the time of their first courtship.

Young jackdaws begin to court and mate chiefly in the first autumn of their life, at the age of about five months, although they do not become ready to breed until their second year. Many individuals wait until their second autumn for the inception of courtship. These young birds occupy the "lower ranks" of the flock society, but if they get worked up in a passionate frenzy in the autumn before some of the adults, and mate before them, they may reverse their respective ranks. In other words, the males, regardless of age, after their second autumn, assume a rank in the social organization according to the order in which they become sexually aroused and become mated. In fact Lorenz found that often the first intimation he had of courtship was the fact that an individual formerly of relatively higher rank assumed, with respect to another individual, a subordinate position.

After becoming fully fledged, the young jackdaws remain for a long time in the immediate vicinity of the nest. This association, especially later, at a time when the young of other passerine birds are totally independent of their parents, maintains in the young jackdaws the nestling reaction of returning to the parents, a parent-returning instinct that reaches the same intensity and definiteness as that shown by most nestlings, an ontogenetically infantile fixation. This instinct on the part of the fully grown young alters and displaces or suppresses so many other reactions, normal to grown birds, that, if deprived of their guiding parents, they appear very helpless and falter in the actions; they may then simulate ravens or magpies of similar age but more mature habits.

It is not until autumn that the parent-return instinct begins to die down; then the young birds very abruptly begin to conduct themselves psychically exactly like adults. This late psychic maturity in the jackdaw, and also in the rook, is almost unique among birds. In other words, the overlapping of successive generations, so essential to the idea of social breeding, is carried to an extreme in these birds.

During the whole year the flocks of jackdaws and rooks appear to have sentinels to warn them of danger, but the nature of turning certain birds into sentinels, the "change of guards," etc., are still unknown.

In some other members of the crow family we find that year-old birds, not yet in breeding condition, nevertheless have the nest-building, incubating, and rearing instincts, and actually assist the older, breeding birds at their nests. This has been observed in some Central American brown jays of the genus *Psilorhinus* by Skutch, to whom I am indebted for this as yet unpublished information, and in the Australian white-winged chough, *Corcorax melanorhamphus*. In the latter this occasionally leads to more than one hen's laying in a single nest—a condition not essentially unlike that found in the ani, among the cuckoos. The social implications in these cases have to do not only with the clinging-together of two successive generations for an unusually long time, but also the breakdown of private territory in these birds.

An essentially similar condition to that of the chough has been reported for one of the Australian babbling thrushes, *Pomatorhinus temporalis* (Timelliidae). North (1904, pp. 358-560) writes that this bird is known in New South Wales as the "Happy Family" bird because of its social habits. He observed that several birds often assist in building a nest but that apparently only one hen lays in it. Söderberg (1918) found five birds building the same nest and concluded from their behavior that their joint action was evidently an expression of a rather intimate social union.

A South African pied babbler, *Turdoides bicolor,* is colonial in its nesting; as many as fifty nests may be found in one large tree, but there is no indication of a corporate social life.

In the thrushes (Turdidae) solitary nesting is the rule, but, as with most rules, there is an exception. The European *Turdus pilaris,* the field-fare, nests in loose, rather formless colonies, and each pair seems to be an entity in itself without any consideration of a social whole. However, as Seebohm (1883) has stated, when their nests are approached, the birds become very noisy and fly around the head of the intruder in a faint attempt to drive him off. However, they quickly lose their defensive urge and retire from the colony leaving the nests and their contents to the mercy of the invader if he is at all persistent.

In the palm chat (Dulidae), a peculiar bird of the island of Hispaniola, we find a highly gregarious mode of life. Wetmore and Swales (1931) have given the fullest account, from which the following may be extracted.

> The palm-chat is a gregarious species that lives in little bands, each group being made up of several pairs, at the proper season accompanied by their young, and having as the center of its activities the communal nest, which serves as a resting place when the

PLATE IV

THE DOMINICAN PALM CHAT (*Dulus dominicus*) AND ITS COMMUNITY NEST
(Drawn by Allan Brooks)

Reproduced, by permission, from Wetmore and Swales's *The Birds of Haiti and the Dominican Republic.*

birds are not searching for food or otherwise engaged and as a roost at night. Their communal habits and nests have attracted universal attention from early travelers who came to Hispaniola from Oviedo down, so that the species is mentioned frequently in older works of travel.

Oviedo noted that this species built a communal nest as large as that of the stork in Spain, made of twigs closely interlaced, in which structure each pair had its separate compartment. Vieillot describes the nest in similar words, as does Sallé in an account furnished to Lafresnaye. The large size of the structure has been truthfully recorded by many observers but the number of individuals that frequent each nest, at least in modern times, is usually only eight to sixteen, and according to Wetmore's observations the largest bands seen did not include more than twenty individuals. Statements of various travellers that two hundred or three hundred were seen in company seem to be exaggeration.

*   *   *

The nests were constructed of twigs from half the size of a lead pencil to a little larger, ranging from 250 to 450 mm., in length, with occasional twigs 600 to 750 mm. long. It seemed remarkable that a bird the size of the palm-chat, having the dimension of a cedar waxwing, could rise from the ground to a nest from twelve to fifteen meters from the earth with such burdens. The first nest examined was obviously under construction, and not yet complete. The twigs were interlaced rather loosely particularly at the sides and top. The structure was the size of a bushel basket and was evidently occupied by only a few pairs. There was a roughly defined central tunnel 100 to 125 mm. in diameter leading through the mass of sticks from side to side, opening at either end to the outside. Near the end was a slight accumulation of shredded bark that made a little platform on one of which had rested an egg, unfortunately broken. The nest padding was barely sufficient to protect the egg. This nest seemed to have been entirely newly formed and was evidently not yet complete. A second structure secured on this day was much larger and had evidently been used the year previous with much material recently added. Eight individual birds were observed flying away from it and it appeared to contain four separate units each 450 to 500 mm. in diameter with stick ends projecting in every direction, and the separate sections loosely interwoven about the trunk of the palm. In each unit a tunnel led to a central chamber 100 to 125 mm. across with the bottom well filled with fine shreds of bark and other soft materials to form a distinct cup. Though each nest was a separate unit with its own portal to the exterior there were roughly defined channels or passages running through the interlacing twigs at the top of the nests that could permit the birds to creep about under cover. The separate nests were very compact so that it was necessary to cut and break away the twigs to get at the interior. Subsequent examination of a number of other completed nests indicated that this was the normal type of construction, each communal structure consisting of several separate compartments opening separately to the outside. The twigs used in construction were usually slightly smaller in diameter than a lead pencil and were dead twigs of light wood, orange and coffee twigs being usual in the lowlands. The nest lining was always the smallest possible amount of fine grass and shredded bark that would serve to support the eggs.

Though each pair had occupied a separate domicile in a common structure, that may be likened to an apartment house, work on this domicile was carried on to some extent in common as it was not unusual to see half a dozen of the birds resting near together, perhaps with two or three so close as to actually touch, all pulling and twisting at the sticks about them to work them more firmly into place. Occasionally birds clung back down to the bottom of the nest to pull and tug with much fluttering of wings at refractory bits of material. The twigs are carried into the trees in the bill of the bird and not in the feet as some have stated. The stick is held crosswise in the bill and the bird flies with steady direct flight at a sharp angle upward, often stopping to rest for a moment on some limb before reaching the nest. The stick nest is without question a safeguard against owls and other similar predators.

As far as the available data permit of a conclusion, we may say that the palm chats reveal a social organization only in the collective structure of the nest; there are no data suggesting corporate behavior or any form of subordination of the individual pairs to the colony as a whole.

In the wood swallows (Artamidae), one aberrant species found in West Africa, *Pseudochelidon eurystomina,* nests in large numbers in sand bars and banks, each pair having its own tunnel nest, very much like the arrangement found in the bank swallows mentioned above. The Australian wood swallows (most of the species live in the Australasian region) are not colonial nesters, but form great flocks at times during the non-breeding season.

In the starling family (Sturnidae) we find some instances of gregarious breeding habits although most of the species are solitary nesters. The wattled starling of southern and eastern Africa, *Creatophora cinerea,* is perhaps the most gregarious of its family. Stark (1900, pp. 23-25) writes that in the Cape Province these birds usually breed in very large colonies, chiefly in localities in which the locusts have deposited their eggs (the birds feed largely on locusts). "For hundreds of yards every thorny bush is packed full of cup-shaped nests, even the spaces between the nests being often filled up with sticks or rubbish, through which narrow passages are left for the ingress and egress of the birds. Many starlings that can find no room in the bushes build on the ground, or under stones, or in holes, and these unfortunates, together with their eggs and young, ultimately become the victims of the smaller carnivorous mammals or of snakes. It frequently happens also that either the young locusts are hatched in insufficient numbers or that they migrate before the young starlings are fledged. In either case large numbers of birds perish of hunger, the majority of the old birds and the more advanced young following the locusts." This species has a social flock-feeding habit of interest in the present connection. The flock may be pursuing a large swarm of locusts and, starting in a dense spherical mass, may suddenly, ". . . open out into a fan-shaped formation, then assume a semi-circular arrangement, and finally end by forming a hollow cylinder in which a portion of the locusts are enclosed; as the imprisoned insects are destroyed, the starlings gradually fill up the hollow of the cylinder until they again assume their 'ball' formation and proceed to follow the remaining locusts. The ground below the flock is covered with the droppings of the birds and the sniped-off legs and wings of locusts."

An Australian glossy starling, *Aplonis metallica,* also nests in large colonies. Mathews (1926, pp. 290-295) writes that at Lockerbie, Cape York, as many as 200 nests were counted hanging from the limbs of one tree. The nests are large affairs, often measuring two feet in length and one foot in width, so they must have been very close together indeed. Unfortunately nothing has been recorded by which we may judge the presence or absence of a social organization here.

The weaver birds (Ploceidae) are among the best examples of gregarious nesting birds. A large number of species are colonial, often nesting in groups of a hundred or more pairs. Most of the forms nesting in trees in open country are gregarious, the solitary nesters being forest birds or species that build their nests on the ground or in low bushes. In some of these arboreal colonists the males build a number of nests and the number of mates they acquire depends directly on the nests they have built for them. Such a case is the baya weaver, *Ploceus philippinus,* studied by Ali (1931), whose general conclusions are as follows: the male baya is polygamous, not in the usual meaning of the term, but in a special manner. The number of his mates depends on the number of nests he is able to build for them, a factor dependent on the force and intensity of his breeding instinct; the hen takes no part in nest-building except to alter the lining at a late stage; incubation is carried on solely by the female who also does most of the feeding of the young. Van Someren (1916, p. 409) found that the males of Speke's weaver in Africa were similarly addicted to building extra nests. "Dozens of nests are built by the male, but only one is occupied; thus there are always plenty of old nests in all stages of completion." In some species the nests are placed so close together that they are in actual contact with each other and become woven or otherwise bound together. This is true of the buffalo weavers of the genus *Bubalornis* and reaches its climax in the huge, many-compartmented nests of the social weaver of southwestern Africa, *Philetairus socius.* Personal study of the latter, reported on elsewhere (Friedmann, 1930b), led to the following description.

As the common name of the bird implies, *Philetairus* is very gregarious in its habits; in fact, it is probably as gregarious as any bird could possibly be.

> It is always found in flocks, feeds in flocks, and breeds in large, "many-apartmented" compound nests. The smallest flocks that I saw contained about twenty birds; the largest one at least a hundred and fifty. The flocks seem to stay pretty much in the same general vicinity all the year round, and the birds use their huge, massive nests as roosting places during the nonbreeding season. With this extreme sociability and sedentary habit of life the territorial relations of the species have been modified in a way that is remarkable, perhaps unique, among birds. Instead of each pair of birds having its own breeding territory, each flock seems to have a definite territory, and as the individual flocks are usually far enough apart not

A TYPICAL NEST, CONTAINING ABOUT FORTY INDIVIDUAL NEST HOLES

ONE OF THE BIRDS BELOW A CORNER OF THE COMMUNITY NEST, TO SHOW THE SIZE OF THE STRUCTURE COMPARED WITH ONE OF ITS BUILDERS

PLATE V

THE SOCIABLE WEAVERBIRD (*Philetairus socius*) OF SOUTH AFRICA
Photographs by the author.

A LARGE NEST, PORTIONS OF WHICH HAVE FALLEN DOWN BECAUSE OF EXCESSIVE WEIGHT, LEAVING THREE PARTS STILL IN USE

UNDER SIDE OF NEST TO SHOW INDIVIDUAL NEST-HOLE ENTRANCES

PLATE VI

THE SOCIABLE WEAVERBIRD (*Philetairus socius*) OF SOUTH AFRICA
Photographs by the author.

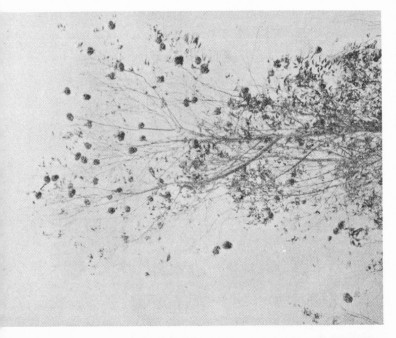

PART OF A COLONY OF SPOTTED-BACKED WEAVERS (*Ploceus spilono-tus*) IN ZULULAND   NESTING COLONY OF BLACK WEAVERS (*Ploceus nigerimus*) IN UGANDA

PLATE VII
COLONIAL HABITS OF WEAVERBIRDS
Photographs by the author.

to compete with one another, the boundaries of these territories are seldom crossed by individuals of other flocks and other territories. However, in a few cases in my own experience two nests were on trees not very far apart and the birds mingled more or less while feeding, but in these cases far more fighting and quarreling was observed than in all the others together. . .

The nests observed varied in size as did the flocks. The smallest nest found measured some three feet in diameter at the base, was about three feet high, and had perhaps ten entrances on the under surface, indicating that it contained that number of individual nests. The largest one found was incomplete, i.e., a piece of it had broken off, breaking its supporting branches by its weight, but the remaining part was a large, flat, horizontal mass of straw, more or less repaired at its broken edge, and measuring about twenty-five by fifteen feet at the base and about five feet in height. The part that had broken off must have been about five feet in diameter each way. This nest contained about ninety-five nests within it. . .

Although the birds live in compound "apartment-house" nests, feed and fly in flocks, and are at all times exceedingly gregarious, they mate in regular monogamous fashion as far as my field observations indicate. If they were promiscuous they would be forever in one another's way getting in and out of the entrance holes of the individual nests in the large communal structures. As a matter of fact the harmony of life within each colony, the lack of what may be likened to "traffic congestion," that is, the coming and going of birds in the task of providing food for the young, the fact that out of numbers of individual nests examined by various observers none were found with unusual numbers of eggs or young, all argue for the actuality of monogamy.

There have been several attempts to explain the structure of the large, composite nests of this species, some writers claiming that each pair of birds builds an individual nest, all of them close together, and then the flock builds the common roof over all the nests, while other writers have recorded that the flock builds a large structure and then each pair builds its individual nest into this structure. I have never seen the actual beginning of a nest and the smallest nests I found were, as mentioned above, complete structures with numbers of nests within them.

We may therefore quote the account of the building process given by Sir Andrew Smith, from Shelley's *Birds of Africa* (Vol. IV, 1905, p. 131).

"The most striking peculiarity observed of the species is the extraordinary manner in which a number of individuals associate, and build their nests under a common roof. When a nesting place has been selected, and the operation of building the nests is to be commenced *ab initio,* the community immediately proceed conjointly to construct the general covering which interests them all; that being accomplished, each pair begins to form their own nest, which like the roof, they construct of coarse grass; these are placed side by side against the under surface of the general covering, and by the time they are all completed, the lower surface of the mass exhibits an appearance of an even horizontal surface, freely perforated by small, circular openings.

"They never breed in the same nests a second time, though they continue for many years attached to the same roof. With the return of the breeding season, fresh nests are formed upon the lower surface of those of the previous year, which then forms an addition to the general covering. In this manner they proceed, year after year adding to the mass, till at length the weight often becomes such as to cause the destruction of its support, upon which a new building-place is selected. They appear to prefer constructing the nests upon large and lofty trees, but where such do not occur, they will even condescend to form them upon the leaves of the arborescent aloe (*Aloe arborescens*), as occasionally happens towards the Orange River. The commencement of the roof is firmly interwoven with the branches of the trees to which it is intended to be suspended; and often a great part of a principal branch is actually included within its substance."

The only point that I can add to Smith's description is that not only do the birds build their individual nests, but during the non-breeding season, all the members of the flock do a certain amount of roof building and repairing of the whole structure. All the birds work together, the males as well as the females, and even during the breeding season, when they have eggs or young in the nest, the birds may be seen carrying straw to the roof or other parts of the common structure, not necessarily close to their own respective individual nests. The huge, massive affairs are composed chiefly of small twigs and of dried grasses of a rather coarse, tough sort that grows commonly in southwestern Africa, and the seeds of which enter very largely into the diet of the weavers. The material is not really woven or even plaited on the surface of the nest, but is rather roughly put together into a well-made hay rack, but with a fairly definite thatching arrangement, causing the rain to run off and not to soak through. The under side of the nest presents the rough, hard ends of the coarse straws, and forms a very uneven surface.

In the colonies of social weavers we find several other vertebrates living in close relations with the weavers. The pygmy falcon, *Polihierax semitorquatus,* lives in the nests with the builders, and seems to have established a most remarkable type of symbiotic relationship with them. I never saw more than a single pair of these little hawks at any one nest, no matter how large the nest was, and I never saw any sign of the slightest hostility between the weavers and the falcon. Frequently I noted both species perching side by side close together on the same branch, not more than a few feet apart, and yet in the stomachs of all the *Polihierax* I collected (three individuals) I found nothing but feathers and bird bones, but the feathers were certainly not those of *Philetairus!* It looks as though the hawk, while feeding largely on small birds, did not molest the weavers. The only good the weavers could possibly derive from this curious symbiotic arrangement is that they would be assured that any other small bird coming to their nest would not usurp any breeding space there. In some nests the rose-collared love birds, *Agapornis roseicollis,* usurp an unused nest and breed in it. In such cases there seems to be no particular advantage to the weavers. I do not know of any instances of the love bird and the pygmy falcon nesting together in the same colony of social weavers. I personally never found the love bird at all, but it has been recorded by several observers as a regular breeder in these large nests.

There is no corporate, social organization for defense or for care of the young; the truly social aspect of these birds' mode of life is confined to actual nest-building.

In the troupials (Icteridae) the ecological counterpart in the New World of the weaver birds of the Old World, we find similar instances of colonial nesting although none go so far as to join their nests together in a common structure. Recently Chapman (1928) has studied a nesting colony of Wagler's oropendola, *Zahrhynchus wagleri,* in detail, with very interesting results, from which the following may be quoted:

> The question of territorial rights while nesting apparently does not enter into the location of an oropendola colony. On Barro Colorado three nesting colonies of these birds are known. One is 400 yards from the laboratory colony, the other nearly two miles from it in the opposite direction. Birds apparently en route to the nearer colony sometimes stop in the laboratory tree and mingle with the local birds without their presence being questioned.
>
> Nor do groups within the colony appear to be concerned by the question of boundaries. The first bird to arrive selects its group location from the unoccupied field, the choice being made by the females. Each year of my observations the first group to arrive has selected a different location. Always, however, a situation was chosen that had been used before. Here the point of attachment, which is usually all that is left of the preceding year's nest, offered an attractive place for the beginning of a new nest.
>
> The nests are always built on the southerly and westerly, which is the leeward, side of the tree during the period of tradewinds that prevail in the dry season. Here the nests receive some protection from the windward side of the tree, and it is probable that the birds can enter there more readily flying up, than they could when flying down wind.
>
> The tree is large enough to afford sufficient space for subsequent groups without arousing the enmity of those already located, and I have seen no ill-feeling displayed between the members of different groups as such. Size is, indeed, to be desired in a colony, and the larger its population the more protection do its component individuals receive from their common enemies.
>
> It was soon evident that the birds were not monogamous, but it was by no means clear whether they were polygamous or promiscuous. The relationships of the males to one another were also to be determined. No reference to these subjects has been found in the literature concerning oropendolas and caciques . . .
>
> If the birds of a group arrive and work together they usually build nests as near to one another as the available sites permit. The selection of a site may be made at once and peacefully, it may cause the display of some animosity accompanied by actual fighting, or it may be the occasion of a remarkable performance extending over several days. In the first instance, nest-building proceeds at once without friction and it is possible that these birds have been associated before. In the second instance the birds grapple claw to claw and, fighting with their bills, whirl downward like a single bird with set wings extended. When within ten to twenty feet of the earth they separate, fly to the nearest perch and sit there quietly for a few seconds side by side. Then they usually return to the site. These conflicts may be repeated from time to time but cease when nest-building is under way and right to the possession of a site is acknowledged . . .
>
> Building birds often take material from another bird's nest either in their own or an adjoining group. Some birds, indeed, are chronic robbers and steal a large part of their material. Slovenly builders are more apt to be robbed than those that leave no loose and tempting ends about their structure. A poor builder is often, therefore, heavily handicapped, for a day's work may be undone in a short time by her thieving neighbors. Birds that do not work continuously and which consequently have their nests unprotected are frequently robbed. There is a limit, however, beyond which it does not pay to try to

secure material from another bird's nest. Only the looser, partly
woven ends may be easily taken. After that the robber may tug
and pull, adding her weight to her strength, but she gets little or
nothing for her labor . . .

* * *

The females outnumber the males about six to one. If this disparity
of the sexes is an actual characteristic of the species it may be the
cause of the colonial association that permits one male to mate with
several females. The males show no marked sexual jealousy. Courtship begins with nest-building. A male may woo several females but
he apparently has but one mate at a time; the length of this association covering only the period when the ova are ready for fertiliza-
tion. A similar type of sexual relation appears to exist in the hum-
mingbird and cotinga that nest in the oropendola tree.

The males take no part in the selection of the site, gathering of
building material, construction of the nest, incubation of the eggs or
care of the young. They are, however, in constant attendance on the
females either as wooers or accepted mates until the eggs are laid.
As watchmen of the colony they play an important part in the protection of the females, particularly in the early stages of nest construction.

Other species of this family, such as the yellow-headed blackbird, *Xanthocephalus xanthocephalus,* and the red-winged blackbird, *Agelaius phoeniceus,* nest in fairly close proximity to others of their kind and form
loose colonies, but apparently without any true social organization such as
the sentinels, etc., found in the oropendola just described.

Just as in the cuckoos and honey-guides we find here (and also in the
weaver birds) a few species of social parasites, in this case, the cowbirds.
The cowbirds are very gregarious during migration and throughout the
winter, but scatter during the breeding season when they have no true
socal life except as parasites of other birds.

Now, having surveyed the world's birds, in an admittedly hurried way,
what generalizations and conclusions may we derive with regard to social
behavior? In the first place, the fact that the great majority of birds are
more or less gregarious in the non-breeding season suggests very strongly
that birds are essentially, and probably were originally, gregarious in their
tendencies. In other words, it seems that solitary nesting rather than colonial nesting is the more recent development, and, on the whole, this is
borne out by the fact that the great majority of the "higher" groups of
birds (58 out of 67 families of passerine birds, and the bulk of the species
of most of the other 9) are solitary nesters, while the bulk of gregarious
breeding species belong to the "lower," ostensibly more primitive, groups
of birds. This must be regarded as only a very general statement; exceptions readily occur to the mind and may be culled with ease from the systematic survey embodied in this paper.

We have already touched upon the matter of territorialism. This is
obviously a feature coincident in origin and development with that of solitary breeding. However, it would be inaccurate to say that territorialism
does not occur in any colonial species. Colonial (not necessarily social)
breeding birds are really of two kinds with respect to this factor—there
are those that never had any territorial instinct, and those that either lost

it or compromised it with other factors during the course of their evolutionary history. This compromise may, in turn, have been of two types; either it may represent an actual diminution of territorialism with the development of colonialism or it may mean an impeded development of territorialism within a gregarious state. A few examples may clarify these distinctions. Of birds that are gregarious in their nesting and that apparently never had any territorial instincts, we may cite the pelican colonies as a typical example; of those that, while gregarious, have developed a slight amount of territorialism, we may recall the gray herons studied by Verwey; of those that apparently lost or compromised their territorial instincts on becoming colonial, we may recall the jackdaws, weaver birds, and oropendolas. Inasmuch as the colonial breeding habit is primary in some groups and secondary in others, it at once follows that social nesting, or even mere colonial nesting, is a habit that originated independently a number of times in widely divergent groups of birds.

The development of a true social structure from a purely gregarious breeding condition has similarly come about independently in the relatively few groups of birds that possess it. One generalization may be drawn in this regard; social evolution has progressed in only two of the three types of gregarious breeding colonies—in primary aggregations where territorialism has not developed even at an impeded rate, and in secondary aggregations where an actual loss or diminution of territorialism took place. In the third type—the primary aggregation with the incipient territorialism—the territorial instinct has developed at the expense of true social coordination (as far as the available data indicate, as in the gray heron). If we take the first type and examine the pelican colony as our example, we find that social development has come about only in the matter of procuring food; if we take the penguins as another example, we find social evolution with regard to care of eggs and young as well as food-getting. If we examine the secondary aggregation developed at the expense of individual territorialism and take as our illustration the jackdaw and the rook assemblages, we find no social development in either food-getting or care of eggs or young, but merely in the relation between component pairs or families, and in connection with concerted action in the face of danger; if we take such cases as the monk parakeet or the social weaver, we find corporate action in regard to the group nest, but not to the individual nests within the group.

On the whole it may be said that birds whose reproductive area is the same as their feeding area are solitary nesters, while colonial nesting has persisted or developed in those whose nesting and feeding grounds are spatially distinct. Here, as always, there are exceptions; for example, birds that feed on the wing, catching insects in mid-air, cannot nest also in mid-air and so might be expected to be colonial breeders. We find that this is true in many cases such as some swifts, swallows, martins, etc., but not in others equally aerial in the feeding such as goatsuckers, and a number of forms of swifts and swallows.

It has been stated as significant that large, colonial, ground-nesting birds breed only on islands or in inaccessible places such as marshes. This is really a secondary and not a primary thing; such aggregations have survived to the present day only in such situations, but this is due to selective factors wholly foreign to the social growth itself.

As a rule colonial breeding does not involve a breakdown of monogamy; on the contrary, it seems in most cases that monogamy is essential if a large number of pairs of birds are to live close together. The densely massed nests in colonies may sometimes be only the result of a scarcity of suitable nesting sites, but even in such cases it gives each individual nest and bird greater security from outside danger. As Stresemann (1928) has pointed out, in small tern colonies rather few sets of eggs usually materialize into birds as long as the few adults are unable to defend them from the rapacious gulls; only a large colony is a defense against them as the excited mob of terns tends to frighten away the marauders, even though there be no real cooperative action against the latter. Each of the members of the colony fights merely against its individual enemies, but in such cases it happens that the invader is the enemy of many individuals simultaneously.

Except for a few cases of collective food-gathering as in pelicans and the South African wattled starling, and for the case of the penguins, where we find collective care of the young, colonial nesting brings the birds no real advantage other than increased protection from enemies. Aside from the penguins, the communal activities do not involve the incubation of the eggs or the care of the young. As Stresemann points out, it was formerly asserted that in colonies of murres (*Uria*) communal caring of the young prevailed, but this is not the case; more recent observations show that each murre feeds and cares for only its own young and drives off, by biting, every strange one that comes too close to it. Young murres that have lost their parents are left to die of starvation. In the same way other colonial breeding sea birds, for example the gulls and terns, recognize their own eggs and young and can distinguish them from the others in the colony. In this they are aided by a very highly developed sense of locality in which every little peculiarity of the nest surroundings seems to be retained, but also by the individual variations in egg color and nestling down. The eggs of colonial nesting auks, murres, terns, and gulls are noted for their great variability; scarcely two clutches resemble each other in their markings; they differ also in the ground color. In many terns this is true also in the natal down. In such colonies one can distinguish at least two sharply different color groups of downy young.

There are some cases on record that appear, on the surface, to be examples of sympathy or compassion for other birds, a truly social attribute. Thus, some parrots, eminently gregarious in their feeding habits, exhibit what looks like strong mutual attachment between the members of a flock. If one of their number has been killed or wounded by a hunter, the others, instead of flying away in terror, hover over the fallen one calling vociferously ("shrieking," as some writers have put it) and themselves fall the victims of the gunner who continues to shoot. Similarly, in some tern colonies, if one bird is hurt, the others fly near by in apparent excitement and often come very close to the dangerous aggressor. It is known that some species of birds come towards a source of commotion while others fly away from it. In gregarious birds there is more of a tendency to stay, at least for a short time, near the scene of trouble, as their gregarious inclinations tend towards making a unit of all the members of the flock. We have, in such cases as these, not true sympathy and compassion in the human sense, but the feeling from which these emotions originated, that of a sense of injury to a part of the social unit of which the individuals are members, and to which, as members, they respond by excited behavior.

The matter of the formation of a colony is naturally a vital topic in a consideration of gregarious nesting, but is one on which we have insufficient information. In general it appears that the group begins with a family to which other families are added as increments. Also it is true that social life depends on the overlapping of successive generations, that is, on the duration of the family life. However, where the family endures too long it may be an actual barrier to group development in that it tends to resist amalgamation in the flock or colony. Geese, for example, are known for their unusually intimate and lasting family unions, and geese are not colonial nesters. Heinroth (1912) has studied them intensively and finds that the family union persists after the young are already fully grown. Katz (1926) has reviewed the whole question of parental, maternal, and paternal families and its social implication. A maternal family is one in which the male parent leaves his mate when the eggs are laid; in the paternal family (rarer) the reverse is true. Katz concludes, with Deegener (1918), that the formation and existence of the family as a unit is primarily and principally conditioned by sexual ties, although not exclusively so in higher animals, including birds. However, it is just this sexuality that resists the formation of corporate groups, and, as a disassociating force, often dissolves them into their component parts when the sexual urge increases in the spring. Only where this impulse, uniting within the family, but dividing within the race, is kept within the required bounds or is overcome by other instincts can the gregarious flock persist as a colony during the breeding season. Only when the sexual instincts are somewhat thwarted and are not all powerful is it at all possible for a colony to form from members of both sexes from several families. Deegener and Katz both agree in the opinion that the family as a lasting unit cannot be due wholly to sexual instincts, but must rest on another instinct as well, an instinct such as cannot be entirely denied to have exerted an influence within the family, but that, on the contrary, must be assumed to have found there a most favorable soil for its higher development and strengthening. This has been called "family egoism" by Heinroth, who sees in it the distant forerunner of human pride in family, ancestry, etc. That this family consciousness (a term I suggest as an improvement on "egoism" in this use) may exert an anti-social influence is shown by Heinroth's observation that it is exceedingly difficult to introduce a new individual into a group of geese otherwise than by mating to one of the members.

Bierens de Haan (1931) has studied the psychological and sociological importance of vocal utterance in birds, a field that offers too many contradictions to be of great value to us at present. It by no means follows that extensive vocabulary formation is either accelerated or impeded by social life; it is true that vocalizations do act as common signals to birds whether in colonies or not. If the birds are massed together in a small area, as in a colony, a greater number of individuals hear the sound than is otherwise the case.

We may conclude this paper with a few notes on symbiotic or commensal relations in which birds figure. We have already discussed the social parasites—cuckoos, honey-guides, cowbirds, etc., and need only say here that the parasitic habit has undoubtedly arisen independently in each of the five families of birds exhibiting it.

There are numerous cases on record of one species of bird nesting close to another for protection or shelter. We have already mentioned the pygmy falcon living in one of the compartments of the compound nests of the social weaver in South Africa; tree ducks sometimes occupy chambers in the nests of the monk parakeet; grackles have been known to build their nests on the sides of ospreys' nests, apparently for the protection against enemies they derived from the proximity of the ospreys; burrowing owls and prairie dogs have been found together in holes in western United States and petrels and the lizard *Sphenodon* are said to share burrows in New Zealand.

A number of birds associate with mammals for purposes of food. The cowbirds gather around cattle (originally buffalo) to get the insects scared up by the grazing beasts; tick birds, *Buphagus,* cling to the elephants, rhinoceroses, buffaloes, zebras, and antelopes in Africa and feed on the ticks that infest them; cattle herons, *Bubulcus ibis,* perch on the backs of buffaloes, elephants, etc., and feed on the insects frightened up by the ponderous animals; a tyrant flycatcher in Argentina, *Machetornis rixosa,* accompanies horses and cattle as the cowbirds do. In many of these cases the mammals derive some benefit from the association also as the birds rid them of insect and other pests or even, perhaps unwittingly, warn them of approaching danger by their actions.

Finally, we find mixed assemblages of various kinds of birds associated for feeding. Of these the variations are endless. These flocks are especially noticeable in the tropics where they assemble to feed on the driver ants or on fruiting trees, etc. They may be simple mixed flocks composed of related species with similar food preferences and sameness of general habits, or they may be compound mixed flocks in which we find a great variety of species often with very divergent habits. The latter type is frequently found in the forests. Stresemann considers the origin of the simple mixed flocks as bound up with mutual aid in looking for food; while the compound flocks he suggests are due to the general gregariousness of most small birds.

On the whole, most birds, at least when not breeding, prefer not to be alone.

BIBLIOGRAPHY

ALI, S. A. 1931. The nesting habits of the Baya (*Ploceus philippinus*). *J. Bombay Nat. Hist. Soc.,* **34**, 947-964.

BATES, G. L. 1930. Handbook of the birds of West Africa. London: Bale & Danielson. Pp. xxiv+572.

BENT, A. C. 1922. Life histories of North American petrel and pelicans and their allies. (*U. S. Nat. Mus., Bull.,* 121.) Washington, D. C.: Supt. Documents. Pp. xii+343.

BIERANS DE HAAN, J. A. 1931. Der psychologische Wert der Sprache bei den Vögeln. *Abh. d. VII. int. ornithol. Kong. zu Amsterdam,* 1930, 186-196.

BURKITT, J. P. 1924-26. A study of the robin by means of marked birds. *Brit. Birds,* **17**, 294-303; **18**, 97-103, 250-257; **19**, 120-124; **20**, 91-101.

BUTTS, W. K. 1931. A study of the chickadee and white breasted nuthatch. *Bird-Banding,* **2**, 1-26.

CHANCE, E. 1922. The cuckoo's secret. London: Sidgwick & Jackson. Pp. 239.

CHAPMAN, F. M. 1905. A contribution to the life history of the American flamingo. *Bull. Amer. Mus. Nat. Hist.,* **21**, 53-77.

————. 1928. The nesting habits of Wagler's oropendola (*Zahrhynchus Wagleri*) on Barro Colorado Island. *Bull. Amer. Mus. Nat. Hist.,* **58**, 123-166.

COKER, R. E. 1919. Habits and economic relations of the Guano birds of Peru. *Proc. U. S. Nat. Mus.,* **56**, 449-511.

CORNISH, C. J. 1896. Animals at work and play. London: Seeley. Pp. xi+323.

DEEGENER, P. J. B. 1918. Die Formen der Vergesellschaftung im Tierreiche. Systematisch-soziologischer Versuch. Berlin: Verein wiss. Verleger. Pp. xii+420.

ESPINAS, A. 1877. Les sociétés animales. Paris: Ballière. Pp. 389.

FISHER, W. K. 1903. Birds of Laysan and the Leeward Islands, Hawaiian Group. *U. S. Fish Comm. Bull. for 1903.*

FRIEDMANN, H. 1927. Notes on some Argentine birds. *Bull. Mus. Comp. Zool.,* **68**, No. 4, 177.

————. 1929. The cowbirds. A study in the biology of social parasitism. New York: Thomas Publ. Co.; London: Baillière, Tyndall & Cox. Pp. xvii+421.

————. 1930a. The new study of bird behavior. *Bird-Banding,* **1**, 61-66.

————. 1930b. The sociable weaver bird of South Africa. *Nat. Hist.,* **30**, 205-212.

————. 1932. The parasitic habit in the ducks. *Proc. U. S. Nat. Mus.,* **80**, article 18.

————. 1933. The size and measurement of territory in birds. *Bird-Banding,* **4**, 41-45.

GREEN, J., & FLINTOFF, R. J. 1932. The desertion of rookeries. *Naturalist,* 369-371.

GRISCOM, L. 1932. The distribution of bird life in Guatemala. *Bull. Amer. Mus. Nat. Hist.,* **64**, 154-155.

GURNEY, G. H. 1930. The mentality of birds with some notes on sexual selection. *Trans. Norfolk Norw. Nat. Soc.,* **13**, 3-13.

HAMER, A. H. 1922. Territorialism and sexual selection. *S. African J. Nat. Hist.,* **3**, 54-59.

HEINROTH, O. 1912. Beiträge zur Biologie, namentlich Ethologie und Psychologie der Anatiden. *Verhandl. V. int. Ornithol. Kong.*, Berlin, 1910, 589-702.

HERRICK, F. H. 1909. Organization of the gull community. *Proc. 7th Int. Zool. Cong.*, Boston, 1907.

HOWARD, H. E. 1907-14. The British warblers. (2 vols.) London: Quaritch. Pp. xv+203; ix+260.

————. 1920. Territory in bird life. London: Murray. Pp. xiii+308.

————. 1929. An introduction to the study of bird behaviour. New York: Macmillan; Cambridge, England: Univ. Press. Pp. xi+135.

HOWELL, A. H. 1932. Florida bird life. Tallahassee: Fla. Dept. Game & Fresh Water Fish. Pp. xxiv+579.

KALMBACH, E. P. 1916. Winter crow roosts. *Yrbk. for 1915, U. S. Dept. Agric.*, 83-100.

————. 1932. Winter starling roosts of Washington. *Wils. Bull.*, 44, 65-75.

KATZ, D. 1926. Sozialpsychologie der Vögel. *Ergeb. d. Biol.*, 1, 447-478.

KROPOTKIN, P. 1902. Mutual aid. A factor in evolution. London: Heinemann. Pp. xix+348.

LEVICK, G. M. 1914. Antartic penguins. London: Heinemann. Pp. 140.

LORENZ, K. 1931. Beiträge zur Ethologie sozialer Corviden. *J. f. Ornithol.*, 79, 67-127.

LUCANUS, F. v. 1912. Beiträge zur Psychologie der Vögel. *Verhandl. V. int. Ornithol. Kong.*, Berlin, 1910, 288-302.

MATHEWS, G. M. 1926. The birds of Australia. Vol. 12. London: Witherby. (See esp. Pt. 7, pp. 290-295.)

MERSHON, W. B. 1907. The passenger pigeon. New York: Outing Publ. Co. Pp. xii+225.

MESSER, D. V. 1926. A partial history of fifteen tree sparrows. *Bull. N. East. Bird-Banding Asso.*, 2, 28-31.

MOUSLEY, H. 1919. The singing tree, or how near to the nest do the male birds sing? *Auk*, 36, 339-348.

————. 1921. Which sex selects the nesting locality? *Auk*, 38, 321-328.

NICE, M. M. 1931. Returns of song-sparrows in 1931. *Bird-Banding*, 2, 89-98.

————. 1933-34. Zur Naturgeschichte des Singammers. *J. f. Ornithol.*, 81, 552-595; 82, 1-96.

NICHOLSON, E. M. 1927. How birds live. A brief account of bird life in the light of modern observation. London: Williams & Norgate. (See esp. Chap. 3, pp. 19-38.)

NICHOLSON, E. M., & NICHOLSON, B. D. 1930. The rookeries of the Oxford district. *J. Ecol.*, 18, 51-66.

NORTH, A. J. 1904. The nests and eggs of birds found breeding in Australia and Tasmania. Vol. 1. London: Quaritch. (See esp. pp. 358-360.)

PERTY, M. 1876. Ueber das Seelenleben der Thiere. (2nd ed.) Leipzig: Winter. Pp. viii+719.

PICKWELL, G. B. 1931. The prairie horned lark. *Trans. Acad. Sci. St. Louis*, 27, 1-153.

PORTIELJE, A. F. J. 1931. Versuch zu einer verhaltungs-psychologischen Deutung des Balz-Gebarens der Kampfschnepfe, *Philomachus pugnax. Proc. 7th Int. Ornithol. Cong.*, Amsterdam, 1930, 156-172.

SCHMID, B. 1931. Biologische und psychologisch Beobachtungen an Jungreihern und Ibisvögeln. *Zool. Jahrb. Jena (All. Zool.)*, 49, 463-508.

SELOUS, E. 1927. Realities of bird life. London: Constable. Pp. 351.

————. 1931. Thought transference, or what? in birds. New York: Long & Smith; London: Constable. Pp. xi+255.

————. 1933. Evolution of habit in birds. London: Constable. Pp. 288.

SMITH, W. P. 1926. A study of the tree sparrow's migration in the Connecticut River Valley. *Bull. N. East. Bird-Banding Asso.*, **2**, 19-22.

SÖDERBERG, R. 1918. Studies of the birds in North West Australia. *Kungl. Sv. Vet. Akademiens Handlngr.*, **52**, No. 17, 92.

STARK, A. C. 1900. The birds of South Africa. Vol. 1. (See esp. pp. 23-25.)

STEINMETZ, H. 1931. Brutbiologisches vom Monchsittish. *Zool. Garten* (V. F.) **4**, Pts. 3-5, 140-153.

STRESEMANN, E. 1928. Vögel. In Vol. 7 of *Handbuch der Zoologie*, ed. by Kukenthal. Berlin: de Gruyter. (See esp. pp. 404-415.)

STRONG, R. M. 1914. On the habits and behavior of the herring gull. *Auk*, **31**, 27-31.

VAN SOMEREN, V. G. L. 1916. A list of the birds collected in Uganda and British East Africa. *Ibis*, 409.

VERWEY, J. 1930. Die Paarungsbiologie des Fischreihers. *Zool. Jahrb., Abt. f. allg. Zool. u. Physiol. d. Tiere*, **48**, 1-120.

WETMORE, A. 1926. The migration of birds. Cambridge, Mass.: Harvard Univ. Press. (See esp. pp. 79-84.)

————. 1934. A systematic classification for the birds of the world. (Rev. & amended.) *Smithsonian Misc. Collection*, **89**, article 13, 1-11.

WETMORE, A., & LINCOLN, F. C. 1934. Additional notes on the birds of Haiti and the Dominican Republic. *Proc. U. S. Nat. Mus.*, **82**, article 25, 44.

WETMORE, A., & SWALES, B. H. 1931. The birds of Haiti and the Dominican Republic. *U. S. Nat. Mus. Bull.* 155, 345-352.

WHITTLE, C. L. 1926. On the nature of the relationship existing among land birds during sustained migration. *Auk*, **43**, 493-500.

WILSON, E. A. 1907. Aves. In *National Antarctic Expedition, Natural History: Vol. 2. Vertebrata*. London: British Mus. Pp. 66.

YEATES, G. K. 1934. The life of the rook. London: Allan. Pp. 95.

CHAPTER 6

THE BEHAVIOR OF MAMMALIAN HERDS AND PACKS

FRIEDRICH ALVERDES

Zoological Institute, Marburg

INTRODUCTION

Among most mammalian species every male, as a rule, exhibits a temporary or lasting relationship to one or several females; such a relationship is spoken of as either monogamy or polygyny, as opposed to promiscuity. Promiscuous sexual intercourse, though it may be observed occasionally in these species, never appears as the normal form of sexual relation but only as an accessory phenomenon. The monogamous or polygynous mateship may be either seasonal, i.e., ending after every mating-period, or permanent, i.e., outlasting even the annually recurring periods of sexual rest. It may be either solitary, as when the male forms a separate group with his female or females, or it may take the form of mateship within a herd, as when several (monogamous or polygynous) mated animals join to form a herd. Through combinations of these various possible relationships there result eight different forms of mateship which are characteristic of mammals. Unfortunately many facts are not yet known, and therefore, in regard to many species, we do not know whether they live in monogamous or polygynous relationships or in seasonal or permanent mateships.

PROMISCUITY

Genuine promiscuity seems to exist among bats which live in herds. Cases have been observed in which several males covered the same female one after another, the surplus males showing complete indifference. Promiscuity is also said to exist among the North American bison, but the data on which this statement is based have not been verified. This relationship has likewise been attributed to rabbits, although it is possible that mateship exists in this case, too, but has been overlooked by observers because the males do not keep the mating bond strictly. For a long time foxes were said to be promiscuous, but it has recently been shown that they live monogamously. The fact that house dogs pair promiscuously is the result of domestication, inasmuch as their characteristic way of living with men makes it impossible for them to form a regular mateship. It has not been ascertained whether wild boars form polygynous mateships during the mating period or whether promiscuity exists among them. During the mating-season individual males or packs of males unite with packs of females. These females may be intermixed with younger animals which are not yet capable of reproduction. Combats which last over long periods of time develop among the males and lead either to the expulsion of rivals by one male or to the mutual tolerance of equally strong male individuals in the same pack. In the latter case it is possible that the pairing is promiscuous (it might be permissible to call this a kind of "group-mateship"), but it is also possible that the rivals settle their rights of possession over individual females.

MONOGAMOUS SOLITARY SEASONAL MATESHIP

A monogamous solitary mateship of the seasonal type does not last longer than a reproduction period, and at the beginning of each such period every male and every female looks for a new partner. There are no relations between a partner in this mateship and individuals outside of this union. A few beasts of prey live in a monogamous relationship, but none continue so throughout life. With many species of cats and martens the two sexual partners remain together during and after the mating-season in order to protect and feed the young. Lions choose a new partner in each mating-season, but throughout one season they live in a monogamous union. Male and female jaguars form such a mateship for four or five weeks; during the rest of the year they are solitary. Foxes are also monogamous and remain together after the young are born; the fathers, contrary to earlier opinions, defend their young and bring them food. Wolves live in couples during the spring, but form packs during the winter. Wolves, foxes, and bears live in pairs for a short while even after the mating-period.

In the case of many mammals it has not been determined whether seasonal or permanent monogamy is the customary relationship. They are seen in pairs during the whole year, part of the time accompanied by their young. Certain species of dolphins, sirens, pigs, stags, antelopes, and blue whales belong to this group. Many of them, especially the small antelopes, probably live in permanent monogamy. Our lack of knowledge in regard to the duration of mateship is in part due to the fact that we do not have exact information concerning the oestrous and parturition seasons of many tropical wild animals. According to Berger (1922), the theory that many African animals may bear young during the whole year is incorrect. The duration of pregnancy differs according to the species; the oestrous period likewise varies from species to species. Schuster, contrary to Berger's opinion, believes that at least antelopes show no periodical oestrus and that, accordingly, the parturition season extends over the whole year. Unfortunately, animals in captivity give us no reliable information about such matters because the environment is so totally changed.

MONOGAMOUS SOLITARY PERMANENT MATESHIPS

In the case of many mammalian species which are found in couples during the entire year it has been impossible to determine whether they live in seasonal or permanent mateships. However, it seems that at least the various species of rhinoceros form solitary permanent mateships. It is possible that the permanency of these mateships is related to the fact that, according to Schuster (1923), the oestrus of this animal is not interrupted during the whole year. Deeg (1922), however, reports a periodic oestrus for these animals. However this may be, we must not neglect the importance of the urge for mateship which operates together with the propagative instinct.

Monogamous Seasonal Mateships within a Herd

The very nature of such mateships makes it very difficult to determine whether monogamous animals which live in groups during the entire year form seasonal or permanent unions. To obtain satisfactory information it would be necessary to mark paired animals in some harmless way and observe them year after year. It is known that many rodents which build their dens in colonies and, within a stationary community of this nature, keep up distinct relations with one another are found in couples in their structures during the reproductive period; this is true for instance of the marmots (*Arctomys*), rabbits, ground-squirrels (*Spermophilus*), prairie-dogs (*Cynomys*), chinchillas, beavers, and rats. Since rabbits are said to live in mateship for several years, we may expect the same to be true of some of the other species mentioned above. *Oryx* and many species of whales are monogamous in wandering herds. The whales live in pairs within their herds and each pair is accompanied by one young animal. The sea-cows (*Rhytina stelleri*), which are now extinct but formerly lived in the Bering Sea, were also monogamous within a herd. Steller, who discovered them, reported that a male came to the shore for two days to a female which had been killed. The otters (*Latax*) are likewise monogamous within the herd; a male, a female, and a young animal keep together within the larger group. In all these cases it is not certain, as we have said, whether the mateship is seasonal or permanent; if it is the latter, then the species in question does not belong to this section but to the next.

Monogamous Permanent Mateship within a Herd

This form of mateship is an especially important one because it is the characteristic relationship in many races of men. If we analyze a herd of a species in which this type of mateship exists we may observe that it is not an unorganized group of individuals but consists of monogamous couples. Domesticated guinea pigs exhibit this type of relationship. The oestrus of this species is continuous throughout the year. There may be combats between unpaired males for the possession of an unpaired female, but one of the males will eventually pair with the female in question and the others will respect his right from then on. A mated male and female of the maras (*Dolichotis*), a species related to the guinea pigs and, like them, living in herds, form such a close association that they find one another again even after months of separation, during which time each one has been locked up with an individual of the opposite sex (Brehm,

1914-16). Wild rabbits build their dens in colonies, and within a colony the tunnels which serve as dwellings are interconnected. These animals are said to be monogamous over a period of many years; the males, however, seem to adopt accessory promiscuity inasmuch as they occasionally have intercourse with unpaired females. Further investigation of rodents which live in colonies may reveal other species which are monogamous over a period of years.

Polygynous Solitary Seasonal Mateship

Many mammals observe this form of mateship, and the following behavior is typical of many species. Outside of the mating-period males are not interested in females and live in packs or alone. When the mating-period begins they look for the females, join their packs, or drive together as many females as possible. They combat each rival and only young males which are not yet capable of reproduction are tolerated. The Indian arnibuffaloes separate from the herd and form small groups at the beginning of the mating-period, each group of females being joined by a bull. Such packs of females, watched by a single male and followed eventually by young animals, are called "harems." It is characteristic of a seasonal harem that at the end of every oestrus it is deserted by the possessor of the harem. The harem scatters then (e.g., as in the elks) or stays together as a "mother's herd." As to the organization of solitary seasonal harems it may be said that in many cases the male assumes the leadership; frequently, however, the function of leadership is retained by an old experienced female that has been at the head of the pack when it was without a male. Strong stags drive away all younger males and rivals from the packs of six to twelve females which they have chosen. At the head of the pack there is always a female who determines the behavior of all the other females. This is also true during the oestrus. During the lively combats between grown-up stags young males sometimes succeed in approaching the pack and covering the females; they also appear and cover the females when the grown-up males are sexually exhausted. (This phenomenon should be considered as accessory promiscuity.) Other species of deer and many species of antelope, wild sheep, and wild goats behave similarly during the oestrus. The harems of Indian and African elephants, of mufflons, and of waterbucks (*Kobus*) also have female leaders. The male belonging to the harem is only a beneficial companion of the females. In earlier times such an elephant harem consisted of from thirty to fifty grown-up females, but due to the destruction which they have suffered during the last few decades we now find some harems that are much smaller. It has been observed that most deer, many species of antelopes, wild sheep, and wild goats form solitary harems, but it has not been possible to determine in every case whether a male or a female leads the group. The data existing are in part contradictory. In the case of gaurs, an Indian species of wild buffaloes, every herd of from eight to ten individuals has two bulls during the time when the females are not in oestrus. During the mating-period, however, a bull, which at other times lives solitarily but which proves himself to be superior to the bulls already in the herd, joins the herd and becomes absolute ruler. The two other bulls remain in the herd in spite of his presence.

POLYGYNOUS SOLITARY PERMANENT MATESHIPS

In the case of guanacos and vicugnas every pack consists of a number of females and only one male except for the duration of the mating-period. Only young males not yet capable of reproduction are tolerated by the old male who leads the herd (the harem), sees to its security, and covers its retreat. If this leading bull is killed, the female vicugnas roam about aimlessly.

Among Asiatic aboriginal wild horses every herd consists of a leading stallion and a harem of from five to fifteen mares. The same organization may be observed in the herds of zebras; if the leading stallion dies, the mares find refuge in another harem (Schillings, 1906). Several zebra herds, each consisting of a leading stallion and several mares, may unite temporarily to form a larger herd, but such unions are loose and separate easily into their constituent elements, the individual polygynous mateships. During such a temporary union of herds the strong leading stallions watch their harems zealously. Zebras have no definite period of oestrus and parturition. Deeg (1922) has observed copulation and newly born animals in every month of the year. In countries where domesticated animals live in the half-wild state, as for instance in South America, every stallion is given from twelve to eighteen mares which he will keep together. Each group lives separately, and, after an incidental jumble, such as may occur when they are driven together, the individual groups immediately separate again. The superfluous stallions are castrated; these castrates live in groups by themselves. All stallions, even those who were living in stables until the time of observation, show the instinct of driving together a number of mares and of taking possession of them (Brehm), and the latter submit to it; evidently stallions as well as mares are directed by an instinct for polygynous mateship. The leading animal of Kulan herds, an Asiatic species of wild ass, is always a stallion; the older he gets the more females he keeps together and the number so kept may vary from three to fifty. If the leading stallion is killed the herd breaks up. The leaders of Nubian wild asses, herds of from ten to fifteen mares, on the other hand, are said to be old mares (Brehm), but each herd is accompanied by one male, who defends his rights stubbornly. Every kangaroo herd keeps one or several definite pasture-grounds that are connected by well-trodden paths. One herd always remains together and never mixes with another. Every herd is led by an old male and follows him blindly when looking for food or when fleeing. At the beginning of the mating-period the leading male demands the females of the herd for himself but has to establish his supremacy by combats with males that have grown up since the previous mating-season. Sometimes a herd divides, forming several herds that keep separate and are each led by a male.

POLYGYNOUS SEASONAL MATESHIPS WITHIN A HERD

If individuals of a certain species live in herds during the whole year, then the structure of the herds may differ greatly according to the season. During the period of sexual rest the individuals may separate into a male and a female herd, or the males and females may keep separate in two groups within one herd. The awakening of the sexual urge, however, brings about a complete change, inasmuch as the herd then consists only of harems. The fur-seals (*Callorhinus*) represent an especially clear example of this type. Outside of the mating-period the bulls live in separate herds in the open sea, and so do the "bachelors," i.e., those males who have had no chance to pair; some of the bachelors, however, seem to join the females with their young ones. At the beginning of the mating-period the old bulls come to the shore every year and occupy there the same rock they have occupied before. Multitudes of females appear later, and the males begin at once to form harems of from fifteen to twenty-five, at most forty. The females either are far advanced in pregnancy, or, if only one year old, are still virgin. The males enter violent combats, until gradually equilibrium, mutual recognition, and a division of interests are established. The old defeated and expelled bulls and the bachelors who were excluded from reproduction by the owners of the harems form two separate groups. When all females are covered the harems break up, and all animals move out into the open sea. The mating of other species of seals takes place in a similar manner.

POLYGYNOUS PERMANENT MATESHIPS WITHIN A HERD

This form of mateship has been established by many human races. In regard to other mammals the following facts are known. The tarpans, extinct European aboriginal horses, lived in herds of many hundred animals. Each of these herds separated into a number of families, each one consisting of a leading stallion and several mares; no stallion would tolerate any younger stallion or older rivals capable of begetting in his harem. The stallions frequently drew away domesticated mares, and it was for that reason that the South Russian peasants pursued them. In the case of zebras, Kulans, and South American horses which have become wild, several stallions may unite with their harems and form more or less loose unions, but each one keeps his females for himself.

FAMILIES

From mateship a family may originate, but that is not necessarily so. Parental, paternal, and maternal families may be distinguished, depending upon whether both parents, the father, or the mother remains with the offspring. If the offspring are deserted by both parents, but keep together for a while, they form what is called a "children's family."

Among many mammals not only the mother, but both the father and the mother guard and train the young; it is probably due to the nature of the subject in question that monogamous fathers take more care of their young ones than do polygynous fathers. In the case of mammals which have a long period of development two or more litters may remain with their parents. In the case of many beasts of prey the fathers remain with their mates and children for a certain time. Male lions are said to gather food and to protect their mates and young ones. Many beasts of prey learn the methods of hunting under the supervision of their parents. Foxes, too (in contrast to earlier opinions), defend their females and young ones. On the other hand, it is uncertain whether male wolves take part in supplying their young ones with food. The males of many monogamous ungulates (peccaries, *Phacochoerus,* certain deer, antelope, gazelles, etc.) also defend and lead the young ones. In the case of wild rabbits one reads that males protect their young ones and that the females hide them from other males. It is possible that their behavior varies according to regions. In the case of ungulates living in polygynous permanent mateship the leading stallions always protect their whole harem and their young. With catlike beasts of prey the mothers drag in small living and half-living animals for their young, but sometimes the fathers take a share in the training. With most beasts of prey, however, the mothers have to keep the males from the young ones, or else they will eat them. The mothers release their prey in the presence of their young ones, who thereby get practice for their future occupation of killing such animals. Later the mothers take their young along with them when they hunt. Such instruction may take months. Only when they are fully trained do the young separate from their mothers. While the prey-seeking instinct is inherited, its development depends upon instruction. Female foxes, like the females of catlike animals mentioned, train their young with living prey. Female ice-bears and seals carry their young ones into the water and teach them how to swim.

Solitary maternal families exist among many ungulates (e.g., the elks). There, where mammals which live in large herds are often pursued by their enemies, herds sometimes separate to form maternal families. Among elephants Schillings frequently observed small herds consisting of a mother and six to seven younger animals of varying size; in all probability these young animals were young of the elephant mother born during the past twenty to fifty years. When many mothers and their offspring unite without the fathers, the group is called a "mother herd." There are also children families among mammals. Rather young individuals of sperm-whale (*Catodon*) keep together in groups up to sexual maturity. Young deer remain with their mothers until the next mating-period and then are driven away by their mothers and frequently form independent groups. Young male and female reindeer which are not capable of reproduction unite to form strong packs led by an old virgin female.

HERDS

Among many mammalian species living in herds one can find old solitary males, the *"Einzelgänger,"* who probably are unable to be members of a herd because their sexual urge has weakened. It is quite possible that the other members of a herd drive away the individuals that are getting old. Solitary individuals can be found among elephants, buffaloes, deer, antelopes, giraffes, hippopotami, kangaroos, rodents, etc. It has been observed that strong male gnus drive older males away from the herd and keep them away permanently. Those driven away remain as if they were sentinels at a distance of a few hundred meters from the herd and warn it by their behavior in case of danger. Very old bulls later separate entirely from the herd and pass the rest of their lives solitarily. It has been reported that old bulls of the bantengs (*Bos banteng*) are driven away by the young ones. Old male individuals either keep strictly isolated or look for their equals of their own species or of others. Thus old gnu bulls and male elephants unite to form groups of two or three. Schillings observed two old elephant bulls in company with an old giraffe bull for weeks. As a matter of course there are always a large number of males among polygynous animals that are excluded from reproduction either temporarily or even for their whole lives. In the case of fur-seals and related species, where every male gathers a large harem, the excluded males unite to form two groups: the old expelled or wounded bulls make up one group, and the younger males, the "bachelors," who have not yet been permitted to pair, form another group. Young mature males of the guanacos, driven away from the herd by the leading stallion, unite with their equals and with young immature females. Young male vicugnas remain with their mothers until they are grown up, but then the entire pack of females drives away the young males which are capable of reproduction by biting and beating them. These males unite to form herds of twenty to thirty head, admitting a few individual defeated males. In such groups there are no leaders, and there is continual quarreling, especially during the mating-period. Such bachelor packs are to be found among deer, antelope, gazelles, buffaloes, and the castrate horses in South America.

Males and females of many mammalian species form common herds outside of the mating-season. Wolves, jackals, and hyena-dogs (*Lycaon*) live in packs and hunt together. It has been observed during wars that in periods of stress domestic dogs instinctively form hunting packs. When a certain section has been deserted by its inhabitants, the farms burned down, and the cattle and most of the dogs have perished, the remaining dogs frequently form packs; these groups hunt on the fields in a formation that looks like a line of skirmishers. A group may be made up of dogs of different races, colors, and sizes. Hunting in long arrays is no tradition among dogs; they unite to form such hunting companies in times of stress, driven by an old instinct. Related wild species of the domestic dog hunt in a similar way. Wolves live in packs during the winter and the members of a pack go in single file; in snow one animal treads in another's footsteps. When hunting together they divide into two packs; one pursues the prey, while the other cuts off its path. The African hyena-dogs (*Lycaon*) hunt large prey in packs. The rear animals of the pack cut off circuitous paths and relieve those animals that were leading before, and this is repeated until the prey is exhausted. In countries rich in wild animals, lions hunt together, sometimes accompanied by their young ones; some drive and come catch the prey; roaring seems to play an important part in their driving.

After the mating-season the two sexes of many animals live in separate herds, but in the case of pronghorns (*Antilocapra americana*) and saiga-antelopes (*Antilopa-saiga*), males and females form a common herd throughout the year. Also males and females of mammals living in colonies remain together. Many rodents and coneys (*Procavia*) live similarly in herds. Within such colonies individuals, either alone (ground-squirrels) or in pairs (wild rabbits), build separate dens and structures, which may be connected to one another, or several individuals build a common dwelling. Common dormice (*Muscardinus*) build skilfully constructed nests in bushes. In the case of jumping-rats (*Dipodinae*) and related species, marmots, wombats (*Phascolomys*), and kangaroo-rats (*Bettongia*), several individuals live together in dens which they dig. Viscachas (*Lagostomus*) and beavers live in colonies with the members in close contact with one another.

In a number of species living in herds the two sexes live separately except for the duration of the mating-period. It is not unusual that the males unite to form one herd, and the females another. When young ones join female herds, one calls them maternal herds. We can see, therefore, that not only with men, but also with animals, individuals of the same sex may unite for purposes other than sexual. According to Schillings many species of antelope form herds divided according to sex during seasons other than the mating-period. Wild sheep, steinbocks (*Ibex*), and other ungulates also live in packs separated according to sex outside of the mating-period. African and Indian elephants form separate packs of males and females. The female herds have a female leader and are accompanied by the young ones. In earlier times it was possible to see herds of several hundred head, but they were really temporary associations of several herds. In recent times the greatly reduced herds of Africa no longer observe the same strict division as before when there were a great many elephants. When occasionally a male and a female herd unite, the separation of the two sexes remains unchanged; this can be clearly observed during rest periods of their marches. The two sexes enter into a close relation only during the oestrus when a male takes possession of a female pack. The millions of bison that were living in North America did not form large disorganized herds, but every herd, when carefully observed, showed a subdivision into individual groups, bull herds with six to sixteen head each and cow herds with thirty or more head each. The female groups were led by a young male, and every male group had a leader as well. The male groups formed the edge of the entire herd, while the female groups were in the center. While marching and eating, the bison were generally in file. It has been observed that the animals did not form pairs or harems during the oestrus, and yet the order as described before must have been disturbed considerably for some time. During other times than the mating-period one can find the two sexes of the seals separated into different herds, the females being accompanied by young ones and sometimes by "bachelors." The old males of mule deer (*Caria-cus*) unite to form packs, but young males join packs of females. The females of many species live with their young ones in maternal herds, the young males capable of reproduction join to form male packs, and the old males live solitarily and care for female packs only during the mating-period. Wild boars, stags, and fallow bucks belong to this group. The males of bats live alone after the mating-period, but they live in groups at other times. The females form special groups; up to the present time no male has ever been found in these female herds. The female herds of the European bison, now completely extinct as a wild animal, consisted of ten to twenty head and were always led by an old cow and accompanied by two to three bulls. Young bulls lived in packs of fifteen to twenty head, but old ones solitarily. Female European bison rarely were solitary, and, if so, it probably was due to the destruction of this species. During oestrus the old bulls joined the packs of females, and violent combats developed among the rivals. Similar facts have been reported regarding other buffalo species. The males and young animals of the elk unite to form packs of fifty individuals at most, while the females and their young ones frequently remain apart. Typical maternal herds have been observed among many whale species. Sperm whales appear in schools consisting of twenty to thirty animals, all of which are females and their young ones; the leading animal of each school is an old male. Sometimes several schools and their leaders unite. Schools of gray whales (*Rhachianectes*) have been observed to have female leaders and they have no males at all. In the case of otters (*Lutra*) living solitarily, several females with their young ones not infrequently join to form a maternal herd. Sometimes two or three lionesses with their young are observed to form a group.

In one herd there may be individuals of different species. Dolphins of different species join and form troops that are led by individuals; sometimes whales follow a ship, propelled by such an "escort instinct." Antelopes of different species sometimes mix, but water-antelopes (*Redunca*) offer an exception, for they always remain apart. Peruvian brockets (*Hippocamelus*) and elks join herds of horned cattle. Wild zebras follow domestic horses and graze among them. Gazelles mix with herds of cattle. Sometimes one can see Kulans, antelopes of different species, yaks (*Poëphagus*), and scattered horses joining together. Wild buffaloes join elephants. Zebras chum with various species of gazelles, with ostriches and balearicans. Such cases have been considered as "mutual insurance," for the long-legged birds just mentioned are "eye-animals," while the hoofed mammals in question are "nose-animals"; that which the eyes cannot see the nose may detect, and vice versa. We do not know yet to what degree experience and tradition play a part in this form of association. In a similar way antelopes and ostriches sometimes stay among herds of baboons for hours.

One may distinguish between closed and open groups. New members are not accepted without resistance in groups of the former type, and individuals that have been accepted separate only under special circumstances; there frequently exists a distinct hierarchy among the members of a group, but members of open groups join and separate without special difficulties. Solitary monogamous mateships, families, and solitary harems are closed troops, excluding other individuals. Parents always know their young ones and many parents bite or kill strange young animals. Herds occupying certain sections and defending them against intruders belong to the type of closed groups. Different animals put into one cage may form a closed group in the course of time. Mutual recognition and acceptance of individuals in cases as mentioned above depend upon the fact that one individual knows another. But with the increasing number of individuals, closed groups come to be open ones. The half-wild pariah-dogs of the Orient, according to Brehm, quarrel at once with their equals who have not grown up among them. And every alley of an Oriental city has a group of half-wild dogs of its own who never forsake their headquarters. If a dog enters a strange alley all the dogs living there attack and kill him, unless he saves himself by fleeing instantly.

Frequently a group has a leader, which may be a male or a female according to the species. Frequently it is the strongest and most experienced individual that occupies this rank. But we must nevertheless not assume that experience is the only factor, but that there are specific "qualities of a leader" playing a part. When an animal tries to enter a closed group, it is usually received in a very unfriendly manner. Schulz added a third rhinoceros to a couple of other ones already accustomed to one another; the two attacked the newcomer at once and only later became friendly. Similar attitudes can be observed when a new animal is brought into a cage of a zoological garden. Beasts of prey, and also other species, as for instance prairie marmots (*Cynomys*), attack a newcomer of their own species or genus at once, and maltreat him or bite him to death. If the newcomer survives this reception, the animals frequently make peace; the meaning of these combats probably is the establishment of a hierarchical order.

It is not always possible to draw a sharp line between closed and open groups. Marmots build structures underground and even during seasons other than the mating-period live together in large numbers. But when these animals appear on the surface they place sentinels. The several viscachas connect their underground dwellings. Such a settlement is called a "viscachera." An old male seems to play a leading rôle in every one of them. Neighboring viscacheras are connected by paths that are used by the animals for visiting one another. When a viscachera is demolished the members of a neighboring settlement dig out the inmates. The few beavers still living in Europe usually live in couples, but beavers in rather quiet countries, as for instance in Canada, may live in small or large groups. · In thickly populated countries they usually live in simple tunnels underground and do not build houses (Burgen), but in sparsely settled countries they may build houses.

The houses are hills which look like baking-ovens and have thick walls; they are built from peeled pieces of wood, branches, earth, clay, and sand; they contain a dwelling and a storeroom for food. In places where animals can work without being disturbed a great number of individuals usually work together in the building of one structure. The females are the builders, the males rather the carriers and hands. When the level of the water changes during the course of a year, or if the water is not of the proper depth, the beavers build dams across the brook. The dams are made out of the same material as the houses and have an almost vertical wall on the side of the water, while on the opposite side they have a slope. Holes in the dam are discovered and filled in. Canadian beavers sometimes reinforce the first dam by building other dams below the first one. It is said that the dams of European and Canadian beavers become hundreds and thousands of years old. Innumerable generations cooperate in building them and caring for them.

In captivity individuals of species that when free have no relation with one another develop friendly relations, being impelled by an urge for company. Animals in captivity usually become friends of the person who takes care of them. Schillings was able to improve the degree of comfort of a young rhinoceros which was in captivity for a short time by giving him a grown-up goat as a companion. They soon were such good friends that the goat frequently rested on the rhinoceros.

The herds and groups of mammals that are formed during other seasons than the mating-period frequently are open groups. One individual is the leader, and some serve as sentinels during the stops of a trip. Gnus and buffalo herds not infrequently rest on hills which permit a view of the surrounding territory. Giraffe and cervine antelope (*Bubalis*) herds are led by a male or a female. Cervine antelopes frequently post their sentinels on termite hills. The saiga-antelopes live in large herds and the old bucks remain with the herds at all seasons. There are always some animals watching; no watching animal rests without disturbing another animal. Only when the other animal gets up and watches does the first lie down to rest. In case of danger these antelopes gather and then flee in the order of a long line, with usually a male, but sometimes a female, leading. With other species the leader is either always a female or always a male. The female leader of a reindeer herd always stands when watching, even if all the other individuals of her herd rest; when she goes to rest, another female gets up at once. In case of danger, the leading reindeer sometimes pushes some individuals of the herd with her antlers to stir them up. It is well known that animals living in herds sometimes follow their leaders blindly, even down an abyss if the leader falls into it. If a leader is killed a herd may be headless for a time. A herd of bottle-nosed whales has an old male as leader whom they follow blindly. Brehm says that a bottle-nosed whale (*Globiocephalus*) who escaped a massacre committed by the inhabitants of a certain shore returned again and again to his dying and dead comrades. In the case of cows the herdsman places the largest bell on the leader. The cows know the bells of their herd very well and individuals that have gone astray find their way back again with the help of the ringing bells. The leading cow shows a certain pride regarding her rank and does not permit any other animal to walk ahead of her. In South America where large herds of llamas are used for the transport of foods a male richly decorated with blankets serves as leader. In the same way leading animals of South American caravans of mules are richly decorated. A leading sheep carrying a bell can keep together from three to four thousand individuals. If the bell is missing, the herd separates into groups of six to twelve head, each one under the leadership of one individual. By marking one of the leading animals so that it may be seen from afar, man enables this one to lead several thousand.

General Attitudes of Mammals Living within Herds

The subject of mutual help in the realm of animals, and the opposite, mutual injury, have frequently been discussed in the field of animal sociology (see Kropotkin). Cases of mutual help are not rare; on the other hand one should not generalize such cases too much and look at them in a sentimental way, for mutual injury is also fairly frequent in the realm of animals. This occurs even among individuals of the same species or group. Mutual help is shown in the case of an animal that rushes to the aid of another animal, setting up cries of warning and distress, and helps without being attacked itself. Schulz reported that when one of his two young rhinoceros was attacked, the other one rushed to the spot and took part in resisting the attack. Prairie marmots (*Cynomys*) and viscachas pull wounded comrades into their dens. According to Berger no species but the apes have as strong an instinct to help their sick comrades as the elephants have. If an elephant is wounded by shooting, other animals support him and, if he falls, his comrades kneel beside him and push their tusks under his body, while others put their trunks around his neck and try to put him on his legs. Mutual help of animals can be observed when they pair and care for their nestlings. The males defend their females; one or both parents protect their young ones. Young animals that have lost their mothers are sometimes adopted by another mother without any fussing. This is true of elephants and wild sows. It is well known that one can foist young ones of very different species, such as young rats, mice, rabbits, wild rabbits, dogs, foxes, squirrels, etc., upon a female cat, on account of her well-developed nursing instinct.

Many sick or wounded animals are thrown out of groups of their former class, or even killed. Before moving into their winter quarters the marmots join, and, according to Girtanner, it sometimes happens that several individuals attack an old thin animal and bite it to death. The biological significance of such a phenomenon is clear, for when an individual dies during hibernation the whole troop is endangered by its dead body. It has been observed that beavers sometimes drive an old, or sometimes even a young, animal out of their colony by biting it. Such animals live in a special house from that time on. There has been much talk about so-called "executions" among animals. The following facts are verified with regard to mammals. "Executions" occur occasionally among many species of beasts of prey and even among cattle. Groos believes that they cannot always be traced to an instinct, useful to the species in question, that urges the animals to remove an individual that has become dangerous to the entire group, for it would be sufficient to expel that individual. The phenomenon rather manifests an inborn instinct of destruction. Cannibalism, i.e., the killing and eating of animals belonging to the same species, occurs frequently in the realm of animals. A condition for such an act is, of course, that one individual is able to overpower another, i.e., the defeated animal must either be weaker than the other or must be hindered in its defense. Individuals of solitary species, e.g., shrews (*Sorex*), and beasts of prey are relentless against other individuals of their species; even male hamsters (*Cricetus*) kill females when they meet them at times other than the mating-period, without, however, eating the dead bodies. The individuals of many species eat their young ones; the parent who does not participate in the care of the young attacks the offspring. Many beasts of prey do this. Animals in captivity leave each other alone as long as they are of equal strength, but if one gets sick it may be attacked and sometimes eaten. This may even happen among brothers and sisters. When a muskrat (*Fiber zibethicus*), or a brown rat (*Mus decumanus*), or a water rat (*Arvicola amphibius*) is caught in a trap, it is torn to pieces while still living and eaten. Sometimes, if one pinches the tail of a rat in captivity so that it shrieks, the rest of the animals in the cage attack it and bite it to death.

If many individuals are together, the entire herd may join a few animals in action. Herds of horses and domestic pigs fight successfully against a wolf, while an individual horse or pig is frequently lost. Similarly wolves organized as a pack are much bolder than individuals hunting alone. Animals living in herds, e.g., half-wild horses of South America, are frequently seized with a panic. Hundreds or thousands of horses gallop along as if mad, running against rocks and into abysses. They carry away with them draught animals and mounts of travelers who may happen to rest nearby (Brehm). Sheep run like mad away from wolves and, in Australia, from dingos. Many ordinary activities are intensified by group practice. This is true for eating; farmers are familiar with the fact that many animals, e.g., pigs and horses, especially when young, eat better when with companions than when alone.

Many species of mammals show characteristic phenomena of courtship and mating. Males usually are stronger, more conspicuous, and more aggressive than females. They fight for and strive to win the females, while the latter remain passive. In the case of some species the urge to fight has developed to excess. The combat of stags appears to be a goal in itself during the mating-period. Stags not infrequently forsake their harems in order to meet their rivals whose call they hear. Combats are jousts, though they may sometimes turn out to be serious. We may say in a general way that many mammals with antlers and horns enter this kind of combat during the oestrus. European bison, intoxicated with the sex drive, tear up medium-sized trees by the roots; not infrequently slain bisons, bulls and cows, can be found during the oestrus.

All animals may be said to play together, young ones especially, but old ones as well. Not only individuals of the same species play together, but also those of different species, especially in captivity. We must be careful, however, in interpreting these activities not to confuse real hunting, or pairing, or similar activities with playing. In games an element of rivalry can frequently be observed, as for instance in sham fights and hunting games. According to Groos hunting games may be classified as follows: those with living prey (a cat with a mouse); those with living mock prey (one dog hunting another one); and those with lifeless mock prey (playing with a ball). According to Pfungst young wolves and dogs arrange jousts and hunting games with living and with lifeless mock prey, in which young wolves without any kind of training show some elements of fetching and carrying. According to Schmidt the impulse to play may come from the young ones, or from the mother. The latter brings a half-dead mouse or something similar, and the young ones practice with it. Dogs (more social animals) take up games more easily than cats. Dogs, cats, and other mammals play more and also more intensively with youthful persons than with grown-up people and submit to rougher treatment when playing with children. They seem to have a certain amount of understanding for the awkwardness of children. If the playful activity of young mammals turns to earnest, their mothers sometimes separate the young fighters. Brehm reported a certain activity of chamois that can be interpreted only to be play. These animals, completely undisturbed, would glide in a crouching position, one by one, over a slope of snow. The distance would sometimes amount to 150 meters. Then they would climb back to the starting-point and glide down again.

Animals now and then produce sounds in common. These sounds may be interpreted as imitation pure and simple, as rivalry in the case of males, and as shouts of greeting. The latter are expressions of excitement and are heard when two or more animals meet. When a lion, free or in captivity, roars, other lions nearby join at once in roaring. A donkey may cause all other donkeys of his neighborhood to bray. In a similar way entire herds may roar. Tamias have the habit of calling one another with chirping sounds for hours. Sometimes one can recognize a certain rhythm. This habit probably has no relation to sex. Two bats that meet call one another.

Many mammals claim a certain territory for their residence; when two dogs meet they may fight one another. Every kangaroo tries to keep a certain territory or several territories connected with each other.

Every herd of the North American pronghorn (*Antilocapra*) occupies a certain area which it claims for itself. They undertake long trips into various sections of it. Many animals keep a supply of food and consider it more or less strictly as property of their own. According to Schillings leopards have the habit of hanging the flesh of an animal which they have killed on the branches of trees and bushes, after having eaten its heart and liver and buried the intestines. Now and then they climb up high to do this. Hamsters, living solitarily, build one or several storerooms in their houses; moles, also solitary, gather earthworms, biting off their front ends to prevent them from escape; squirrels (*Sciurus*) hide supplies of food.

Imitation plays an important part in animals living in herds. It has been frequently observed that, if a trained beast of prey attacks a tamer, all other animals of its group join in the attack. According to Sokolowsky animals of a herd do not stop a common action, but obey some kind of "agreement," and observe the motions of the animal that started the attack. In a similar way many animals living in herds imitate one another when fleeing or attacking, and the majority are not aware of a cause of the change. A horse, hearing the sounds of galloping caused by another one, reacts very distinctly. Many animals have a characteristic warning call: chamois and marmots whistle, wild rabbits beat the ground with their hind legs, and kangaroos show alarm in a similar manner. Many solitary and gregarious species understand each others' calls of warning (Schmid). When reedbucks (*Redunca*) warn with a whistling sound, not only animals of the same species, but also other mammals and many birds flee.

Von Uexküll studied carefully the manner in which dogs make known their home place to other dogs. The spots they distinguish by means of their "marks of odor" are identical with those that men use to remember places by sight. If two dogs take a walk with their master, they start a regular contest in urinating. A high-spirited dog is inclined to provide the next outstanding object with his "mark of odor" whenever he meets another dog. Also he will try to cover "flags of odor" of other dogs whenever he enters their home territory. A dog without temperament, however, will timidly pass the "marks of odor" when he enters the territory of another dog and will not reveal his presence by placing marks of his own. The tall bears of North America also mark their territory. Bears, standing erect, rub with their backs and mouths the bark of trees that stand alone and are visible from considerable distance. These marked trees serve as warnings to other bears to avoid these signals and the territory marked by them. In the case of many mammals, odors and excretions of special glands serve the individuals to establish and to maintain a mutual relationship. The white spots on the posteriors of many deer also have been said to be marks by which individual animals are enabled to follow their leading animal and their pack. In the case of deer the white spots are distinct in winter only; this is said to be due to the fact that the females are alone with their young ones during summer. The white spots of wild sika (*Pseudaxis*) are invisible while the animals rest, but very distinct while they flee. According to Berger those species that have no white spots usually have tails which are light-colored on the lower side. The beating movements of the tails are supposed to be signals to show the way. According to Schillings giraffes wave their tails vigorously right and left when they flee or become suspicious.

According to Pfungst wolves have various sounds at their disposal, about half of which express anger; even young wolves kept in complete isolation develop real barking when they are menaced. This is sufficient to prove that wolves do not learn barking by imitation from dogs or from the voice of men. Domestic dogs evidently bark more frequently because they are without the restraint of wild animals forced to be silent; and therefore they learn to make use of barking as an expression of various emotions, e.g., of joy, while originally it expressed only anger. Female wolves throw themselves on their backs to express helplessness.

According to Darwin the scratching of dogs and wolves after completed defecation is a rudiment of an urge to hide the excrements. Pfungst believes, however, that it is impelled by the animals' instinct to spread their scent. The fact that many animals leave their excrements on elevated spots or stones is said to verify this theory. If we accept von Uexküll's opinion with regard to the meaning of urinating of dogs, we may conclude that excrements also mark the territory. Free hamsters, badgers, martens, and rabbits have definite dung places. All llama species and various species of antelopes pile up their dung. Guanacos start a new pile of dung when one has reached a certain size. Cervine antelopes (*Cape hartebeests*) deposit their dung on certain places that have the shape of a circle and are made even by treading. The center of such a place is a small ant-hill covered with dung. These level places come into existence because a pack of animals gather on or beside an ant-hill, use it as a playground, and trample it down. Schillings reports that African rhinoceros show a certain preference in leaving their excrements at fixed places and spreading it by scratching with their hind legs. According to Schillings these dung places serve the widely scattered individuals as "posts" and as means of orientation in finding one another. The hippopotami display a peculiar behavior which is said to have the same meaning. They hurl their dung high up on bushes by means of their tails, which have the appearance of brushes and are provided with stiff bristles. It is possible, however, that they, too, wish to mark their territory in this manner.

Only animals which are capable of adaptation, such as horses and donkeys, could be domesticated. Zebras, for instance, are very difficult to tame; in training them for shows it is necessary that ponies be used as companions and "instructors." Indian elephants, even if captured in old age, will establish a friendly relation to men in a few weeks and will willingly perform work they are taught to do. African elephants qualify much more poorly for such a purpose. Schulz, who has lassoed zebras and antelopes from horseback in East Africa, has given us an illustration which shows how well animals may learn to understand their masters by means of suggestion. A horse rapidly learns to recognize the goal of his rider, flies into a very ardent hunting passion, and sometimes even bites the captured zebra. Many antelopes turn sharply at full speed when they are pursued and a horse will make the same turn. Hunting dogs behave in a similar way. Due to their versatility, dogs are also used for the watching of cattle and sheep. They change their behavior properly according to the situation, being much more gentle in dealing with lambs than with sheep. Only animals who offer a special advantage to man have become domesticated in the proper sense of the word.

Man has not brought about anything new by breeding domestic animals, but has only transmitted certain variations of quality especially agreeable to him from one generation to later generations of domestic animals by means of selection and elimination. It is impossible to create something entirely new, but the breeder must have the ability to pick out those morphological, physiological, and psychological variations of quality which are favorable. Pfungst thinks dogs originate from wolves and jackals, not from foxes, and makes the statement that the domestication of dogs did not produce anything new. He mentions the fact that young wolves at play show elements of fetching and carrying without any training. By consistent selection man has made near-automats out of some of his domesticated animals, who perfom his work willingly and sometimes go to the limit of their ability. That which training can add every generation has to learn again (hunting in dogs, training of horses, etc.). Habits acquired by learning are not passed on by inheritance, but dispositions for learning such habits are. By associating with man many domesticated animals have completely lost their original inclination toward certain sociological structures of mateship, family, and herds. Accordingly, in most cases, it is not permissible to draw conclusions regarding the behavior of the original species ("das Tier" überhaupt) from the behavior of domesticated animals.

BIBLIOGRAPHY

ALVERDES, F. 1927. Social life in the animal world. London: Kegan Paul; New York: Harcourt, Brace. Pp. ix+216.

———. 1932. The psychology of animals in relation to human psychology. London: Kegan Paul; New York: Harcourt, Brace. Pp. viii+156.

BERGER, A. 1922. In Afrikas Wildkammern als Forscher und Jaeger. (2nd ed.) Berlin: Parey. Pp. xvi+327.

BREHM, A. 1914-16. Tierleben: Säugetiere. Vols. 1-4. (4th ed.) (Ed. by O. zur Strassen.) Leipzig & Vienna: Bibliog. Instit.

DEEG, J. 1922. Ueber Brunst- und Setzzeit in der Tropen. *Wild u. Hund*, **28**.

DEEGENER, P. 1918. Die Formen der Vergesellschaftung im Tierreiche. Leipzig & Berlin: Verein. wiss. Verleger. Pp. xii+420.

DOFLEIN, F. 1914. Das Tier als Glied des Naturganzen. Vol. 2 of *Tierbau und Tierleben*, by R. Hesse and F. Dolflein. Leipzig & Berlin: Tuebner. Pp. xv+960. .

ESPINAS, A. 1879. Die thierischen Gesellschaften. (Trans. by W. Schlosser.) Braunschweig: Vieweg. Pp. xiii+561.

GIRTANNER, A. 1903. Aus dem Leben des Alpen-Murmeltiers. *Zool. Garten*, 44.

GROOS, K. 1930. Die Spiele der Tiere. (3rd ed.) Jena: Fischer. Pp. ix+348.

KROPOTKIN, P. 1908. Gegenseitige Hilfe in der Tier- und Menschenwelt. (Trans. by G. Landauer.) Leipzig: Thomas. Pp. xvi+294.

PFUNGST, O. 1914. Versuche und Beobachtungen an jungen Wölfen. *Ber ü. d. VI. Kong. f. exper. Psychol.*, 127-132.

SCHILLINGS, C. G. 1905. Mit Blitzlicht und Büchse. Leipzig: Voigtländer. Pp. xvi+558.

————. 1906. Der Zaubér des Elelescho. Leipzig: Voigtländer. Pp. xiv+496.

SCHMID, B. 1921. Von den Aufgaben der Tierpsychologie. (*Abhandl. z. theoret. Biol.*, No. 8.) Berlin: Gebr. Borntraeger. Pp. iv+43.

SCHULZ, C. 1922. Auf Grosstierfang für Hagenbeck. (3rd ed.) Dresden: Verlag dtsch. Buchwerkstätten. Pp. 184.

SCHUSTER, L. 1923. Brunst- und Setzzeit des Wildes in den Tropen. *Wild u. Hund*, 28.

UEXKÜLL, J. V., & KRISZAT, G. 1934. Streifzüge durch die Umwelten von Tieren und Menschen. Berlin: Springer. Pp. viii+101.

ZIEGLER, H. E. 1913. Tierstaaten und Tiergesellschaften. In Vol. 9 of *Handwörterbuch der Naturwissenschaften*, ed. by E. Korschelt, G. Linck, et al. Jena: Fischer. Pp. 1204-1220.

PART III

HISTORICAL SEQUENCES OF HUMAN SOCIAL PHENOMENA

CHAPTER 7

SOCIAL HISTORY OF THE NEGRO

MELVILLE J. HERSKOVITS

Northwestern University

I. INTRODUCTION

One of the simplest ways of grouping large masses of human beings is according to race. In the main, these groupings, which derive from common-sense observation as well as from the scientist's classification, divide *homo sapiens* into three races—Negroid, Caucasoid, and Mongoloid. Whether or not any relationship exists between the differences in physical characteristics that set off one race from another and the mental capabilities or cultural achievements of the races is at the present time a matter of dispute, for the evidence thus far has not been such as to allow a successful correlation of race with culture. That is to say that racial classifications are useful as convenient designations for the great groupings of mankind, the individual members of which, in a general way, resemble each other in certain outward physical traits, and it is in this sense that the word "Negro" will be employed here.

As is the case with other races, Negroes not only differ among themselves in the very physical traits that give rise to the term that distinguishes them, but the cultures of Negro populations also differ from one another to a striking degree. Before discussing these cultural differences, however, the physical characteristics of the several subtypes, the geographical limits of the distribution of these types, and the problems as to the origin of this race, its migrations and the contacts it has had with other peoples may be outlined, so that in the pages which follow these basic facts may be held clearly in mind.

The origin of the Negro race is a secret of the past. Even the region where Negroes first appeared is not known, some authorities holding that Africa was not necessarily the habitat of the first Negroes but that they might have migrated from outside the continent. That Africa was inhabited in the early days of humanity is evident from the finds made by archeologists in eastern and southern Africa, which prove beyond doubt the antiquity of man on that continent. Yet these forms are proto-human, consisting of types which antedate *homo sapiens,* and hence cannot be identified with the Negro race as it exists at present. Almost the only hint that the Negro type may have been differentiated by the end of the paleolithic epoch from other human forms then living is contained in the Grimaldi skeletons, which were disinterred near Monte Carlo, not far from the northern shore of the Mediterranean. Yet there are those who maintain that the Negroid characteristics of the Grimaldi woman and boy are not Negroid in the sense that the skeletal characteristics of contemporary Negroes are Negroid, but rather that these individuals represent chance variations from a type that was prevalent over all Europe in those days.

The Distribution of the Negro Race. In view of the lack of agreement as to the origin of the Negro race, and in view of the fragmentary nature of the available data concerning this problem, the distribution of Negro peoples at the present time may be considered at once, without giving further attention to the question as to where or when or how they may have originated.

This distribution is a vast one. Not only does it comprehend all of Africa south of the Sahara, and, in mixture with Caucasoid forms, northern Africa and Egypt, but peoples having Negroid physical traits are found far to the east, while as a result of the slave-trade millions of persons of African descent now inhabit the New World. The world distribution of the Negro race thus comprehends a broad belt, which, stretching eastward from Africa, includes southern India where millions of Dravidians, classified as Negroid folk, live; reaches the Indonesian islands where groups of Negroid peoples such as the Negritoes of the Philippines or the Semang of Malay are found; and continues farther to Melanesia, where the so-called Papuans of New Guinea, Fiji, and the other numerous islands exhibit distinctly Negroid traits. There are some, indeed, who in making their classification include the Australians among the Negroids, but there is no general agreement as to this, nor is there any agreement as to whether or not the Tasmanians, now extinct, should also be included in this racial group. It may well be asked how these Negroid peoples ever attained such a far-flung distribution, but the question is only another of the many to which the study of prehistory has as yet disclosed no answer.

These eastern Negroids, however, are not ordinarily included in discussions of the Negro race. Their cultures, like their physical types, are too specialized, and their distance from the mass of Negro peoples is too great, to permit of bracketing them and the Africans with any degree of intellectual comfort. In the case of the New World Negroes, on the other hand, it is a different matter, for their migration is one which occurred in historic times and is thus well documented. Hence it is the peoples of Africa and their New World descendants who will furnish the subject-matter of this discussion. And, because it is important to recognize what physical differences can be comprehended within one of these conglomerates of peoples, all designated by a term applied to a single race, a brief list of the physical types of Africa follows.

The Various Types of Negroid Peoples. Five or six African types are variously distinguished by those who have studied the problem; while in the New World, if mixture with whites and Indians is disregarded, one of these six, the so-called "true Negro," predominates. The first of these types which may be named inhabits a wide belt that reaches across Africa, comprising the whole of the Sahara desert and those parts of Egypt included between the corresponding latitudes. It is a mixed Negroid-Caucasoid stock that is usually designated by the term Berber. The Touareg of the desert are Berbers, and so are most of the other nomadic peoples encountered there. Yet the Berbers are not to be regarded as other than of partial Negroid derivation, for full-blood Negroes are found only south of the Sahara. North of the Berbers— in Morocco, Algiers, Lybia, and northern Egypt—a type predominantly Caucasoid lives, though even here Negro characteristics are present to some degree. As one proceeds southward from the extreme northern portion of Africa, the population becomes more and more Negroid, so that the Hausa of northern Nigeria, who live on the extreme southern border of this Berber belt, to take only one example, are almost as Negroid as the fully Negro Yoruba to the south of them.

The type denoted the "true Negro" inhabits the region bordering on what is usually termed the West Coast of Africa but is in reality that portion of the continent which faces south toward the Gulf of Guinea. The physical characteristics of the true Negro are those which are best known in the New World, for it is from these people that the bulk of the slaves brought to the Americas was derived. This type is short and stocky, sturdily built, of heavy pigmentation and frizzled hair. Its facial features are those which are usually meant when the word "Negro" is employed, the true Negro having a prognathous facial angle, thick everted lips, a broad nose, and high cheek bones. This type extends eastward as far as the Cameroons and is separated from a third subgroup of the Negro race, called the Nilotic type, by the Bantu-speaking peoples of the northern portion of the Congo basin. The Nilotic folk inhabit the region bordering the upper reaches of the Nile. They are less Negroid in appearance than the true Negro and represent a mixture with Caucasoid Hamitic peoples who migrated into the area they inhabit. This type, particularly in the region of the great lakes of East Africa, number among them the tallest folk in the world—"strangely enough," the best authorities state, "in spite of the moderate stature of most Hamites" (Seligman and Seligman, 1932, p. 3)—their tallness being accentuated by the extreme slenderness of their bodily build. These mixed tribes also exhibit skins of extremely heavy pigmentation. East and northeast of them, in Abyssinia, are found the Hamitic peoples, who, to a lesser extent than the Nilotes, are the offspring of the mingling of an aboriginal Negroid population that resulted from wave after wave of migration into northeastern Africa from nearby Arabia, which lies just across the Red Sea.

Perhaps the largest single grouping of African peoples comprises the Bantu-speaking folk. This is also the type that is least adequately defined as to its physical form and probably exhibits the greatest variation. Inhabiting the geographical heart of the continent—the whole of the Congo basin and all of southeastern Africa—it also represents a merging of the various tribes who came into contact as a result of the unrecorded population movements that have taken place since the earliest times. If one were to summarize the physical type of the Bantu peoples, one would say that they resemble to varying degrees the true Negro of West Africa. Yet there are such great differences among the Bantu in stature and facial contour, in hair form and bodily build, that the term applied to them is at best a kind of catch-all for these varied physical forms which only future study can differentiate with any degree of exactitude.

The two remaining types, which authorities are now inclined to classify as a single one, inhabit the extreme southern portion of the continent— or did so before the peopling of the area by Dutch and English settlers forced them into less hospitable territory and reduced their numbers almost to the vanishing point. The principal difference between the Hottentot and Bushmen is in stature, the Bushmen being one of the pygmy groups of mankind, Hottentots being of normal size. Otherwise both are marked by rather yellowish pigmentation, by the so-called Mongoloid or "slant" eye, the peculiar "pepper-corn" type of hair, and steatopygy, while their skin exhibits the trait of wrinkling to an extreme degree. Whether or not the pygmy Negroids of the Congo forests are related to the Bushmen is a 'much-debated question; it is another of the large number concerning Africa and its peoples to which as yet no satisfactory answer has been given.

The differences found between the Negro peoples of Africa in physical characteristics are, however, neither as numerous nor as striking as those between the cultures that spread over the continent. The character of these cultural dissimilarities will be discussed below; here it is necessary merely to point out the fact of their presence, to ask how they may have developed. Except for the Arabic-speaking peoples of northern Africa, the Abyssinians, and the Vai of Sierra Leone, Africans do not possess written languages, and their history is therefore largely a matter of reconstruction, something that to the student is unsatisfactory at best. There are those who hold that in early days Africa was populated largely by pygmy folk. These, it is said, were pushed farther and farther to the south by intruders who were not only of larger stature and hence of greater physical force, but who were also equipped with a higher culture and a more efficient technique of warfare which allowed them to prevail over the indigenous inhabitants. The validity of this hypothesis, however, has never been established, even though it is granted that the habitat of the Bushmen was at one time undoubtedly much more widely extended than it was at the beginning of the historic period. Thus it is to be noted again that the question as to whether the true Negro types arose in Africa itself, and, if so, in what part of Africa, cannot be resolved.

Migrations within Africa and Contacts outside the Continent. Only two statements concerning the peopling of Africa and the development of its cultures may be made with any degree of certainty. One of these is that the internal migration of peoples, as evidenced by cultural relationships and by the folk history of tribe after tribe, would seem in general to have proceeded from east to west, from northeast to southwest, and, in the eastern part of the continent, from north to south. The second of these generalizations is that Africa may not be regarded as an isolated, self-contained area, but as one which from earliest times has had numerous and significant contacts with the neighboring continents. In recent centuries Mohammedanism has had most influence on the indigenous folk. The migrations of the Arabs along the east coast have made for the introduction of a lingua franca known as Swahili, while other Arabic influences left by the traders who coasted up and down the East African shore in their dhows can be traced for some distance into the interior. This influence, however, is slight compared to that which has been exerted on the Mohammedanized folk of North Africa. Here the influence of Mohammedanism is to be found, in most instances as a major factor, in all that area which reaches across the continent as far south as a line which, beginning on the Atlantic Coast at about the twelfth parallel of latitude, curves toward the northeast so as to touch the Red Sea at about the sixteenth parallel.

Yet the spread of Mohammedanism is the result only of the most recent of those numerous contacts between Africa and the remainder of the Old World which have been going on for untold centuries. The contacts between Egypt, southern Europe, and Asia Minor are well established and the influence of Egypt, which was exerted to the south and southwest, could not have been other than significant. It must be stressed, however, that contacts between two cultures inevitably leave their mark on both of the cultures involved; hence the influence of the Negro cultures of Africa on Egypt, something rarely taken into account in the study of Egyptian civilization, is also to be reckoned with when the mutual interaction between the cultures of all the Old World is considered. Culture was carried in both directions across the Red Sea, and the same was undoubtedly true of the entire littoral of the Mediterranean. The numerous caravan routes across the Sahara, which have existed from the earliest times, indicate how northern Africa, whose cultural orientation for centuries has been essentially toward Europe, was in contact with the regions south of the desert. Africa has undoubtedly been influenced by Carthage, and through Carthage by Rome; in return, the influence of the African Moors on Spanish culture, and, in earlier times, of Africans who were in contact with Greece, Rome, and Babylon must be given full cognizance.

Africa as a Portion of the Old World Area. This would seem to indicate that a realistic view of the origin, development, and present affiliations of the civilizations of Africa must hold them to be not something separate and unique, but an integral portion of the Old World cultural province. As the history of man goes, it is not so long ago since what is now the Mediterranean Sea was a series of great inland lakes, with several passages from Africa to Europe which allowed communication by land. The Isthmus of Suez facilitated contacts between Africa and Asia Minor, while the Strait of Bab-El-Mandeb at the mouth of the Red Sea is not of sufficient width to have hindered intercourse. Furthermore, the fact that large enough numbers of Indonesian folk were able to make their way by out-rigger canoe either across the Indian Ocean or along the coasts of Asia and Africa to populate Madagascar shows that contacts between the Far East and Africa have also taken place; conversely, the demonstration that the giraffe, an African animal, was exhibited in China as early as the fifth century indicates that the flow of culture assumed an eastward as well as a westerly direction.

Evidence drawn from the distribution of certain aspects of culture go far in supporting this theory of an Old World culture province of which Africa is but a part. The Uncle Remus folktales told by American Negroes, which can be matched by stories from all sections of Africa, are not greatly different from the stories contained in the collection of Aesop's Fables, or which constitute the medieval cycle of Reynard the Fox, or the Indian Panchatantra tales, or the sacred Jataka tales of China. The institution of trial by ordeal which marked medieval Europe and is still found in portions of Asia is a fundamental aspect of African jurisprudence. The mythological organization of the gods in relationship groupings, the widespread use of mechanical means of divination or of the inspection of the entrails of freshly killed animals to foretell the future, the importance of the ancestral cult, and many other cultural traits characterize the whole of this area.

The Problems to Be Considered in This Chapter. This brings us to the problems which are to be considered in this chapter. That the study of human social groups is different from the study of animals and inert matter in that human populations are not subject to experimental techniques—that they cannot be brought into the laboratory for study— is a proposition often put forward. In a sense this is true—thus, no problem of human group psychology can be studied by means of repeated, controlled experimentation. Yet it is nevertheless also true that history sets up experiments for the social scientists that can be regarded as more comparable to the laboratory experiments set up by the natural and exact scientists than is ordinarily thought to be the case.

One such laboratory situation is that which the Negro peoples afford the student, particularly if the behavior of New World Negroes is studied in relationship to their African background. The problems that may be analyzed by the use of this material are numerous, but in the main the ones to be studied most profitably are those that concern the manner in which the process termed "acculturation" goes on and those that have to do with the vitality of the socialized behavior patterns that are called "cultural patterns." These matters will be discussed at the end of this chapter; here we need only outline the reasons why the material for the study of these problems through a consideration of Negro folk is so excellently adapted to this end. To begin with, the presence of adequate historical documentation is of the first importance, since this makes it possible to discover the civilizations from which the Negro slaves who were brought to the New World derived, and thus gives the student a cultural base line against which the behavior of contemporary New World Negroes can be projected. The regions of the New World to which the Negroes were taken are also well known, and the history of these New World regions is similarly documented, so that the peoples and the customs which the Africans encountered in the Western Hemisphere can likewise be studied. These non-Negroid peoples with whom the slaves of the Western Hemisphere came into contact are more numerous and exhibit greater differences than might be thought on first glance to be the case. There were, first of all, the aboriginal Indian tribes, who differed among themselves in culture and physical type and who mixed both physically and culturally to an appreciable degree with the Negro slaves. Of Europeans, there were British, French and Dutch, Spanish, Portuguese and Danish. Thus in North America, in the islands of the Caribbean Sea and in South America, the Negroes came into contact with Europeans who among themselves spoke different languages and had differing customs. Furthermore, within each of the regions of the New World where slavery obtained, the contact of the Negroes with the cultures of their European masters varied in intensity; on the same island, house-servants and field-hands had anything but equal opportunities to know the customs of their masters. Finally, it must not be forgotten that in all parts of the New World the contact, particularly between the younger members of the master class and their personal slave servants, was usually sufficiently intimate to cause the results to be manifested in both directions and on all concerned.

Thus it can be seen how the history of the Negro race affords one of these laboratory situations for the study of acculturation and of the vitality of social behavior patterns. Certain questions must be considered, however, before the wider usefulness of these data becomes apparent. What types of cultures are found on the African continent? To what degree are Africanisms present in the New World? To what extent do the Africanisms found in one part of the New World differ from those in another? Are the differences between the cultures of the African regions from which the slaves were derived reflected in different regions of the New World where these Africans have been in contact with Europeans, themselves of different culture? To what extent can it be said that their behavior reflects the differences between, let us say, British and French traditions? The answers to these questions constitute material which, provided by the accidents of history, can be used to analyze some of the larger considerations in the study of human social processes. Let us, then, enter the laboratory and see what is to be found in it.

II. The Civilizations of Africa

Culture Areas, Their Delimitation and Usefulness to the Student.
Since a knowledge of the cultural achievements of the Negro is essential
for the study of those problems which have been suggested, the first
step in our analysis must be to classify and describe the cultures of Africa.
This is the more necessary since, as has been explained, the historical
development of the hundreds upon hundreds of different civilizations which
are found in Negro Africa is unknown to us, and consequently we can
but analyze them as they are found. The tool best employed in classifying large numbers of cultures showing as great differences as do these
of Africa is that afforded by the concept of the culture area. The
culture area has proved its usefulness to students in North America and
in other parts of the world, and it is on the basis of these areas as they
have been mapped for Africa that this description will be made.

A culture area comprises that region wherein the civilizations of the
peoples who inhabit it are relatively alike when compared to cultures
of other regions. It must be emphasized, however, that though definite
boundary lines between areas may be drawn, and are in fact drawn on
the map, the culture area as such exists as an integrated unit only in
the mind of the student. In making a classification of this type, when
the similarities between the cultures of a region become apparent, the
classifier draws a line about the portion of a continent where these
similar cultures are found. He calls the cultural center that portion
of his area—not necessarily its geographical center—where the cultural
traits that mark the region, as he envisages it, are found in their purest
form. He also recognizes the fact that, as he moves away from this
center, the cultures he encounters become more and more permeated with
traits from neighboring areas, so that he eventually reaches a borderline
region which he terms "marginal" where the cultures exhibit traits of
the adjoining areas. It must be held clearly in mind, however, that
the culture of a people living in a marginal region is none the less complete, nor holds any the less meaning for that people, than a culture in
the very heart of an area. It is merely to the student that the concept
of the cultural center or marginal region has significance; indeed, an
area as such does not exist for those who live in it, and most persons,
of whatever culture, would be hard put to it to indicate the boundaries
of the area in which they reside, or to name a "culture-center" in the
sense in which the student employs the term. The more finely the distinctions between individual tribes are drawn, the more it becomes apparent that the tribe itself is the primary cultural unit; there are even
those who hold that, in the final analysis, the individual is the essential
unit in the study of culture. However, this is principally a matter of
the problem to be studied, for, just as important differences are manifest
between the cultures of different areas, so within any given area smaller
but none the less significant differences between tribal cultures are apparent to the student who intensively studies that area, while to the

student of personality it is the individual differences found within a given tribe which count above all else.

Cultural Focus and Its Socio-psychological Significance. Yet, even though it is not recognized as such by its inhabitants, the culture area nevertheless undoubtedly has objective existence, which may be regarded as the expression of a process of human civilization denoted by the term "cultural focus." This tendency of a people to focus their interests on a given phase of their culture, if considered in terms of cultural change, has socio-psychological significance as a dynamic force. On the other hand, if a culture is described at one period of its existence, cultural focus is to be thought of as that element in the psychology of the inhabitants which gives to an area its peculiar characteristics—the manner in which one phase of culture dominates the interest of a given people at a given time. Thus, as will be seen, the overwhelming significance of cattle in East Africa is the focal point of East African life; in the West African extension of the Congo area a pecuniary motivation not unlike that of Western European and American civilization may be regarded as marking off these peoples from the ones surrounding them. In considering the culture areas of Africa, therefore, it is those facets of culture which are outstanding in conditioning the behavior of the inhabitants—the focal points—which will necessarily be given prominence in the following descriptions.

The Culture Areas of Africa and Their Characteristics. The Hottentots inhabit the first area to be considered. Though their culture does not possess the vitality it had before these people came into contact with the Europeans who occupied their territory, it is sufficiently preserved to allow an adequate description of its principal features. According to some authorities it is to be regarded as essentially the same as the culture of the Bushman area, which will next be discussed. However, even though it be granted that Hottentot culture is a specialized development from cultural beginnings which are the same as those of the Bushmen, the cultures of these two people, since the time of earliest historic contact with them, are sufficiently unlike to necessitate classifying them separately. The Hottentots are exclusively a herding folk. Cattle play a major rôle in their life, so much so that it is precisely on this point that they are most strikingly to be differentiated from their Bantu-speaking neighbors to the east, who also possess cattle but who practice agriculture as well. The position of women in regard to the cattle is important in differentiating their culture from that of these neighbors, since among the Hottentots the women have much to do with the herding, something unknown to the east. Again, the Hottentot drinks his milk sweet, not soured, and utilizes his animals as beasts of burden as well as to provide him with subsistence. Other aspects of their material culture differentiate them from the peoples of surrounding areas; for example, their huts are better shelters than those of the Bushmen, though they are much less adequate than the structures of East Africa.

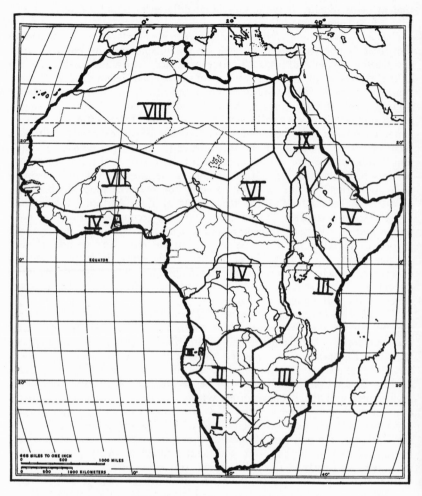

THE CULTURE AREAS OF AFRICA

I. Hottentot   IV-A. Guinea Coast Sub-Area
II. Bushman   V. East Horn
III. East African Cattle Area   VI. Eastern Sudan
III-A. Western Sub-Area   VII. Western Sudan
IV. Congo   VIII. Desert

IX. Egypt

Though the material culture is not of a high order, property is held privately and is inherited from father to son along well-recognized lines. The social organization of the Hottentots is also more complex than that of the neighboring Bushmen, each tribe being composed of a number of patrilineal sibs, that is, of persons claiming descent in the male line, each sib taking its name from that of its first known ancestor or the first ancestor under which it gained its separate identity. Marriage follows the general African pattern of requiring gifts to be given by the bridegroom, but among the Hottentots this is in the form of cattle which furnish the wedding feast rather than the usual type of "dowry." Moon-worship is an important element in their religion, the moon being the most prominent among a number of other supernatural beings. Ghosts are feared and placated, while the belief in magic is strong, with magic and divination being performed by specialists. Linguistically, the Hottentots, like the neighboring Bushmen, are sharply to be differentiated from the rest of Africa because of the employment of a phonetic device known as the "click." These sounds are made not by passing the breath over the vocal cords, but rather by pressing the tongue against some part of the mouth so as to create a vacuum and then allowing the air to rush in with a resulting sharp sound when the tongue is forcibly withdrawn.

The second area is that named for the Bushmen, but this designation must today be regarded as no more than an abstraction of an historical reality almost entirely lost, for there are but few of these people left at the present time. It is not difficult to differentiate their culture from that of their neighbors. The extreme poverty of the material culture of the Bushmen stands in sharp contrast to the flowering of their art and folklore, which constitute its most striking features. The poverty of material culture is perhaps best exemplified by the following statement, which was made many years ago to Bishop Callaway by a Kafir:[1]

> The Abatoa are much smaller than the other children of men; they hide in grass and sleep in ant-hills; they go into the mists; they live in high rocks; they have no settled place of abode; their home is wherever they kill game; they eat it all up and go on. . . .

Agriculture and herding are entirely absent from their culture, the dog being the only domesticated animal they possess; but hunting is pursued with a high degree of skill, and numerous methods employed by the Bushmen to bring down their kill have been recorded. They use the bow and arrow and have developed a poison which is effective in aiding them to kill the larger forms of game; the Bushmen also know how to simulate the movements of animals so as not to disturb a grazing herd until the hunter is near enough to make his shot a telling one. As has been remarked in the quotation given above, they have no fixed homes, and caves and rock shelters are used when available, while their clothing

---

[1]Quoted by Ratzel (1896-1904, Vol. 2, p. 268).

is also rudimentary. The sparseness of Bushman material culture is matched in the slight amouñt of organization which marks all phases of their social life. There are no sibs, the family being the only relationship grouping, and marriage ceremonies are at a minimum. A well-recognized system of worship of heavenly bodies and supernatural beings and of beliefs concerning the dead exists, coupled with the practice of both good and bad magic, their religion thus showing many resemblances to that of the Hottentots. The rock paintings of the Bushmen have long been famous among artists and laymen for their beauty and mastery of technique. Similarly, their singing and dancing is of an intricate character, while a large body of folklore has been collected from these people.

The East Africa cattle area, the third to be distinguished, comprises two and perhaps three subregions. It is principally to be differentiated from the other culture areas of Africa by the complex that gives it its name. Cattle are found in many parts of the continent, but nowhere do they have a place in the life of the people as significant as that which they take in the life of the East Africans. From the southern portion of the eastern coastal region to the great lakes and beyond they determine a man's position and his prestige; they are utilized in ceremonials having to do with the great events, the "crises" in the life of a human being—birth, puberty, marriage, and death—and their care is the prerogative of their owner, who often knows each animal in his herd by name. In the entire area, too, this cattle complex, as it may be termed, is found to be superimposed upon an underlying agricultural civilization which, there is strong reason to believe, historically antedates the presence of cattle. Except for their milk, which is consumed after it has become soured, cattle are not a source of food, for their primary function is to assure the social position of their owners. Only as ceremonial offerings, or at the natural death of an animal, are they eaten. The food on which people rely for sustenance is the produce of the fields, and throughout the area this agricultural work is done mainly by women, who are forbidden to care for the cattle. There is a distinct break in the distribution of cattle and cattle customs in the central portion of the area, where the presence of the tsetse fly effectively prevents the people from possessing them. Here, however, smaller animals play a corresponding rôle in the life of the folk.

In this area, that economic specialization which is the mark of more complex cultures is found, and iron-working, for example, is generally done by men who devote themselves almost solely to their craft. Nevertheless, the economic order is not too complex; though private property is the rule, exchange is ordinarily carried on by barter. Cattle, it must be emphasized, though regarded as wealth, are not considered money; they are not bought and sold but are merely retained as an index of social position and a means of acquiring prestige. Land is ordinarily held by the head of a tribe in trust for the rest of the people, and, though absolute ownership is not vested in individuals, the right to work a certain tract of land for agricultural purposes by a given person is clearly recognized. As a general rule, grazing land is free in all the area. The people live in villages, which throughout much of the region are centered about the cattle kraals. The houses are both thatched and mud-plastered; generally the shape is round, but in certain parts of the region, particularly in the north, rectangular houses are the rule.

The political life of the East Africans is more highly organized than is the case in either of the two preceding areas which have been discussed, resembling to a much greater degree the rest of Negro Africa. But the importance of cattle is again seen in this connection; indeed, in some of the northern tribes of the area the chiefs are appointed to rule over a given number of cattle rather than over human beings. Social organization, in the main, is patrilineal, although in the central section of the area matrilineal sibs are also found. Polygyny obtains, and the number of wives a man may have is based directly upon the number of cattle he possesses, or is able to command, although other animals or objects may be included in the "dowry" that a prospective bridegroom must give for his wife. Age classes are certainly found in the extreme north and south of the area, and there are reports which indicate that these groupings are also found in other tribes of this region. "Initiation schools," where puberty rites are performed and the young people are taught the proper ways of carrying on adult life, are characteristic. As in all of Africa, the use of magic and magic charms is of great importance in the system of religious beliefs, but more important than these are the deified ancestors and the gods who are associated with natural phenomena. One type of rite often met with in the area is the rain-making ceremony. Curiously enough, the cattle figure to a minor degree in the religious and ceremonial life. The languages spoken in this area are two: Bantu dialects are found in the south and central portions, while in the north the Nilotic tongues are heard.

The subdivision of this area which lies westward of its southern portion comprises a comparatively small territory and includes a few tribes of Bantu-speaking peoples such as the Ovaherero, Ovambo, and Ovimbundu. The cultures of these tribes differ markedly from those of the Congo people who live to the northeast of them and from those of the Bushmen and Hottentots to the south and southeast, while, in spite of their present-day separation, they resemble strikingly the cattle cultures of East Africa. The cattle complex, the circular kraal, the tabus on women as far as contact with cattle is concerned, and the place which cattle play in the life of the people, all mark them as being closely related culturally to the East Africans. It must be emphasized, however, that relatively little is known of these folk, and hence their inclusion with the East African tribes must be tentative in the extreme, particularly since in clothing, housing, and certain of their religious beliefs and ceremonial customs a

lack of correspondence is found between them and the larger area from
which they have presumably derived their social behavior.

The Congo area, like East Africa, must be divided into two subregions. The first of these, which includes the territory drained by
the Congo and its affluents, is inhabited by agricultural Bantu-speaking
folk, who comprise numerous independent tribes. By some this is called
the Hylaean area, and these students do not include in it the West
African coastal strip where the culture, though in many respects similar
to that of the Congo, is indeed to be differentiated from it in certain
other striking characteristics. The cultures of the Congo basin proper
are most prominently distinguished from those of the East African area
by virtue of the absence of cattle. This throws the agricultural basis
of Congo economic life into sharp prominence. The people live in villages principally composed of rectangular houses, made of woven or
mud walls and roofed with thatch. They utilize the inner bark of certain trees out of which they make bark-cloth, while they also weave and
embroider cloths of notably beautiful design from raffia-fiber. Basketry
and mat-making have also been developed to a high state of excellence.
Iron-work of fine quality is done in this area; the iron-workers in
a given tribe, who have prominent social position, are usually organized
as a guild and produce many types of weapons and utensils. One of
these weapons, which is also used as currency, consists of the so-called
throwing-knife, an iron object made in complicated outline, the various
prongs being sharpened in such a way that the twirling motion with
which the knife is thrown inflicts great damage when it strikes the body.
Some of the important art provinces of Africa are found in this Congo
area, particularly the region along the Kasai and Sankuru rivers and
the Cameroons, where many notable examples of what has come to be
known as "African art" have been collected. This art consists of carved
wooden figures, masks, and decorated objects of everyday use, both of
human representations and geometric designs. The urge to decoration
manifests itself even on the human body, for, in the central Congo, cica-
trization, found all over Africa, has been developed to an almost unbelievable degree of intricacy of design. The wooden drum is found
in this region, in addition to the skin-head drum, and is employed for
beating the messages of the "drum-language," which is so often prominently mentioned in descriptions of African cultures. In the Congo
basin, as in the West African sub-area, the development of political organization is striking. The courts of the kings, before European occupation, were large in size and rich in ceremonialism; in this area the
king's court was often supplemented by separate courts of the queen
mother and the king's "wife," who was often a sister. Social organization is in most cases of a matrilineal order, totemic sibs being found in
all parts of the area. Other outstanding traits are the more closely
organized structure of religious life, with a more highly developed priesthood than is to be found in the areas heretofore considered, and a resulting

greater complexity of religious belief. Zambi, the Great God in the region of the coast, is worshipped under various names throughout this region; the ancestral cult with its corresponding belief in the soul is found as it is in East Africa; while the use of magic and charms attains great prominence.

In the light of the general problems which have been enumerated above for consideration in this chapter, the West Coast is perhaps the most important region of Africa, since it is from here that the slaves were for the most part derived. This sub-area is to be differentiated from the Congo in a number of traits. In the first place, except in eastern Nigeria the languages spoken here are not Bantu, but of the type usually classified as Sudanese. Again, the density of population is much greater than perhaps anywhere else in Africa, and hence the economic life, with the pecuniary motivation that gives it its underlying psychological drive, is more complex and the degree of specialization greater than in other parts of the continent. In certain parts of the region some of the larger domestic animals are found, though not to any great extent, nor does their economic and sociological importance approach that which they hold for the peoples who live farther to the north. In West Africa, the development of techniques of all kinds is the greatest on the continent. The Benin bronzes, the brass-work of Dahomey, the weaving of the Ashanti, or the wood-carving of the Ivory Coast, Dahomey, and Nigeria are famous, while pottery of a high grade, basketry, and iron-work are found everywhere. The social and political organization also has great complexity, and this region may be distinguished from the Congo area proper in this regard. It was here that some of the great kingdoms of Africa existed from medieval times or earlier to the dates of their downfall before the advance of European colonial expansion; among these were the kingdoms of Benin, Dahomey, and Ashanti, to name only three. In this area we find a well-developed sib organization which, like those of East Africa and the Congo, is totemic in character, and a highly developed ancestral cult which validates and stabilizes these relationship groups. The religions of West Africa are similarly highly developed. Well-coordinated systems of great and lesser deities, served by priests and initiated cult-followers and deriving their sanction from a complex philosophical world view, are characteristic, while a highly standardized method of divination, with its special practitioners, is also found in some portions of the region. In addition to its social significance, the ancestral cult forms an integral portion of the religious system; the belief in magic and the use of magic charms are found to as great an extent as anywhere in Africa. It is this forested belt which lies along the Guinea Coast that is the locale of the high cultures of Africa, cultures that in view of their complexity of structure are to be termed "primitive" only because of the technical definition of the word which makes it applicable to people who have non-written languages. Yet even in this connection it is to be remarked that in West Africa an independent discovery of writing was made, that is

A MARKET-WOMAN IN WHYDAH (DAHOMEY), WEST AFRICA

THE SAME WOMAN IN A GESTURE OF PLEASURABLE SURPRISE
(Note the similarity to New World Negro behavior.)

PLATE I

THE ALAKE OF ABEOKUTA (NIGERIA) AND SOME OF HIS WIVES AND CHILDREN

A DAHOMEAN CHIEF AND HIS YOUNGER WIVES

PLATE II
WEST AFRICAN POTENTATES

to say the syllabary system of the Vai, who are found in Liberia and Sierra Leone.

Moving eastward across the continent, the fifth culture area, denominated as the East Horn, may next be described. Its cultures show no such sharp differentiation from those of the areas·surrounding it as, for example, the East African area shows when compared to the Congo. Between East Africa and the East Horn there is merely a gradual shading, principally manifest in the matter of emphasis placed on those cultural traits which are the focal points of the interests of the people. Thus such an institution as the age classes of the Masai and Nandi who live east of Lake Victoria Nyanza is found in accentuated form among the Galla of the East Horn. Here, too, the sociological importance of cattle slowly gives way before the primacy of other animals, such as the horse and the camel. By some students it is thought that cultural and linguistic affinities between the people of the East Horn and the Hottentots of South Africa may be traced as a reflection of early historic contact. Certain aspects of the grammatical structures of the languages and of the cultures of the two areas—such as the tendency to allow women to care for cattle, the use of skin for clothing, and elements in the social organization—are not dissimilar. However, those who have given most time to studying this problem feel that these similarities are not such as to justify the conclusion that historic contact must have taken place, and the question is thus as yet an open one. The East Horn, like the Sudan, might almost of itself be called marginal, for it includes the southernmost point of the southward march of Islam in this portion of Africa. This involves a consequent interlarding of Mohammedan traits, such as the attitude toward the pig, with the indigenous culture patterns. The social organization is strongly patrilineal, this being perhaps another indication of the influence of Islam. The position of the iron-worker in the East Horn represents an intensification of his position among the tribes of the northern part of the East African cattle area. In all this region he is regarded as a pariah, but the organization of these craftsmen into guilds of outcaste folk reaches its highest point in the East Horn.

The Eastern Sudan, the sixth of the areas denoted on the map, comprises a portion of the southeastern Sahara and is peopled by a nomadic folk who have adapted their culture to the exigencies of life in the desert. Their whole life, as far as can be judged from the rather fragmentary reports that are available, seems to be organized about their livestock and the necessity of seeing that the beasts are properly fed and watered. This is at the base of their nomadic existence, since the camels, their most important animals, to be fed properly must be taken where grass is available, while the other beasts, such as cattle, sheep, and goats, whose primary need is water, are driven to the occasional watering places that are found during the long dry season. The religion of these peoples is Mohammedanism and, as would be expected, this deeply influences other phases of their culture. Thus the head of a family is the father, while the larger relationship groups are all patrilineal. The political head of a tribe is the sheikh, who dictates its movements. The milk of the camel is the principal means of subsistence, and, like the cow in the region to the southeast, the camel represents the principal constituent of the marriage gifts given for a wife. Unlike that in the East Horn region, the clothing is of cloth; the type of habitation is a skin tent which, as might be expected, is so constructed that it can easily be moved from place to place.

The Western Sudan is another of these marginal areas, for here the greatest battles between Mohammedanism and the aboriginal cultures have been waged. In the main the result has been that Mohammedanism has prevailed in name but that the patterns of the aboriginal cultures have been at the same time largely preserved. Thus, in the field of religion, the Mohammedanism that is practiced in the western Sudanese area, particularly in its southern portion, is far from the pure form that is found, let us say, in Arabia, for the ability of the African to assimilate different forms of religious beliefs and ceremonials makes it easy to add a series of beliefs such as Mohammedanism to pre-existing ideas of the supernatural. Hence in such regions as northern Nigeria or about Timbuctoo the religious as well as the other aspects of culture represent a mixture of pagan and Mohammedan forms, or, as in the region about Lake Chad, some localities are inhabited by peoples who have taken on Mohammedan patterns, while others nearby contain folk who have held to their pagan customs. The area, like its southern neighbor, West Africa, is remarkable for the great kingdoms it contained, the Hausa, the Fulbe, and the Bornu dynasties ruling over large populations for long periods of time. The structure of these kingdoms, and their histories, with their tales of internal dynastic feuds and external wars, which supplied the germs of disintegration that resulted in the eventual collapse of one after the other, are reminiscent of the political organization and history of Europe in the Middle Ages. The basic factors in the economic life of the people of this area are agriculture, herding, and trade. All of these are well developed, though here the herds do not hold the same place in the life and esteem of the people that they do in East Africa. As is the case with all great kingdoms, each dynasty reared architectural monuments to itself, and this area contains important examples of native architecture in such cities as Kano, Zaria, and Timbuctoo, to name but three of the best known. Artistically, the region is affiliated with the West African and Congo areas, and it is particularly among the tribes of the French Niger that some of the finest types of African art in wood-carving is done. The decoration of houses by means of designs on the walls in bas-relief is also a distinguishing mark of the art of this area, though this is confined to the urban centers.

This, then, comprises in essence a catalog of the cultures of Negro Africa. Though the Desert and Egyptian areas must be delimited on any map of African culture-types, they need be given but passing mention here. In the former a nomadic people is found, whose livelihood is

A Street in Kano, the Capital of the Ancient Hausa Empire, Nigeria

Hausa Man

PLATE III

gained from trade and from camel- and horse-breeding. They are Mohammedan in religion and, like their neighbors to the south, represent a marginal culture, though in this case the culture points more toward the European-like Mediterranean belt than toward the Negro West Coast. To differentiate the Egyptian area would require volumes, so complex is the culture and so detailed the work that has been done in the field of Egyptology. It is necessary only to state the fact to realize that in it is constituted an area distinct from the rest of Africa. The cultural exchange between Egypt and other portions of Africa, as has already been remarked, has been going on for untold ages. Just what forms this mutual influencing may have taken, both in Egypt and to the south, is at the same time one of the most interesting and one of the most neglected problems in the Africanist's repertoire.

African Institutions and the Psychology of the African. Thus far the traits which differentiate the regional cultures of Africa—the focal points which mark the African culture areas—have been emphasized to give a sense of the differences that distinguish these groups of cultures from each other. When the continent is considered as a whole, however, and when its cultures are contrasted with those of other continents, certain similarities between all the civilizations of Negro Africa become apparent. Though varying in detail from region to region and from people to people, these common culture-traits are nevertheless found in recognizable form throughout the African continent, so that, if to a description which stresses the differences between groups of cultures is added a list of the similarities which mark them all, a more adequate concept of the cultural achievements of the African Negro may be had than would otherwise be possible. This is the more important since these similarities in outward behavior represent those similarities of a psychological order which must underlie all manifestations of culture. And, as no trait of culture exists for a people unless it is validated by the psychological factor of the meaning it holds for that people, an understanding of the drives in Negro psychology that are reflected in widespread similarities in Negro cultures may be most readily attained by indicating those institutions of similar character which are found.

The psychology of the Africans, as perhaps of any other folk, is best seen in their folklore, and it is indubitably not chance alone, but congenial contact, that has given certain types of folktales the widespread distribution over the continent which they show. Generally speaking, African folktales may be divided into three categories. The first of these includes the animal stories, the second the historical tales, and the third the sacred myths. It is the first that is of the most interest and of which we possess the largest collections. In these animal tales, though the characters change from tribe to tribe and from area to area, the themes of the stories, the behavior of the characters, and the reason for telling them are the same wherever these have been reported. These animal tales are primarily told to children and by them, and they constitute the most important single factor in inculcating in the African youth the moral principles of his civilization.

The type of story represented by these tales is one which involves the behavior of a shrewd animal, who as trickster usually outwits his slower, duller, and more heavy-footed rivals. It is true that sharp dealing often characterizes the action, for the African does not regard astuteness of this type as immoral, but rather as an endowment for which the owner should be thankful. Certain of these tales are found everywhere; the Tar Baby has been recorded from a large portion of the continent, while the tale where the little trickster, challenging two huge beasts to a show of strength in a tug-of-war, arranges for a rope sufficiently long so that neither can see the other and both believe the small animal to be their adversary, with the result that the trickster becomes the ruler of the country, appears in almost every collection of African tales that has been published. Thus it is that the African child is taught that wisdom and perspicacity are better than strength. In similar manner he is taught that the old are wiser than the young, that malice often brings about destruction, that impetuousness is dangerous, that obedience is rewarded, and other moral precepts of like character.

This does not mean that these tales are not told by older persons, for often they amuse the elders as they instruct the children, while in some parts of Africa their humor makes them appropriate to be re-counted at funerals or at wakes, to amuse the dead. But it is the his-torical tales which recall the achievements of great men and the events of the past, and those other stories which, semi-mythological in character, give the reasons for the existence of natural phenomena of various kinds, rather than these children's tales, that occupy the time of the elders. Similarly, for grown-ups, the mythological tales which explain the uni-verse and the place of the gods, the ancestors, and man are of even greater importance. But such tales are for those who are versed in the ways of the gods and, if told at all to children, are given them in sim-plified form.

Another aspect of culture found throughout most of Negro Africa is the high development of political organization seen in definite, well-established systems of government. Usually the governmental head is a king or chief, with counselors and retainers to advise and aid him in governing and an army to enable him to maintain his position. The existence of settled dynasties which reigned over great empires has been mentioned in describing certain culture areas; how widely this tradition of political organization is spread over the continent may be realized when it is stated that not only were such kingdoms present in West Africa and the Sudan, but in the Congo and eastern and southeastern Africa as well, as the presence of the important states of Loango and Kongo and such kingdoms as the Balunda, the Baganda, the Banyoro, and the Zulu attests.

Associated with this political organization is a characteristic attitude of legalism. African justice is most often in the hands of a king or chief and his officers; the concept of a primitive society that envisages it as one in which a quarrel, flaring up quickly, results in immediate combat, or where the strong individual takes what he wishes from the weak by right of his strength, is utterly inapplicable to any African group. Here the administration of justice is marked by well-ordered court procedure, where cases are presented with arguments from plaintiff and defendant, where widely understood and accepted penalties exist for given types of crime, and where a system of appeals from lower to higher courts prevails. Among some tribes, furthermore, provision is made for plaintiff and defendant to be represented by those skilled in presentation of cases in court. In the presentation of these cases, another folkloristic form, the proverb, figures largely, for aphorisms are introduced to make a case—cited in much the same manner as lawyers in European tribunals cite volumes of earlier procedure to establish the necessary precedents. One of the widespread legal mechanisms found throughout Negro Africa is the use of the ordeal in trials, where the plaintiff, if judged guilty, may take oath as to his innocence and have the opportunity of giving ultimate proof by drinking poison or putting his hand in boiling oil or being bound and thrown into the water, to cite but a few of the ordeals that have wide distributions. The ordeal may also be used in ferreting out criminals where a suspicion of complicity of several persons in a crime may indicate these tests to be the best method of finding out which of the accused has actually committed it.

But it is not only in criminal cases that the African has recourse to legal action, for a large proportion of the time of the courts is spent in deciding civil suits. Many of these arise as a result of divorce. In all of Africa the prospective bridegroom is required to give valuable gifts and services to the father of his betrothed. As has been seen, in East Africa this takes the form of cattle; elsewhere other objects are presented. Should the wife be mistreated after marriage, she usually returns to her people. Among many tribes, if ill-treatment can be established, the gifts that have been given for her are not recoverable by the husband; court action, however, is often necessary to determine the question of fact. In other instances it is permitted to a husband to return an infertile wife to her parents, and in such a case the husband also claims restitution for the gifts and services that were given. A good example of how complex the ensuing litigation may become is seen if a case of the type commonly reported in East Africa is taken as an example. Here, the matter of the disposition of the offspring of animals originally given for a woman who has left her husband at once arises in the event of divorce, and a dispute often ensues that is not settled for several generations. In West Africa, the ownership of palm trees gives rise to lawsuits that are similarly involved. Throughout this area palm trees are of great value and are owned by the persons who plant them even though such persons may no longer themselves farm the land on which the trees grow. When some farm land which has been deserted is taken up and worked by another, there may be reluctance to allow the owner of the trees to have access to his property, whereupon a suit is brought to compel the occupant to permit the one who planted the trees to reach them.

As a result of their interest in court procedure, most African men have great proficiency in argumentation and in skillful presentation of a case before a judicial body. This argumentation is carried on with a wealth of allusion, characterized by the use of a vivid and often poetic imagery and the employment of many proverbs. The effect of this style of presentation is that it enables the African, in displaying his histrionic ability, to make his points much more strikingly and persuasively than a bare presentation of facts could possibly do.

One phase of the political life of Africa should be given special mention, since it reveals a deep-seated element in African psychology which is also to be seen in many other non-political aspects of everyday life. This is the love of indirection, the tendency to speak in terms of circumlocution and innuendo, the habit of the constant use of inference. It is perhaps best illustrated by the songs of derision which the African employs to make sport of an enemy whom he does not name but whose identity is known to all his listeners. The efficiency of African governments has been commented upon from the earliest days of European contact with African civilizations. Yet so subtly were the processes of government carried on—certainly in many parts of West Africa—that the burdens of taxation and of other demands of the central authority were psychologically lightened by the fact that those subject to them were presented with these demands in masked forms. One of the best examples of this is in the West African kingdom of Dahomey, where an annual census was taken and taxation decreed on the basis of it without those being counted having knowledge of the fact that this was the purpose behind the ingenious inquiries made ostensibly for an entirely different reason.

Another arresting phase of the psychology of the African is his deep religious bent, for African religion pervades all parts of African life. If a field is to be sown, a journey to be made; when a child is born or is to go through the rites of puberty; when a marriage is arranged or a new residence is to be taken up; if iron-working is to be done or hunting engaged in—the good will of the gods and ancestors must unfailingly be obtained so that the undertaking will be a successful one and so that no harm will come to the person concerned. The religious philosophy of the African includes a concept of the world as ruled by forces whose operation is predetermined; this is why the phenomenon of divination has been reported from almost every culture of Negro Africa that has been studied with any degree of thoroughness. Systems vary; divination is carried on by the use of seeds or bones, by consulting the will of the ancestors, by regarding the entrails of sacrificial animals, by water-gazing, and by other methods, but the basic concept which underlies the practice is the same and shows how the African regards his future as something that can be foreseen and directed if proper pre-cautions are taken to put him in accord with the will of higher powers. This implies an attitude toward the supernatural that would seem to follow from such practices, namely, that the gods and ancestors are not regarded as being very different from human beings in their make-up and motivations, so that, if one takes proper care, they are not too diffi-cult to get on with. This attitude is actually found. It is for this reason that religion is so immediate in the life of the individual African, it is the reason why the gods and other supernatural forces are regarded as beings whom it is possible to supplicate, to influence, and on occasion to whom effective hints may even be given. It makes for an ease in the attitude which the African has toward the supernatural forces of his universe; most importantly, it makes for a frame of mind that is far different from the state of fear which those who have casually studied the African have too often attributed to him.

This current opinion concerning the manner in which the African approaches the supernatural, namely, that he lives in trembling and goes through his devotions in a manner to make them a burden to him, has perhaps arisen from the dictum that "the religion of Africa is the fetish." There is but slight evidence that this is a true statement of the case, though there are no African peoples who do not use charms and among whom magic does not figure prominently as one element in their religious belief. The rôle of the charm, however, must be viewed in its proper perspective. Reports from all parts of the continent testify to the fact that the charm is something which, while perhaps deriving its power from more universal supernatural forces, is immediate in its action and special-ized in its applicability. The charm is indissolubly linked with magic and, in West Africa at least, magic is regarded as a gift of the Great Gods—as a power given to man to help him cope with the hostile forces of the universe. But whatever the psychology behind the use of "fetishes"—the word is one of the most ill-used in the vocabulary of African ethnologists, and one of the most confusing—the fact remains that these "fetishes," or, properly speaking, charms, are both good and bad; moreover, it is to be realized that for every evil charm there is a good one which can over-come its malignant force.

If the phrase "the fetish is the religion of Africa" is the one most often heard in discussions of African belief, the other phrase, "the ancestral cult is the basis of African religion," is encountered next most often. Indeed, the religions of East Africa, on the one hand, and of the Congo and West Africa, on the other, are ordinarily differentiated on this basis, it being said that the religion of the East Africans is ancestor worship, while that of the West Africans is the worship of the "fetish." Neither of these statements is more than a half-truth, for, like the belief in magic and the use of charms, the belief in the importance of the ancestral dead in influencing the lives of their descendants is basic to African thought. Yet it would not be putting the ancestral cult in its true light were it to be regarded as merely a religious institution. For, as will soon be

AN ASHANTI (GOLD COAST) DANCER UNDER POSSESSION

ANOTHER POSSESSED DANCER

PLATE IV

seen, it is as intimately associated with social organization and with the political regimentation of a people as with religion.

In the field of religion one striking similarity between the cultures of the continent is the method of worship. It is not too much to say that the essence of African ceremonialism is the dance; further, that religious dancing is invariably accompanied by singing and, among most African folk, by drum-rhythms. The drum is known over all of Africa, and, though the rhythms vary and the types of drums differ, the use of drums to call the gods, to speak to the gods, and to set the rhythms for those who dance for the gods is a widespread trait in the religious complex. The song plays an equally important rôle, and in many parts of Africa subsidiary instruments such as rattles are also of significance. Yet dancing, singing, and drumming, with varied emphasis on each of the three elements, form the basis of African ceremonialism.

The ancestral cult as a part of daily life as well as of religion may now be considered further. In essence, the ancestral cult is to be looked upon as the stabilizing force which makes for the existence and perpetuation of the sib organizations that are characteristic of African social life. To understand the sanctions the ancestral cult exerts, however, the broad lines of African social organization must be laid down. The fundamental unit in Africa, as in all human society, is the family, and throughout Africa the family consists of a father, his wife or wives—for polygyny is universal and is a question of economics rather than of morals—and their children. Unilateral descent is the rule, though whether on the side of the father or of the mother depends on the region and, in some areas, varies with the tribe that is under consideration. Yet African sib affiliation is not to be thought of as possessing so exclusive a character that it precludes the existence of close ties which bind a child to the parent to whom he is not socially related. In those societies where descent is on the side of the father, the mother's family is important to a child, while a member of a group who counts his descent through his mother's line feels a strong bond of relationship with his father's people. In addition to the fundamental relationship group, the "extended family" is usually afforded recognition, so that where patrilineal descent is the rule a group of brothers live together and their children feel closer relationship than might otherwise be the case, while in those tribes where maternal descent prevails the children of sisters regard themselves as forming a unit within the larger clan group. Over the basic family unit and the extended family, however, is the sib. And in the study of the sib, one of its most characteristic and widespread traits is found to be in the extensive power exerted by the sib-head over its members. This power derives from the ancestors. Among many tribes where this type of organization has been investigated, the sib is found to be totemic in character, though totemism has not been reported from all portions of the continent. The totem animal is often the oldest ancestor, and, as such, is the most powerful one. To him and his descendants is ascribed the wisdom that comes with continued existence in the world of the dead, and it is for this reason that the funeral is of such importance in African cultures. The power over their descendants that is exerted by ancestors, then, explains why their will is followed with such meticulous care and why the "ancestral cult" transcends considerations of a purely religious nature.

There are other traits which exhibit wide distribution over Africa. One of these is the relatively complicated form which economic life takes, often including the institution of the market as the nexus of economic activity. Money, in the form of caury shells or metal bars, was known to many tribes of Africans from the times of earliest contact with Europeans and, though not found in all portions of the continent, is characteristic of a sufficient proportion of the tribes so that its importance as a determinant of economic life must be recognized, for money makes it possible to accumulate and mobilize wealth and affords a basis for the kinds of business activity found in the more complex African societies. Similarly, the aesthetic drive of the African as manifested in the graphic and plastic arts exists everywhere on the continent, though it is true that those forms which have come to be regarded by Europeans as "African art" are localized in the Congo, the West African coastal region, and the southwestern Sudan. Yet wood-carving is also done in East and South Africa, while the asymmetrical paintings on the shields of the warlike Masai, Nandi, and other tribes of northern East Africa, and the pottery, carved calabashes, cloths, and basketry that are made by so many tribes testify to the desire of the Africans to embellish all types of objects which they utilize.

With this twofold approach to a summary of African cultures, taking into account the manner in which they are to be differentiated from each other and how they resemble one another, the results of the historic development of the Negro peoples are had. Through the centuries, the contacts resulting from war, trade, or mass migrations have not only made for cultural diversity, but have aided the spread of certain traits over large areas. Furthermore, as has been pointed out, with these outward manifestations of behavior have gone their inner psychological sanctions. To the extent that cultural differences are found among Africans, to that extent differences in the psychological approach to life on the part of the peoples who manifest these differences can be assumed. To the extent that there is similarity between African cultures, to that extent a similarity of psychological "set" may be postulated. What, then, of the Africans who were brought to the New World? What of the differences of Africa did they bring, which of these have they retained? What of the resemblances in the patterns of their life, as in the patterns of the lives of their aboriginal forbears in Africa?

III. How the Negroes Came to the New World

The Slave-Trade, Its Duration and Extensiveness. The introduction of the Negro into the New World followed shortly after the discovery of America by Columbus, for Negro slaves had been known in Europe a half-century before that time. In 1442 the Portuguese explorer Antem

Gonsalves, having seized some Moors at Rio de Oro, returned them in accordance with orders issued by Prince Henry the Navigator and was presented with ten Negro slaves and a quantity of gold. These he took to Lisbon, where he sold the slaves, with the result that numbers of his fellow countrymen fitted out expeditions which, in the course of the succeeding fifty years, brought many slaves to the Hispanic penninsula. By 1481 the Portuguese had built a fort on the Gold Coast, and, continuing along the shore of west and central Africa, they established themselves in Angola near the mouth of the Congo, which also soon became a center for the early slave-trade. The date when Negroes were first introduced into the Island of Hispaniola, the island which today is known as Santo Domingo and which contains Haiti, one of the three independent Negro political entities in the world, cannot be exactly determined. However, by 1502 Negroes were being employed in the mines of the island and were present in sufficient numbers so that further permission to import them was denied on the grounds that they "corrupted" the aboriginal Indian inhabitants. The demand for Negro workers was so insistent by 1517 that Charles the Great granted a patent to one of his favorites to import four thousand slaves annually into the islands of Hispaniola, Cuba, Jamaica, and Porto Rico. In 1562 the English entered the trade, in which they were later to become pre-eminent, the freebooter John Hawkins being the first Englishman to sense what profits might be realized from slaving. In the year named, he brought three hundred Negro slaves to Hispaniola.

Negroes were introduced into continental North America in relatively late times as compared to the date of their introduction into the New World as a whole, for it was not until 1619 when, as John Rolfe tells in his *Generall Historie* of John Smith, "about the last of August came in a Dutch man-of-Warre, that sold us twenty negars." It is to be noted that these first Negroes were brought to Virginia not as slaves but as bondsmen, being simply designated as "servants" in the court lists and falling under the same category as other indentured servants. In 1670, however, Virginia passed a law declaring that "all servants not being Christians, imported into this colony by ships" were slaves for life, following similar legislation elsewhere that decreed the issue of slave women must follow the status of their mothers. From 1619 until 1808, when slaving operations were forbidden by the Constitution, the importation of Africans into North America continued. At the same time, slaves were being brought to the islands of the Caribbean, to the Guianas, and to Brazil, where their labor made their masters wealthy from the sale of the sugar, tobacco, coffee, indigo, and cotton grown on the plantations which they worked.

The numbers of slaves exported from Africa and imported into the various portions of the New World during the period of the slave-trade was undoubtedly very large. Bryan Edwards, whose history of the West Indies is one of the classics of the period, estimated that seventy-four thousand slaves were annually exported from Africa in the decade between 1790 and 1800. E. D. Morel (1920, p. 19), after investigating the most reliable sources, gives the following figures: From 1666 to 1766, the British alone imported three million slaves into British, French, and Spanish colonies. From 1680 to 1786, two million one hundred and thirty thousand were imported to the British colonies in America, Jamaica absorbing six hundred and ten thousand individuals; from 1716 to 1756, seventy thousand slaves per annum were imported into the American colonies, a total of three million five hundred thousand; from 1752 to 1762, Jamaica imported seventy-one thousand, one hundred and fifteen; from 1759 to 1762 the small island of Guadeloupe imported forty thousand slaves; between 1776 and 1800, an average of seventy thousand per annum were imported into all of the American colonies, making a total of one million eight hundred and fifty thousand. Slavery continued in the New World until well after the middle of the nineteenth century. Though the traffic was outlawed at the source, and, as has been stated, was technically illegal in the United States after 1808, it has been estimated that over two and a half million slaves were landed in this country between the years 1808 and 1860.

The guesses which have been made concerning the total number of individuals affected by the institution of slavery in the New World vary fantastically and often differ by millions. It has been said, for example, that for every slave landed in America and the West Indies five or six individuals succumbed to the hardships of the voyage and as many more died or were killed in Africa. Though this is probably an exaggeration, there is no doubt that the conditions under which the slaves were kept in the "factories" on the West African coast while awaiting shipment and the manner in which the slaves were packed into the vessels for the "middle passage" to the New World caused the death of at least 50 to 60 per cent of those who eventually reached their new home. One factor that has been largely overlooked, but which made for great destruction of life among the slaves, was the necessity of taking the slaves to the ships through the West African surf. In the days of slaving there were no piers to which the boats might tie up, so that surf-boats had to be employed. In manoeuvering these vessels through the two or three lines of great rollers that had to be navigated, they often capsized, and the shackled slaves invariably drowned. That this was not an exceptional occurrence is testified by the fact that almost every contemporary account of slaving operations contains descriptions of these tragedies. Even when safely on board ship the chance of arriving in the New World alive was not too great. Diagrams showing how slaves were packed into the holds of the ships speak volumes concerning the manner in which the slaves existed during the crossing, and an impressive mortality must have resulted from overcrowding of this character.

It is to be expected that slavery left its marks on the peoples of Africa themselves, though this is a question which has not been investigated to any great degree. Even today, in the city of Abomey, the capital of the kingdom of Dahomey in the days of its autonomy, when the rituals of the cult for the royal dead are being performed at the palace of the kings, special sacrifices are given to the souls of those ancestors who were sent away. Yet not only members of the royal courts, but common people in West Africa speak the name of the Portuguese when slaving is mentioned. It has been recorded how Africans, when told that the descendants of Negroes taken to the New World are not only alive and free but, in some cases, prosperous, have exclaimed, "Those are people of my family!" It can thus be seen how the slave-trade set its psychological mark on Africa no less than it took its toll of social demoralization and loss of life.

The Slave Markets of the Western Hemisphere. The slaves were distributed more widely in the New World than is commonly held to be the case. In addition to those taken to North America and the West Indies, they were imported into Brazil in great numbers. The ports of the Guianas, particularly Georgetown and Paramaribo, were the destination of many slave ships. Venezuela and other South American countries also found use for Negro slaves, while Negroes were and are found in smaller numbers throughout Central America and along the eastern coast of Mexico. Indeed, among the more obscure groups of Negroes found today are the so-called "black Caribs" of Yucatan, the descendants of West Indian Negroes and Indians who were exiled there because in the islands they revolted against their British masters, while in a neighboring region of Mexico live a group of people called Zamboes, mixtures between the indigenous Indians and the Negroes who were sold there.

Many more slave ships from Africa made for West Indian ports than for the ports of continental North America. Elizabeth Donnan, who has analyzed the manifests of slave ships that discharged their cargoes at the ports of New York, New Jersey, and New England, shows that for the period between 1715 and 1765 only 930 out of the 4551 slaves landed were brought directly from Africa. Similarly, as many slaves were brought from West Indian ports to Charleston, the most prominent southern port for slaving operations, as were landed directly from Africa. The importance of this inter-island slave-traffic, and the traffic between the islands and North America and the Guianas, is something that has been largely overlooked in the study of the history of Negro slavery. It is, however, of the highest significance, principally because it indicates how thorough a mixture of aboriginal types took place in the New World. This fact thus forms the basis for the hypothesis that Negroes who today inhabit the West Indies, the United States, and the Guianas, at least, are derived from the same ancestral types.

The Sources of Slaves in Africa. The question of the African origin of the slaves is one the answer to which has been taken more for granted than as a subject for investigation. And, as so often happens when a question, to which the traditional answer has been uncritically repeated, is subjected anew to scientific analysis, recent study has shown the accepted belief not to have the validity it is commonly assumed to possess. The traditional position holds that the slaves came from diverse parts of Africa —not only Guinea but Madagascar is often mentioned, and East Africa and Morocco and the Barbary Coast, while the name of the Congo appears more prominently than that of any other region. Yet the writers of the eighteenth and early nineteenth centuries who had occasion to query their own slaves and the slaves of their friends concerning their African tribal origins report affiliations which can be traced to but two of these regions, for the tribal names that recur again and again are those of the peoples who inhabit the region which has been designated as the West African subregion of the Congo area, and the northwestern portion of the Congo area itself.

The material contained in a little-known work by C. G. A. Ollendorp, a German missionary who was sent as inspector of missions in the Virgin Islands, may be cited as a case in point. In his two-volume report, published in 1777, he devotes almost two hundred pages to discussing the problem of the tribal origins of the slaves; and the tribal designations he gives are those of peoples who inhabit the region from the Gambia river to the mouth of the Niger. The study of tribal names of the slaves in Jamaica as recorded by Bryan Edwards shows the same facts, while if one investigates the seventeenth- and eighteenth-century writings of the captains of slaving vessels who described their operations—John Barbot, William Bosman, William Snelgrave, William Smith, and others—the only portion of the African coast they mention is Guinea. Even the Portuguese, whose long possession of the Loango area and what had been the Kingdom of Kongo would seem to argue a priori that the slaves sold by them came principally from the Congo, seem on further investigation to have carried on their most intensive slaving operations in the Gold Coast, in the region about the mouth of the Niger, and in Dahomey.

What, then, of the slave caravans so often mentioned, caravans which, coming from great distances inland, toiled for months to reach the coast? These "coffles," as they were called, did, indeed, take a long time to reach the coast, but so slow was the pace at which they moved and so lengthy were the pauses between marches that in the one definite historic account of the movements of such a coffle that is available, that of Mungo Park (1806), we learn that his trip, which lasted over a period of many months, covered a distance of only five hundred miles.

The fact is frequently ignored that Africa did not supply only the New World with slaves. Slaves captured in the interior of West Africa or in the eastern part of the continent were much more likely to be taken to the native states of North Africa, to Egypt, or to Arabia than to be brought by way of the dangerous route overland to the West Coast and the slave-ships or to be transported by sea on the long journey around the Cape of Good Hope. Moreover, that New World slaves could easily have had a preponderantly West African provenience would be logical were nothing more than the density of population in West Africa taken into account. The seat of the most complex Negro cultures of the continent, it is also the region of the greatest concentration of Negroes. Today cities of considerable size exist in this area, some of them upwards of one hundred thousand in population, one even exceeding a quarter of a million souls. In addition, West Africa is dotted with villages and towns, and the bush has long ago given way to the farms necessary to provide subsistence for a population of this size. The fact that the area from which the African slaves exported to the New World were derived was a relatively restricted one is significant for an understanding of the processes of acculturation to which the New World Negroes were subjected in their slave environment. For it must again be repeated, and must be kept in mind for future reference, that the cultures of this area were and are similar in their basic configurations and that the languages of the people who live there, though perhaps mutually unintelligible, are organized in accordance with the same general principles of phonetics, grammar, and idiom.

Types of Africans Sold into Slavery. A further point, which bears upon the validity of another commonly accepted belief concerning New World Negroes, must also be raised. This relates to the social classes in Africa from which the slaves were drawn. It is generally held that those who were sold into slavery were an inferior group, the underlying assumption being that had this not been the case they would not have been captured and sold to the dealers. The ramifications of this belief are widespread. Thus, it is often verbally maintained, if not actually stated in print, that this is the reason for the relatively low standing that American Negroes have made in intelligence tests. For, it is asked, is this result not to be expected in the light of the fact that the ancestors of these Negroes were recruited from among the least able elements of the African population? What, then, is to be expected of their descendants, even though this Negro stock may have been mixed with white strains possessing some degree of ability?

Investigation, however, shows this belief to be as untenable as is its companion hypothesis that large numbers of slaves were derived from all portions of Africa. The fact of the matter is that the social classes from which the slaves were drawn represented all strata of African society. This is readily understandable if the socio-political organization of the West African kingdoms is taken into account and is substantiated not only by oral tradition, but by the writings of those who were actually engaged in the slave-traffic.

There were three ways in which a person might become a slave, and of these three only one might conceivably have had the selective effect that is usually taken for granted, though even this cannot be proved. The principal manner in which slaves were obtained was through warfare, although the term "warfare" may be properly used in this connection only if its real meaning is allowed great elasticity, for these "wars" were nothing more than traditionally sanctioned man-hunts. Thus, in the kingdom of Dahomey, an annual "war" was the rule. Of religio-economic motivation, its actual purpose was to provide slaves for the human sacrifices necessary in the rituals of the ancestral cult, to work the plantations of the king and his nobles, and to satisfy the demands of European slave-dealers. This last, from the point of view of the economy of the native kingdom, was fully as important as the other two, since the sale of slaves constituted the principal source of funds which could be used to obtain the European goods, arms, and gunpowder held so desirable by the natives. The same was true in the kingdom of Benin to the east and in the Gold Coast to the west. The point to be stressed is that in these wars all members of the "enemy" people were fair game, whether they were men, women, or children, and whatever rank or station they occupied; and any citizen, once captured, became a slave.

In this connection it must be remarked that the institution of slavery was itself widespread in Africa. Not only was the type of slavery found that is conventionally recognized as prevailing on the continent—that is, household-slavery, where the slave was to all intents and purposes a member of his owner's family—but in addition there was plantation-slavery such as is ordinarily identified only with the New World. In those regions where stable dynasties ruled large populations, kings and nobles possessed plantations each of which comprised a large area, and these were worked by slaves under the control of overseers. It is not unlikely that one of the reasons why Negroes accepted New World slavery with as much docility as they did is because slavery was the one institution in their new environment with which they were familiar from experience in Africa, and the existence of which they had always taken as an accepted fact.

The majority of the slaves, then, were those captured in "wars," or slave-raids. These "wars" did not take place far from the seacoast as distances go in the great African continent; thus the people of Benin preyed on the eastern Nigerian folk; the Dahomeans warred with the Yoruban Nago of western Nigeria or with the Ewe peoples of Togoland; while the Gold Coast Ashanti and Fanti tribesmen turned to the natives of coastal Togoland and to the people of the eastern portion of the Ivory Coast for their human supplies. In addition to this organized foraging, moreover, it was not unusual for an unprotected person, a traveler or a child who had strayed from home, to be kidnaped and sold to the slave-dealers. It is striking how many tales are told in West Africa today which make the point that a child should not be left alone in the house, or, if he is sent on an errand, should be accompanied by an older child or an adult. That such tales derive from slaving times, when a child left alone was liable to be kidnaped, is evident, for West African natives, when asked why this type of tale is so prominent in their folklore, include this among their reasons.

The second method of enslaving Africans owed its inception and existence to the functioning of the inner political organization of the West African states. Descent in the reigning houses was from father to son, or from the ruler to his sister's son. In both forms of succession, there was competition for the office; in the latter case, sons of the king's sisters contested for the succession. It was, however, in the dynasties where paternal descent obtained that competition was particularly keen. Because polygyny was the rule, sons of a king by different mothers intrigued against each other or waged open warfare once the royal office was vacant. Even in such a highly stable kingdom as Dahomey, where the crown prince was named long before the death of the king and enjoyed well-recognized prerogatives, the demise of the ruler often brought about plots and uprisings in favor of other sons. Here, except in one instance, these uprisings were put down; in the case of the other kingdoms they were occasionally more successful. As far as the point being considered here is concerned, however, the result was the same. The defeated contender was either executed or sold into slavery; in either case, the victor rid himself of possible future malcontents—the family of the unsuccessful one, as well as all his sympathizers and their families—by the convenient and profitable method always at hand, the European slave-dealer.

What is the significance of this in terms of the stuff of which the ancestors of New World Negroes were made? It means that, in all probability, as proportionately great or greater a number of upper-class folk were caught in the net of New World slavery as commoners. For it must be understood that when a prince, his followers, and their families were sold into slavery many priests, many chiefs, many women and children of high rank, and, what is of the greatest significance, many diviners who were among the most carefully trained and highly educated persons in the West African communities were also sold away. It will be seen when African survivals in the New World are discussed how prominently African religious practices figure. It is not too much to suppose that this has been caused by the influence of the large number of priests who were deported. For priests were sold not only because they opposed the accession of a king. After an autochthonous people had been overpowered by an invading native dynasty, the priests were invariably the most intransigent among the conquered. Calling on their indignant gods, they could be counted on to create a frame of mind among their followers that made for unrest in the newly occupied territory. Many native cults were consequently suppressed when their priests were sold into slavery; a notable example of this is the river-cult in Dahomey which, found today in portions of the New World, has been so completely lost to the Dahomeans that they believe the gods of the river are troubling the country because no one is available to impart the knowledge of how these deities are to be placated.

The only group sold into slavery which might have been constituted by the operation of a selective process that took the least desirable element in the West African populations to the New World was the group recruited from those convicted of crime. However, the West African definition of crime is not such as to encourage an hypothesis that even these criminals were any less well endowed than the general population. Thus a man who was detected in an intrigue with a wife of his ruler, if not executed, was sold into slavery as a criminal, just as though he had been a murderer or a thief, and slavery as a result of debt is also known to have occurred.

It is therefore to be seen that the Negro peoples of the New World have not only been derived from a relatively more restricted area of Africa than is ordinarily thought to be the case, but that they represent a cross-section of the total population which, if it represents any weighting, is most likely weighted toward the upper end of the scale. With this historical and sociological background, a consideration of the distribution of the Negroes in the New World at the present time and a description of the cultural behavior they manifest may next be undertaken.

IV. Negro Cultures of the New World

The Essential Unity of New World Negro Cultures and the Differences That Are to Be Seen among Them. It is not possible to group New World Negro cultures by culture areas in the manner in which the indigenous civilizations of Africa have been classified. One reason for this, as already suggested, is that all New World Negro cultures derive from a common base; another is that all of them include at least some non-African cultural traits, and some of them are almost entirely non-African in character. Since these cultures were not established as a result of free action of the carriers, such as happens in the case of voluntary mass migration, but rather in the face of adverse circumstances of the most discouraging character, New World Negro cultures, to the extent that they exhibit any individuality, are recognizable because of the vitality their aboriginal characteristics have manifested despite severe repression. For, as is well known, the Africans brought to the Western Hemisphere were not only not encouraged to hold to their aboriginal beliefs, traditions, or modes of behavior, but were compelled to relinquish many of their own practices. In making any classification, moreover, it must be borne in mind that the majority of New World Negro cultures as such have been subjected to but little study. Only two of them have been described in the detail which marks the manner in which ethnologists have described African or Indian or Polynesian civilizations. This is due partially to the fact that ethnologists have been intent on studying "pure" civilizations and partially to the tradition that Africanisms have disappeared in the New World under contact with European customs, leaving only cultural fragments which do not have sufficient importance to repay investigation.

Yet, in spite of these difficulties, it is possible at the present time to make three divisions of New World Negro civilizations. They are based largely on the names of deities which can be traced to definite West African regions. The Negroes of Brazil and of Cuba have preserved in their religion the gods of the Yoruban peoples of Nigeria; in addition, the Muslem sect of the Male, probably derived from Senegal, is also present in Brazil. In the French islands of the West Indies and especially in Haiti, as well as among the Negroes of Louisiana who were brought from Haiti by the planters who fled the slave rebellion which occurred there at the end of the eighteenth century, the culture seems to partake largely of Dahomean elements. In the British islands of the Caribbean, particularly Jamaica and the Bahamas, in British Guiana, and in earlier times along the eastern seaboard of the United States, notably in the Gulla Islands and Virginia, the culture is largely of Gold Coast origin. Finally, in Dutch Guiana, where the revolted slaves were able to escape into the isolation of the South American bush, all three strands may be discerned, though the Dahomean and Gold Coast influences would seem to be more prevalent than those of Yoruban origin. In all these regions, however, some Congo elements may be found, though not as many as might be expected when the historical importance of the slave-trade from Loango is taken into consideration.

The Distribution and Characteristics of New World Negro Peoples and Cultures in South America, the West Indies, and the United States. In describing these New World Negro cultures it may be well to begin at the southernmost point and, progressing northward, obtain some concept of the extent to which the aboriginal heritage of the slaves has been retained and the manner in which this heritage has been reincorporated into their present patterns of cultural behavior.

The Negroes of Brazil are concentrated largely in the region of Bahia and it is only here that Negro customs have been studied to any extent. Testimony is given as to the African character of the life of a large portion of the Brazilian Negroes, however, by one writer, Sir H. H. Johnston (1910), who significantly enough had had the widest experience in Africa itself.

> Of course in general mode of life, social customs, etc., the educated coloured people of Brazil are scarcely distinguishable from the Portuguese middle or upper classes, according to their means and social status. The peasants, however, away from the towns, lead a more African existence, and except that the house or hut may be a little superior to the average Negro home in Africa, manners and customs in domesticity are very little changed by the standard of the Gold Coast or Dahome—not a very low standard, by the by. (p. 105)

Other than this and some studies of folklore which indicate how many African elements are present in the tales told by the Brazilian Negroes, the reports which have been made concerning their customs describe their religious life. These descriptions of the so-called "fetish-cult" leave no doubt as to its essentially Yoruban character. The gods of this cult are called *Olorum* or *Olorung*. One of those who has written on it, Father Ignace, lists fifteen Yoruban deities who are worshiped in the same manner and under the same names as in West Africa, and whose functions in Brazil are identical with those of their Nigerian counterparts. Thus *Sango* is the god of thunder in both places; *Ogun,* the god of war; *Osun-Maure* the rainbow, and *Ye-man-je* the goddess of the sea, to name but four. *Ifa,* the divining cult of the Yorubans and Dahomeans of West Africa is worshiped in Brazil, and the term *babalao,* which is applied to the Yoruban diviners, appears in Brazil as the designation of priests who at least retain the ability of their African counterparts to understand the permutations and combinations of the seeds they manipulate so as to be termed "mathematicians" by Father Ignace. In Brazil, as in West Africa, each divinity has a color sacred to it, and each divinity is worshiped at a cult-center, where his devotees are organized into a cult-group. Finally, the use of magic charms to prevent ill-luck or to carry evil to an enemy is such as to demonstrate further how closely analogous to African practices are these phases of religious life. Whether an investigation of other than religious aspects of Brazilian Negro behavior would reveal as close correspondences to African culture patterns cannot be said. The quotation already cited from the work of Sir Harry Johnston, however, leads to the belief that this may well be found to be the case if future investigations are made.

As might be expected, the extent to which the Negro cultures of the New World manifest a peculiar African quality differs from region to region in accordance with the degree of freedom from interference that was enjoyed by the Negroes. And, because in Dutch Guiana the Bush Negroes were able to muster sufficient forces to revolt and thus to attain complete freedom, their culture is the most African that exists in the Western Hemisphere. Indeed, it is more than this, for it has retained Africanisms of the period of the slave-trade, so that today in the South American forests an old African civilization is to be seen. How did this come about? The answer must be looked for in the history of their combats with their masters and in their extreme isolation.

The Bush Negroes are the descendants of the slaves who were brought to work the Guiana plantations, which, in the seventeenth and eighteenth centuries, were among the richest in the world. These plantations were mainly located in the coastal region and along the lower Suriname river, but behind them lay the tropical jungle, inhabited only by a few Indian tribes. Under the leadership of men of considerable military ability, the slaves who ran away from the plantations organized and began systematic raids on the outlying coastal settlements, taking the slaves rescued from servitude into the bush and incorporating them into their own groups. The Indians who inhabited the region were driven out, and today they rarely come in contact with these Negroes. Little by little, the Negroes penetrated farther up the rivers, so that by the early part of the eighteenth century they were well established there. A treaty of peace was signed between them and the Dutch that has been faithfully observed ever since, by the terms of which they live under nominal Dutch control. Except for those Bush Negroes who run lumber rafts to the city of Paramaribo to sell, and who use the proceeds to buy cloths and iron pots and ornaments, they have extremely infrequent contacts with Europeans; indeed, in the case of the women and most of the younger people, it may be said that almost none of these have ever seen a white person.

This means that the cultural contacts that have taken place in West Africa during the last two centuries have exerted no influence in the Guiana bush; similarly the influences which have brought about changes in African cultures—influences such as increasing contact with Europeans —have not been operative in South America. In accordance with the cultural conservatism that is a concomitant of isolation, these Negroes, therefore, have the same cultural patterns that marked the life of their ancestors in Africa, so that the civilization of the Guiana Negroes reflects more faithfully than any other the modes of life as lived in Africa three

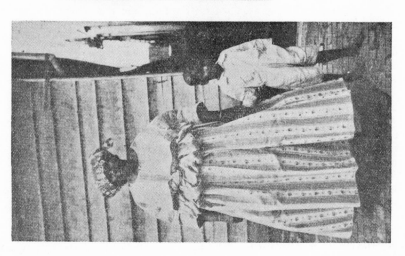

LEFT—A PARAMARIBO (DUTCH GUIANA) WOMAN AND HER GRANDCHILD
(The child is of Negro-Chinese parentage.)

ABOVE—"YARD" OF A NEGRO COMPOUND IN PARAMARIBO

PLATE V

centuries ago. Needless to say, such a people constitutes the key point in the "laboratory experiment" which is being considered here, since the African words in their language, place-names, sib designations, and customs of various sorts, give the most direct evidence available as to the African areas from which they derive.

There are three tribes of Bush Negroes, and their language is a mixture of African, Portuguese, Dutch, and English words, pronounced in accordance with the rules of West African phonetics and organized grammatically into the structure of their ancestral languages. These tribes manifest the Gold Coast type of social organization, descent and membership in the clan being on the maternal side, the relationship between father and children being of a spiritual order, children inheriting their souls from their fathers. In similar fashion, the entire Gold Coast system of "day names" is found unchanged in Suriname. These names, given according to the day of the week on which the owner was born, are regarded here, as in West Africa, as having the most intimate connection with the souls of the individuals who bear them. The West African market is not found, for the villages are too small and scattered too widely up and down the river to permit of this kind of economic interchange. The pattern of agriculture, however, which constitutes the economic foundation of Bush Negro civilization is characteristically West African, the men breaking the ground for their farms and the women doing the planting and caring for the growing crops.

The political organization of West Africa has likewise been preserved, though in the Suriname bush the overwhelming power of the king that characterized the West African empires has been diluted by means of a decentralized system which places power in the hands of sib and village chiefs, and only through them in the hands of the tribal head. This, however, is a direct consequence of the experience of slavery. The Bush Negro is proud of having regained his freedom, and this is why the institution of slavery is not present in the Suriname bush. This also explains the reason why the culture of the Bush Negroes manifests a greater degree of democratic control than is now found or probably ever existed in the ancestral lands.

The religious life of the Bush Negroes is entirely African. *Nyankompon,* or *Nyame,* the Great God of the Fanti-Ashanti peoples, *Asaase,* the Earth Mother, *Osai Tando,* the ancient name for the sacred Tano river, *Opete,* the vulture, and other deities of the Gold Coast are found there. The Dahomean gods named *Legba, Gedeonsu, Afrikete, Aisa, Aido Hwedo,* and others are worshiped in the same manner and for the same reasons as in West Africa, while the serpent cult is found in the worship of the *Dagowe, Vodun,* and other snakes in the Suriname bush. The Loango deities *Zambi* and *Ma Bumba* are also known. The complex of worship by dance and song, with the drums representing the voice of the gods themselves, obtains in full force among the Bush Negroes. Furthermore, these drums are given recognizably African names, and the most important one, the *apinti,* is also called in the sacred language of the Kromanti men's society, *asante kogbwa,* "the Ashanti drum." As in portions of West Africa, twins are held sacred and are called by the Dahomean word *hohobi,* while the palm fronds that stretch across the path leading to a village or are found in front of a house where illness or death has occurred, to "disinfect" it spiritually and to prevent evil spirits or those who would enter with evil intentions from working their malice, are given the Dahomean name of *azang.* Social dances as well as religious ones are of the West African type and some of these found in Suriname can be identified as those which are no longer danced but are only traditionally remembered in West Africa. More important, the world-view of the Bush Negroes is that of their African forbears. The first element in this is the conception of the world as having been created by the Great Gods who govern it today; next, the rôle of the ancestors is held to maintain the equilibrium between man and the forces of the supernatural; while, finally, there is the belief in magic, which thrives in Guiana as it does wherever Negro cultures are found and is regarded in true West African fashion as having been given by the Great Gods to man to help him against the malignant forces of nature and of the universe.

The Bush Negro songs which have been collected show strong retention of African melodic line and rhythm, while other aspects of the aesthetic life of these people demonstrate how faithfully they have held to their aboriginal heritage. The region from which they came in West Africa is the seat of the high arts, and, though they have lost the techniques of brass- and iron-working and weaving, they have transmuted the West African wood-carving styles so that their art in this medium, though unique in the manner of its execution, is still recognizably affiliated with the sources from which it has sprung. In the villages of the Bush Negroes the artist holds an enviable position, and the good carver is sought after in marriage and often wins the most desirable young woman for his wife. This is because Suriname wood-carving is a part of all phases of life. The utensils of a woman—her food-stirring paddle, her fire fan, her clothes beater, the tray on which she carries rice and cassava from the fields, the boat in which she travels and the paddles she and her husband use to propel it, the doorway of her house—are all embellished with the intricate ribbon-like decorative designs that the Bush Negro artists have evolved. More than this, these designs, which on analysis are seen to be highly stylized concepts of human and animal figures, often in sexual congress, are held by the operation of principles of sympathetic magic to contribute to the fertility of the woman who uses them. Thus the artist who can carve these symbols most beautifully is believed to possess a power whose operation not only affords aesthetic pleasure but is associated with supernatural manifestations. Africanisms are present not alone in music and carving, but in folklore as well. The use of the proverb in everyday life and in the native courts is as prevalent here as anywhere in West Africa. Riddles are found, and innumerable folktales told which deal with the exploits of the Gold Coast trickster, the spider *Anansi,* and with men and women of the early days, and with the gods. The game of *wari,* a form of draughts common to numerous African cultures, is played in Suriname. That not only the game but its social setting has been preserved is evidenced by the fact, to take one example, that as in West Africa it is never played at night for fear that this will bring on the death of the player when the ghosts of the dead take part in the game.

Guiana holds further importance for the study of Negro peoples and cultures and the manner in which they throw light on larger problems of acculturation because of the fact that a control group exists in the same colony. These are the Negroes whose forbears, never escaping from slavery, have been in contact with the whites since the earliest days of the colony and who have therefore absorbed European culture to a much greater extent than the Negroes of the interior. This does not mean that the coastal Negroes have not retained much of aboriginal African custom. Their language exhibits a difference from that of the Bush Negroes which is one of degree rather than kind. Thus in *taki-taki,* as this coastal Negro English is called, there are few African words, fewer words of Portuguese derivation, and many more taken from Dutch and English. Yet the phonetic system of *taki-taki* retains many Africanisms, while the grammatical structure is almost as African as is that of the language of the Bush Negroes. In material culture, however, the difference is at once immediate. The town Negroes wear European dress instead of the loin cloths, tunics, or cloths thrown over the shoulder that are worn in the bush. Indeed, the dress of the women of Paramaribo is famous for its picturesqueness, for it preserves the voluminous skirts known in Europe in the late eighteenth and early portion of the nineteenth centuries. Similarly, the coastal Negroes lived in wooden houses, not in huts of palm and thatch, and the occupations are those of any group of people in a European town, with the single exception of the market, which retains a flavor that is distinctly African.

The inner life of the coastal Negroes, however, resembles that of the interior to a far greater degree than appears on the surface. Though many, perhaps a majority, are affiliated with the Christian denominations found in the colony, nevertheless a very considerable number remain who engage in the worship of the African spirits—called *winti* in the coastal strip—and attendance at one of these "*winti* plays," as they are called, is sufficient to convince the student that the cult of these spirits is as living as it is in the bush. Though the organization of the gods is not as clear in the minds of many of the coastal folk as it is in the bush, the system by which these gods are transmitted to succeeding generations, the manner of their worship, the drum-rhythms by which they are summoned, and the songs that are sung to them are well understood, though these matters are known in detail only by the considerable number of *winti* priests who specialize in directing this type of worship. The use of magic flourishes in the town and, as elsewhere, operates in accordance with a well-recognized set of principles. The social organization of the town Negroes, though influenced by European patterns and prevailing economic conditions, has retained elements that are distinctly African. Here, as in the bush, the soul of a child is inherited from its father, and with the soul goes the food tabu, violation of which is believed to bring on leprosy. Though actual matrilineal descent has been set aside by the patrilineal character of the dominant Dutch culture, in inner family relationships the importance of the female members and their brothers as those who exert the essential stabilizing force shows how strongly in attitude, if not in outward form, matriliny has persisted. The folklore of the town Negroes is as rich in all its forms as that of the bush, and their amusements include dances and games that are present in Africa.

In the adjoining colony of British Guiana a Negro culture of similar African tone exists. A study of the speech of the British Guiana Negroes shows many correspondences with that of the Negro inhabitants of Dutch Guiana, both in town and bush. Relatively nothing concerning the inner life of these British Guiana Negroes has been recorded, and it is not known to what extent they worship in recognizable form the gods of their ancestors. Hints here and there would seem to indicate that this worship is far from extinct, and certainly magic—the use of charms, potions, and other objects to cure or harm—flourishes here. The British Guiana Negroes tell many African folktales, while proverbs and riddles are also found in great numbers. As in Suriname, the Gold Coast spider *Anansi* gives his name to all tales. A final point of information concerns the game of *wari* which has been recorded in British Guiana, where it is played with the same rules and in the same fashion as in West Africa and Dutch Guiana.

Thus in those parts of South America where Negroes were imported in large numbers, their socialized behavior patterns mark them off from the other peoples, both aboriginal and those derived from Europe and elsewhere, among whom they live.

Trinidad is the island of the Antillean group which lies closest to South America; north of it is Barbados, while the strands of the Windward and Leeward Islands continue in almost a straight line. Except for Martinique and Guadeloupe, which are French, all these islands are British possessions, though in earlier days many of them were under French control, and French influence is manifest in the *patois* spoken by the Negro inhabitants of many of them. Thus, in the back country of Trinidad a Negro-French dialect is heard, while on such islands as Dominica, St. Lucia, and St. Christopher this dialect constitutes the prevailing mode of speech among the Negroes.

Few accounts concerning the life of the Negroes who inhabit these islands are available; only in the case of their folklore and speech, which the recent work of Dr. Elsie Clews Parsons has shown to have numerous traits in common with the lore and linguistics of the Guianas, the northern islands, North America, and West Africa, is satisfactory information available. In Trinidad, for example, aboriginal religious practices undoubtedly exist in some form, though their existence can only be inferred from casual quotations, such as the following, which appeared in the *Trinidad Guardian* for September 7, 1929:

> For seven nights the town of St. Joseph will be *en fete*. A Shan-
> goo sect is affording the amusement. . . . The tambours send forth
> their blatant sounds in the still air, accompanied by dancing and
> barbarous intonations of "Way hee, Way hee, Alladoe. . . .!"

Here two references to Africanisms are found; Shango is the Yoruban god of thunder, while Allada, the name of a city in Dahomey, is also the designation of a member of the thunder pantheon of the Suriname Negroes as well.

The island of Barbados has been an English possession since the earliest days of its settlement, and here the British character imparted to the life of the people, whether Negro or white, is striking. Bridgetown, the capital and port, is the counterpart of an English city. Nevertheless, on going ashore from the ships that lie at anchor some distance off the break-water, it is possible to see Negroes on the wharf playing the same West African game of *wari* that has been mentioned as being present in British and Dutch Guiana. Similarly, even a casual visitor to Barbados may learn of the yam festival that is celebrated at Christmas, a festival which in the display of colored cloths, in the wrestling bouts that are held, and in the fact that a certain individual must take the first yams which are then "given back" to the field, shows a series of traits which link it with the yam festivals that have been reported from Nigeria. Anansi stories are told on the island and these are "cut" in typical African fashion with songs, thus resembling, both in content and in the manner of the telling, the tales told in Suriname and British Guiana. The funeral practices of the Guianas and of West Africa are similarly observed in Barbados, a wake held eight days after death, when *wari* and other games are played, being an outstanding element in the rites of death. Both social and religious dances of an African character are danced by the Barbadian Negroes, and the inquirer may hear the names of dances that he has heard in Guiana and West Africa. To what extent these are surface indications of a more deep-seated series of Africanisms which are present in the inner life of the culture cannot be said, but, when in addition to the facts cited it is discovered that magic flourishes among the Negroes, that water or rum is poured on the ground as a libation before dances begin, that the ant-hill is feared, or that the names of drums are African, it would seem that even in Anglicized Barbados a Negro culture exists with a greater proportion of Africanisms than is ordinarily thought.

Of the other eastern islands little can be said. Two forms of the game of *wari* are played in all of them, and not only the motor behavior in making the moves but the cultural setting and traditions usually associated with the game in West Africa are found. On the island of St. Lucia, the yam festival mentioned as occurring in Barbados is also held, and dances similar to those seen and spoken of in the other islands are danced to the *apinti* drum and the sound of the rattle. These are only hints of what may be present, however, and one must turn to the larger islands in the northwestern part of the Caribbean Sea for fuller accounts of Negro life.

The studies made in Haiti, Cuba, and Jamaica give much more information concerning the Negro cultures than are available for any other islands of the Caribbean. As has been remarked, Jamaica offers to the student not only the best documented data, but reports which extend over the longest period of time. Bryan Edwards, Monk Lewis, and others in the early days, and, in recent years, Martha Beckwith have all made important contributions to Jamaican Negro ethnology. Their writings clearly show that in spite of the amount and quality of European education afforded the Negroes of the island, and in spite of long and close contact with British culture, Negro behavior persists in distinctive form. Magic, named by the generic term *obeah*, flourishes in Jamaica to an extent that has caused it to occupy a major portion of the considerations of all those who have written of the Negroes there. What has been written of the social organization, however, discloses characteristics which could not have derived from contact with Europeans, particularly in its emphasis on the mother's side of the family, while the respect paid the dead, the fear of ghosts— *duppies,* as they are called—and the elaborateness of the rites in connection with the burial of the dead are all distinctly African. As a result of the successful slave revolts of the Maroons, though the majority of these people were deported first to Nova Scotia and later to the West African colony of Sierra Leone, those who remained were accorded by treaty the right of settling on a reservation of their own in the interior of the island, where they maintain their identity to this day. From the information available concerning this group it is evident that their culture stems principally from the Gold Coast. The Maroon town named Accompong derives its name either from the Ashanti deity *Nyamkompon,* a designation listed above in connection with the description of Dutch Guiana Bush Negro culture, or, more likely, from the name of the Gold Coast town Akropon. The "Kromanti" pact of drinking mingled blood and rum with a former enemy to seal a treaty is known in Dutch Guiana, while the word *kromanti,* in Jamaica as in Guiana, derives from the name of the West African kingdom of Coromantyne. This word *kromanti* also gives its name in Jamaica to a so-called secret language in which, according to Miss Beckwith, the Maroons know songs "strong enough to bewitch anybody." The name of "Old Nanny," who was "queen" of the Maroons at the time of their first treaty with the whites, probably comes from the Ewe (Togoland) term *Nana,* used there to this day with the significance of ancestress, "mother," or from the Ashanti word *nana,* which means grandparent, or ancestor. The "day names," the importance of which has already been discussed in connection with the discussion of Suriname Negro cultures, are heard throughout Jamaica, while the sacredness of great trees, such as the silk-cotton, is a direct Africanism. In Jamaica, as in Africa and elsewhere in the New World, worship is ordinarily carried on by dancing to the accompaniment of songs and rhythms made on percussion instruments—drums, tambourines, or rattles. Though many English lays and ballads of the eighteenth century are sung by the

Negroes, yet the Kromanti songs that have been recorded show a musical structure and melodic line that is far from European.

At this point the culture of the Virgin Islands and of the Bahamas may be mentioned in passing. Though but little work other than in the field of folklore has been done there, it seems that the behavior of the Negroes who inhabit these islands resembles that of the Jamaicans to a marked degree.

The customs of the Cuban Negroes reflect the effect of acculturation to the patterns of Spanish culture with which they have been in contact. Despite the relative freedom with which these Negroes, when compared with Negroes on the British and French islands, have mingled with the rest of the population, there are large numbers of them who have retained, certainly in their religious beliefs, many practices that mark them off from the population as a whole. These practices, which have been best described by the Cuban historian, Fernando Ortiz, are markedly similar to those of the Negroes of Brazil, and analysis of the Cuban and Brazilian "fetish cults" show both to be of Nigerian derivation. The African character of these religious traditions has been recognized by Ortiz, who has traced them to their point of origin, and the gods that he mentions in his works are those that have already been spoken of in connection with the Brazilian cult. As in Brazil, and, indeed, in portions of West Africa itself where Negroes have come in contact with Catholicism, certain identifications are made as, for example, that of Santa Barbara with the aboriginal Thunder-gods. Similarly, the worship of these deities, as in Brazil, follows aboriginal practice. In the employment of horns, carved wooden figures, and the like as amulets; in the beliefs concerning the soul; in the ritual of the worship of the gods; in the masked dancers who wear girdles of palm fronds, there is presented to the student a further series of configurations that are traceable in accordance with the requirements of an hypothesis of West African origin of these rituals.

The culture of the great mass of Haitian Negroes follows that of the Suriname Bush Negroes in the number of Africanisms it exhibits. As will be recalled, the Haitian slaves, revolting under the leadership of the military genius Toussaint l'Overture, early in the nineteenth century drove out their French masters and established an independent republic. French culture has been carried on faithfully by the educated classes of the cities, but in the villages and in the back country the peasants have retained the full flavor of their aboriginal traditions. A large portion of the writings concerning Haitian culture exhibits a marked hysterical quality as a result of the misunderstanding of the religious rites, which are known under the generic name of *voodoo*. So intent have students investigating Haitian culture been on discovering the secrets of *voodoo* that there are few sources to which the student can turn for information concerning aspects of Haitian culture other than these religious ones. In the field of religion, however, serious studies have been published by several Haitian scholars, notably Dr. Price-Mars (1925) and Dr. Dorsainvil (1924), and from their writings, as well as from one or two other papers by American students, it is possible to see how unlike any form of European worship are the practices of *voodoo,* despite the infusion of elements of Catholicism into the cult.

The word *voodoo* itself is of Dahomean derivation, and in its aboriginal home is used as the generic term for "deity." The gods have been traced to the African regions named here again and again, though in Haiti the Gold Coast deities are few in number, with Dahomean and Nigerian gods predominating. Within the cult, investigation has shown that there is a well-defined pantheon of gods and a well-regulated system of worship. Dancing is an integral portion of the ritual, and the internal structure of the songs that accompany the dances is principally African. Dahomean twin worship is followed even to the item of naming the child born after twins by the aboriginal term *dosu,* while the principal ceremonial object associated with the twins, here as in Africa, is the double pot, the two portions of which are connected by a ligature. Little is known of the social organization of the Haitian peasants, yet remarks here and there in the literature indicate that a West African sib organization, if not present in recognizable form, has at least left substantial survivals, while the economic institution of the Combite gatherings, which carry on cooperative agricultural work, represents the retention of a basic tradition in West African life.

In North America—that is, in the United States itself—the peculiar African patterns of Negro behavior are not as easily discerned as they are in the West Indies. As has been observed, one reason for this is that a large proportion of the slaves reached the colonies by way of the Caribbean islands rather than directly from Africa, and each additional step away from the homeland must have lessened the tendency to retain aboriginal behavior traits. Another reason is that even before the Civil War, but certainly after emancipation, the Negroes in the United States have had closer contact with whites and greater opportunities to absorb European cultural patterns than anywhere else in the New World. This acculturizing process has been so strong, indeed, that among the Negroes of the large cities of the North and South it is practically impossible to discern Africanisms in any aspect of outward manner except in certain phases of motor behavior. Certainly, as far as the psychology of the Negroes of the United States is concerned, the sanctions of the white population are the accepted sanctions of Negroes; white behavior patterns are not only automatically adhered to but consciously striven for. Thus a study of Negro-white crossing in the United States has demonstrated to what extent light color is valued in selecting a mate, a point of view seen in such an expression as the following, taken from a Negro magazine of poetry:

> I love the black and rippling hair
> Of little Nina Clark,
> I love her beauty, fresh and rare,
> But oh! her skin is dark.

I love the eyes, the lips, the teeth
Of little Nina Clark,
I love the virtue underneath
That skin which is so dark.

I might have married her some day,
This lovely Nina Clark,
But this one thing stands in the way—
Her skin, which God made dark.

This acceptance of the cultural values of the majority group is also evident in the tendency of urban Negroes in the United States to employ hair-straightening devices to achieve a coiffure that is non-Negroid in appearance, or in a terminology which denominates a European-like cast of countenance as having "good" features. Similarly, in dress and occupation, in the manner of home life and in occupational pursuits, the force which the acculturating process has exerted is apparent. No stronger testimony of this fact is necessary than that offered by the recent achievements of Negroes in the United States in the fields of literature, of higher learning, of music, and the graphic and plastic arts.

The Gulla Islanders, who live off the coast of the Carolinas, are one of the few groups of Negroes in the United States who have lived in any degree of isolation from their white fellow-citizens, and the character of their life differs decidedly from that of other Negro groups. As described both by scholars and in literary presentations, Gulla Island culture shows many aspects strange to the ordinary patterns of American behavior. These fall not only in the African-like elements in their social organization and their religion, but are also to be seen in the speech of these people, which, though almost incomprehensible to persons from other parts of the United States, is actually English spoken with a West Indian Negro accent and based on vestiges of African grammatical and idiomatic configurations.

This is not to say that non-European peculiarities in Negro behavior are confined to the Gulla Islanders, for many elements in the behavior of most rural, and some urban, Negroes differ from corresponding patterns of the white population among whom they live. Accounts of these are most often found in works which discuss the "superstitions" of the less-educated strata of the Negro population in both North and South. The importance of the mother's family, though not institutionalized, is so great when compared with the significance of the father and his people that it must be considered as one of these special types of tradition, as must the care taken of orphaned children by relatives, usually on the mother's side, and the reluctance of Negroes to allow orphans to be taken to institutions which shelter such children. Negroes in the United States are Christians, yet it is possible to see among certain groups of them expressions of Christian worship that are unknown in Europe. The songs of the American Negroes—the spirituals—have long been thought of as African, though there are many today who hold that these are merely borrowings of well-known European hymns. Whether or not these represent in their imagery simple borrowings, or have taken on "accretions," the place of the song in the religious service, and its accompaniment by hand-clapping, tapping the feet, and instruments of percussion such as the tambourine, do not partake of European religious cultural behavior.   Spirit possession (by the Holy Ghost) manifested through dances—"shouts"—in which the motor behavior is clearly African, is found in some Negro churches, while among these "shouting" sects the communion service partakes largely, in both psychological implications and outward ritual, of very different elements than are found to mark the corresponding rite in white churches.

Thus some Africanisms may be isolated even in the culture of the Negroes in the United States, in spite of the fact that their behavior in large part parallels more closely that of the white population among whom they live than is the case anywhere else in the New World.   The significance of this for the problems being considered here will be discussed in the pages which follow.

V. Conclusion

Old and New World Negroes—the Beliefs Concerning the Retention of Africanisms in the New World and Their Validity.   The social history of the Negro, as it has been sketched in the preceding pages, has indicated how internal migrations of peoples on the African continent and cultural contacts that can only be conjectured have made for the several types of social behavior that can be found in the various culture areas.   In the discussion of New World Negroes it has been shown how these people, deriving in large measure from a more or less restricted African region, welded their historical experiences into a series of cultural patterns that reflect their historical background.   As was pointed out, this material offers unique opportunity to understand the workings of the socio-psychological mechanisms involved.

Before finally analyzing the theoretical significance of these data, however, certain further points must first be considered, of which the most important relates to the accepted tradition concerning what has happened to the aboriginal heritage of the Africans who were brought to the Western Hemisphere as a result of the slave-trade, and the validity of this position. The current tradition may be briefly set forth, for it is a familiar one. On the whole, it is assumed that the African who was imported into the New World came as a "naked savage," with a cultural background which had neither sufficient depth nor enough vitality to stand against the impact of the experiences of slavery. It is further assumed, as a corollary to the preceding concept, that even though these "naked savages" might conceivably have had a strong cultural heritage the practice of separating slaves belonging to the same tribe, coupled with the fact of the diversity of African languages and their lack of mutual intelligibility, would in any case have made it impossible for these slaves to preserve what they might have brought with them in the way of cultural endowment.   Therefore, in considering New World Negroes, the problems that arise from daily contact between Negroes and whites have absorbed the attention of students, and few attempts have been made to determine whether or not the behavior of this folk exhibits anything that may be referred to African origins. Indeed, the matter has gone farther than this; it has been taken for granted by most students, both Negro and white, that the behavior of New World Negroes is essentially European behavior—though, to be sure, of a more or less infantile order. Moreover, the point that African culture could be sufficiently tenacious so that not only might Africanisms have been retained by Negroes in the New World but that African influences might have infiltrated into certain elements in the behavior of the white population has been regarded as so improbable as to require no verification by students.

Yet it has been demonstrated above how, by a combination of historical and ethnographic methods, it is quite possible to trace New World Negroes to specific points of origin despite the fact that scholarly tradition has had it that these regions from which Negroes were derived might not be recovered except in the most general way. Similarly it has been seen how the Negroes who were brought to the New World, far from being "naked savages," were the carriers of the high cultures of Africa, cultures that, as one student puts it, display "on the average, a more complex development of government, art, industry, and material culture than the non-literate inhabitants of any other great continental area" (Murdock, 1934, p. xiv). Not only that, but it has been seen how the individuals sold into slavery represented at the least an adequate cross-section of the population, with possibly a weighting to include more than its proportion of the upper strata, while, finally, Africanisms have been pointed out again and again in discussing the life of the various New World Negro groups described in the previous section. To make the point more clear, however, it may be well to review some of these Africanisms that are found in the region as a whole.

Culture-Patterns, Their Retention and Change, as Illustrated in the Study of Negro Culture-Patterns. That segment of culture which affords the most prolific material, it has been seen, is the religious life. The "fetish cult" in Brazil and Cuba, the *voodoo* of Haiti (and also of Louisiana), the religious beliefs and ceremonies of Jamaica, the Windward Islands, and, above all, of the Guianas have been briefly described. These New World Negro religions have been seen to exhibit great similarity, particularly in the use of magic and charms, in the importance of the priest, whether he be fetish worshiper or preacher, and in the belief in the strength of supernatural spells worked by those especially trained for this calling. The faithfulness with which Negroes in all the New World resort to practitioners of magic who employ non-European curing devices is also worthy of remark. The importance of baptism in the ritual practices of Negro Christians has often been commented upon. It is not unreasonable to relate the strength of adherence to this practice to the great importance of the river-cults in West Africa, particularly in view of the fact that, as has been observed, river-cult priests were sold into slavery in great numbers.

The vitality of Africanisms in folklore must also be emphasized, though it must be indicated that this has not only been granted by folklorists, but is perhaps the one African element in New World Negro culture that has been recognized as such by all students. The animal stories, best known to whites, form only one portion of New World Negro folklore, however. The Bible tales that have obtained vogue in recent times, particularly those of the Gulla Islanders, are essentially non-European not only in the action they depict, but also to a large degree in the characters found in them. The widespread use of the proverb and riddle has been remarked, while songs and games of an African character have also been commented upon. In music the problem has been particularly difficult. As has been stated, there are those who consider the spirituals African; others, however, hold them to be the result of Negro borrowing from European musical motifs. Yet the extent to which the spirituals form only one group of the body of music peculiar to North American Negroes is not generally recognized, for work-songs and the songs of social castigation and ridicule are quite as important to the Negroes themselves. Comment has already been made upon the fact that the place of the spirituals in the rituals of Negro Christian churches is markedly non-European. This is even more apparent in the case of these other types of songs, where the underlying psychological sanctions that furnish the reason for their existence, rather than their exterior musical structure as such, give these songs significance for the problem being discussed here. The dance is another aesthetic form that preserves numerous Africanisms. The well-known "Charleston" can be seen in the cult of the royal ancestors among the West African Ashanti at the present time; it can also be witnessed in the West Indies and Dutch Guiana. In Dutch Guiana, indeed, a motion picture of this dance was interpreted as a manifestation of spirit possession such as is known to the Negroes there.

One of the reasons that Negroes are as concerned with their position in the family, their relations, and their forbears as they are found to be may easily be referred to the fact that the only social position in African societies is that derived from family affiliation, while the forms which some rituals of death take among Negroes do not impress one as European. The most striking examples which refute common belief concerning the retention of Africanisms in the New World, however, are perhaps to be found in the field of language. This is especially the case in the survival of African grammatical patterns, for here the curious turns of phrase in Negro-English and Negro-French, ordinarily accounted for by a supposed inability of the child-like mind of these African "savages" to grasp the intricacies of European modes of expression, can clearly be shown to have resulted from a process of placing European words in an African grammatical frame. As is well known, the educated Negro has no trouble in speaking the language of his country perfectly; it is only where formal education has been denied Negroes that they speak the language of their adopted land with a non-European idiom. The proof of this lies in the fact that whether in French, in Spanish, or in English the turns of phrase employed by Negroes are the same. In all these languages, to do a thing "softly" means to be careful, to do it "one time" means to do it at once; in all of them the use of sex gender is disregarded, while the use of such a construction as "make we go" for "let us go" is found. These are, however, but literal translations of expressions found in all West Africa—idiomatic configurations into which the new words were fitted as the early slaves learned them.

If one regards the history of slaving in the New World objectively, a number of reasons why these Africanisms should have been carried over become apparent. The plantation system which was universal in the New World and the conditions of life of the Negro workers were such that large numbers of them were constantly thrown together. Though supervised in their labor, what they did during the evenings was of no concern to their masters as long it it did not affect their efficiency and their acquiescence to control. The Negroes on the plantations must, therefore, have led an inner life of their own, as would seem to be indicated by the fact that among the first specimens deposited in the British Museum was a Gold Coast type of drum, collected in Virginia during the late eighteenth century. It must also be understood that slave children were not ordinarily separated from their mothers, for such cases were sufficiently unusual to give rise to comment. Even when a child was sold away from his mother, he remained in contact with other Negroes whose behavior was not greatly dissimilar from that of his parents. Since the mechanism by means of which tradition is handed down from one generation to the next is the contact of a child with his elders, slave-children thus absorbed and perpetuated the behavior patterns of their parents and associates rather than those of their masters.

Again, the cultural unity of West Africa, which was pointed out in the discussion of African culture areas, is much greater than is commonly conceived. This unity, of course, does not mean that dissimilarities are not present, for they are often sufficiently great to bewilder the student. Yet, for example, though descent may be on the father's side in one tribe, and on the mother's side in another, unilateral descent is the rule. In economic life, in fundamental religious beliefs and practices, and in manifestations of the aesthetic, this underlying unity is also apparent. Granting that the slaves could not at first understand each other, this difficulty must have been surmounted when they learned the tongue of their masters sufficiently well to speak the pidgin dialects that arose, and once pidgin was created, it was natural for the unity of West African cultures to become a significant factor in the maintenance and perpetuation of aboriginal patterns.

A third reason for the retention of Africanisms in the New World was the leadership that Africans of the ruling, warrior, and priestly classes continued to exert in their new home. This leadership was principally evident in the numerous revolts which occurred wherever slavery obtained.

In the Caribbean and Guianas, in Brazil and in the United States—even on the slave-ships—these revolts went on intermittently, as recounted in contemporary records, and indicated by the increasing severity of the penalties for rebellion that, as time went on, were authorized by the New World makers of law.

This, then, is the problem: to what extent have the various phases of the traditions, beliefs, and techniques which the slaves brought with them been preserved in the various regions of the New World? The question involves fundamental aspects of the psychology of culture, and it is best approached through a further consideration of the nature of cultural patterns, a phrase which has been repeatedly employed in the preceding discussions. In a sense, cultural patterns may be regarded as the socialized behavior patterns peculiar to every culture which enable the student to differentiate a given culture from all others. These patterns are functions of the psyche of their carriers, and, though they have outward existence only in so far as they are reflected in the personalities who go to make up the group that manifests them, they exhibit great vitality. The patterns of culture become so deep-seated that, though today we know they manifest themselves in the individual as automatic or habitual responses, earlier students felt them to be a part of one's innate endowment, with the result that long catalogs of "instincts" were prepared—"instincts" which now are recognized as something resulting from the process of cultural conditioning. Though the learned reactions of a given group of persons are deep-seated, they are far from fixed, for a primary fact concerning culture is that, while custom is conservative, it is never static, and, though change in the accepted patterns of behavior is always resisted by a folk, change nevertheless does take place. By invention, by the adoption of new ideas and new techniques, and, to a larger extent, by contact with other cultures, this change in the patterns of a given civilization is brought about. The question then resolves itself into this: to what extent do the patterns of a culture resist change; to what degree are they hospitable to it?

It is here that the value of the data summarized above becomes evident when we ask to what extent, in the history of the Negro, we can discover the operation of the forces of cultural conservatism and culture change. To what extent can it be maintained that the aboriginal cultural patterns of the Negroes have been preserved, or have given way, in the face of stress such as few peoples have experienced during the history of man?

It is obvious that the answers to these questions can be neither decided affirmatives nor clear negatives. Indeed, the greatest importance of the study of the Negro for the understanding of the theoretical points just made is that it furnishes data which indicate how clearly differing situations dislodge the traditional types of belief and behavior to differing degrees. Yet, though the answer cannot be clean-cut, the discussion of the African Negro cultures and those of the Negroes of the New World have made two facts apparent. The first of these is that there is no such thing as Negro culture, but that, developing from a basis of certain deeply lodged configurations, the processes of cultural change have caused variations in pattern that have brought about important differences between the civilizations that are found on the African continent. In the second place, and conversely, it must be evident that in the New World these African patterns of behavior have exhibited a vitality and a tenaciousness that far transcends the concept ordinarily held concerning their living quality.

Certain cautions must here be entered. Just as it must not be thought that Negro cultures in Africa are in the process of dissolution in the face of European contact, so it must not be held that contact with Europeans in the New World has not enormously modified the African behavior of the Negroes brought here. The point that cannot be emphasized too greatly is that cultural contact is a matter of give and take, and that although Africanisms have persisted in the New World they are to be seen only as a result of extended analysis, while in Africa European expansion and conquest have left their mark on the indigenous civilizations. Similarly, both in Africa and the New World, the degree of interaction between European and African cultures varies with geographical regions and according to the aspect of culture under consideration. Europeanization of South and East Africa is occurring much faster and to a greater degree than in West Africa or the Congo, whereas the Africanisms of the Guianas and Haiti have persisted more strongly than elsewhere in the New World, the amount of Europeanization of New World Negroes increasing as Jamaica, Brazil, and Cuba are reached, being more intensive in other West Indian islands and the southern portions of the United States, and becoming almost complete when the culture of the urban northern Negroes is considered.

In the light of the description of New World Negro cultures that has been given, it is apparent that the survival rate of cultural patterns lying within different fields of culture has shown wide variation. Thus, in the realm of material culture, little if anything African has been preserved except in the Guiana bush and possibly in the interior of Haiti. In dress and in occupation, Negroes are like other citizens of New World nations of European descent; in the implements they use, or in the kinds of houses they occupy, they are very generally no different than their white neighbors. In the graphic and plastic arts almost everything that is distinctly African has been lost, while in the field of social organization even the relatively little that can be found is difficult to discover except by inference. It is in music and folklore, in religious beliefs and ceremonialism that Africanisms are most readily seen. Yet even here, certainly in the United States, direct comparisons between New World Negroes and those of Africa cannot be made. For it may be stated that, in the majority of cases, those traits which survive the longest under cultural contact form the least tangible manifestations of culture. The most difficult, because the most complex, aspects of the study of culture lie in this field, particu-

larly where the matter is one of attitudes and points of view and underlying sanctions. The reluctance of the Negro to give a quick answer to
a question and his ability to act diplomatically in difficult situations and
to give the answer his questioner wishes to receive are aspects of his
psychology that have persisted in the New World and are found in
full flower in Africa. The phrasing of the Dutch Guiana Bush Negro,
who said, "Long ago our ancestors taught us that it is unwise for a
man to tell to anyone more than half of what he knows about anything,"
would hold significance for any African or New World Negro. The
elaborate system of etiquette which marks the contact of the Negro with
his fellows—etiquette which demands politeness of outward behavior even
when this may mask an inner resentment—and other dictates of a similar
order, manifestations of the ability to meet "social" situations with the
urbanity that characterizes Negroes wherever they are found, reflect other
of those more subtle but deeply persistent cultural configurations.

Thus it would seem that both geographically and from the point of
view of the various inner elements of culture a scale of cultural tenacity
for Negro cultures can be set up which may perhaps point to similar
scales for the cultures of other folk. In the instance of the peoples being
considered here, these propositions may at least be set forth: Where there
has been the greatest opportunity for isolation, the most Africanisms have
been retained; while in all cases it is the tangible aspects of culture that
have been the first to be sacrificed, the intangible ones which have persisted most strongly and longest.

The Give and Take between Civilizations in Contact. However, the
principle that has been laid down concerning the fact that cultural contact
involves a give and take must not be neglected. The extent to which New
World white populations have derived aspects of their present cultural
behavior from Negroes is not generally recognized. The English dialect
spoken in the South of the United States, though unquestionably based on
the speech of old England of the eighteenth century, is vastly different
from the English dialect spoken in New England, where the speech is also
based on British pronunciation of the same words at the same period. The
difference is the element of African phonetics, which was transmitted to
the Southern whites by their Negro nurses. The distinctive dishes which
mark the cuisine of the Southern states and of the West Indies derive to an
unrecognized extent from the African cooking traditions introduced by
the slaves into the kitchens of their masters. The religious hysteria that
marks the manner of worship by certain white groups in the United
States is so different from the kind of evangelical excitation found in
Europe that it can be referred only to influences—in some cases, indeed,
two or three times removed—which emanated from Negro religious
gatherings. On the other hand, the things which the white man brought
to Africa, like the tobacco and maize which came from America, or the
guns and gunpowder and machines introduced from Europe, have deeply
influenced many of the aboriginal cultures of the Continent. Thus on all

sides a process of mutual give and take is to be noted, a process the importance of which is not to be held the less because in Africa European influences are relatively slight and in America the African patterns have not changed the behavior configurations of the whites to any major extent. *Psychological "Set" and Traditional Modes of Behavior and Thought.* From the point of view of the attémpt to understand psychological processes of human social life, then, the Negro peoples of the world afford unusually pertinent data. Even a cursory review of this material indicates how it throws light on the importance of the psychological "set" which characterizes a people and the manner in which traditional modes of behavior are inculcated into each of the individual members of a given society. In the case of the Negro, his social history has provided him with a background of tradition that has seemed to persist more vigorously and to be dislodged less readily in the face of cultural contact than is the case with other stocks that have been studied. Yet it is possible that, with greater emphasis on the study of what has been retained by a people in contact with another folk than has in the past been given such retentions, culture may be found to exhibit greater tenaciousness than has been credited it. It may then be more strongly realized that every culture provides in its inner sanctions the means for its own perpetuation and that the qualities of Western European civilization are perhaps not as evident to those of other cultures to whom it is brought as to those whose heritage it constitutes.

BIBLIOGRAPHY

1. *General Works, Periodicals, and Works on African Prehistory and Negro Physical Traits*

Africa, Journal of the International Institute of African Languages and Cultures. London: Oxford Univ. Press.

BEARDSLEY, G. 1929. The Negro in Greek and Roman civilization. Baltimore, Md.: Johns Hopkins Press; London: Oxford Univ. Press. Pp. xii+145.

BENEDICT, R. F. 1934. Patterns of culture. Boston & New York: Houghton Mifflin. Pp. xii+291.

BURKITT, M. C. 1928. South Africa's past in stone and paint. Cambridge.

BUSCHAN, G. 1922. Illustrierte Völkerkunde. Vol. 1. Stuttgart: Strecker & Schröder. Pp. xvi+686.

CATON-THOMPSON, G. 1931. The Zimbabwe culture. London: Oxford Univ. Press. Pp. 324.

CUNARD, N. [Ed.] 1934. Negro anthology. London: Wishart. Pp. 863.

DELAFOSSE, M. 1931. The Negroes of Africa; history and culture. Washington, D. C.: Asso. Publs. Pp. xxxiii+313.

DUBOIS, W. E. B. 1915. The Negro. New York: Holt; London: Williams & Norgate. Pp. 254.

HADDON, A. C. 1925. The races of man and their distribution. New York: Macmillan. Pp. viii+201.

HARDY, G. 1922. Vue générale de l'histoire d'Afrique. Paris.

HERSKOVITS, M. J. 1930. The culture areas of Africa. *Africa,* **3,** 59-77.

————. 1934. Freudian mechanisms in primitive Negro psychology. In *Essays presented to C. G. Seligman.* London: Kegan Paul. Pp. 75-84.

JOHNSTON, SIR H. H. 1913. A survey of the ethnography of Africa and the former racial and tribal migrations in that continent. *J. Roy. Anthrop. Instit. Great Britain & Ireland,* **43**, 375-412.

Journal of American folk-lore. New York: Amer. Folk-Lore Soc.

Journal of Negro history. Washington, D. C.: Soc. Stud. Negro Life & Hist.

Journal of the Royal Anthropological Institute of Great Britain and Ireland. London: Roy. Anthrop. Instit.

KEITH, SIR A. 1931. New discoveries relating to the antiquity of man. New York: Norton; London: Williams & Norgate. Pp. 512.

LAUFER, B. 1928. The giraffe in history and art. *Field Museum Anthrop. Leaflet,* No. 27. Chicago. Pp. 100.

LEAKEY, L. S. B. 1931. The stone age cultures of Kenya Colony. Cambridge, England: Univ. Press; New York: Macmillan. Pp. xiii+287.

————. 1935. The stone age races of Kenya. New York & London: Oxford Univ. Press.

LINTON, R. 1928. Culture areas in Madagascar. *Amer. Anthrop.,* **30**, 363-390.

RATZEL, F. 1896-1904. The history of mankind. New York & London: Macmillan. (See esp. Vol. 2. Pp. xiv+562.)

REISNER, G. A. 1923. Excavations at Kerma. (*Harvard African Stud.,* Vols. 5 & 6.) Cambridge, Mass.: Harvard Univ. Press.

ROOME, W. J. W. (n.d.) Ethnographic survey map of Africa. London: Stanford.

SELIGMAN, C. G. 1930. Races of Africa. New York: Holt; London: Butterworth. Pp. 256.

————. 1934. Egypt and Negro Africa. London: Routledge. Pp. 82.

THEAL, G. M. 1891. History of South Africa. London.

TORDAY, E. 1930. African races. In Herbert Spencer's *Descriptive sociology.* London: Williams & Norgate. Pp. 395.

WORK, M. N. 1928. A bibliography of the Negro in Africa and America. New York: Wilson. Pp. xxi+698.

————. 1931. Negro year book. (8th ed., 1931-32.) Tuskegee, Ala.: Tuskegee Instit. Pp. xiv+544.

2. *African Ethnology*

BURTON, SIR R. F. 1893. A mission to Gelele, King of Dahome. (2 vols.) London: Tylston & Edwards. Pp. xi+256; vii+305.

CALLAWAY, H. 1870. Religious system of the Amazulu. London: Trübner. Pp. 448.

CARDINALL, A. W. 1931. Tales told in Togoland. London: Oxford Univ. Press. Pp. 290.

CUREAU, A. 1912. Les sociétés primitives de l'Afrique equatoriale. Paris: Colin. Pp. v+420.

DANQUAH, J. B. 1928. Gold Coast: Akan laws and customs. London: Routledge. Pp. v+272.

DAPPER, O. 1933. The early Cape Hottentots. Cape Town: Van Riebeeck; London: Edwards. Pp. vi+xx+309.

DENNETT, R. E. 1910. Nigerian studies: or, the religious and political system of the Yoruba. London: Macmillan. Pp. 235.

DESPLAGNES, L. 1907. Le plateau central nigérien. Paris: Larose. Pp. 504.

DOKE, C. M. 1931. The Lambas of northern Rhodesia. London: Harrap. Pp. 407.

DRIBERG, J. H. 1923. The Lango, a Nilotic tribe of Uganda. London: Unwin. Pp. 468.

————. 1930. People of the Small Arrow. New York: Harcourt, Brace; London: Routledge. Pp. 338.

EINSTEIN, C. 1920. Afrikanische Plastik. Munich: Wolff. Pp. xxvii+108.

FROBENIUS, L. 1913. The voice of Africa. London.

FROBENIUS, L., & WILM, R. v. Atlas africanus. Munich & Berlin: de Gruyter.

GUILLAUME, P., & MUNRO, T. 1926. Primitive Negro sculpture. New York: Harcourt, Brace. Pp. 134.

HERSKOVITS, M. J. 1926. The cattle complex in East Africa. *Amer. Anthrop.*, **38**, 230-272, 361-380, 494-528, 633-664.

————. 1932. Some aspects of Dahomean ethnology. *Africa*, **5**, 266-296.

————. (With Sie Tagbwe.) 1930. Kru proverbs. *J. Amer. Folk-Lore*, **43**, 225-293.

HERSKOVITS, M. J., & HERSKOVITS, F. S. 1933. An outline of Dahomean religious belief. (*Amer. Anthrop. Asso. Mem.* 41.) Menasha, Wis.: Amer. Anthrop. Asso. Pp. 77.

————. 1934a. The art of Dahomey: I. Brass-casting and applique cloths. *Amer. Mag. Art*, **27**, 67-76.

————. 1934b. The art of Dahomey: II. Wood carving. *Amer. Mag. Art*, **27**, 124-131.

HILTON-SIMPSON, M. W. 1911. Land and peoples of the Kasai. London: Constable. Pp. 356.

HOLLIS, A. C. 1909. The Nandi, their language and folk-lore. London: Oxford Univ. Press. Pp. xl+328.

JUNOD, H. A. 1927. The life of a South African tribe. (2 vols.) (2nd ed., rev.) London: Macmillan. Pp. 559; 660.

KIDD, D. 1906. Savage childhood. London: Black. Pp. 314.

LeHERISSÉ, A. 1911. L'ancien royaume du Dahomey. Paris: Larose. Pp. 384.

LINDBLOM, K. G. 1920. The Akamba, an ethnological monograph. (*Arch. d'Études orientales*, Vol. 17.) Upsala: Appellbergs Bolatryckerei. Pp. xii+607.

LINDBLOM, K. G., *et al.* 1926-1933. Riksmuseets etnografiska avdelning, Smärre Meddelanden. (General papers on problems of distribution of various African culture-traits.) Nos. 1-11. Stockholm.

LUSCHAN, F. v. 1919. Die Altertümer von Benin. (3 vols.) Berlin: Verein. wiss. Verleger. Pp. xii+522; plates; plates.

MAES, J. 1924. Aniota-Kifwebe. Anvers: Editions "De Sikkel." Pp. 64+60 plates.

MAIR, L. P. 1934. An African people in the twentieth century. London: Routledge. Pp. xv+300.

MIGEOD, F. W. H. 1927. A view of Sierra Leone. New York: Brentano's. Pp. 361.

MOFOLO, T. 1931. Chaka. London: Oxford Univ. Press. Pp. xv+198.

RATTRAY, R. S. 1923. Ashanti. London: Oxford Univ. Press. Pp. 347.

————. 1927. Religion and art in Ashanti. London: Oxford Univ. Press. Pp. xviii+414.

————. 1929. Ashanti law and constitution. London: Oxford Univ. Press. Pp. xix+420.

————. 1930. Akan-Ashanti folk-tales. London: Oxford Univ. Press. Pp. xx+275.

RICHARDS, A. I. 1932. Hunger and work in a savage tribe. London: Routledge. Pp. xv+238.

ROSCOE, J. 1911. The Baganda. London: Macmillan. Pp. 547.

SCHAPERA, I. 1930. The Khoisan peoples of South Africa: Bushmen and Hottentots. London: Routledge. Pp. xi+450.

——. 1934. The present state and future development of ethnographical research in South Africa. *Bantu Stud.*, **8**, 219-342.

SELIGMAN, C. G., & SELIGMAN, B. Z. 1918. The Kababish, a Sudan Arab tribe. (*Harvard African Stud.*, Vol. 2.) Cambridge, Mass.: Harvard Univ. Press. Pp. 105-187.

——. 1932. Pagan tribes of the Nilotic Sudan. London: Routledge. Pp. xxiv+565.

SMITH, E. W., & DALE, A. M. 1920. The Ila-speaking peoples of northern Rhodesia. London: Oxford Univ. Press.

SPIETH, J. 1906. Die Ewe-Stämme. Berlin: Reimer. Pp. 80+962.

——. 1911. Die Religion der Eweer in Süd-Togo. Leipzig: Hinrichs. Pp. vi+316.

STAYT, H. A. 1931. The Bavenda. London: Oxford Univ. Press. Pp. 410.

TALBOT, P. H. 1926. The peoples of southern Nigeria. (4 vols.) London: Oxford Univ. Press. Pp. xii+366; xx+424; x+425-976; viii+234.

WATERLOT, E. M. 1926. Les bas-reliefs des bâtiments royaux d'Abomey. Paris: Instit. d'Ethnol. Pp. vi+16.

WERNER, A. 1933. Myths and legends of the Bantu. London: Harrap. Pp. 335.

3. The Slave Trade and New World Negro Life

BECKWITH, M. W. 1929. Black roadways. Chapel Hill: Univ. N. Car. Press; London: Oxford Univ. Press. Pp. xvii+243.

——. 1924. Jamaica Anansi stories. (*Mem. Amer. Folk-Lore Soc.*, Vol. 17.) New York: Stechert. Pp. 295.

——. 1929. Jamaican folk-lore. (*Mem. Amer. Folk-Lore Soc.*, Vol. 21.) New York: Stechert. Pp. 347.

BOSMAN, W. 1721. A new and accurate description of the coast of Guinea. London. Pp. 456.

BOUET-WILLIAUMEZ, E. 1848. Commerce et traite des noirs aux côtes occidentales d'Afrique. Paris: Imprimerie nationale. Pp. v+230.

BRAWLEY, B. G. 1927. A short history of the American Negro. New York: Macmillan. Pp. xvii+284.

CRUICKSHANK, J. G. 1916. Black talk: being notes on Negro dialect in British Guiana. Demerara: Argosy Co. Pp. iv+76.

DALLAS, R. C. 1803. The history of the Maroons. (2 vols.) London. Pp. xii+ xiii+357; xi+514.

DONNAN, E. 1928. The slave trade in South Carolina before the Revolution. *Amer. Hist. Rev.*, **33**, 809-828.

——. 1930-32. Documents illustrative of the history of the slave trade to America. (3 vols.) (*Carnegie Institution Publ.* No. 409.) Washington, D. C.: Carnegie Institution of Washington. Pp. x+495; xii+731; xiii+ 553.

Do RIO, J. (n.d.) As religiões no Rio. Rio de Janeiro & Paris: Livraria Garnier. Pp. 245.

DORSAINVIL, J. C. 1924. Une éxplication philologique de Vodū. Port-au-Prince: Pierre-Noël. Pp. 40.

EDWARDS, B. 1801. The history, civil and commercial, of the British colonies in the West Indies. (3 vols.) London: Stockdale. Pp. v+576; iii+617; iii+477.

FREYRE, G. 1934. Case-Grande & Senzala. Rio de Janeiro: Maia & Schmidt. Pp. vlix+517.

GASTON-MARTIN, —. 1931. Nantes au xviiie siécle. L'ère des nègriers (1714-1774). Paris: Alcan. Pp. 448.

GONZALES, A. E. 1922. The black border. Columbia, S. Car.: State Co.

HALL, R. B. 1929. The Société Congo of the Ile à Gonave. *Amer. Anthrop.*, 31, 685-700.

HARRIS, J. C. 1911. Nights with Uncle Remus. Boston & New York: Houghton Mifflin. Pp. 404.

————. 1929. Uncle Remus. New York: Appleton. Pp. xxiii+283.

HERSKOVITS, M. J. 1927. Acculturation and the American Negro. *Southwestern Pol. & Soc. Sci. Quar.*, 8, 211-225.

————. 1930a. The Negro in the New World: the statement of a problem. *Amer. Anthrop.*, 32, 145-156.

————. 1930b. The anthropometry of the American Negro. New York: Columbia Univ. Press; London: Oxford Univ. Press (1932). Pp. xiv+283.

————. 1930c. The social organization of the Bush-Negroes of Suriname. *Proc. XXIII Int. Cong. Americanists*, New York, 1928. Pp. 713-727.

————. 1932. Wari in the New World. *J. Roy. Anthrop. Instit. Great Britain & Ireland*, 42, 23-37.

————. 1933. On the provenience of New World Negroes. *Soc. Forces*, 12, 247-262.

HERSKOVITS, M. J., & HERSKOVITS, F. S. 1933. A footnote to the history of Negro slaving. *Opportunity*, 11, 178-181.

————. 1934. Rebel destiny, among the Bush-Negroes of Dutch Guiana. New York: Whittlesey House; London: McGraw-Hill. Pp. xvi+383.

HURSTON, Z. 1931. Hoodoo in America. *J. Amer. Folk-Lore*, 44, 317-347.

IGNACE, A. E. 1908. Le fétishisme des négres du Brésil. *Anthropos*, 3, 881-904.

JOHNSON, G. B. 1930. Folk culture on St. Helena Island. Chapel Hill: Univ. N. Car. Press; London: Oxford Univ. Press. Pp. xi+183.

JOHNSON, J. W. 1927a. The autobiography of an ex-coloured man. New York: Garden City Publ. Co. Pp. 211.

————. 1927b. God's trombones. New York: Viking Press. Pp. 187.

JOHNSTON, SIR H. H. 1910. The Negro in the New World. London: Methuen. Pp. 499.

KENNEDY, R. E. 1925. Mellows. New York: Boni.

LEWIS, M. G. 1929. Journal of a West India proprietor. (New ed.) Boston: Houghton Mifflin; London: Routledge. Pp. vi+356.

LINDBLOM, K. G. 1924. Afrikanische Relikte und Indianische Entlehnungen in der Kultur der Buschneger Surinams. Göteborg: Wettergreen & Kerber. Pp. 120.

MOREL, E. D. 1920. The black man's burden. London.

MURDOCK, G. P. 1934. Our primitive contemporaries. New York: Macmillan. Pp. vii+614.

NINA-RODRIGUES, —. 1900. L'animisme fétichiste des négres de Bahia. Bahia: Reis. Pp. vii+158.

————. 1932. Os Africanos no Brasil (Bibliotheca Ped. Brasileira Ser., Brasiliana, Vol. 9.) Saõ Paulo: Companhia Editora Nacional. Pp. 409.

OLLENDORP, C. G. A. 1777. Geschichte der Mission der evangelischen Brüder auf den caraibischen Inseln S. Thomas, S. Croix und S. Jan. Barby. Pp. 10+1068.

ORTIZ, F. 1916. Hampa Afrocubano. Los Negros esclavos, estudio sociologico y de derecho publico. Havana: Revista Bimestre Cubana. Pp. 531.

————. 1917. Hampa Afrocubano. Los Negro brujos (apuntes para un estudio de etnologia criminal.) Madrid: Editorial-America. Pp. 406.

―――. 1924. Hampa Afrocubano. Glosario de Afronegrismos. Havana: Imprenta "El Siglo xx." Pp. xxviii+558.

PANHUYS, L. C. VAN. 1914-17. Art. Boschnegers, in *Encyclopaedie van Nederlandsch West Indië.* 'S Gravenhage & Lieden.

PARK, M. 1806. Travels into the interior districts of Africa. London.

PARSONS, E. C. 1918. Folk-tales of Andros Island, Bahamas. (*Mem. Amer. Folk-Lore Soc.,* Vol. 13.) Lancaster, Pa. & New York: Amer. Folk-Lore Soc.

―――. 1923. Folk-lore of the sea islands. (*Mem. Amer. Folk-Lore Soc.,* Vol. 16.) Cambridge, Mass. & New York: Amer. Folk-Lore Soc.

―――. 1933. Folk-lore of the Antilles, French and English. Part I. (*Mem. Amer. Folk-Lore Soc.,* Vol. 26.) New York: Stechert. Pp. 521.

―――. Spirit cult in Hayti. *J. de la Soc. d. Amer. de Paris,* 20, 157-179.

PETERKIN, J. M. 1927. Black April. Indianapolis, Ind.: Bobbs-Merrill. Pp. 316.

―――. 1932. Bright skin. Indianapolis, Ind.: Bobbs-Merrill. Pp. 348.

PHILLIPS, U. B. 1918. American Negro slavery. New York: Appleton. Pp. xi+529.

PRICE-MARS, ―. 1925. Le sentiment et le phénomène réligieux chez les Nègres de St. Domingue. *Bull. de la Soc. d'hist. et de géog. d'Haiti,* 1, 33-35.

PUCKETT, N. N. 1926. Folk beliefs of the southern Negro. Chapel Hill: Univ. N. Car. Press. Pp. xiv+644.

SCARBOROUGH, D., & GULLEDGE, O. L. 1925. On the trail of Negro folk-songs. Cambridge, Mass.: Harvard Univ. Press. Pp. 289.

STEDMAN, J. G. 1796. Narrative of a five years' expedition against the revolted Negroes of Surinam, in Guiana, on the wild coast of South America. (2 vols.) London: Printed for J. Johnson. Pp. xviv+407; iv+404.

STONEY, S. G., & SHELBY, G. M. 1930. Black Genesis. New York: Macmillan. Pp. xxix+192.

UNITED STATES BUREAU OF THE CENSUS. 1918. Negro population, 1790-1915. Washington, D. C.: Govt. Print. Office. Pp. 844.

WOODSON, C. G. 1927. The Negro in our history. (4th ed.) Washington, D. C.: Asso. Publs. Pp. xxx+616.

CHAPTER 8

SOCIAL HISTORY OF THE RED MAN

CLARK WISSLER

Yale University

Everywhere and at all times there arises the demand for an understanding of a people. The aboriginal inhabitants of the Americas, when seen in contrast to peoples in other great world areas, are judged distinctive, if not unique. The observed biological homogeneity of this aboriginal population is often taken to necessitate a like or even greater unity in mind and spirit. Not infrequently the specialist in American anthropology is pressed to reveal the soul of the Red Man, or the spirit of the aboriginal world. We suppose this idea arises from the feeling that there must be something universal and pervading in the things Indians do. However this may be, we are sure that no satisfactory statement of this kind has been made, nor can anthropology offer more than a tentative answer. What the history of the Old World does suggest is that in more or less distinct geographical units of the world's land surface centers of national life and culture are to be found which may be taken as the culminating types in civilization. It may then be that in the New World there were at any given time two or more such centers. In so far as we are able to reconstruct the scene in 1492, or thereabout, no large areas were uninhabited. The aboriginal population thus spread from the Arctic circle to Cape Horn, a region embracing about every type of climate and topography known in the Old World. Likewise the state of society ranged from the very primitive to nations of barbaric splendor. If, therefore, there be something universally American, it should pervade all these forms of society and at the same time stand out as unique. We take it that the reader of this volume may first wish for a general picture of this range of social life, after which he can proceed to an interpretation.

THE THREE MAIN TYPES OF ABORIGINAL SOCIETY

It seems desirable, at the outset, to use a simple classification as:

1. City-States and Empire Builders
2. Agricultural Tribes
3. Hunting Tribes

The objections which may be raised to such a procedure are, first, the objections to classification of any kind, and, secondly, the vagueness of the terms used, with the consequent arbitrariness of procedure. Yet this, like all similar classifications, is designed for use, rather than for explanation. Reference to Figure 1 suggests that this classification could be expressed in geographical terms as well as in those of social behavior, since it so happens that when the various political groups are plotted upon a map

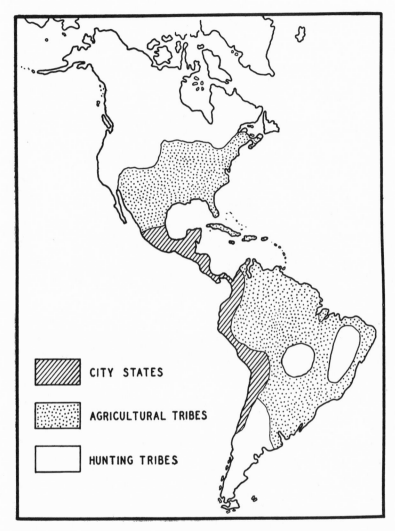

FIGURE 1
DISTRIBUTION OF THE THREE TYPES OF ABORIGINAL SOCIETY

the three classes we have designated tend to be geographically separate. So, from the geographical point of view, we could designate our three classes as Middle America, Intermediate America, and Marginal America, but as we are committed to the discussion of society we prefer the terms as given above.

THE AREA OF GREAT EMPIRES

When Spanish explorers arrived in Middle and South America they found two outstanding political organizations, the Aztec of Mexico and the Inca of Peru. The literature on these nations is vast, and it may be assumed that the reader knows the general outline of the Spanish conquest of Mexico and Peru. We have used the term "nations" because in many respects the patterns of political organization and control were at least analogous to those of the then contemporary Old World. In part, the proof of this lies in the ease with which the European conquerors took over the control of these governments. The extent of territory controlled was even greater than the ranges of many ancient kingdoms in the Old World. The Aztec approximated that of modern Mexico; the Inca at one time held the whole stretch of the Andean highlands from Ecuador into Chile, a territory in extent and form similar to that of Lower California, the states of California, Oregon, and Washington combined. The area of the Inca territory was about 380,000 square miles, and its population in Inca times has been estimated at 16,000,000, or about 45 per square mile.

The term "city-states" is frequently used to designate a political pattern prevailing in this area. The so-called empire of the Inca was an organization of city-states subject to the city of Cuzco. In Mexico Cortez found a similar organization under the control of the Aztec city, Tenochtitlan, now Mexico City. In Ecuador, at this time, Quito dominated; in Colombia, Bogota; etc. Apparently the history of government in this area conformed to the pattern of a city, becoming militant and extending its authority over surrounding cities; in turn, these small city-states each fell before a larger one, until a single city ruled a large geographical area. This is the significance of the term "area of city-states."

The Inca Area

When the Spaniards conquered the Andean country of South America, the native government was headed by a man to whom the name "Inca" is now applied. The original meaning of the word is not quite clear, but in such discussions as we are now to take up the term means the ruler, the state, or the culture, as may be indicated.

Naturally the Inca régime was the last aboriginal development in this area, but archeological research reveals a number of preceding civilizations, a situation similar to that in parts of the Old World. However, the limits of our study preclude the consideration of anything antedating the Inca period. It may be noted, however, that, despite the remarkable culture of the Inca, most scholars are agreed that the highest attainments in Andean cultures were reached before the beginning of the Inca period. It is further believed that the decline of Inca culture itself had set in before the Spanish invasion.

For the details of Inca history the reader should consult the literature of the subject. In brief, the tendency is to regard the Inca Pachacuti

(1400-1448) as the greatest of the Inca rulers and the one who gave final form to the organization of the state. The list of traditional Inca rulers is as follows:

1. Sinchi Rocca	7. Uriacocha
2. Lloque Yupanqui	8. Pachacuti
3. Mayta Ccapac	9. Tupac Yupanqui
4. Ccapac Yupanqui	10. Huayna Ccapac
5. Rocca	11. Huascar
6. Yahuar Huaccac	12. Atahualpa

Authorities generally agree that, while Pachacuti was clearly the greatest Inca, the last great ruler was Huayna Ccapac, approximately from 1484 to 1524. The cycle of the empires was something over 400 years and while the exact time interval is not certain a conservative estimate would put the beginning at about 1000 A.D. The Spanish conquest began about 1530 A.D.; hence it is fair to say that the cycle of development for the Inca was a period of about 500 years. As just stated neither as an empire nor as a culture was the Inca the initial development in the area. Scholars have proposed several chronologies, of which the following is one:

1540	Historic Peru
1000–1540	Inca
500–1000	Tiahuanaco
200 B.C.–500	Pachacamac, Nazca, Trujillo
....–200 B.C.	Archaic Period

Whatever differences one may have with the details of this chronology, it remains that the Inca régime stands as the historical culmination of the aboriginal Andes.

In approaching the exposition of Inca society a few gross characteristics may be serviceable as giving orientation. The achievement of this society, as indicated by the material accumulations of the time, may be characterized by the following incomplete enumeration:

Textiles. Weaving and spinning had reached a high level in quality and beauty of product, using cottons and woolens. The mechanization was simple, but all the known types of weave were practiced.

Food. Agriculture was well developed, but of the "hoe" type. Maize, beans, squashes, potatoes, tomatoes, manioc, agave, alligator pear, coca, cherimoya, chili pepper, cotton, guava, peanuts, oca, quinine, sweet potato, and tobacco are some of the more important plants cultivated by the Inca.

Domestication. Llama, dog, and guinea pig. It is here that this culture is weakest in contrast to some Old World cultures.

Ceramics. No pottery wheel used, but modeling excellent; no true glaze; production increased by the use of molds.

Metals. No iron; gold, copper, silver, the chief metals; bronze made; great skill in smelting, casting, and shaping.

Transportation. Llama for packing; most freight carried by men; no wheeled vehicles; roads and bridges.

Architecture. Buildings were of stone and brick, massive but simple; symmetry and solidarity were their chief characteristics; the use of columns was practically absent, as was the true arch. Sculpture in stone rare.

Inscriptions. Writing non-existent; consequently no inscriptions; arithmetical calculations by string records, or quipu.

The absence of writing has puzzled scholars, but there is reason to believe that pictures were used on boards as mere pictorial records. However, none have survived. Some pen and ink portraits were made in early Spanish days, which seem to be copies of true aboriginal paintings. In any case it is correct to say that writing did not exist. The method of preserving historical and current materials was by professional memorizers.

Markham (1911, p. 142) states that large relief maps were made for administrative purposes and as guides in the planning of roads and the allotment of agricultural lands. There are traditions that as population increased towns were moved from easily tillable to the less tillable lands, thus increasing the yield. Extensive aqueduct systems were established for irrigation, and terracing was resorted to on a large scale.

The empire was self-contained, but the variations in topography and elevation offered many special environments. Advantage was taken of these: thus cotton was raised near the coast, maize and potatoes in the upland; wool was produced at relatively high altitudes. The Inca even invaded and exploited parts of the forest marginal belts on the eastern slopes of the Andes from which they drew supplies of wood, bamboo, and feathers, and where they established plantations for the production of coca and other tropical plants. A controlled exchange of such goods was maintained. This cannot be called commerce in the modern sense, because it was carried on by the state. Here and there were public stores from which cotton, wool, food, etc., were issued to meet legitimate needs.

Nature of the Empire. We now turn to the political and social organizations functioning with the materials listed above. The fundamental political set-up has been stated as follows:

> The government, however mild in character, was a pure despotism. The Inca, a chief ruler, as the representative of the Sun, was at the head of the priesthood and of the army, making all the laws and appointing judges to enforce them. In short, he was a superior being, owning everything, and the source of all power in the Empire. No one dared approach him unless barefoot and carrying some token of homage. (Mead, 1932, p. 17)

The empire seems to have been handled in four subdivisions or provinces, for each of which there was a deputy of the Inca in charge. All land was the property of the Inca, or of the State; in theory everything seems to have been the property of the State.

> The land was divided into three parts, one for the Sun, another for the Inca, and the third for the people. The proportion differed in each province. The lands assigned to the Sun furnished a revenue to support the temples and the multitudinous priesthood. The Inca's portion supported the royal establishment and the remainder was divided, per capita, among the people. The tenant's lease of this land expired at the end of the year, and he had no power to alienate or add to his possessions. All lands were cultivated by the people; those belonging to the Sun were attended to first; next came the lands of the old, the sick, widows and orphans, and of soldiers in actual

service. The people were then allowed to work their own grounds, and lastly, all joined together, and with many ceremonies cultivated the Inca's portion.

As has already been said, everything in the Empire belonged to the Inca. The mines were wrought exclusively for his benefit. At the time of shearing, the wool was all put in public magazines and, by direction of the Inca, dealt out by officers appointed for that service, to the women of each family to spin and weave into clothing. In like manner cotton was divided. Accounts of these things were accurately kept by means of the quipu, a simple device by which any given number could be registered by tying knots in strings. The quipu was also useful in connection with the collection of revenue. Each province was required to furnish a certain proportion of the products grown or manufactured there, the assessment for each locality was regulated by the quantity it produced and an inventory was taken every year and the results recorded on knotted strings, which were taken to the capital and submitted to the Inca. (Mead, 1932, pp. 61-62)

Scheme of Organization. Notwithstanding the incompleteness of our knowledge, we have enough data to indicate that the Inca Empire grew by adding lesser empires and marginal tribes, many of which seem to have preserved their original community organizations. Yet, throughout, the basic unit was the family group or *ayllu,* a small group of related families in contemporary usage. Usually such units were federated and, in their most primitive form, functioned under an elected chief. Such a grouping is essentially a tribe, as we find in the more primitive parts of the New World. Again, such tribes were enlarged, as two or more tribes federated under the rule of an hereditary chief or family, and it was of such units that the Inca Empire was built. The theory of the Inca seems to have been that all land belonged to him, but the communal right of the *ayllu* and the tribe to use land in a certain locality seems to have been respected so long as they cooperated with the Inca. While the individual did not own land, the group did, and this was fundamental in the sense that the group fought for and in turn defended the lands necessary to its maintenance. The Inca seems to have been most successful in coordinating these units, in exercising arbitrary power to direct and to organize labor to produce goods for the state as a whole, and to exchange the products of labor, so that the various environments might be used to best advantage and the goods produced distributed widely. Public works were executed on a large scale, their archeological remains standing as sufficient evidence of the successful administration of the Inca.

The scheme of social and political integration seems to have been as follows:

1. *Ayllu*—family group.
2. *Sinchi*—a kind of tribe, composed of *ayllu* in a single hamlet, but which might extend into a number of such hamlets under one head.
3. *Curaca*—an hereditary chief, ruling a fair number of hamlets.
4. A kingdom.

The more or less complete integration of all individuals and institutions not only astonished the Spanish conquerors but still impresses the scholar.

The individual was submerged and his routine habituated almost to the level of the social insects. Patterns of response were rationalized for types of situations and the people drilled in their execution. Markham (1911, p. 166) tells us that once a certain district was laid waste and the people killed by Spanish soldiers: this was after the Inca power had been smashed, yet the neighboring districts automatically told off labor to repair the damage and settlers to repopulate the lands. The mistake of the Spaniards, if such it was, was in not sensing the Inca system and letting it work.

Labor. All labor was for the Inca, in the sense that the product went into the public store. This does not necessarily mean that no private property existed, because it may be doubted if a society flourished anywhere in which the individual did not claim something as his own. The chief industry was agriculture. We are told that all the land was divided into three types according to the distribution of the crops. Thus, here and there certain plots were reserved for the Sun or for religious purposes; certain others for the support of the royal family; and, finally, plots for the population at large. These assignments were temporary and subject to revision at any time. On the other hand, the family had a guarantee in that the head of each was assigned a plot, the size of which was determined by the number of persons in the family.

However, it is in the labor system that the power of the Inca is best seen. All lands were worked in common, which is to say that all laborers in a community were mobilized under captains, and so operated. Nor was the captain free to choose a plan of procedure, for we are told that the prescribed order was first to work the religious lands, next the fields of widows, the aged, and the sick, then the lands for the laborers, and, finally, the royal lands. Garcilasso tells us of an incident according to which a certain captain was executed for varying the order. The order, as given, seems to reflect the social values of the time, first to work for the gods and religious institutions, which seems to have included a large part of such literature and learning as the Inca culture possessed. The humanitarian motive is next in order, then the people, and, finally, the Inca. We suppose that putting the Inca last was a fine gesture since he seems to have had the power to seize any and all goods if he so wished. Further, from the crown lands came the produce stored as reserve and for the use of the army.

Since we are now discussing labor it should be noted that the whole population was regimented, implying a working system to the last detail. Discipline was rigid and unrelenting. Entire communities were executed for irregularities. We cannot give space to the details of this system, but note that the individuals in each so-called family group were classified as follows:

1. Punuc rucu (old man sleeping), sixty years and upwards.
2. Chaupi rucu ("half old"), fifty to sixty years. Doing light work.
3. Puric (able bodied), twenty-five to fifty. Tribute payer

and head of the family.
4. Yma huayna (almost a youth), twenty to twenty-five. Worker.
5. Coca palla (coca picker), sixteen to twenty. Worker.
6. Pucllac huamra, eight to sixteen. Light work.
7. Ttanta raquizic (bread receiver), six to eight.
8. Macta puric, under six.
9. Saya huamrac, able to stand.
10. Mosoc caparic, baby in arms.

From these classes, according to fitness, were recruited all agricultural laborers, male and female, artisans, shepherds, hunters, soldiers, etc. For every kind of service individuals were drafted by the representatives of the Inca, and it was they who decided upon the occupational fitness of the individual.

We are accustomed to think of labor as for individual reward, but here all labor seems to have been forced, or to be a form of tribute. Units of labor were not in terms of time but in units of production: in this way industry and ability were rewarded by the increase of leisure. Thrift of a kind was encouraged by credit given for excess production as against future tribute. On the other hand, everyone could be called at any time to complete the quota of the sick and unfortunate. During the period of tribute labor, food, and other necessities were issued from the public store, not only to the worker, but to all dependent upon him.

Religion and Ceremonialism. The main outline of the Inca religion and ritual can be stated with some certainty. To begin at the bottom, every family had a number of sacred objects (conopas) which varied in form and number and which were often buried with the dead. In the fields similar charms were buried with accompanying ceremonies to bring good crops. Maize was supposed to be under the care of a special power or spirit to which every agricultural family offered prayers. Then, whatever its origin, there was a kind of state religion and a priesthood, the leading god being the sun. Of somewhat lower rank was the moon, wife of the sun, in other words, a kind of holy mother, the stars being her children. Again, the moon seemed to be goddess of the ocean and to watch over germination and childbirth and many other details of life.

The spiritual and administrative head of the Inca religion was said to be a close blood relation of the Inca, perhaps a brother, thus affording a convenient berth for a near heir to the throne. He presided in the temple of the sun where the Inca officiated, but there seem to have been many temples scattered throughout the empire, each presided over by a head priest and in which the local ruler worshiped. What is suggested is a kind of pattern in which religious organization was closely integrated with the political and social set-up. It is interesting to note that women were not permitted to enter the temples of the sun. Nevertheless, women had a place in religious service; buildings like convents were provided in which lived women drafted for this purpose. Selected young, they were expected to be virgins. These establishments were under the control of elderly experienced women, and men were forbidden to enter. A great deal of uncertainty surrounds these so-called convents. The duties of the occupants seem to have been exacting enough, such as producing the clothing of the royal family and preparing food as well as other prerequisites for the authorized ceremonies in the temples. No doubt the general resemblance of this institution to the nunneries of the Catholic church conditioned the descriptions in the Spanish accounts. One of the first acts of the Spanish invaders was to turn their soldiers loose in these convents, an act no doubt sanctioned by the church as destroying a pagan institution.

In general, the picture we get is that of an elaborate priesthood paralleling the equally elaborate political organization. Studies of Roman religion show us how many local gods were incorporated into the priestly system of pagan Rome; in much the same way the Inca fitted into his scheme the tribal and local gods his subjects brought with them, however subordinated to the state priesthood.

Of temple observance and general festivals there was the usual long list one expects in association with such a priesthood; convenient lists of these have been given by Markham, Means, and others. The grand ceremony seems to have been in the summer, the most spectacular part being a greeting to the rising sun, which, as in the case of others of its kind, ended in riotous feasting and drinking. In the matter of sacrifices, the authorities differ, but some fruits and grains were offered and domestic animals killed. Further, human sacrifice is both affirmed and denied by the Inca régime; the evidence suggests this practice before the Inca period, nor is there good proof that such sacrifices had ceased with the Inca régime. We can, however, be certain that the importance of human sacrifice was relatively small as compared with its place in the religions of ancient Mexico.

The educated and ruling classes seemed to feel the need of a less objective deity than the sun, and, in keeping with their own type of organization, assumed that a single power ruled the world. Even the sun and moon were regarded as subservient because they followed a fixed routine; at least certain Inca hymns, as translated by Markham, express the idea of a great, supreme, unseen god who rules all (1911, pp. 101-103).

Literature. The use of the term "literature" may be questioned for a culture that possessed no writing or other methods of keeping records (except for the quipu), but it is scarcely conceivable that so well organized an empire as that of the Inca should have been without a body of oral tradition comparable to literature. Like all peoples, they maintained a body of mythology and composed hymns of which Markham gives us samples. True dramas are said to have existed, the most famous being the much-debated Ollantay (Markham), which, though rejected by some, is usually admitted to contain true Inca elements. Of plainer practical lore were historical accounts, moral philosophy, and rules of conduct, among which is the oft-quoted statement concerning the rearing of the young (Mead, 1932, pp. 111-112).

One need scarcely comment that, had a system of writing been in vogue and manuscripts preserved, our knowledge of these cultures would be more satisfactory. Had the European conquerors been less occupied in the destruction of all things native, they might have recorded more. What we have are tantalizing glimpses of an interesting civilization.

Concluding Remarks. The foregoing is too brief an account to go far except in a superficial general view of Inca society. The reader of books dealing with this society will find attention focused upon the Inca system as an example of state communism, or socialism, according to the point of view. The good points usually emphasized are that every adult had a piece of land to till, was subject to draft for labor in whatever the State required, that public stores were maintained from which food and raw materials were issued according to the judged needs, and that absolute authority was vested in the Inca. It is usually overlooked that the standard of living among the masses was low, that punishments were brutal and drastic, that attempts at revolt were frequent because of increasing demands in production and service to the State.

The reader should consult at least one of the following works, wherein are given additional titles: Markham (1911, esp. Chaps. 8-11), Means (1931, Chaps. 8, 9, and 12), Joyce (1912, Chaps. 4 and 6), Mead (1932—a brief account), and Murdock (1934*a*).

The Aztec

The first of the great aboriginal states to fall before the Spanish invaders was that of the Aztec. Though contemporaries of the Inca, the Aztec operated in another continent, sufficiently isolated to avoid coming to blows. As military powers the two states were perhaps equals, and had one or both of them taken to the sea it is conceivable that a much greater aboriginal empire would have resulted, spanning the highlands of the two continents, but as matters stood in 1500 A.D. the Inca and the Aztec were so widely separated that there seems to have been almost no direct communication between them. Nevertheless there are many basic similarities in the culture of the two, which indicates that these two states came into existence by organizing smaller units among which wide diffusion of culture traits had been and was in progress.

The seat of the Aztec state was a city on the site of the modern capital of Mexico. The central plaza in the modern city is the approximate site of the great temple and other public buildings of the aboriginal capital. Chapultepec, a great hill nearby, was their stronghold and the source of the Aztec water supply, brought down by an aqueduct.

The origin of the Aztec is still a matter of debate, but they seem to have been a somewhat barbarian tribe among small .cultured states in central Mexico. About 1325 they seem to have occupied Chapultepec, and after strengthening their position began to fight with their neighbors. They suffered severely and retreated into the swamps and lagoons of the lowland. Here they began to build a Venice-like city, made agricultural lands and floating gardens. When Cortez came he found here a city with a wall, internal canals, lighthouses, and other conveniences. It was the builders of this small city-state who eventually ruled over all the central highland of Mexico.

Aztec chronology is usually given as follows:

Acamapichtli	1376-1396
Huitzilihuitl	1396-1417
Chimalpopoca	1417-1427
Itzcouatl	1427-1440
Moctezuma I	1440-1469
Azayacatl	1469-1482
Tizoc	1482-1486
Ahuitzotl	1486-1502
Moctezuma II	1502-1520
Cuitlahua	1520
Cuauhtemoc	1520-1521

These personages are designated as war-chiefs, and, while the most conspicuous and important of them seem not to have been as supreme and powerful as the Inca, nevertheless everyone had to approach the Aztec ruler with bowed head and bare feet. As in the case of the Inca, he was provided with many luxuries and attended at all times. As in Inca land, great palaces were provided for this war-chief and his court. Among other things, a zoological garden was maintained, in which curious and interesting animals, birds, and reptiles were confined, some for eating, some for feathers, etc.; it is reported that the bison was observed in confinement here, though his range was farther north. The collection of these curiosities alone would suffice to reveal the presence of a powerful state.

Apparently the state built up by the Aztec was less homogeneous than that of the Inca and far less socially integrated, but this may appear to be the case because we know more about the Aztec situation than the Inca. Like the Inca, the Aztec were the latest development in their area. For one, they were the heirs of the great Maya civilization, considered the high-water mark of aboriginal society, but whose center of development was in southern Mexico and adjacent Central America. Preceding the Aztec there had flourished a number of small states, probably mostly city-states, among which were federations of varying duration and magnitude. The first step of the Aztec was to form a federation of their immediate neighbors, taking care that their own dominance was maintained. Then one by one all the surrounding cities and towns were subjected. Tribute in men, houses, and goods was levied upon all these subjected units. All of this is best read in the special works upon the Aztec.

The Materials of Civilization. In the case of the Inca we enumerated the main categories of property and goods; the same list, with certain exceptions, will do for the Aztec. Agriculture was again the chief industry, maize, beans, and cotton being the crops of first importance. Again no iron was used, but gold, copper, and silver were skilfully worked. The number of copper weapons and tools seems to have been relatively fewer than with the Inca, obsidian offering good material for many kinds of edged tools. One clear distinction between the Inca and Aztec is that writing was used by the latter. Parchment and a kind of paper were made for preserving the written texts. We are told that each official had a map of his jurisdiction, lists of tribute to be exacted, census data, etc.; also that in the capital similar documents were on file. Rubber was used for many purposes. There were no large domestic animals like the llama, so all transportation was upon the backs of men. Here, as among the Inca, the wheel was unknown. Canoes were used when internal waterways were available, but the topography of the Mexican highlands did not encourage water transport. Architecture was grossly similar to that of the Inca, save that more use was made of the pyramid, and columns supported lintels and roofs. But the most striking difference is that, whereas the Inca walls were chiefly plain, those of the Aztec were covered with stone carvings, often in bold relief. We see in the carved façades of Aztec temples their heritage from the Maya.

Aztec Organization. The best authority on Aztec social organization is Bandelier (1878, 1879). The capital city was divided into four quarters according to the conventional points of the compass. Each quarter had a war-chief and a temple, and these four chiefs formed a kind of cabinet, next in rank to the supreme war-chief. The fundamental social unit was the *calpulli,* a kind of ward, originally a kind of family group. Each quarter held five of these wards, or twenty in all. The numbers four and twenty suggest that these divisions were arbitrary, corresponding to ceremonial concepts, a feature observable in many primitive societies.[1] One leader from each of the twenty wards constituted a council, and this body seems to have been the legislative unit.

The *calpulli* is thus the basic social unit and probably began in the primitive substratum of aboriginal society. It does not differ much from the Inca *ayllu.* In Mexico each *calpulli* seems to have had its own temple, which may mean certain individuality in ritualism. A kind of public hall was maintained where meetings were held and where war materials and tribute were kept. In the matter of land ownership the situation is not clear, save that the title to land seemed vested in the *calpulli* and not in its individual members.

There has been some dispute as to the status of the supreme war-chief, some giving him absolute power, others insisting that he was little more than commander-in-chief. Part of the confusion is due to the fact that there was a civil chief of almost coordinate rank who had the curious title of Snake-woman. Both offices seem to have been filled by election by the council of twenty chiefs, who, however, had to choose one of a single family line. There is nothing improbable in this arrangement, because the pattern of a war and a civil chief and their restricted election is found among many tribes of North America.

The judicial system of the Aztec city seems to have provided a court in each of the four quarters, where one chief and two associate judges sat continually. There was a higher court of appeal to which certain

---

[1] The Inca empire was divided into four parts also named after the four world quarters, and the capital city was in four quarters.

matters could be referred.   Conquered cities were provided with a court, if the Aztec considered such advisable.

The Aztec population seems to have consisted of freemen and slaves, though perhaps not quite in the sense in which we use these terms.   A person could sell himself or a member of his family into slavery.   Punish-ments for crime were often enslavement for the offender and frequently for his next of kin also.

The attitude toward land next claims our attention.   Land use seems to fall under three categories: the *calpulli* owned certain agricultural lands in common, from which allotments were made to families, and other lands reserved; on the reserved lands the able-bodied members of the *calpulli* labored under direction to maintain the priests, temples, and other public functions.   So far as we know the family owned the produce of its allotted land.   Under a second head fall lands allotted to warriors; these were plots in conquered districts where the owners were expected to form settlements.   These could be inherited but not sold, since they belonged to the war-chief in the capital of the state.   A third class con-stituted lands given to members of the aristocracy or relatives of the rulers, such lands forming private estates.   Though the data are con-flicting, it appears that these last were private property which could be sold.

> The Mexican social system therefore comprised a landed aristoc-racy who paid no definite taxes, but owed service to the king; associated with them was a military nobility who held lands at the king's good will, and whose tenants paid royal taxes.   Lower in rank were the calpulli freemen, who paid taxes in common; still lower, the tax-paying rent-holders, and finally the serfs, who paid taxes only to their feudal lords.   In addition to these there was the official clan, their sons and descendants, who, ranking as warriors and nobles, paid no definite taxes, but contributed their personal services and formed the suite of the ruler.   (Joyce, 1920, p. 117)

So, notwithstanding the contrary opinions held respecting the un-king-like position of the Aztec war-chief, we see an efficient empire held together by military force, the army being the vital mechanism in the organization of the state; all of which should have enabled a strong war-chief to seize power and consolidate a state, and there is every reason to believe that such a chief and his four advisers dominated the situation.

Social discipline was no less drastic than among the Inca.   Adultery was punished by death; unusually troublesome children were sold as slaves and those given to falsehood were marked by a cut in the lip. Only old people were permitted to get drunk, younger offenders were executed.   Disloyalty or revolt among subject cities and towns led to wholesale executions.   Prisoners of war were usually killed.

Labor.   Military service was universal for the Aztec, and levies were made upon all subject cities for soldiers as well as laborers.   Directly responsible to the rulers were a host of overseers under whom the popula-tion was brigaded somewhat after the Peruvian pattern.   Boys and girls in the schools were put to work according to their ages, to keep the temples in order, to care for their own dormitories, and seem to have been led by priests to engage in public works and in the fields. Crafts called for special training, but we are not informed as to the details of procedure. *Business*. In Inca land the distribution of goods seems to have been handled by the state; there may have been private traders, but, if so, no account of their doings has come down to us, but among the Aztec private traders flourished. Nevertheless these traders seem to have dealt in luxuries rather than in necessities. Tribute in food, clothing, and other necessities was exacted by the official tax gatherers and kept in the public stores, nor is there reason to believe that anyone was allowed to starve. On the other hand, there were differences in wealth, in size of houses, in furnishings, ornaments, presence of slaves, etc., and one source of such wealth was trade in distant cities and countries. The traders formed a recognizable class according to their costume and the kind of canes carried. There was a special god to whom they looked for prosperity.

> [He] was the one who started trading among those people, and for this reason the guild of the merchants adopted him as their god and honored him in different ways, one being to offer him paper with which they covered his statues wherever they found them. They also venerated the cane (stick) with which they walked, which was a solid cane called utatl (also otate). They have still another kind of cane or walking stick made of a solid light black cane without a knot, and which looks like reed such as is used in Spain. All merchants used that kind of cane on the road. When they reached the place where they were to spend the night, they would gather all their canes and tie them into one bundle, which they then stuck at the head of the sleeping place or camp. They would sprinkle blood in front of this bundle, which blood they obtained by bleeding their own ears, tongue, arms or legs. Then they offered incense by building a fire and burning copal in front of this bundle of sticks, which they considered as the image of the god Yiacatecutli, and by this means they asked him to protect them from all danger. These merchants traveled over the whole land, bartering, trading, buying in some place and selling in another what they had purchased. They also travel through towns, along the seashore, and in the interior. There isn't a place they do not pry into and visit, here buying, there selling; it is neither too hot for them in this place nor too cold in that one. They don't shun a road because it is too rough nor too difficult to search for whatever is there, either pretty or valuable or advantageous to buy and sell again. These traders suffer great hardships and are exceedingly daring; they go anywhere, even if it should be an enemy's domain and they are very sly in their deals with strangers, in learning their languages, as well as in their tactics, attaining through kindness what they want, thus gaining their confidence.
> (Sahagún, 1932, pp. 41-42)

The successful traders sacrificed many slaves in the temples since they could best afford such display. Youths were taken on trips as apprentices, to bear burdens, man canoes, etc.

The towns maintained markets where food and all kinds of useful objects were exchanged, from which it appears that individual trade flourished even in the common household. Special markets were maintained for gold, feathers, and other expensive wares brought in by the traveling merchants. We are told that the market in the Aztec capital had numerous stalls in which assorted goods were displayed, thus facilitating trade. That the market was controlled is clear, since there were inspectors going about and three magistrates ready to hear all cases. A full enumeration of the objects, slaves, and goods offered for exchange will be found in the account by Bernal Diaz (1908-16).

There was nothing in the way of true money, but coca beans were sometimes used as a standard of value and so as a kind of exchange unit. Since these beans were consumable goods, they cannot be considered as on a level with money.

The Priesthood. The list of Aztec gods is somewhat disconcerting, and their functions are far from consistent, so one may suspect that they represent accretions from other peoples—as was the case in the Roman Empire. The chief god of the Aztec was Tezcatlipoca, but we learn that the war god, Huitzilopochtli, was worshiped in the chief temple, leaving one in doubt as to which was really the superior. Then follows a long array of other gods, including the sun, moon, earth, etc. Most cities had individual gods, and so did many of the *calpulli*. As in the case of Peru, the priests seem to have groped for a single supreme unseen god, but such played no part in public worship.

To support so much ritualism a large body of priests was maintained. As in the case of the political state, there were two high priests, one to represent the war-god, the other the gods of Tlaloc, or those having to do with water supply, rain, weather, etc. Taking the subject peoples of the Aztec collectively, it was generally true that each god had a high priest and a flock of subordinate priests. While on the surface we seem to have less integration than among the Inca, still ceremonialism was systematized to the extent that all recognized festivals and ceremonies were facilitated by the state.

As in many cultures, education was in the hands of the priests. The nobility among the Aztec attended a school of their own under the direction of the chief temple and so of the high priest. This was for boys only and the training was designed to prepare them for prominent positions in the temples and the army. Since the army was always accompanied by priests there is nothing strange in their association in a training school. Boys for this school were taken from home when young, and, as they lived continuously in the school until ready for marriage, we note an institution comparable to the men's house of more primitive societies. Their religious training was as rigorous as any other; service in the temples, care of equipment, and frequent self-torture in offering their own blood were parts of the routine of school life. School ended with the making of a warrior or a priest. War training was not merely in a play school but on the fighting front, and the graduate became a warrior only after having the regulation achievements to his credit.

Daughters of the nobility were trained in a school of their own where deportment, domestic arts, and religious duties held a prominent place in the educational program. They were subject to strict discipline and carefully chaperoned.

As may be expected, these schools set the pattern for schools found in all parts of the Aztec territory in association with the temples.

Sacrifice. One of the spectacular aspects of Aztec society is the ceremonial killing of human beings. We have remarked upon the making of slaves as a punishment, and when we note that slaves were frequently sacrificed the significance of the penalty is apparent. There is available an English translation of Sahagún's classical work, the perusal of which will give a realistic idea of the place of the human sacrifice in Aztec religion. Not only on important feast days, but at any time were such sacrifices made. Even a merchant about to go on a trading trip would bring a slave or two to the temple to be sacrificed in order that his good fortune might be guaranteed. It is difficult to estimate the number of victims, but we are told that several hundred at a time was not unusual. Children and adults, male and female, according to the ritual in the case, were brought to the temples. Their hearts were burned and the blood collected as an offering to the gods. Some accounts state that the flesh was often eaten. Victims were secured from subject cities as tribute levies and by sending out the army to take captives. Thus it was necessary to wage continual war in order to perpetuate this religious ritualism, and we are told that the method was so formalized that the armies of certain cities met regularly to take captives from each other. These captives were either sacrificed immediately or taken home to the temples.

It was blood that the gods sought, in return for which rain, crops, health, good fortune, etc., were expected to be showered upon the living. Further, the human sacrifice was only the climax of far more numerous other sacrifices: priests and the multitude, even children, pierced their skins to draw blood for the gods; animals were sacrificed, and, lastly, grains, fruits, etc. For example, at the feast of Tochilhuitl the populace appeared at the temple and at noon cut off the heads of many quail, bled their own ears, and thrust thorns through their tongues, all for blood offerings. Then bread, fruits, and honey were offered. Finally, slaves were delivered to the priests for the sacrifice. Thus we read:

> When the temple was again full, the youths of the nobility came forth. Each one had some small knives in one hand, and in the other a bundle of thin smooth sticks of osier. Sitting down in their correct order, they practiced a peculiar form of self-sacrifice. This consisted of making wounds in the fleshy part of the left arm above the elbow. . . . Through these they passed the sticks one by one, drawing them out covered with blood. (Thompson, 1933, p. 217)

The sticks were then offered to the sun.

Thus the Aztec seems to have paid a heavy price for permission to live, even in the lives of his children and fellowmen. The highest kind of sacrifice was that in which the victim was a willing participant, fired with religious zeal. One is perhaps shocked at the loss to society of so many men and women sacrificed in the prime of life, but it is far from clear that no thought was given to the conservation of good human stock. It is true that for some of the important ceremonies the finest physical types were chosen, yet there are statements that the most undesirable slaves and the criminally inclined of all classes sooner or later met death at the temple. The barring of diseased victims seems to have been chiefly due to the custom of eating the bodies of those sacrificed, which also accounts for the careful fattening of intended victims. Further, the greater part of those sacrificed seem to have been captives and tribute slaves of non-Aztec origin, that is, from subject cities and tribes.

Fatalism and Sin. According to Sahagún after a child was born it was the custom to call in a priest who determined, according to certain rules, what would be the fate of this new personality. Some were doomed to maladjustment, some to drunkenness, some to various kinds of crime, etc. Apparently some steps could be taken to improve the prospects of these children, but, for the most part, nothing could be done about it. Though nothing is said about it, one may suspect that children sold into slavery and given for sacrifice would include many such unfortunates. On the other hand, value was placed upon moral training in the schools, and punishment used to inhibit evil doing.

Frequent comment is made on the practice of confession to a priest, indicating an idea of sin comparable to that entertained by European nations. This is probably going too far in the matter of interpretation, but the accounts we have reveal some recognition of guilt. A form of procedure was provided by which one could make a full confession of guilt to a priest who represented the goddess Tlazolteotl. After hearing the penitent, the priest decided upon the sacrifices and self-denials required to atone for these sins. Strangely enough, though such a procedure wiped the slate clean, the process could not be repeated. We are told that most such confessions were made in old age or to escape execution, since the confession stayed the arm of the law. Note should be taken that real overt acts are confessed, not merely feelings of unworthiness.

One or more of the following references should be read to supplement the information given in this chapter: Bandelier (1878, 1879), Diaz (1908-1916), Sahagún (1932), Spence (1912), Spinden (1922, chap. on the Aztecs), Thompson (1933, Chaps. 4 and 5).

General. Not all of the area we have set off as the region of city-states was under the sway of the Aztec and the Inca. In fact, their frontiers were many miles apart. They thus stand as two independent political developments, the culminating peaks of the sixteenth century. For completeness' sake we should note that between Mexico and Peru and on their respective margins were a number of lesser political units, interspersed here and there with primitive agricultural tribes. These smaller states in a way constituted the substratum out of which the two great aboriginal military governments arose. As in the Old World, a succession of these smaller states must have arisen and fallen, federations formed and dissolved, furnishing the political materials for the making of empires. The span of time was considerable, certainly several thousand years, and it was during this period that the basic elements in the cultures of these central highlands were developed, such as cultivation of maize, work in copper, gold, silver, weaving of fine cloth, building with stone, etc. So there is little need of reviewing the cultures of these smaller states, the essentials appearing in the history of the two great empires just considered.

A few of the common social characteristics of the Aztec and Inca invite comment. Certain aspects of the family seem identical. Though it is difficult to decide what form of marriage prevailed throughout the area, monogamy seems to have led, for when, for reasons of wealth or power, additional wives were taken the original one tended to be the real wife. In Peru, the Inca in his immediate domain had from time to time a census made of the marriageable, and forthwith they were married. That the Aztec resorted to such state-directed marriages is not clear, but we are told that persons seeking divorce had to apply to a designated court, where a judge heard the case, doing everything possible to adjust the difficulty and prevent separation. On the whole, inheritance seems to have been through the father in Aztec and Inca society, though there may have been examples of female descent among many of the subject tribes. There was no individual ownership of land in the European sense, though this was in a fair way to develop among the noble and warrior classes to whom special grants were made from the lands of newly conquered areas. The main support of the people was agriculture, carried on in family plots and in public areas tilled by mobilized labor. Each civil government was paralleled by a priestly organization, on similar patterns, though the civil head was usually superior to the corresponding priest. Ritualism was developed to a degree strange to European thought, as in these great aboriginal empires every day seemed to call for its appropriate temple ceremonies. The necessary mathematics and methods of precise astronomical observation were used to keep track of this religious routine.

THE AGRICULTURAL TRIBES

The area of great empires is surrounded by a larger territory in which most of the tribes practice some agriculture, but engage in such hunting and fishing as the environment permits. Maize was raised in most every part of the area. In North America this was the chief domesticated food; in Central and South America it was often overshadowed by manioc. A few plants of lesser economic importance were raised, wild foods being drawn upon when available. Agricultural labor in the area of city-states was carried on by men, or at least men did the heavy work, whereas in the area we are now discussing the tendency was in the other direction. In northern Mexico and our Southwest the fields were chiefly tended by men, but elsewhere in the United States the work of men was usually limited to assistance in clearing the land. Where hunting was strongly developed, men were not disposed to work in the fields.

It should not be assumed that life was uniform throughout this area. The differences are often contrasting enough, as between the village Indians of New Mexico and the less sedentary Indians of Massachusetts, or again between the Creeks of our southern states and the tribes on the Rio Negro. The one characteristic they had in common was the cultivation of maize, a practice originating somewhere in the area of city-states. Most of them produced pottery, attempted some weaving, but rarely indulged in the building of temples or other public works. Their dwellings were often of simple structure and easily moved or rebuilt. Many tribes in fact were seasonally nomadic. Metal work was almost completely absent. There were among them no great nations, but occasionally federations approaching such levels. Finally, the material equipments possessed by these tribes were meager as compared with the Aztec or Inca civilizations.

The term "city-state" is no longer applicable here, as we now find the population in relatively small independent civil units to which the name "tribe" is given. It is true that a few villages on the margins of the great empires had populations of a thousand or two, but no one of them seems to have hit upon the idea of building up a state in the sense in which we have used the term. Perhaps the units were not big enough. For the most part, the population was scattered in small camps or communities of a hundred persons or less, and a number of such organized loosely into a civil unit, or tribe. Two thousand seems an unusual number for a tribe, though it is not always easy to draw the line between a tribe and a subdivision. Each camp was largely self-sufficient, except in matters of defense and ceremonial procedure. The economic interrelations of the camps or villages has not been studied as it deserves, but it seems that within the tribe economic aid was forthcoming so that the line of defense was against want as well as war and pillage. A fair picture of this belt of agricultural peoples is a population functioning in small local civil units; here and there peace federations were set up, but most tribes were jealous of their freedom and unwilling to be integral parts of larger civil organizations.

We have noted that tribes were small aggregates of population, and, as we shall see later, were composed of still smaller units, such as camps, communities, or villages, made up of families in the usual sense of that term. Whatever one may think of civilized man, everyone will agree that such groups as we are now to discuss are biologically a predatory fauna. They live off the country; they exploit their immediate environment according to the corresponding patterns in their cultures. There is reason to beleve that such populations will be sparse or dense according to the kinds of their economic patterns. However this may be, the great empires of the central area were relatively dense in population. Estimates of population for the agricultural tribes in the United States have been made, from which estimates of density can be calculated. In terms of the number of square miles per capita available for sustenance we have the following:

New England	2.6
Middle Atlantic States	3.2
South Atlantic States	2.7
Central States	2.8
Gulf States	2.7
New Mexico and Arizona	3.2

It is not to be assumed that population was evenly distributed, but rather bunched in camps or villages according to the culture pattern prevailing. Thus in New England a village of 100 persons might range over some 260 square miles. The amount of land cultivated would probably not exceed 20 individual plots, or 10 acres. The remaining land was used for foraging, fishing, and hunting. In the Gulf States, where climate is more favorable to agriculture, the area cultivated was not much greater. Finally, in New Mexico and Arizona, where there is much waste arid land and the villages depended largely upon what their fields produced, the proportions were not greatly different. It would be a mistake to assume that food was the sole determinant of population, because war and the chase took a steady toll and internal homicide a somewhat less but still depleting ratio.

To an agricultural people like the Inca, land is the most important possession, but we see that most of these tribes cultivated so small a fraction of the land that no one need worry about a place to put his field. It was more important that the tribe hold sufficient land for hunting and forage. In any case, the land seems everywhere to have been regarded as tribal, open to the free use of every member of that tribe. Usually possession was determined by ability to defend. Open trespass upon hunting land resulted in a fight, so that the hunter was not infrequently hunted. Under such conditions the value of an unoccupied area surrounding a camp or village is clear.

The tribe is usually governed by a council of the older men. The subdivisions of the tribe are usually hereditary units, often called sibs. When the child belongs to the sib of the mother the divisions are called "clans," and when he goes with his father's sib, "gentes." Another characteristic of the sibs is that they are exogamous, which brings it about that mother and father are from different sibs. It does not follow that all sibs camp or live apart, but in many cases the sibs function in civil units in the tribe. In such cases there are often sib leaders, or chiefs, and a sib council, usually exclusively male. The tribal council may then be made up of the heads of the sibs. These councils designate leaders who thus become tribe chiefs. The allegiance of the sib chiefs is largely voluntary, and the power of the tribe chief such as his personality can command. This type of organization is apparent in the Aztec scheme.

Looking at the tribe from another angle we find certain age distinctions, as the unmarried men, the warriors, and head-men. The chief control seems to be in the head-men, the warriors standing by, more or less, as against the youths or unmarried. The reactions of these groups to each other form the main structure of tribal society. No courts are maintained, nor is there anything like a school. Instruction is usually individual and a part of the regular routine.

In such a society the individual possesses great freedom, as there is ample scope for individualism. It is true that custom and tabu have their say, but often these protect the individual as well. Economic living may be collective and communistic in the main, but on the other hand the individual is allowed great freedom of action. He may or may not join a war party; if a member of a council, he may take any side of a question he chooses; he may determine his own religious beliefs, etc. When he threatens to act anti-socially he may be reasoned with, but rarely forced. Of course, if too overt, the group will take drastic action, often spontaneous.

As in most primitive societies, the sib or even the community unit possesses such solidarity that it assumes certain responsibilities for the acts of its members. If a man from one village or camp injures a person from another village, the reaction of the injured one's sib is to retaliate against the other sib as a whole, and so against any or all such members as it may lay hold of. This response is given various names, but probably means no more than that the camp is accustomed to act as a social unit toward all external situations. Within the sib, a quarrel tends to draw in all the immediate families of the contenders, but the responsibility is less clearly placed than when two camps or sibs are involved. When the tribal philosophers rationalize such procedure, they seem to feel that since a community attempts to control its own members, it should assume the responsibility for individual acts. This is not to say that the practice grows out of a rationalization; it may be far more spontaneous than that.

Sibs and Relationship Systems. General discussions of sibs, clans gentes, and relationship systems hold a prominent place in the literature dealing with primitive society; it is among the tribes now under consideration that sibs come to the fore. It may well be that the frequent coincidence between civil units and sibs stimulates curiosity as to the part these sibs may play in the development of large political units such as were discussed in the preceding section. Some theories of society have proceeded on the assumption that sibs were the foundation stones of civilized society, but these are questions not to be considered here. Our task is to review briefly the sib as it appears among these aboriginal agricultural hunters. The sib is an ancestral class and is of two kinds: those inheriting their class through the mother and those inheriting it through the mother's husband. The name "clan" is usually given the former and "gens" to the latter. They thus differ in whether the line of descent is female or male. Theoretically at least, all in a sib are relatives and may be considered as an enlarged family. It so happens that in the area under consideration the prevailing type of sib is the clan, but gentes do exist. When we turn to a discussion of the nonagricultural hunters we shall find them for the most part lacking in both clans and gentes. The detailed data for aboriginal America have been used in attempts to show that the more complex societies take to the gens, the simpler to the clan. However, since both forms existed here and in Mexico, the argument resolves itself into the statement that the sib may be an important institution among the more complex. Thus the question of male versus female inheritance becomes secondary.

An interesting feature of the sib is its use in defining marriage restrictions, which are usually exogamous. Another peculiarity is that in the case of clans the husband goes to live with the wife's people and in the case of gentes the reverse holds. There is nothing strange about this, since the married pair thus live where the children belong.

Another feature of this society is that the tribe is frequently divided into two parts, or dual divisions, sometimes called "phratries." This distinction does not cut across the sibs, but divides them more or less evenly.

Thus the sibs (clans) in the Seneca tribe were divided as follows:

First division

| 1. Bear | 2. Wolf | 3. Beaver | 4. Turtle |

Second division

| 5. Deer | 6. Snipe | 7. Heron | 8. Hawk |

The methods of classifying relatives have long intrigued students of society. In fact, the possible significance of differences in these methods was first cited by Morgan, one of the great social philosophers of his time. In our own strictly monogamous system of marriage it is considered important to distinguish clearly between the children of the respective pairs, but in most of the tribes now under consideration the emphasis seems to be on the generation or age level rather than upon strict blood descent: thus, under a sib system all girls born of mothers in the same sib may be spoken of as sisters. However, the systems used by the tribes in the area under consideration seem in no wise peculiar to them.

Turning back to the sib as a social institution, we find that members of a sib tend to live together, either as a separate community or in a definite part of the camp or village. Sometimes this grouping is associated with religious and other concepts; the dual divisions may be on the north and south sides of the village respectively, one in some way associated with winter, the other with summer, etc. If there are restrictions upon the office of tribe chief, these restrictions may take the form of limiting choice to a single sib, in other words, a kind of royal lineage.[2] Further, certain priestly and ceremonial functions may likewise belong to a single sib. Agriculture encourages permanent village or camp sites, and in turn may support the segregation of sibs.

Federations. When discussing the Inca and Aztec we observed their rise to power by conquest and federation. While we find no great nations in the area now under consideration, interesting examples of federations come to notice. One of the best known is the so-called League of the Iroquois, or Five Nations, in what is now New York State (see Morgan, any ed.). There was another and perhaps older federation of Iroquois-speaking tribes, the Hurons, living northeast of Detroit. In 1615 this group was composed of four tribes and a number of outlying communities They were destroyed by the League after the latter had received firearms.

The League is supposed to have taken its final form about 1570. This

---

[2]Note the Aztec restrictions in electing a war-chief.

was after the discovery of America but before direct contact with European peoples. The original constituent tribes were Cayuga, Mohawk, Oneida, Onondaga, and Seneca. For the scheme of civil organization the literature should be consulted, but it is usually regarded as a relatively ideal plan of federation. Our chief interest here is in its history. The apex of power was about 1670, at which time the population of the five tribes was about 16,000, living in some twenty-four villages, occupying the greater part of New York State and adjacent parts of Canada, Pennsylvania, and Ohio. They exacted allegiance from many tribes surrounding this territory.

Although possessing an effective civil organization, these tribes had no system of writing, built neither temples nor public buildings, lived in cabins of bark and poles, raised maize, squash, beans, etc., but depended largely upon hunting. Work in the fields was mostly woman's work; men hunted and went to war. The objectives of the League seem to have been security from attack when at home and abroad, the extension of their hunting territories, and the increase of power and prestige. What they might have accomplished had Europeans not interfered, one can but guess. That they had a long road to travel before reaching the level of the Aztec is clear. Their culture differed little from that of the weaker tribes around them.

Possibly in imitation of this federation, certain Algonkian-speaking tribes east of the Hudson River formed a loose federation usually passing under the name "Abnaki." When the English settled in Virginia they came into conflict with the Powhatan confederacy, which quickly broke down under pressure of the colonists. In the southern states two strong groups were functioning, the Cherokee and the Creek confederacy. The first was a large well-organized tribe numbering about 14,000 in 1730; the latter was a true confederation of tribes, in which the Creeks dominated. Some fifty towns were included. Most of these spoke Muskhogean languages, though there were among them representatives of two other language stocks. This was a powerful confederation containing tribes with interesting culture traits, to be noted under another heading. A few much weaker combinations of closely related tribes and subtribes were to be observed in other parts of this area. All these confederacies, great and small, seem to have been formed primarily for defense, miniature leagues of nations within relatively small areas. The anarchy of ever-warring tribes is perhaps sufficient explanation for their being. They were not strictly non-aggressive, for the Iroquois entertained ambitions of conquest.

When we turn to South America almost no trace of such federations occurs outside of the Andean region.

The Pueblos. In the New Mexico and Arizona of today survive some twenty-six separate Indian villages to which the distinctive name *pueblos* is given. The advantage of this name is that it defines a group of villages with closely similar cultures, thus distinguishing them from aboriginal villages in other parts of the New World. The peculiar housing structure of these pueblos is well known; the population of each such village formerly lived in one or two large buildings of separate rooms, designed to afford protection, like the castles and walled cities of Europe. If a relief map of the pueblo area is consulted, one perceives a rather high plateau enclosed by mountain ridges, and it is within the limits of this table land that all the historic pueblos are located. They are found in groups, bound by ties of language and sometimes other relationships, but for the most part each pueblo remains politically independent. Their chief support formerly was maize, beans, and squash; they domesticated the turkey, raised cotton and some tobacco; most of the meat consumed came frqm hunting. The men did most of the farming and most of the weaving; the women bore most of the burden of building and repairing the houses, and made pottery and baskets. Consistently enough, the woman owned the home and when the harvest was brought in took possession of the grain, it being up to her to prepare and serve the food.

The plan of organization included for each pueblo a civil chief and a war-chief, chosen or appointed annually. The former stood as the executive of the pueblo, met all visitors, etc. The latter, of course, led in war and defense, acted as chief of police, and was also in charge of all communal labor. However, there was a more powerful person, locally called the *cacique,* who seems to have served for life; this functionary was a kind of high priest, whose superiority is attested by the fact that he usually appointed the chiefs. There was a council of the older men, the war chief being their executive agent. The people of the pueblo are grouped in clans, and, though the villages are independent and often of different speech, the names used for these clans are about the same, suggesting cultures of common origin.

The ceremonial life is largely in the hands of men. Each village contains a number of ritualistic secret societies, each of which conducts public ceremonies such as, for example, the celebrated snake dance. There are no temples, but simple circular rooms called kivas are used as ceremonial places, and altars are set up from time to time in these. At sundry places outside the village are shrines where offerings are made. The chief concern of the people is the maize crop, hence their concern with rain and favorable weather.

Not only was this area marginal to Mexico, but similar village cultures have been found south of the Rio Grande, leading some students to assume that the great empires of the Mexican highlands were composed of just such units. There is doubtless some truth in this contention, but archeological research in the pueblo country reveals a long and gradual development from simple cultures to the complex villages of historic time, for which reason we must expect some degree of individuality in even this marginal area.

Good descriptions of pueblo life and history may be found in Goddard (1931), Hewett (1905), and Kidder (1924).

The Lower Mississippi Tribes. Another region in which village life was well organized was the country around the lower Mississippi River, particularly among the Natchez. Unfortunately our information is fragmentary because the French wars with the Natchez destroyed their villages and scattered the survivors, but all the available data have been reviewed by Swanton (1911, 1922).

As in the Southwest, agriculture was intensively practiced and the turkey domesticated. Maize was the chief crop, and it appears that certain parts of the land were tilled for communal purposes and for the support of the ruling class, labor being brigaded for the latter. The harvest was stored in a public warehouse. The French writers speak of a temple in which, a perpetual fire was kept, attended by priests. The architecture of these temples, however, was simple, like that of regular houses. The ruler was supposed to have descended from the sun and could be approached only ceremonially. He was carried in a kind of chair similar to that used in Mexico and Peru; when dead, his body was deposited in the temple. At his funeral, too, his wives and many male subjects were executed. Head-flattening as in Mexico and Peru was in vogue. Some human sacrifices seem to have been made.

No extensive use of metals has been noted, though copper ornaments have been reported. No cotton was cultivated, but some fine cloth was woven from native materials. Pottery was made. Thus, though their material culture was simple, these village peoples had gone farther in some of the forms of life than the other agricultural tribes in the area under consideration. Further, the cultures of these people bear resemblances to both the Pueblos and to the Aztec and Inca.

The Amazon Country. East of the Andes is a large area drained by the Amazon and Orinoco river systems, comprising half the continent. The region is for the most part low and a tropical forest. While a number of linguistic stocks are found here, four dominate: the Arawak and Carib in the northwest, and Tupi and Tapuya in the southeast. The first two extend into the West Indies.

Manioc vies with maize here as the chief staple, but tobacco, coca, yams, pumpkins, peppers, etc., are raised. This is the aboriginal home of the hammock, the cigar, and snuff. Cannibalism was a widely practiced custom in this area. As to the forms of society, our information leaves much to be desired, but the general pattern seems to be autonomous, if not independent, villages. Usually certain formalities accompany the installation of a chief, but in most cases his authority is nominal. The shamans exercise a good deal of power, their equipment containing, among other objects, cigars of tobacco and calabash rattles. Well-defined sibs appear here and there, some paternal, some maternal. Ordeals are prominent, such as ceremonial whipping and biting by ants. The reader should consult Whiffen (1915) and im Thurn (1883) or Murdock (1934b, Chap. 15).

Summary. This outlying fringe of agricultural hunters hung on the frontiers of the area of city-states, as did the barbarians around Greece and Rome. They were, in the main, still primitive hunters, but toyed with the economic techniques of the city-states, here and there approaching the level of true agriculturists. Some of these tribes, encouraged by the new food economy, set up control by conquest and possession, forming federations and thus making a feeble gesture toward following the road that leads to empires. On the lower Mississippi were cultures vaguely reminiscent of Inca and Aztec ceremonialism and social discipline; farther north the Pawnee conducted human sacrifices on the pattern of the Aztec; in northern Mexico and adjacent United States were villages recalling those of the immediate Aztec fringe, raising cotton, keeping turkeys, etc.; and again on the southern borders of the Inca were other villages strikingly similar. The somewhat erratic outer boundary of agricultural practice, and the still more erratic extension of city-state culture traits, as temples for the sun, carrying the chief in a chair, keeping of a sacred fire, regimenting the population to labor in the fields, the Aztec form of human sacrifice, etc., is what might be expected when we take a sixteenth-century cross-section of the New World. Ceremonial cruelties were numerous. The individual was about as free as among the true hunters, only now and then for an interval submitting himself to civil discipline. The family group was more in evidence than among the city-states and the tendency was toward a clan organization. It was chiefly among tribes in this belt that Morgan found the data to project a theory of society.

THE HUNTING TRIBES

We now turn to the inhabitants of the marginal continental areas distinguished by not engaging in the cultivation of food plants. They, in common with all aboriginal Americans, domesticated the dog; in some places the dog was used for transport, in some eaten, and in others as an aid in hunting, but above all, the dog was a companion and a watchman.

The term "hunters" may be too emphatic for these tribes, because vegetable food was used in varying amounts. In California, for example, the acorn and certain wild seeds played an equal if not greater part in the domestic economy of certain tribes than did maize among some of the agricultural hunters. Nevertheless the ceremonial and mythological maize complex had no place in the culture of these hunters.

The North Pacific Coast. One of the first regions to demand our attention is a stretch of coast land from Oregon to the Aleutian Islands. In the popular mind this is the home of Indians who erected great carved wooden totem poles, made large dug-out canoes, etc. The coast is skirted by islands and indented by numerous inlets. As may be anticipated, travel is chiefly by canoe. The climate is mild and moist, the people go barefoot and lightly clothed, if at all, but often wear large hats. They live in villages on the seashore and along the wide mouths of rivers, build rectangular houses of planks, live chiefly upon sea food and salmon, though there was some hunting on land. What vegetable food they used was gathered from wild plants. We have said that they were non-agricultural, which is true, save that some of these tribes raised a little tobacco. No pottery was made; food was boiled in baskets and wooden boxes into which hot stones were dropped. Basketry and wood-carving were the chief arts.   Some coarse weaving was attempted with strands of shredded cedarbark and with wools of wild goat and a certain breed of dog.

In social matters they remind us of the city-states, since we find a lower class, or slaves, an upper rank of chiefs, etc.   Captives were made slaves, required to mate among themselves and so perpetuate their class. The ownership of these slaves seems to have been vested in individuals, usually of rank.   On certain ceremonial occasions, owners would sacrifice their slaves and not infrequently kill them in public demonstrations of their wealth.   There are even traditions that slaves were formerly eaten.

Those we call chiefs inherited their positions as heads of family groups, each cherishing more or less mythical ancestors and certain painted and carved figures, called crests.   By tradition, such family groups are ranked one over the other, thus automatically arranging the chiefs of these families in a kind of hierarchy.   Naturally, there was rivalry among such chiefs and the families they represented, as expressed in certain curious complicated institutions known as potlatches, by which a great deal of property was given away or loaned, the expectation being that it would be returned with interest.   It was the display of such property that recorded the prestige of the owners.   Yet the idea of such formal exchanges of property was so integrated in the society of this area that births, marriages, deaths, etc., were all celebrated by the exchange of property, in some cases by the destruction of property.

Shamanism was highly developed and the men maintained a number of secret societies which at stated times staged ceremonies of masked dancers.   The family ancestors, mostly animal gods, took a leading position in supernatural beliefs.   The idea of a supreme god, though vague, was not entirely lacking.   In some parts of the area each stream was supposed to have a goddess and in the sea the killer-whale god headed the list.   Naturally considerable variety in such beliefs was met with.   For the most part all animals were believed immortal and so not far removed from the human plane.

The following books will give additional information: Goddard (1934), Boas (1921).

People of the Plains.   West of the Mississippi River lies the familiar area of the plains, and in South America, chiefly in what is now Argentine, is another great grass-land area.   The aboriginal life usually associated with these areas is that of semi-nomadic horsemen, but the horse was introduced by Europeans.   On the other hand, the cultures of these Plains tribes indicate a prehistoric existence, during which they became adjusted to the plains and were not greatly changed by the introduction of the horse in historic times.

In North America the plains were the habitat of the bison, a never-failing food for the aboriginal tribes.   On the eastern and southern margins of these plains lived tribes who raised some maize and so were included in the discussion of agricultural hunters but whose cultures were primarily adjusted to bison hunting.   Out in the plains, however, the tribes were true hunters.   They made no pottery, rarely made baskets, dressed in skins, used skin tents. Before the horse was introduced they traveled on foot with dogs as pack animals. These tribes were warlike and aggressive, living in large camps of from one to two hundred tents. The tribe was under the leadership of a chief—in some cases two, a civil and a war-chief. The chief authority rested in a council representing all the constituent bands. These bands were, for the most part, groups of relatives and their leaders, but, as such, constituted the basic political and social units. If for any reason the tribal camp broke up temporarily, these bands camped apart. Frequent quarrels resulted in one or more bands withdrawing for a time and camping alone. The hunting of bison called for team work, which in turn called for organization and discipline. In a large camp each band had its fixed place in the circle, so that the pitching of camp was orderly and prompt. A number of police, as soldiers, were always on duty to enforce the orders of the chief, and heralds went about from time to time crying out orders. Such discipline not only insured the fruits of the hunt but success in war also. The chief property was the horse, some individuals boasting large herds. Ceremonialism was well developed, the rituals having mostly to do with health, food, and war. For the most part, rituals were the property of individuals, rarely rising to the level of a tribal status. The one outstanding ceremony was the so-called sun dance, in which the whole tribe participated. This ceremony is not in any way associated with agriculture, but with the buffalo, war, and the well-being of individuals, suggesting that it arose and functioned under a hunting economy. A series of societies for men were maintained, in some cases in age grades.

In the South American plains the original food animals were the guanaco and the rhea, but with the coming of Europeans cattle ran wild and the Indian took to horses. Indian life was then semi-nomadic; the Indians did not till the soil, worked in skins chiefly, lived in rude tents of skins or mats, carried babies in cradles similar to those used by the Plains Indians of North America, etc. Among some tribes civil and war-chiefs were maintained.

For further details read Wissler (1927) and Dobrizhoffer (1822).

California. California and a fringe in adjoining states was the home of a fairly dense population of relatively simple culture. The tribes clustered in valleys, and, strange to say, the linguistic diversity of these tribes far exceeds that in any other part of North America. These tribes were not agricultural, but in the use of acorns found a good staple substitute for maize. No pottery was made, nor cloth woven, but basketry was highly developed. Ceremonial life was simple. With a few exceptions the tribes were composed of simple bands, taking on no such form as the clans and gentes of the agricultural areas. We have used the term "tribe" here, but true political organization was almost non-existent. "Ethnic groups" has been proposed by Kroeber as a California substitute for the term tribe.

The reader should consult Kroeber (1925) for further information concerning these tribes.

Moose and Caribou Hunters. In Canada, stretching from the St. Lawrence to Alaska, are great forests of conifers in which range moose and
caribou, not to mention other animals. The winters are long and severe,
during which travel is by snowshoe and goods are transported by tobog-
gans, pulled by men or dogs. Hunting and fishing are the chief activities.
Clothing is rather elaborate, made entirely of skins and furs. Shelters
are crude, for the most part tipis covered with bark. Birchbark was
utilized for pails, cooking vessels, containers, and for covering tipis and
canoes. In summer, travel was as far as possible by the light birchbark
canoe, the use of which made the Indians about as mobile as the horse
users of the plains. Large camps were impossible in winter, hence these
hunters scattered in small bands. In keeping with this, we find no well-
developed leadership and little in the way of tribal organization. Yet
the use of a common language, similar culture interests, and ties of blood
defined an ethnic group which may be spoken of as a tribe. Shamanism
of the simpler kind was universal.

The following quaint account of an early observer not only presents
a vivid picture of hunting life in this area, but when stripped of its local
color may serve as a pattern for all primitive hunters. The narrator is
Joseph la France, recorded by Arthur Dobbs, a fur trader, at Hudson
Bay, 1744.

> The Indians West of the Bay, living an erratick Life, can have no
> Benefit by tame Fowl or Cattle; they seldom stay above a Fortnight
> in a Place, unless they find Plenty of Game. When they remove,
> after having built their Hut, they desperse to get Game for their
> Food, and meet again at Night, after having killed enough to main-
> tain them for that Day; they don't go above a League or two from
> their Hut. When they find Scarcity of Game they remove a League
> or two farther, and thus they traverse through these woody Countries
> and Bogs, scarce missing one Day, Winter or Summer, fair or foul,
> in the greatest Storms of Snow, but what they are employed in some
> kind of Chace. The smaller Game, got by Traps or Snares, are gen-
> erally the Employment of the Women and Children, such as the
> Martins, Squirrels, Cats, Ermins, etc. The Elks, Stags, Rain-deer,
> Bears, Tygers, wild Beeves, Wolves, Foxes, Beavers, Otters, Corcajeu,
> etc. are the Employment of Men. The Indians, when they kill any
> Game, for Food, leave it where they kill it, and send their Wives next
> Day to carry it home. They go home in a direct Line, never miss-
> ing their Way, by Observations they make of the Course they take
> upon their going out, and so judge upon what Point their Huts are,
> and can thus direct themselves upon any Point of the Compass. The
> Trees all bend towards the South, and the Branches on that Side
> are larger and stronger than on the North Side, as also the Moss
> upon the Trees. To let their Wives know how to come at the killed
> Game, they from Place to Place break off Branches, and lay them
> in the Road, pointing them the Way they should go, and sometimes
> Moss, so that they never miss finding it. London 1744. (pp. 41-42)

Consult Jenness (1932) for further information.

The Arctic Circle and Cape Horn. Upon the Arctic shores of America
live the Eskimo, too well known to need ordinary description. In the
main they are a seashore people in winter, hunting inland in summer.

Their life is thus ordered in correlation with the seasonal round. The routine is hard and the food supply subject to fluctuations, the margin between starvation and existence being narrow enough. Explorers often comment upon the good humor and jollity of the Eskimo, but fear of starvation is ever in the background, as they will betray when confidential. The supernatural world of the Eskimo was peopled with numerous beings all more or less antagonistic to human welfare. Of political organization there is but a skeleton; each camp is an independent unit in which the individual claims great freedom of action. Though the entire population is spread thinly from Greenland to Siberia, the linguistic and culture differences are relatively small. The Eskimo recognize certain ethnic groupings, but these have little political significance. War is largely a matter of personal feuds, hence there is little in the way of military organization; on the other hand, team work is shown in hunting caribou, whaling, and in taking walrus. Yet no true chiefs are recognized, probably because their self-contained communities are too small. Their family life is likewise simple, the man usually living with his wife's people. The burden of making adequate skin clothing placed the woman in a strategic position, because only with the united labors of both man and wife could the family survive. It remains to be added that in keeping with the exacting environment we find the Eskimo clever and ingenious, possibly superior in this respect to all other primitive peoples in the hunter class.

At the southern extremity of South America, in an uninviting environment, live a number of linguistic and ethnic groups often passing under the name Fuegians. The climate is far less severe than in the Arctic, so the Fuegians got along by merely muffling their bodies in skins. Not infrequently they tramped through the snow barefoot. They, too, lived by the sea, from which came much of their food. With many writers Fuegian is but another name for the most primitive human level of life, but this is hardly fair to these aborigines, though in material equipment they were poor enough. As in the Arctic north, there was nothing like a tribal organization, no chiefs were recognized, though the shamans at times exercised some control. A community of a few families was thus the unit of organization. In ceremonialism and religion these Indians were weaker than any other people in the New World. It was once doubted if they conceived of a soul but it now appears that they had at least something approximating that concept. They peopled the supernatural with many spirits, mostly antagonistic to man, but among them a kind of superior who created all things.

Consult Jenness (1932) and Lothrop (1928) for further details.

The Hunters in General. We have now glanced at the main groups of aborigines forming the area of hunting peoples. For one thing the boundary between these peoples and those who do some agriculture is wavering, as when a few outlying tribes plant tobacco only. Yet certain differences do prevail, since the most poverty-stricken cultures are found in parts of this area. The environments are often harsh and exacting, the wonder being that a human community could survive at all.

For the most part, social organization does not transcend the family group, nor are there complicated relationships and other social distinctions. Neither does the civil organization take enough form to outline a scheme of tribal government, the exceptions being among the plains people and those of the North Pacific coast. Federations for defense and war are conspicuously absent, in contrast to the agricultural hunters. However, too close a correlation should not be assumed because of the arbitrary nature of the classification. On the other hand, a well-organized system of chiefs with a scheme for integrating the units of a tribe is usually accompanied by clans, gentes, or bands in which one inherits a place. Further, a well-integrated scheme of ceremonial functions will accompany an elaborate civil set-up. In geographical position these hunters are outlying and in that sense marginal to the central areas of the more conspicuous Inca and Aztec cultures. For the most part, culture stimulation could come to them from only one direction, whereas the intermediate tribes were exposed to influences from two main directions.

GENERAL ABORIGINAL CHARACTERISTICS

We have now passed in rapid review the varieties of aboriginal life in 1492 and may well concern ourselves with how it would be to live in such a world. To the European of that time, life in the New World presented certain contrasts. Thus the wheel as a driving principle was wholly absent, and the same may be said of the plow and the broadcast sowing of grain. The ox and the horse were conspicuously wanting. Iron was unknown; but in a limited area, copper, and in Peru, bronze, was used. Neither glass nor true pottery glaze was known. While it is true that a form of writing was known to the Aztec and their immediate predecessors, its distribution was too limited to go far in shaping thought and action. Sea-going vessels had not passed the canoe stage. Temples were built, but the arch was wanting. Though there was some barter among the agricultural and hunting tribes and more systematic trade among the city-states, the use of gold and silver as money was unknown; in fact, the modern idea of money as a medium of exchange was not entertained. It remained for the early European traders to introduce such concepts. The use of tobacco was unique in aboriginal America; we are told that as Columbus first approached its shores he saw Indians awaiting him, smoking cigars. Cigarette and pipe smoking were regionally known, as was snuff and tobacco chewing. While the Indian associated tobacco with various religious procedures, he also valued it as a symbol of good will. It is surprising how completely the Old World fell for this one phase of New World culture.

Observers having experience with natives in the Old World as well as the New think they sense something in Indian personality expressible in general terms. For one, the serious, dignified mien of the Indian has been felt and interpreted by the European according to his own intellectual level. As a quality this seems highly valued by the Indian himself. True, other peoples according to their cultures put value upon dignity, but often surround themselves with external arrangements of costume, housing, etc., in the faith that these externals will convey the desired impression, whereas the Indian depends chiefly upon his own control. In other words, he looks the part even when alone on the trail in breechcloth and moccasins. The art of the Maya and the Inca seems to portray this same personal dignity. Finally, this attitude is observable in the many varieties of ritualistic procedure practiced by the Indian.

Aboriginal mentality must be gauged by achievements. As an inventor the Indian has much to his credit. His chief economic contributions were domesticated plants. He not only sensed the potentialities of the wild flora, but improved the species by domestication. Modern man has possessed the lands of the Indian, but so far he has scarcely added an important domestic plant to the list already controlled and exploited by the prehistoric Indians. Full lists are given by many writers, particularly by Merrill (1933), of which we need but mention a few—maize, tobacco, potato, coca, and peanut. The contrast with the Old World is chiefly in the botanical origin of these plants rather than in the technique of production, each great world area having exploited its floral resources and built up large political units and relatively dense populations by specializing in cereals. On the other hand, the use of domestic animals for power and transport was singularly weak in the New World. Yet in the matter of mechanical devices the Indian can qualify as an inventor (Nordenskiöld, 1929). Among those commanding our approval are the hammock, the cigar, the tobacco pipe, the birch canoe, the lacrosse game, toboggan, rubber ball, bola, tipi, maple sugar, lye-hominy, whistling-jar, cassava squeezer, etc. All of these have met with recognition in the modern world. To them could be added a respectable list of value to native Indian culture and serving to set off the material cultures of the New as against the Old World.

It is frequently asserted that society in the New World was universally communistic, and as respects land and natural resources this seems to be true. Lewis H. Morgan conceived the "law of hospitality" as a more precise expression of this attitude, and, while it may be difficult to prove that the more primitive Indian emphasized this attitude more than other peoples, it is clearly a fundamental aboriginal trait. To the accumulation of wealth this attitude was antagonistic, leading to such a formalization as "the richest man is he who gives away the most." The ideal was thus in giving and not in hoarding. Even in Mexico and Peru this attitude was foremost respecting certain kinds of property.

Turning to the concept of the family, we find the usual forms of association of the sexes and the tendency for two or three generations to form a household, but perhaps more than elsewhere the concept of a family ritual, a ceremonial bundle, and the inherent right of the family to perform certain ceremonial and religious functions in the village and the tribe.

But what of the aboriginal mental world? Magic, the symbol of ignorance, the method of desperation, was everywhere. Here and there a few of the most intellectual groped for unity in the universe and for the unseen but necessarily logical supreme power. The early history of the Old World gives examples of the same growing dissatisfaction with the lack of logical consistency in the beliefs respecting the unseen world. Yet in the New World such power was conceived, if at all, as impersonal and implacable, too remote to be moved by the misfortunes of men. Some emotional satisfaction may have been experienced by the few entertaining such thoughts, but in real life they were ever mindful of the traditional gods and powers, various and antagonistic, upon whose whims and passions the fortunes of mere man seemed to depend. For the most part these gods were thought of as vindictive to the extent that the individual must walk warily among the senseless prohibitions and tabus these malevolent gods were believed to have invented to plague and to test out the Indian. As a defense technique the Indian devised a bewildering array of charms, songs, rituals, and sacrifices. It mattered not that even the gods he sought to placate were themselves the creations of the imagination of his ancestors, the residual rationalizations growing out of experience with the world in which the Indian found himself. In all this the generality of Indian beliefs differed little from those of the primitive Old World, but the visions were his own and the types of response he cultivated belonged to his own environment. In this specific sense the unreal world of the Indian was original.

Yet it would be a mistake to think that the Indian lived in a state of fear. Of bravery he had a man's share; but he looked upon the phenomena of nature with respect and awe, often finding therein great emotional satisfaction. As a hunter he knew animals and birds well; he matched his wits and strength against them and endowed them with more intelligence than we in this prosaic age are willing to concede. He believed that on occasion individual animals manifest great powers and speak to man face to face. Indeed, much of Indian wisdom was supposed to have been transmitted in this way. When the Indian spoke, his language was colorful, most of his figures of speech resting upon nature as he saw her.

The quest for a vision seems to have no close parallel in the Old World. There are many records of such in the New World, the patterns of which center around this speaking face to face with living creatures. The idea is not that the mere animal speaks, but that through it, as the best medium he can conceive, speak the unseen powers of nature. The sincere vision-seeker goes out from the haunts of his kind and cries aloud in the loneliness of the night. It is a mournful, supplicating cry. Such notes of sadness and supplication can be sensed in many Indian ritual songs. The points of difference as between Indian and non-Indian attitudes are not to be found in the gross pattern, but in certain integrating qualities of thought and emotion.

One approach to the kind of an unseen world the Indian entertained is through his mythology and folklore, a large body of which has been recorded, especially from the hunters and simple agriculturists. Little has been done in the way of interpreting this material, but there is some obvious homogeneity. As Brinton pointed out long ago, there is widespread belief in a bearded god, prominent among the city-states, but spreading far out toward the margins of both continents. Sometimes confused with this concept is what is called the "trickster culture hero," a super-being who transforms the world and the social order as well, but who at the same time indulges in immoral, trivial, and obscene conduct, which to our minds is shockingly inconsistent. The unseen world is peopled with animal gods who appear, if at all, in the corresponding animal form— a bear, bison, jaguar, condor, eagle, serpent, etc. The chief patron saint of the medicineman in Mexico, the Andes, and throughout the Amazon was a great cat—the puma or the jaguar, according to locality—and in the United States and Canada, the bear.

Further, in aboriginal mythologies, the pre-human form of the world is conceived as quite unfit as the habitat of man. Little attention is given to the creation of a world in a void, its existence in some form being taken for granted. What these mythologies are concerned with is how an unsuitable world was transformed into a home for man. Most tales embodying this conception deal with specific details, as raising up certain mountains, changing the form and habits of certain animals, etc., which in the aggregate may account for the more important features of the tribes' environment; but such transformations call for a transformer, usually conceived of as man possessed of unusual magical powers, and he is the hero in such tales. Students of aboriginal mythology and folklore designate this character as culture-hero, transformer, trickster, etc. Usually he is all of these and more; he may show great wisdom in setting culture patterns, set ideals of conduct, and again do stupid things, resort to unbelievable vulgarity, obscenity, and crime. Many of his pranks are intended to excite humor. He is venerated for the great service rendered in making the world a fit place to live in, but laughed at and reviled for his follies and his crimes. He may have several names, according to the plot of the particular tale recounting his doings.

While in most tribal mythologies a definite culture-hero is designated as responsible for many of the transformations recorded, not all transformer tales are necessarily his exploits (Alexander, 1916, 1920; Thompson, 1929). There are other heroes, usually dealt with in a single narrative, who make important changes by overcoming monsters or introducing new rituals. Often the pattern of the transformer myth so dominates that adventure tales end with the statement that with these events came certain specific changes. Such are sometimes called secondary explanations. Yet the plots of tales and the methods of composition, among most Indian tribes, have much in common so that an experienced student has little difficulty in recognizing a New World tale.

It has been said that every American Indian possesses a guardian spirit or maintains an individual relation between himself and some supernatural power. To say that such was universal would be going too far, but it is clear that the concept was strong among many of the hunting tribes and the agricultural hunters, and is implied in the ceremonialism of the city-states. Such guardians were acquired in visions and dreams.

By some this was considered a form of totemism, the name totem having been derived from an Indian word. This assumed personal relation is perhaps the most fundamental thing in aboriginal belief, and is elaborated in many forms of ritual. The so-called medicine bundle is based upon this idea, and it may be noted that even the Aztec seem to have had such bundles during their migrations. This individualism may account for the religious tolerance so striking among the hunters and agriculturists where every man's guardian and every serious ritual is respected. Even the first missionaries to North America complained that the Indians saw no difficulty in continuing pagans and being good Christians at the same time. On the other hand, the Inca and Aztec seem to have approached a level where they were beginning to demand observance of the rituals belonging to the ruling family as a form of submission to the state; yet we observe that this is the extension of a family religion rather than otherwise, and, so far as the data go, no objection was raised to the observance of other rituals, so that the principle of tolerance was apparently recognized.

This broad tolerance may account for the numerous cults and societies met with in various regions, for the most part ceremonial and ritualistic. These cults have individuality and freedom to perform their ceremonies at regular intervals or in response to definite situations, but rarely are they identified with civil functions. Each ritual is the possession of a family, a society, or even of a single individual, as the case may be, and stands for a technique in magic, or, as an aboriginal may say, "has some kind of power." Individuals, families, and the tribal government may call upon such of these owners of rituals as they choose to do what they can in the situation or crisis at hand. Even under the rule of the Aztec and Inca this system seems to have operated, notwithstanding the demands of the state that the rituals of the ruling family be respected.

While we have characterized the above attitude as tolerance, the reality of the phenomena may lie in the culture patterns involved. The culture of Europe, at least at the time of Indian contact, supported a number of closely similar religious systems, actually conforming to a single pattern. As elements in this pattern were regard for the Bible as the commands of the Supreme God, the integration of these commands with all behavior and culture activities, and, finally, as a corollary, the intolerance of all other beliefs. The different sects and churches differed somewhat as to the interpretations placed upon biblical texts but were a unit in demanding that all other sects be forsaken. The religious patterns of the Indians, especially in what are now the United States and Canada, were quite in contrast. In the first place, the various mythologies, rituals, and cults were not integrated as an all-embracing scheme of life, but were, for the most part, looked upon as special separate entities in which functioned some kind of supernatural power. The charm had a place in this scheme; in fact, was an integral part of it. It is in the above sense that the term "medicines" is used in white speech, when referring to the ceremonial affairs of the Indian. In almost literal terms the Indian expected each ritual to be "good for something" and part of his life was spent in seeking knowledge by experience or otherwise as to the specific "good" in each case. So when the Indian saw rituals performed, or the objects obviously associated with one, he treated them with respect, in part because of the unknown latent powers therein.   There is abundant evidence in narratives of the time that in early white contact the Indian looked upon baptism, the crucifix, the raising of the dead, etc., as merely new examples of specific rituals.   Friction arose not from the preaching of church doctrine, but when by pressure and force the whites tried to degrade and destroy native rituals.   Further, the appeal to forsake all other gods and images was so different from the Indian pattern that, if he grasped the idea at all, his resentment and contempt were aroused.

Apparently much the same pattern prevailed among the agriculturists and hunters of South America.   Whether a similar condition prevailed among the primitive peoples in the Old World is not certain, but the evidence points that way.   Our earlier remarks about the multiplicity of ceremonials in Aztec and Inca lands are little more than an assemblage of more or less specific rituals, integrated into a calendar and rationalized as in the case of an organized priesthood.   The pattern here is still at odds with that of the Christian religion.

Additional information may be obtained from the following books: Lowie (1924, Chap. 1), Goldenweiser (1922, Chaps. 1-3 and other sections dealing with American natives), Morgan (1904, 1881), Radin (1927).

HISTORICAL PERSPECTIVE

The title of this chapter implies that something in the way of history be attempted. Such treatment for the accompanying chapters on Old World societies is feasible, especially in the one devoted to the white man, but in case of the New World we have little in the way of true history before 1492, and after that date the dissolution of aboriginal cultures sets in. However, the data of New World archeology and certain inscriptions left by the Maya in Yucatan enable us to present a gross relative chronology. So far as we know, man entered the New World from the Old near the end of the last glaciation.   Some scholars assume this migration was from an early Asiatic neolithic horizon, though it may turn out that aboriginal neolithic culture originated in America independently.   In any case, since all domesticated plants are derived from flora peculiar to the New World, we are constrained to believe that the marginal belt of hunter tribes represents the substratum of aboriginal society.   This is not to say that any specific society lately observable in this hunting area is the initial aboriginal type, but that, in so far as these Indians lived by hunting and gathering and so were committed to a society of small self-contained groups, a part of whose material equipment can be defined by archeology, they stand as the point of departure in subsequent social history.

History demands time sequence as a chronological framework into which data can be filed.   In our field of inquiry we naturally turn to the archeologists for an established sequence to integrate with social data, for in so far as archeology gives true time perspective it contributes to social history. While it is obvious that the materials of archeology are the bare fragments of culture equipments, yet these materials give data as to the size of towns, the density of populations, the housing of the family, etc., all telling something of social life.

Stratigraphy is the foundation for all such time perspective set-ups. Yet it so happens that stratigraphy is still in the making, scarcely out of the tentative stage, approaching completeness in two localities only, New Mexico–Arizona and the Valley of Mexico. The Lake Titicaca area in the Andes is probably next in order, but the chronologies so far proposed for the Andean area have not been adequately checked by stratigraphy. In the Maya area of Central America dated inscriptions give a chronology which is yet to be harmonized with stratigraphy. Tables for these four chronologies will be found in the literature.

As an example we present the general sequence as agreed upon by archeologists working in New Mexico–Arizona (Kidder, 1924). (See Figure 2.) The dates are for the most part based upon the so-called tree-ring method, applying to Pueblo Periods II to V; for the earlier periods the dates are estimates. For Pueblo Periods these can be taken as closely accurate; for the earlier periods they seem conservative (Roberts, 1931, Introductory Chap.). For our purpose the sequence is sufficient and this is empirically established by stratigraphy alone. The type of hous-

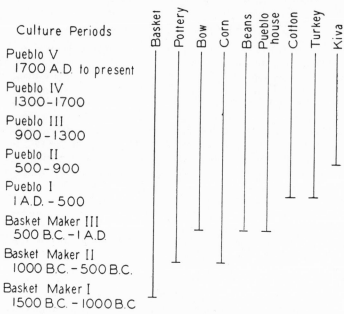

FIGURE 2

SEQUENCE OF CULTURES IN NEW MEXICO–ARIZONA

ing changes in Pueblo II and culminates in Pueblo III, and, since it continues to the present, we assume that the social framework for the group and the family has held to the same gross patterns. In ritualism we note that the kiva, a kind of men's house around which all modern ritualism is organized, came with the above type of housing. Agriculture, domestication, weaving cloth, pottery, the bow, all precede the kiva and pueblo housing.

What we can be sure of is that the large organized village appears after agriculture, pottery, etc. We see nowhere evidence that inland tribes maintained large towns without these important equipments. This implies that the more formalized social and ceremonial organization was, historically at least, a concomitant of the economic systems maintained by large organized groups.

Quite aside from stratigraphic data, attempts are made to set up general time perspectives in the social history of the New World as a whole; the procedure is to interpolate outlines in assumed sequence based upon geographic distribution and the logical relations of the customs involved.

As an example of such tentative time correlations we have adapted the accompanying table from Kroeber (1923, Chap. 13). Bearing in mind that this is a working hypothesis, the picture implies a moderately long course of development during which the respective cultures were well integrated with their environments. In any case this is about as far as we can go in the matter of an historical outline.

Sequences in Culture Complexes

Bronze	loom with shed	empires	human sacrifice
Copper and gold	true loom	city-states	temples
		confederacies	
	weaving frame		priesthood
Bow	weaving downward	exogamic rites	secret societies
Pottery and agriculture			
Atlatl	basketry	bands	shamanism

These are to be read independently, and vertically rather than horizontally. In some parts of this table the sequence is quite like that in the Old World, suggesting parallels in social behavior. On the other hand, the single-origin school claims that each change in aboriginal culture was the result of a migration from the Old World comparable to that initiated by Columbus; but the majority opinion seems to prefer the interpretation that the successive social changes arose locally and that the main Old World contribution lay in the lower ends of each column in the table. If we are primarily concerned with historical sequence, the place of initial origin is of no consequence, since each successive increment, to survive, must have found a functional place in one or more cultures.

All of this means that the conclusions of authorities in New World problems tend to a view that aboriginal society is largely indigenous and whether the particular sequences proposed for culture change ultimately stand the tests of repeated checks with new data, or give way to a somewhat different order, they have the virtue of sketching in the composition for the final triumph of research.

BIBLIOGRAPHY

ALEXANDER, H. B. 1916. North American. Vol. 10 of *The mythology of all races*, ed. by L. H. Gray. Boston: Marshall Jones. Pp. xxiv+325.

――――. 1920. American (Latin). Vol. 11 of *The mythology of all races*, ed. by L. H. Gray. Boston: Marshall Jones. Pp. xvi+424.

BANDELIER, A. F. 1878. On the distribution and tenure of lands and the customs with respect to inheritance, among the ancient Mexicans. *11th Ann. Rep. Peabody Mus. Amer. Archaeol. & Ethnol.*, **2**, No. 2, 384-448.

――――. 1879. Social organization and mode of government of the ancient Mexicans. *12th Ann. Rep. Peabody Mus. Amer. Archaeol. & Ethnol.*, **2**, No. 3, 557-699.

BOAS, F. 1921. Ethnology of the Kwakiutl based on data collected by George Hunt. (*Bur. Amer. Ethnol., 35th Ann. Rep. to the Secretary of the Smithsonian. Instit.*) (2 vols.) Washington, D. C.: Govt. Print. Office. Pp. 1481.

DIAZ DEL CASTILLO, B. 1908-16. The true history of the conquest of New Spain: By Bernal Diaz del Castillo, one of its conquerors. (Trans., with introduction and notes by A. P. Maudslay.) London: Hakluyt Soc. Vol. 1 (1908). Pp. xlv+396. Vol. 2 (1910). Pp. xvi+343. Vol. 3 (1910). Maps. Vol. 4 (1912). Pp. xiii+395. Vol. 5 (1916). Pp. xiv+463.

DOBBS, A. 1744. An account of the countries adjoining to Hudson's Bay, in the north-west part of America: containing a description of their lakes and rivers, the nature of the soil and climates, and their method of commerce, . . . with an abstract of Capt. Middleton's Journal, etc. London: Robinson. Pp. ii+211.

DOBRIZHOFFER, M. 1822. An account of the Abipones, an equestrian people of Paraguay. (3 vols.) London: Murray. Pp. 435+xii; 446+v; 419+vi.

GODDARD, P. E. 1934. Indians of the Northwest Coast. (2nd ed.) (*Amer. Mus. Nat. Hist., Hdbk. Ser.*, No. 10.) New York: Amer. Mus. Nat. Hist. Pp. 175.

――――. 1931. Indians of the Southwest. (4th ed.) (*Amer. Mus. Nat. Hist., Hdbk. Ser.*, No. 2.) New York: Amer. Mus. Nat. Hist. Pp. 205.

GOLDENWEISER, A. A. 1922. Early civilization: an introduction to anthropology. New York: Knopf. Pp. xiv+428.

HEWETT, E. L. 1905. A general view of the archaeology of the pueblo region. In *Annual Report of the Smithsonian Institution for 1904*. Washington, D. C.: Govt. Print. Office. Pp. 583-605.

IM THURN, E. F. 1883. Among the Indians of Guiana. London: Kegan Paul. Pp. xvi+445.

JENNESS, D. 1932. The Indians of Canada. (*Nat. Mus. Canada, Bull.* 65.) Ottawa. Pp. 446.

JOYCE, T. A. 1912. South American archaeology. London: Macmillan. Pp. 292.

————. 1920. Mexican archaeology, an introduction to the archaeology of the Mexican and Maya civilizations of pre-Spanish America. New York & London: Macmillan. Pp. xvi+384.

KIDDER, A. V. 1924. Introduction to the study of southwestern archaeology; with a preliminary account of the excavations at Pecos. (*Phillips Acad., Dept. Archaeol., Papers of the Southwest Expedition*, No. 1.) New Haven Conn.: Yale Univ. Press. Pp. vii+151.

KROEBER, A. L. 1923. Anthropology. New York: Harcourt, Brace. Pp. xi+523.

————. 1925. Handbook of the Indians of California. (*Bur. Amer. Ethnol. Bull.* 78.) Washington, D. C.: Govt. Print. Office. Pp. xviii+995.

LOTHROP, S. K. 1928. The Indians of Tierra del Fuego. (*Mus. Amer. Indian, Contrib.*, Vol. 10.) New York. Pp. 5+244.

LOWIE, R. H. 1924. Primitive religion. New York: Boni & Liveright. Pp. xix+346.

MARKHAM, C. R. 1911. The Incas of Peru. (2nd ed.) London: Smith, Elder. Pp. xvi+443.

MEAD, C. W. 1932. Old civilizations of Inca land. (2nd ed.) (*Amer. Mus. Nat. Hist., Hdbk. Ser.*, No. 11.) New York: Amer. Mus. Nat. Hist. Pp. 141.

MEANS, P. A. 1931. Ancient civilizations of the Andes. New York: Scribner's. Pp. xviii+586.

MERRILL, E. D. 1931. The phytogeography of cultivated plants in relation to assumed pre-Columbian Eurasian-American contacts. *Amer. Anthrop.*, **33**, 375-382.

MORGAN, L. H. 1881. Houses and house-life of the American aborigines. (*Contrib. N. Amer. Ethnol.*, Vol. 4.) Washington, D. C.: Govt. Print. Office. Pp. xiv+281.

————. 1904. League of the Ho-dé-no-saunee or Iroquois. (2 vols. in 1.) (Ed. by H. M. Lloyd.) New York: Dodd, Mead. Pp. xxiv+332.

MURDOCK, G. P. 1934a. The organization of Inca society. *Scient. Mo.*, 231-239.

————. 1934b. Our primitive contemporaries. New York: Macmillan. Pp. xxii+614.

NORDENSKIÖLD, E. 1929. The American Indian as an inventor. *J. Roy. Anthrop. Instit. Great Britain & Ireland*, **59**, 273-309.

RADIN, P. 1927. Primitive man as a philosopher. New York: Appleton. Pp. xviii+402.

ROBERTS, F. H. H., JR. 1931. The ruins at Kiatuthlanna, eastern Arizona. (*Bur. Amer. Ethnol. Bull.* 100.) Washington, D. C.: Govt. Print. Office. Pp. viii+195.

SAHAGÚN, B. DE. 1932. A history of ancient Mexico. (Trans. by F. R. Bandelier from the Spanish version of C. M. de Bustamante.) Nashville, Tenn.: Fiske Univ. Press. Pp. 305.

SPENCE, L. 1912. The civilization of ancient Mexico. New York: Macmillan. Pp. 121.

SPINDEN, H. J. 1922. Ancient civilizations of Mexico and Central America. (*Amer. Mus. Nat. Hist., Hdbk. Ser.*, No. 3.) New York: Amer. Mus. Nat. Hist. Pp. 7+242.

SWANTON, J. R. 1911. Indian tribes of the Lower Mississippi and the adjacent coast of the Gulf of Mexico. (*Bur. Amer. Ethnol. Bull.* 43.) Washington, D. C.: Govt. Print. Office. Pp. vii+387.

————. 1922. Early history of the Creek Indians and their neighbors. (*Bur. Amer. Ethnol. Bull.* 73.) Washington, D. C.: Govt. Print. Office. Pp. 492.

THOMPSON, J. E. 1933. Mexico before Cortez: an account of the daily life, religion, and ritual of the Aztecs and kindred peoples. New York: Scribner's. Pp. x+298.

THOMPSON, S. 1929. Tales of the North American Indians. Cambridge, Mass.: Harvard Univ. Press. Pp. xiii+386.

WHIFFEN, T. 1915. The Northwest Amazons. London: Constable. Pp. 319.

WISSLER, C. 1927. North American Indians of the plains. (3rd ed.) (*Amer. Mus. Nat. Hist., Hdbk. Ser.*, No. 1.) New York: Amer. Mus. Nat. Hist. Pp. 172.

CHAPTER 9

SOCIAL HISTORY OF THE WHITE MAN[1]

W. D. WALLIS

University of Minnesota

The moving finger writes; and having writ,
Moves on; nor all your Piety nor Wit
Shall lure it back to cancel half a line,
Nor all your Tears wash out a Word of it.

I. INTRODUCTION

To get our bearings in the social history of the white man we may consider first the historical and geographical compass of our subject. Who is the white man, when and where did he emerge above the horizon of history, and what has been the geographical range of his activities? When we have answered these inquiries, of necessity summarily, we shall survey his social history and ask its meaning.

By white man we shall refer to that portion of the human race which anthropologists classify as Caucasoid, a group set off from the other great divisions of mankind, the Negroid and the Mongoloid, (1) by virtue of possessing certain physical traits not possessed by either of the latter groups, and (2) by the absence of distinguishing physical traits which are found among either Negroids or Mongoloids. Nearly all of these distinguishing physical traits are superficial; they are literally only skin deep. They consist of a smaller amount of pigmentation than is commonly found in either of the other two races and of an intermediate amount of hairiness, or pilosity. The hair of the Caucasoid is wavy rather than straight or kinky. The face is not as projecting as in Negroids and not as wide in comparison with height as in Mongoloids, who have protruding cheek bones. The nose of whites is prominent, long, and slender, with considerable elevation of nasal bridge and comparatively small nasal apertures which turn downward to a greater degree than in the other races. The lips are thinner and less everted, that is, have a smaller amount of mucous surface turned outward, than those of either Mongoloids or Negroids. The skeletal characteristics which distinguish the white race are not so easily determined. Though there may be differences in some race means, there is much overlapping in practically all skeletal dimensions and proportions. Such is the case with respect to the various skull indices and proportions.

Perhaps by degree of alveolar projection and type of teeth any large series of Mongoloids can be distinguished from any large series of whites; and any large series of Negroids can be distinguished from any large

---

[1] I am indebted to Ruth Sawtell Wallis for much assistance in the preparation of this chapter.

series of whites by type of nose, eyebrow ridges, facial proportions, and facial projection.

We do not know when the white man originated. There is, for example, no certainty that Cro-Magnon man, who lived in Europe during the Upper Paleolithic, some twenty thousand to twelve thousand years ago, was or was not white or proto-Caucasoid.

In the early Neolithic, which began in Western Europe about 8000 B.C., there are skeletal types which can with assurance be assigned to the Caucasoid division. There then appear in various parts of Europe long-heads and short-heads which are essentially the same in general characteristics as some of the types found in Europe today. There is no evidence that from that time to the present any type other than the Caucasoid has been prevalent in Europe. The place of origin of the white man has, however, not been revealed. Probably the Caucasoid evolved in Western Asia from an earlier type which specialized into Mongoloid on the one hand and into Caucasoid on the other. Fossil evidence, both positive and negative, suggests an Asiatic origin of the white race, with subsequent specializations in the Euro-Asiatic area. Anatomic, morphologic, and anthropometric evidence indicates that the white man is ancestrally more closely allied with the Mongoloid than with the Negroid. The overlappings of type are predominantly with the Mongoloid rather than with the Negroid.

When the whites enter the stage of history they occupy a large continuous area of the Old World. The racial boundaries are Mongoloids to the east and Negroids to the south. In Greenland, when Europeans first reached the island, were Eskimo, a Mongoloid, people. The Lapps probably represent a Mongoloid intrusion into an area previously settled by Caucasoids.

An irregular and to some extent indeterminate geographical line separates white from Mongoloids. There have been numerous minglings and interpenetrations of the two races along the eastern front and one cannot draw the boundary between them with any precision. A southern portion of Caucasoids juts farther to the east than the northern mass. It is represented by peoples of Iran and of Northern India, who are bounded to north as well as to east by Mongoloids.

Asia Minor and Arabia are other Asiatic regions which have belonged to the white man since the beginning of the historical era. Egypt and the northern strip of otherwise Negro Africa has been white territory from the earliest historical period to the present.

Early Relations with Other Peoples. History starts with written records, but we do not assume that the earliest records are records of earliest achievements. At the dawn of the Neolithic the white man certainly inherited the technology and traditions of Paleolithic man. This heritage must have included, among other things, the techniques of polishing bone, which began in the Paleolithic, and in the Neolithic were highly developed and applied to stone. Probably Neolithic white man domesticated the dog. The sheep, goat, pig, and cattle, also of

Neolithic domestication, probably came into Europe from Eastern Central Asia; but whether the white man or the Mongoloid first domesticated them is not known. A similar statement applies to the horse.

The donkey, first known in Mesopotamia, may, in our ignorance, be credited provisionally to the white man, but those other important domesticated animals of the Far East and the Near East, the camel and the dromedary, almost certainly came from Central Asia. Chickens, first found in the Indus valley, were possibly a contribution from Mongoloids, and perhaps also ducks, swans, and geese. Agriculture was perhaps the invention of the whites, and probably pottery-making also was first practised by whites.

The Negroids were never a "problem" of early whites. The desert regions of North Africa prevented direct contacts on a large scale and the contacts which were made were almost always initiated by the whites. The whites have had contacts with Mongoloids throughout the historical period. Not until the eleventh century, however, were there great incursions of Mongoloids into Caucasoid territory. In 1071 the Seljuk Turks captured Jerusalem, and Mongoloids reached the shores of the Mediterranean. In subsequent centuries Mongoloid conquerors carried the banner of the Tartar from the Arctic circle to the Persian Gulf, from the China Sea into Central Europe. The Turks conquered Southeastern Europe as far west as the Adriatic and penetrated Central Europe.

Turkish conquests, however, introduced comparatively little Mongoloid blood into territorial Europe save in the region proximate to the Bosphorus. The invading Turks may, indeed, have been partly Caucasoid in racial composition. But they came from the region of Central Asia and certainly they were not sharers to any great extent in a Caucasoid tradition. In this chapter we shall assume them predominantly Mongoloid rather than Caucasoid and therefore, as a group, not members of the white race.

Expansion of the World of the White Man After 1600. The travels of the Polos, the coasting voyages of southern European navigators, and, most of all, the discoveries by Columbus were invitations to new lands. These voyages and others which they inspired increased the area of the known world. The fruits of that knowledge were reaped by whites. They circumnavigated the globe, discovered the Western Hemisphere and many, to Europeans, unknown lands in the Eastern Hemisphere. These new lands were claimed for the country under whose flag the voyager had ventured. Discovery was followed by exploration, exploration by settlement. European colonies were planted in North and in South America, in the larger islands of the South Seas, in South Africa, and in most of the islands near Asia and America. Thus millions of square miles of territory outside of Europe and the Asiatic and African continental areas of the Old World were colonized by Europeans during the last three centuries and made white. History has never before witnessed in such magnitude the spread of peoples and such rapid growth in population as have characterized the whites in Europe and in European-settled lands since the beginning of the seventeenth century. The migrations of whites and the great increase in their number imparted a new turn to world history and to the fates of all peoples.

The Varied Physical Characteristics of Whites. We have spoken of the whites as a race, and such indeed they are when contrasted with Mongoloids or with Negroids. Race, however, is a concept rather than an objective fact; or, if one likes, it is a fact the character of which depends upon our concept. The concept implies the selection of certain characteristics from the totality of physical traits. All of them are in a sense as much racial as are the traits chosen as the criteria, since they, too, are the characteristics of individuals in the group. Everywhere man is variable, so variable that no individual is like any other in every respect. Within the Caucasoid division of mankind there are, moreover, marked local differences in physical type; a North European can generally be distinguished by appearance from a South European, a Welshman from a Great Russian. Anthropologists recognize three main types among Caucasoids: Nordics, Alpines, and Mediterraneans. To these some add Dinarics, and some consider the North Indian ("Hindu") a locally distinct variety or subrace. These respective types are to some extent localized. Nordics predominate in Northern and Western Europe; Alpines in Central Europe; and Mediterraneans in the Mediterranean region, including Asia Minor, Arabia, and North Africa.

This localization, however, merely describes the relative frequency with which the respective types occur in these regions. Nordics are found with greatest frequency in the Baltic area and in parts of the British Isles; but some districts of France have a higher percentage of Nordics than do some districts of Northern Germany; and some districts of the British Isles are predominantly Alpine. Each of these subraces has great variabilities. Some Nordics, for example, are long-headed, some are short-headed; some have light eyes, some have dark eyes; some are short, some are tall. The actual combinations of traits which result from fluctuations in these and other physical characters give rise to a large number of subtypes within the Nordic group. This is true of the other Caucasoid subraces. The white race therefore is not so much a fixed congeries or constellation of physical traits as elements of a pattern in which there is almost infinite variety of specific combination of constituent traits.

Absence of Social or Political Integration of the White Race. The whites are not a unified group either socially or politically. During the period of recorded history there has never been a complete integration. The ancient civilizations knew little of peoples beyond their own borders and were unaware of the existence of whites beyond the ambit of the areas of trade or conquest.

There was no concept of the white man, much less any exploitation of such a concept. At the present day there is no social or political unification of the white race.

Varied Achievements within the White Race. The achievements of the component units of the white race are as varied as the localities which members of this race have occupied and as the physical types of the race. Achievements differ greatly from one locality to another and from one period of history to another, and without any consistent regard for specific physical type. The achievements of the Mediterranean area are not those of the British Isles or those of the Baltic region; the achievements of Eastern Europe differ from those of Western Europe. Local developments of white civilization do not, however, differ in the same respects at all periods of history; their character shifts with every century. The differences between ancient Greece and ancient Egypt, for example, are not the differences between modern Greece and modern Egypt; only the land and some of the monuments remain fundamentally the same.

The respective periods at which some of the more important civilizations of the white man have reached the height of their respective achievements are indicated in the accompanying table. The dates are only approximate.

TABLE 1

CHRONOLOGY OF THE HEIGHT OF ACHIEVEMENTS IN SOME OF THE MORE IMPORTANT CIVILIZATIONS OF THE WHITE MAN

Century of highest development	Civilization
B.C.	
27th	Sumerian
14th-12th	Babylonian, Egyptian
14th	Aegean (Minoan)
10th-9th	Hindu, Persian
9th	Jewish
5th-3rd	Greek (Athenian)
3rd	Hellenistic
A.D.	
1st	Roman
6th	Byzantine
17th-	Western European

These peaks are but moments in the incessant changes in the respective cultures. They suggest the shifting character of the differences between any two contemporary civilizations when compared at different periods of history. Almost equally great are the differences in a civilization in the same locality at different periods of history: as witness ancient Egypt, Roman Egypt, medieval Egypt, and present-day Egypt; the Athens of the Periclean age and the Athens of today; the Rome of Augustus, and the Rome of Mussolini.

II. TYPES OF EARLY ACHIEVEMENTS BY WHITES

Early Mediterranean Phase. Early history seems to play into the hands of the geographical environmentalists. The earliest achievements of the white man were in regions highly favored by nature, namely, the fertile self-irrigated flat lands of the Tigris-Euphrates and Nile valleys, where the agriculturist had merely to plant the seed and reap. Two considerations, however, should be weighed before nature is given the credit for early civilization.

First is the fact that similar river environments in Europe are not the home of early civilizations. These grew up around or north of the Mediterranean. Climatic conditions are similar in Crete, Greece, Italy, Egypt, and Mesopotamia; but the conditions of soil and the demands of toil are contrasting. The civilizations north of the Mediterranean are not built on river effluvia. Of equal significance is the fact that neither Egypt nor Mesopotamia has always harbored the same kind of civilization. In each region the civilization changes incessantly and not always in the same direction. The spade of the archeologist turns up with each deeper thrust much the same kind of earth; meanwhile it reveals a constantly shifting culture scene. Whereas historical geography tells the archeologist substantially the same story through successive centuries with only slight variations of the theme in regard to rainfall and deposits of surface soil, archeology discourses of different things at every spade-depth. Thus a given soil and climate have the capacity of producing contrasting civilizations; or, more accurately, they support civilizations but cannot produce them or perpetuate them. If the soil is the source from which they spring it is also the grave into which they retire.

Two civilizations developed in Mesopotamia on the Arabian peninsula some five thousand years ago. The older of these was the Sumerian, a southern kingdom erected on deposits built up near river mouths as the rivers filled the adjacent shallow bed of the Persian Gulf. This encroachment of the land upon the sea has continued to the present day until places situated in early historical times on the Persian Gulf are now some eighty miles inland. The archeology indicates that these early Sumerians were not old occupants of the land but intruders. No distinct Neolithic culture is found in this locality. The stone implements are apparently copied from metal ones, and none of premetal type have been found. The first occupants, therefore, were presumably users of metal and brought with them a technology probably recently acquired from some nearby people, perhaps together with the domesticated horse. The peoples to the north were Semites, but the Sumerians were non-Semitic; their tongue has no known affiliation with that of any other people. In the course of time the northern Semites, Babylonians, conquered and absorbed the Sumerians. At least they absorbed many elements of Sumerian civilization, which became characteristically Babylonian. The Babylonians, in turn, were conquered by Assyrians, who followed precedent and adopted the civilization of the conquered. Sumerian-Babylonian-Assyrian civilization is the civilization of Mesopotamia from about 3000 B.C. until the sixth century B.C. or later.

Egyptian civilization closely parallels its Mesopotamian rival. It likewise was once conquered from outside, by the Hyksos, but later expelled its conquerors. There is an unbroken continuity in Egyptian civilization from at least 3000 B.C. to Roman days. These two river-valley civilizations have much in common, or, at least, much that is very similar. In both areas the economic life utilizes irrigation, barley, wheat, and the date tree. Both accomplish great feats in construction and in the transportation and placement of heavy materials. The gods are diligently cultivated, temples are built and adorned, the priesthood becomes powerful, kingship is exalted and sanctified, aristocracy flourishes, the poor are oppressed.

Babylonia excels in the promotion of commerce, business organization, contracts, and the elaboration and codification of law. Under Assyrian tutelage the armies of Mesopotamia are invincible. Egypt builds huge monuments of stone, still unmatched in magnitude and some of them unrivaled in impressiveness. Attention to the fate of the dead through provision of rock-hewn tombs and elaborate funeral equipment, embalming, and detailed prescriptions for the conduct of the soul in the afterworld are among the outstanding traits of Egyptian civilization. To these should be added the elaboration and magnitude of the cults of animals, an accomplishment far exceeding anything of the kind in Mesopotamia.

Aegean civilization reached its height about the fourteenth century B.C., before the fall of Knossus and the eclipse of Minoan culture in Crete, when the scepter probably passed to the mainland. Aegean civilization flourished for at least three thousand years, during which period there was unbroken continuity in culture traits. The Minoan civilization of Crete excelled in palaces which outrivaled in luxury and artistic finish those of Egypt and Babylonia. Minoans provided a water supply with modern plumbing and bathrooms; fine mosaic work; beaten gold work of unexcelled artistry; windows; folding doors; and plural-story houses. They built the first paved roads. There is evidence of elaborate registration, the keeping of accounts, and secretarial work. There probably were a wide-flung commerce and manifold commercial transactions. Cretan writing has not yet been deciphered, but one may infer the existence of a large body of commercial law.

Early Indo-Persian Phase. The earliest skulls identified as of Mediterranean type were found in the valley of the Indus at Mohenjo-Daro, in a horizon subsequent to 2500 B.C. From about 2400 B.C. to about 1500 B.C. there was, presumably, a migration of Aryan peoples into India. The date of their advent in Persia (Iran) cannot be definitely determined. A typical Aryan culture probably flourished in Persia and India when civilization was at its height in Egypt, Babylonia, and the Aegean area. The notable accomplishments are not of an engineering or artistic character, so far as information has come down to us, but rather of a religious and social character. Among the Indian Aryans there developed an elaborate nature religion with special powers or phases of nature associated with some particular god. The god of the sky and the gods of the winds were among the most powerful. In social life the Indian Aryans developed a fourfold caste system, of which the Brahmins, the priests or learned men, were one, and non-Aryans an outcaste.

Iranian civilization emphasized dualism in nature and in religion. The forces of good are led by Ahura Mazda, the forces of evil by Ahriman. The struggle is cosmic; human beings are but pawns in the great game. Ultimately Ahura Mazda and his assistants will conquer and Ahriman will be vanquished. Both Persian and Indian Aryanism exalt the family group, a patriarchal family sharing a common fireplace. The family circle includes all those who are within its ambit, even the domesticated animals. Those within the family circle share a common life, the members bound to one another with mystic bonds.

Early Semites. To the west of these Aryans were the early Semites— Babylonians, Assyrians, Jews, Phoenicians, and nomads of the Arabian peninsula, who were not members of any highly advanced civilization. Jewish nationalism has a long history of trial and travail in a territory between Egypt and Babylonia, an anvil for both hammers. In the ninth century B.C., during the reign of Solomon, Jewish civilization attained its grandeur. Its outstanding contribution is the law, religion, ethics, and literature embodied in the Old Testament. These books describe the changes in social life from nomadism and patriarchal families, in which kinship groups play a dominant rôle, to agriculture, settled abode, city life, temples, priesthood, warfare, and international relations. Two other Semitic groups, the Phoenicians and the Aramaeans, were predominantly commercial and were the media of the dissemination of many culture traits around the Mediterannean and through Asia Minor, Syria, and the Arabian peninsula. The dialect of the Aramaeans spread from Syria, through Palestine, into Mesopotamia and became the *lingua franca* throughout that region. Aramaean, probably the language of Jesus and the disciples, was known from Damascus to Babylon. The Phoenicians, whose Semitic affiliation has been challenged, though accepted by most scholars, were primarily seafarers. They traded from the Bosphorus to the Straits of Gibraltar and even, it is believed, to the British Isles and the western coasts of continental Europe. To their god Moloch they offered infants as human sacrifice. On the other hand, they must be credited with the dissemination if not with the invention of the alphabet which came to be used in all the classical, Hindu, Buddhist, Persian, Arabian, Turkish, and Mohammedan world, eventually supplanting all others except Chinese and its derivatives. The most emphatic element in the social life of the Semites, especially as represented in early Arabian and Jewish life, is the emphasis upon the family, the kin group, and the patriarchate.

Later Mediterranean (Classical) Civilization. The later Mediterranean civilizations are not completely autochthonous developments. They have their roots in the soil of the older Mediterranean civilizations and are in a sense their fullest flowering.

In the classical civilizations, however, new notes become dominant. These cultures produce forms of thought, life, and accomplishment which are so different in emphasis from the cultures which preceded them that the centuries in which they flourished may be considered the dawn of an epoch in human civilization. Western civilization begins with the

Greeks. The *Iliad* and the *Odyssey,* which antedate 1000 B.C., are heroic compositions which embody history, dramatic action, adventure, and great poetry. They have moved men for centuries and are today among our most prized literary possessions. "The same Homer, who pleased at Athens and Rome two thousand years ago, is still admired at Paris and London. All the changes of climate, government, religion, and language have not been able to obscure his glory." This observation is as applicable today as when David Hume made it in the eighteenth century. The subsequent civilization of Athens produced history, tragedy, and comedy which sound a modern note and still serve as great exemplars. In the concepts introduced by Greek philosophers and scientists are to be found much if not most which is fundamental in those fields of thought today. Their sculpture is unsurpassed, their architecture the most appealing which any civilization has achieved. They developed the concept of relativity in social life; and Plato and Aristotle elucidated most of the philosophical, social, and ethical problems which subsequent students have recognized.

Herodotus was a student of other civilizations as well as of Greek culture and is entitled to be called Father of Anthropology as well as of History. The Greeks wrote treatises on the gods and on religion, and, after the Egyptians, were the first to enunciate an ethical doctrine of the belief in a life after death. Sir Henry Maine's famous dictum, "Except the blind forces of nature, nothing moves in the world today that is not Greek in origin," seems scarcely an exaggeration. If any exception is to be made it is their failure to develop experimental investigation and their neglect of technology. The Greeks gave us democracy in theory and in practice. Athenians developed and practiced self-government with a thoroughness never equaled before or since.

If a single contribution of Athenians is deserving of primary stress it is probably their exaltation of the individual and of individual freedom. The older civilizations knew nothing of the freedom of mind and soul which was exalted by the Greeks. The Athenian mind traversed realms of thought which left untouched nothing in their world. Its citizens challenged conventional religion, conventional ethics, conventional social life, conventional political life, conventional scientific concepts.

The Greeks, however, never achieved political unification. There were many Greek city-states, there was no politically united Greek civilization. Leagues and alliances they knew, but not federation.

Social life was an amalgam of the old and the new. The kinship groups of earlier days still functioned in the democratic city-state where political obligation demanded the unqualified allegiance of the citizen. Only now and then does even the greatest of their citizens, a Socrates, a Plato, or an Aristotle, think politically in larger terms than the affairs of the immediate Athens.

This limited intellectual and political orientation was to prove the undoing of all of the Greeks, for it made each city-state a potential enemy of all the others. These local patriotisms brought weakness where a larger political orientation would have insured strength. The lack of cohesion among the Greek city-states enabled Philip of Macedon to conquer the more powerful city-states and his son Alexander to complete the conquest of all Greece. The latter extended his empire to include the whole of the eastern Mediterranean, Egypt, Asia Minor, Syria, Arabia, and part of India.

Hellenism, as the culture of this new empire was called, destroyed the old Greece but erected on larger if shallower foundations a new civilization; and the new Hellenism was more cosmopolitan in spirit than the older Greek culture.

It did not despise the conquered barbarian but imparted freely to him the Greek culture and rapidly Hellenized the entire Empire. Libraries were established in Alexandria and in Pergamum; Greek architecture graced Asia Minor, Syria, Trans-Jordania, and Egypt. The new spirit found fullest expression in the Stoics, who developed the concept of the equality of all peoples, the desirability of a World State, and the fuller cultivation of reason.

West of Greece, in the Italian peninsula, was a contrasting civilization, weak in the phases in which the Greeks were strong, strong in the phases in which the Greeks were weak. The backgrounds of Roman civilization lay in an early Italian, or Latin, culture, with roots in prehistoric times; and it was deeply indebted to the Etruscans. The Etruscans wrote in Greek script, but the inscriptions have not yet been translated, for the tongue is still an unknown language. Presumably, though the form of the script is Western, the main elements in the culture are Eastern. The Etruscans utilized the structural element of the arch which had been developed and widely utilized in Babylonia and was known to the Mycaenaeans; they practiced haruspication, taking the omens from the liver, as it was practiced in Babylonia, and in taking the omens they paid much attention to the flight of animals. Their drainage works were copied by the Romans and became the prototypes of later Roman engineering construction in aqueducts and sewers. They conquered Latium in the sixth century B.C., but were driven out of Rome about 500 B.C. For a thousand years, approximately from 500 B.C. to 500 A.D., Rome knew no conqueror. Proudly calling herself the Eternal City, she bowed the knee to none and demanded that the whole known world acknowledge her sovereignty. Through almost unintermittent conquest she enlarged her borders until by the first century B.C. all Mediterranean lands were under her control and her legions had penetrated Germanic and Celtic lands to what is now France and Britain.

Ultimately she extended her frontiers to India on the east and to the Baltic and the Irish Sea on the north and west. Practically the whole known world was vassal of Rome. Such an extensive conquest of territory by a city-state has remained a unique event in history. It was made possible by consolidation of gradual accretions of territory and by absorbing into the governmental unit the conquered Italian territories. Military organization, a well-equipped and a well-trained fighting force, and good generalship were among the elements which made this conquest possible. Of all the contributions which Rome has made we could least afford to dispense with her contributions to the field of law. Legal doctrine was refined and built up through many centuries. It is a logical system and, more important, embodies rules of equity and procedure evolved by compromise and pragmatic modification in the indispensable school of practice. The Code of Justinian became the inspiration of later Continental jurists. In England and America it is still the basis of much of the legal code. The second century A.D. was the happiest century which men were to know, at least in Europe, for a full thousand years. In spite of the prevalent ease and riches, however, and of the culture and intellectualism prevalent in the Roman Empire, there seemed to be no drive or purpose in Roman life.

During these peaceful and prosperous times there were no great men and there were no great accomplishments which might become a heritage for subsequent centuries. Wealth and a high level of refinement produced no great artist, man of letters, historian, no great religious or ethical leader. The Roman world took its ease, the ease of a career that was well-nigh over, which sighed for no worlds to conquer and found no great undertaking in which to incorporate its placid, if magnificent, accomplishments.

In the fourth century Constantine built on the Bosphorus the new capitol which was to bear his name. Here a modified Roman culture, the Byzantine civilization, developed, For two hundred years, from 850 to 1050, Constantinople was the world's leading commercial and shipping center. Here East met West and Orientalism amalgamated with Western civilization. Byzantium became the medium through which Roman civilization passed to Eastern Europe, as Rome gave her civilization to Western Europe. The separation of Eastern from Western Europe in the fourth century continues to the twentieth century in religion as in culture—an Eastern Greek Orthodox Europe and a Western Roman Catholic Europe with its impenitent rebel child, Protestantism. In 1453 the beautiful city on the Bosphorus was captured by the Turks, who made it their capitol until 1919.

Pagan Europe beyond the Mediterranean. Ancient history is the story of civilizations which bordered upon the Mediterranean or had direct or indirect contacts with that nursery of early cultures.

Beyond the northern borders of this inland sea lay vast stretches of territory of which Mediterranean peoples knew, even by hearsay, practically nothing. Yet that great reach of unknown and forbidding forest and steppe land was destined to influence the fate of the future world more than would those Mediterranean peoples who had blazed the trail to higher civilization. By the fifth century A.D. most of the Mediterranean cultures were already fading into the background, and more virile, if cruder and more savage, peoples were stirring in the forests to the north. Henceforth the region north of the Alps was to have ever greater weight in European affairs; and the center of gravity of European civilization was destined to shift westward as well as northward. Cisalpine sovereignty gives way to Transalpine, the Straits of Gibraltar become more important strategic avenues of ingress and egress than the Straits of the Bosphorus; the Pillars of Hercules are the portal from which an inland civilization passes into an oceanic culture. Isolated and autonomous groups become connected units in an intercommunicating and interdependent, if disunited, European continent.

The present largest group of these early pagan peoples beyond the Mediterranean and the group which now occupies the largest amount of Euro-Asiatic territory is the Slavs. Possibly a branch of them was known to Herodotus. Certainly Roman historians were aware of their existence. Nineteen hundred years ago, however, they were probably a small group northeast of the Carpathians. During the next few centuries they were expanding and probably were displacing, at least in Central Europe, masses of Germanic peoples. At present the Slavic people occupy practically the whole of Eastern Europe, eastward from a border represented by a line drawn from Danzig, on the Baltic, to the northern shore of the Adriatic. The western portion of such a division of Europe would, of course, include many millions of Germans, Magyars, Hungarians, Albanians, Greeks, and Roumanians, who are not Slavs, although many Slavs are to be found in all of these nationality groups. The Slavs occupy not only Eastern Europe but also a territory stretching from Western Asia into Central Siberia, a great wedge-like thrust into Mongoloid peoples. Indeed, the Slavic people have traversed Asia to the Pacific and planted colonies on her shores. About their culture which antedates influence from Mediterranean lands little is known. Apparently they lived in small village units and the kinship tie was strong. They had little genius for political development and were watchfully jealous of local autonomy. They dominated, it seems, primarily by virtue of sheer force of numbers and by continual thrusts into adjacent territories.

Another large unit, linguistic and to some extent cultural but not political, is the Celts, who formerly occupied the territory of Gaul, or France, and the British Isles, where the culture as well as the language still flourishes, notably in Ireland, Wales, and Brittany.

The Celts seem to have carried on most of their migrations during the prehistoric Bronze Age, when they invaded Britain. They display the familiar characteristics of the strong kin (clan) group, absence of organization into large social or political units, and absence of the traits which characterized the higher achievements of the early Mediterranean civilizations. During the centuries following upon the expanse of Roman power into northern and western Europe the Celtic peoples lost territory and political independence. One might imagine that Europe is destined to be Pan-Slavic, Pan-Germanic, or Pan-Latin; one can scarcely imagine that it will ever be Pan-Celtic.

A great block between the Slavic peoples to the east and the remnants of Celtic peoples to the west is the Germanic peoples of Central, Western, and Northern Europe.

They were Rome's neighbors to the north, but not neighborly. They conquered the Roman Empire which had conquered but had not subdued them. A wandering folk, they penetrated southern Europe into the Balkans, the Italian peninsula, and Sicily, and sent marauders and settlers from northern Europe into the British Isles and along the entire western coast of Europe. Today they are the physical backbone of every major country of Europe east of the Slavs, although Germanic is not the dominating language in all of these countries. Their social life shows strong development of the kinship unit and marked individualism.

The Latin peoples occupy territory to the south and west of the Germanic-speaking peoples, west of the Adriatic and north along the western shore of Europe into the lowlands of Belgium. There has, however, despite the language similarity, never been any marked similarity in the culture or social life of these Latin lands. The northern lands have been essentially Germanic in culture, and Italy and the Iberian peninsula have had little in common. Roumania stands apart, essentially Slavic in all but language; and modern Greece is an even more marked idiosyncracy.

Religious Cultural Movements. With the notable exception of Judaism, the religions of the ancient world were not identified with important social, intellectual, or ethical movements. They were, in the main, cult organizations rather than throbbing cultural movements. The world religions which have survived to the present day are, however, not merely cults, but cultural movements that have embodied social, ethical, and intellectual patterns of thought and life which have profoundly influenced all recent historical civilizations.

One of the earliest of these religions is the Brahmanic movement which began in India some two thousand years B.C., was elaborated by the priesthood during the period 800-500 B.C., and experienced a renaissance almost a thousand years later, from 100 to 400 A.D., and a marked resurgence during the last half century through the various *Samaj* which have displayed nationalistic aims as well as cultural and intellectual urges.

Brahmanism and the more comprehensive Hinduism which developed from it are essentially intellectualistic and therefore aristocratic. They give religious sanction to the social and economic caste system. Contemplation is both an intellectual and a religious function; and religious tabus enforce social discriminations.

Buddhism, which developed out of Hinduism in the sixth century B.C., emphasizes through the doctrine of rebirth the continuity of life. Its *dhatu* concept stresses the essential unity of things which are joined together by some bond, such as locality, community, kinship, or even antagonism. The monastic ideals of Hinduism are cherished by Buddhism. Priesthood flourishes, and the separation of the religious from the worldly is emphasized in many ways.

Religion is the most important tie which binds together the peoples of India, as, conversely, religious differences and discriminations are powerful factors in fomenting discord and disunity.

The Oriental cults which flourished around the eastern Mediterranean during the days of Greek and Roman civilization have disappeared except as weak survivals in country districts or as elements which have been incorporated into later religions.

Many of these cults emphasized the revival of the spirit of vegetation and probably were basically fertility cults. Some Oriental cults utilized the appeal of mystery and so are often called Mystery Cults. Some formally and ritually initiated the novitiates into the mysteries and thus laid the foundations of conversion psychology.

One of these cults, Mithraism, was for a century or more the main rival of Christianity, upon which it has left a permanent influence. Mithraism was difficult to combat for the reason that it contained many elements of belief and ritual which were very similar to those of Christianity.

Inasmuch as the Oriental cults never succeeded in identifying themselves with a culture, they were destined to fall before cults more powerful because cultural as well as religious movements. The most vital of early Oriental religious cults was Judaism, which was indissolubly linked with Jewish culture at many points. It developed high ethical doctrines and gave sanction to law, custom, and political and social enterprises. The Jews who scattered about the Mediterranean in Roman times kept alive the culture of Palestine in their respective colonies in the Hellenistic and later in the Roman Empire. Subsequently numerous European centers of Jewish settlement became centers of Jewish culture. The faith has lived to the present day and has carried with it the language, folklore, customs, and habits of life which characterized Palestine more than two millennia ago. The humblest and ultimately the most powerful of these Mediterranean cults was Christianity. It started with a small nucleus of culture, other than the religious ideas which inspired the founders of the religion; in the course of time, however, it absorbed the culture of surrounding peoples and became the greatest exponent of culture in Europe. Those who today carry the faith to foreign lands are disposed to introduce with Christianity the civilization with which it is mainly identified at the present day, that is, Western European capitalistic civilization, rather than the early Mediterranean communistic atmosphere of *Acts* and the New Testament. This religion has been so intimately interwoven with civilization that an account of Christianity as an historical phenomenon would involve an account of Western European civilization.

Mohammedanism (Islam) has some two hundred and fifty million adherents in various parts of the world, although many of these are not members of the white race. Like Hinduism, Brahmanism, Judaism, and Christianity, Islam is one of the great world religions. Like its great rivals, it, too, originated among the whites, from whom it took all of its distinctive features.

Mohammedanism is both a view of life and a way of life. When one moves from another religious sphere into the ambit of Mohammedanism one moves into an essentially different type of civilization. Wherever

Mohammedanism has gone it has carried along with the faith many traits of its distinctive civilization.

III. THE MODERN WORLD

However much we refine the analysis, the period taken as the beginning of the modern world is inevitably arbitrary. It began with Adam or with *Pithecanthropus erectus* or at any subsequent time which one chooses to select as the beginning.

If, however, the modern world is compared with the ancient world, a few aspects show significant differences.

Among the distinctive characteristics of the modern world are: large political units; great mobility of individuals; numerous large centers of population; a technology remarkable both for its intensive development and its extensive applications; the prevalence of the printed word and the commonness of the ability to read and write; the ease of communicating at great distances and the brevity of the time required; the great variety of associations and ties which knit groups together; the variety of the natural and artificial products which are utilized by a local group; and the rapidity with which changes of all kinds take place. There is also a modern attitude different in essence from that which characterized the ancient civilizations. The modern attitude, in contrast with ancient or medieval attitudes, may be characterized as one in which inquiry is more dominant and the mind plays with greater abandon over the subjects which it contemplates. The modern age is characterized also by a greater readiness to trust in reason rather than in dogma, in experiment rather than in authority, and by a more prevalent intellectual skepticism. These traits of the modern world are mainly matters of degree, yet in their totality they produce a world so different from that of the ancient civilizations as to constitute a veritable difference in kind. The totality of the difference is momentous in human history. Modernity, if we may call it that, has been acquired most fully and almost exclusively by the white man or by peoples who wittingly or unwittingly have learned from him.

Renaissance. The period during which the transition from the old order to the new can be clearly detected, though only certain phases of the new order can be observed there, is the period of the Renaissance. The term is perhaps a misnomer; for a new civilization was being conceived rather than born, and the period marks the beginning rather than the completion of a process. Had the cultural movement ended with the Renaissance no such book as the present one would have been written in this twentieth century. The centuries which followed upon the Dark Ages that were ushered in by the fall of Rome witnessed a resurgence of civilization as well as a rediscovery of civilization.

An intellectual ferment was the leaven that agitated the whole loaf. Italian scholars brought to the attention of contemporaries the writings of the Greeks and Romans and themselves produced literary works inspired by the classics.

Literature, history, political science, philosophy, were the result; and there was a revival in the fine arts.

Italian painters copied and created; Italian architects brought Greece to Italian cities and introduced to North Italy the structures of Rome. Hovels, a few of them, gave way to palaces, and much drabness and ugliness to beauty of form and finish. Florence, Milan, Assisi, Perugia, Ferrara, were born, and have not been reborn. They remain the artist's urban paradise.

The mariner's compass was introduced. With its spirit-like guidance the seaman could sail uncharted seas. By means of it he could chart and knowingly traverse unknown waters; and his tracks remained to be seen by subsequent adventurers. The compass pointed the way to the Cape of Good Hope, to distant Indian waters, and ultimately to the New World and the myriad mystic isles of the limitless Pacific.

The navigator who possessed the compass had fallen heir to a magician's wand; when he waved it he could be wafted to lands afar previously beyond human ken, and beyond reach even if their whereabouts were vaguely known. The compass took Europeans to all parts of the world and ultimately made that world basically European. As Montesquieu (1748) remarks, "the compass opened the universe. Asia and Africa were found, of which only some borders were known; and America, of which we knew nothing. . . . A consequence of the discovery of America was the connecting of Asia and Africa with Europe; it furnished materials for a trade with that vast part of Asia known by the name of the East Indies."

Thanks to the compass and the lands to which it led, "Europe has arrived at so high a degree of power that nothing in history can be compared with it [and] Europe [now] carries on the trade and navigation of the other three parts of the world."

Men's imaginations had been stirred by travelers' stories of other lands. Marco Polo's accounts were among the incentives to visit far-off lands. Stronger incentives to sail the seas came from articles of trade which were now reaching Europe from distant lands, especially from farthest Ind and that mysterious land beyond, Cathay. The growing volume of trade provided a powerful motive for financial venture and geographical adventure.

While the compass pointed the way to new lands beyond the seas, gunpowder made new social and political trails and ultimately new trials for all mankind. It made the armed knight helpless and ridiculous; it placed in the hands of the common man a weapon as effective as any which could be wielded by the nobility; it made stone walls and stone castles, hitherto impregnable, a source of danger rather than a bulwark of protection, and reduced the castle's occupants to the status of inmates in a prison. The knight was driven to hang his mailed armor on the castle wall and call the place a museum; for gunpowder made dust of castle walls and upturned the very foundations of the feudal system, which was thereby condemned to a lingering death as a futile system. Thanks to gunpowder,

Europeans were able easily to conquer any and all of the newly discovered lands and to establish themselves firmly on foreign territory; for no other people, save only the Turks, had learned its virtues in war. Had other peoples anticipated Europeans in the fruitful utilization of gunpowder the story of world conquest would have had a different *dénouement*.

Social and Political Effervescence. The Renaissance was essentially pagan. It introduced into Christian thought pagan ideas and ideals, namely, those of the Greeks. Many of these ideas and ideals were inconsistent with those of traditional Christianity. The result was a challenge to old standards and the adoption of new ones. Without the Renaissance there probably would not have been a Reformation; certainly a Luther and his doctrines of faith could not have survived in pre-Renaissance days. Stoic ideas of natural rights were revived; the idealism of Plato's philosophy challenged modern thinkers, once they had passed beyond the *ipse dixit* of Aristotle. Schemes of social reconstruction were set forth in detail and some of them attained great popularity. Sir Thomas More described in the *Utopia* (1516) a society in which there was no personal property, no money, no leisure class, no long hours of work, no militaristic or imperialistic designs. In the early seventeenth century Companelli portrayed in the *City of the Sun* an ideal community of city-state form in which communism, including community of wives, was the underlying basis of social life, and science and education had come into their own. The scientific ideal was expounded by Bacon in the *New Atlantis,* wherein the material conditions of living were remade. Winstanley and Harrington inject into the troubled years of the Commonwealth new schemes of social life, the one emphasizing the redistribution of property, the other the redistribution of political privileges.

Cooperative enterprises are advocated by other seventeenth-century writers, and in the following century socialistic schemes are advanced by Morelly and Mably. In France, Rousseau, Voltaire, and a score of able writers challenge the social order and some of them specify plans for its fundamental reconstruction. The ferment is not only in ideas but in acts as well. In the sixteenth century the Anabaptists establish a communistic form of government. Seventeenth-century England teems with movements which challenge the social, political, or religious order— Levellers, Anabaptists, Fifth Monarch Men, Quakers, Puritans. France, Germany, and Russia are troubled by numerous sects; and most of these sects have a social as well as a religious program. The spectacular culmination of these movements, at home and abroad, is the political revolutions which shook the old regime to its foundations in France and set up in the English Colonies of America the first great democratic country in English-speaking lands.

The objects attained by each revolution were much the same—freedom from monarchical control; freedom of speech and of religion; rule by the people through representatives; fundamental rights of the individual guaranteed in written constitutions; and, in France, universal suffrage.

In France the privileges of aristocracy were swept away, and Liberty, Equality, and Fraternity became at least the verbal triumvirate.

In each country the revolution ushered in a new order, and in each country it was the beginning of a new epoch, the end of an old. The principles which it embodied were not immediately realized in practice, but many of them progressively developed in succeeding decades when the fruits of strife were garnered. If any note may be taken as marking the change most significantly it is the new determination to make social life conform with the demands of reason and of justice rather than, as had previously been the case, to maintain the *status quo* and read the future in the past. This determination was embodied in the Frenchman's reiterated conviction of the eternal potentiality of human progress and in the fertile plans for reconstructing and reorienting social life.

Closely linked with these social and political ideas and movements was the new science of economics, making headway in France during the reign of Louis XVI and receiving its first comprehensive and systematic expression from Adam Smith in 1775. From that day to this men have contemplated the economic laws of society and have attempted to reconcile economic, social, and political demands in a world in which each sphere of interest seeks mastery.

Nationalism. Until about the beginning of the seventeenth century there was little sentiment of nationality among European peoples. Culture, religion, and the humanities cut across local boundaries and respected national frontiers as little as community frontiers. Such, for example, was Latin, the language in which the learned communicated, and to some extent Greek, which many read and some wrote. The Church was a bond of unity· until the Protestant revolt, known as the Reformation, challenged the authority of Rome, declared faith superior to dogma and authority, and incidentally started religious wars which ruined whole populations. The consciousness of unity among a people as a more important bond than any tie binding them to other groups, that is to say, a consciousness of nationality, appears in England in literature soon after the Norman Conquest and has an uninterrupted history to the present day. Essentially, however, nationalism and the patriotism which is associated with it were created in and of the French Revolution, which made nationalism a religion and set the pattern which other countries adopted. Nationalism is shown in an exaltation of the interests of the nation above those of all other peoples and above those of constituent units of the nation; in the use of symbols of national unity, such as a flag, a hymn, a marching-song, a motto; in the medium of a common language, at least for purposes of state; and in an attempt to inculcate common ideas and common convictions on national affairs.

Missionary zeal led the Convention to declare their intention to carry the doctrine of the new French nation to all lands and to impose upon the ruling houses of Europe the democratic doctrines of the French. French nationalism blatantly challenged the European world. Today nationalism is rampant in many of the countries of Western civilization and is increasing in parts of the Westernized Orient, Near and Far.

Science and Technology. From a world point of view, the white man has, perhaps, during the last nineteen hundred years made no great achievements in art, literature, ethics, or religion, at least none which clearly surpass those of other peoples. In science and technology, however, his accomplishments have been beyond comparison the world's outstanding achievements. Especially momentous were the descriptions of the solar system by Copernicus, Giordano Bruno, and Galileo. More than two thousand years ago the Greeks knew that the earth travels around the sun, and the moon around the earth; they estimated the size of the earth and the distance from the earth to the sun. They gave a naturalistic rather than supernaturalistic interpretation of such startling phenomena as earthquakes, eclipses, comets, and meteors. But a knowledge of these interpretations had been lost during the Middle Ages, and early Jewish (biblical) interpretations had been substituted. The effects of the new astronomic interpretations were tremendous.

Man seemed no longer a godlike creature in a universe made for his benefit, as had been his assumption during the theological dominance of the Middle Ages. His world was now but one of many, not established on firm foundations which supported the canopy of the heavens, but a sphere which swung through space around a central body on which he and all terrestrial existence were directly dependent. His lot became but a transitory existence on one of the meanest of planets, his sun but one of many suns in manifold universes so widely scattered through the immensities of space that imagination could scarcely traverse the distances. What place was there in this heliocentric system for Heaven? Heaven had been above the earth. But if there was no above or beneath, since the earth constantly changed its position and, moreover, revolved on its axis, where indeed was the Heaven in which man's soul would reside forever? Bruno was burned, Copernicus' ashes were scattered to the winds, or to the waters, and Galileo was forced to recant. Heaven and the religion of the Fathers must be saved. The Renaissance, however, had done its work too thoroughly. Intellectual curiosity was not to be stayed by killing or suppressing its outstanding exponents. Scarcely less significant than Copernicus was Newton, whose *Principia* brought all heavenly bodies, and the earth also, into a system of invariant law of motion. The law of gravitation was the ever present force which held the stars in their places, the earth to its orbit, and regulated the movements of the planets and their satellites. The falling of the apple to the ground and the shifting of the seasons had one and the same cause. All were part and parcel of a rigidly determined mechanistic system.

In the eighteenth century the foundations of most of the modern sciences were laid. Lavoisier established chemistry as the science of the composition of bodies out of simpler elements, and Dalton later introduced the Democritean theory of the atom. Physics found brilliant exponents in England and America; zoology and botany adopted schemes of accurate and comprehensive classifications; anatomy, human and comparative, flourished in France, Germany, and England; Hutton, Smith, and Lyell founded modern geology and paleontology.

Through Buffon, Cuvier, Lamarck, the Darwins, Wallace, and Huxley evolution came into its own, and Spencer made this realm all-inclusive. Soon Samuel Butler was showing the evolution of theories of evolution and incidentally exposing some of the biases in the fields of science.

Surgery and medicine accompanied the rise of anatomy and the exact sciences. Less than a century ago the use of ether as an anesthetic made further great advances in surgery possible, and chemistry, the microscope, and knowledge of microörganisms gave the bases of the germ theory and the knowledge of means of combating man's most insidious foes.

Scientists, indeed, have taken upon themselves "the mystery of things as if they were God's spies." Technology, too, has wrought wonders in changing the conditions under which man lives in the civilized world. Science and technology have in fact developed together, each influencing the other.

Without science, modern technology is impossible, in fact, almost inconceivable; conversely, much of our science would be impossible without the technology which has been developed along with science. The lens is an example of this indissoluble partnership.

Remove the microscope and you remove half of modern medicine; remove the telescope and you remove half of modern astronomy, nay, nearly all of it which was not known to the ancient Greeks. Without the spectroscope we would not know the composition of the stars, and nothing would be known of the movements of the more distant stars and constellations. The interrelations of science and technology are as intimate as those of Siamese twins and much more mutually helpful. To sever this relationship would be to kill both children of a common scientific-technological parentage. Technology, to speak of it apart from its twin, science, has brought us a new world of material things. It enables man to move and live and have his being in a universe as different from that of ancient man as ancient man's world was different from that of men of Paleolithic times. Technology makes it possible for us to utilize power, through steam, electricity, and the internal-combustion engine, which equals, for the average American, the power of nearly two hundred human beings. And much of this power requires comparatively little supervision.

Technology, thanks to science, enables us to travel comfortably, if not always safely, at great speed, to communicate freely throughout the entire world in the fraction of a second, to see into immensities of space until now beyond the reach of man's sense perceptions, to observe the infinitesimal and snatch the secret of its composition; to make fertilizer from the air; to dig into the bowels of the earth and bring to the surface materials which only a superior technique could uncover, secure, and utilize; and to make of them and of other substances a million things which did not exist in the world of handicrafts. Technology alone has not accomplished these things, but without technology perfected and supplemented by science they could not have been realized.

Literature and Learning. All peoples have literature, but until recently only the white man has used the printed word on any large scale, and few peoples in other areas have, until recently, made extensive use of writing. Writing or printing and a suitable material for its record and preservation do not create literature, but they facilitate continuous literary and intellectual development. The accomplishments of the Greeks demonstrate that the absence of a printing-press does not preclude high literary endeavor. Even so, with all its facile evils, the printing-press makes possible the recording for large numbers of people of the fructifying thoughts of men. Great literature is the creator's reflection in artistic form upon life and its vicissitudes; it is, therefore, always to some extent a reflection of the times in which the writer lives. Certain literary creations come into favor, are read by many, and become a heritage for future generations. Thus literature creates a life of its own and exerts an independent effective force.

Learning, in the sense of scholarship, is not the sole possession of the white man, but it has flourished extensively in Western civilization and is almost as typical of the culture if not as frequent as are mechanical devices. It would require a series of volumes as compendious and as numerous as those in a recent edition of the *Encyclopaedia Britannica* even to mention the special fields or problems which have engaged the concentrated and prolonged attention of scholars in the Western world during the few centuries which have elapsed since the Renaissance. The titles of the papers and books published during two decades in sixteen sciences require one hundred ninety-seven volumes of the *International Catalogue of Scientific Literature.* The range of the universe of present-day scholarship is amazing; and there are no signs that this universe is shrinking.

IV. The Rôle of Culture Contacts and Culture Diffusions

Culture was not made to live alone and cannot be made to live alone. Every culture bears evidence of having been influenced by other cultures. This generalization applies without exception to the cultures which have been developed by the white man.

That similar traits sometimes develop independently in two areas is a demonstrable fact. The more common occurrence, however, is the diffusion of a trait from one area to another. Seldom are two virtually identical traits invented independently in two culture areas or in a given culture area. When, therefore, a trait shows practically continuous distribution through a large area, in the absence of direct historical evidence we explain its presence in most of the area as due to diffusion.

Similarly, when two traits in separate areas are almost identical we usually explain this striking similarity as due to diffusion from one region rather than to independent inventions. Thus if a philosophic concept of Greece is practically identical with one in India we suspect that it has gone from Greece to India, or from India to Greece, or from some third place to these two areas—in a word, that it has had a single origin. When, however, direct historical evidence of the travels of a trait are lacking, inference of origin based on distribution can be made only with appropriate caution, for certainly some similar traits have independent origins. Similarity in traits is, therefore, not indisputable proof of common origin. We have, however, for the historic and even for the prehistoric civilizations much direct evidence of diffusion and some which though inferred can scarcely be challenged. A great deal of this evidence is documentary.

The Ancient World. The cultures of the ancient world were not isolated areas of civilization. Each built upon its own foundations, but each secured from other cultures much of the material which went into its edifice. In Neolithic Knossos, for example, the center of the famous Aegean Minoan culture in Crete, are objects made of *Tridacna* shell, the nearest habitat of which is the Red Sea. Neolithic deposits in Italy yield exotic shells, among them the mother-of-pearl, whose present habitat nearest to Italy is the Persian Gulf and the Indian Ocean. The presence of these shells in prehistoric lands distant from the place of origin betokens trade.

The sailboats which plied Mediterranean waters during the early Metal cultures probably originated in the Aegean area rather than, as Hesiod alleges, in Egypt. The close similarity between the water craft used in Early Minoan Crete and during the early historic phase of Egypt is convincing evidence of common origin. Egyptian vessels of stone were imported into Crete and were imitated by Early Minoan lapidaries. The Cretans copied the Egyption forms of cups, figurines, hair-dress, and loin cloth.

Early Egyptian cylinder designs inspired the Cretan exotic forms of animals and monsters, among them the Minotaur, which are found on Early Minoan seals. These in turn had originated farther east and had passed through a Nilotic medium. Oriental and Egyptian influences in prehistoric Crete were not limited to material things. Religious forms and symbols were borrowed. The Egyptian cult of Hathor affected that of the Minoan goddess probably in more than externals; the Hippopotamus goddess, Taurt, was progenitor of a beneficent race of Minoan genii.

> The hieroglyphic writing of Egypt stimulated the growth of an independent Minoan script which included a certain number of borrowed signs, such as the *ankh,* or life symbol, the libation vase, the bee of the royal title, and the Palace sign itself. The long-spouted teapot-like crocks of the Early Minoan household were modelled after the copper ewers of contemporary Egyptian usage. Even the humble Cretan used ointment pots of Egyptian shape, and to complete his toilette had the choice of two varieties of depilatory tweezers in vogue [in Egypt] under the Old Kingdom. Beneath the ilex shade he played his favorite "backgammon," such as had been popular at a much earlier date on the banks of the Nile, and he went to bed with the aid of a candlestick of [Egyptian] proto-dynastic shape. (Evans, 1925, p. 228)

We do not know to what extent students of early Mediterranean culture will accept Waddell's (1930) theory that the Sumerian Menes, his father, and his predynastic forefathers introduced Sumerian civilization into Egypt, and that the Sumerian script was the basis of the early Egyptian script.

Certainly there are marked similarities in traits in the two areas. The similarities include, among other traits, "agriculture with plough and hoe and irrigation works, brick buildings with recessed walls, metallurgy and copper chisels, etc., cylinder-seals, stone-mace-heads, polished stone-vases, carved slate-palettes, potter's wheel pottery, painted pottery, incised pottery decoration, animal and bird-form vases, clay-figurines, lapis lazuli beads and inlayings, style of jewelry, use of cosmetics, weaving of linen, chambered tomb-burials, with votive offerings of food, dress and tomb-furniture, stone sculptures and statues, Sumerian hieroglyph writing, radical words in Sumerian language, Sun worship and symbolism, mythology, etc." (Waddell, 1930, pp. 33-34). This is an imposing list of similarities. Whether or not we accept the theory of the Sumerian origin of early Egyptian civilization, the large number of similar traits compels the conclusion that the traits which these two contemporary civilizations had in common cannot in their entirety have developed independently in Egypt and in Mesopotamia.

The excavations in the Indus valley reveal a civilization of the early Bronze Age which was in contact with Babylonia and had borrowed traits from Mesopotamia. Seals from the Indus-valley culture at Mohenjo-Daro which have been found in Mesopotamia establish the date of approximately 3250-2750 B.C. for that phase of Indus culture. The similarities between this early Indian culture and Mesopotamian and Egyptian culture of the period are striking and undoubtedly are the result of many influences between India and the Mediterranean area. These prehistoric Indus people utilized wheat, barley, and dates, and ground their grain on a saddle-quern, or metate, with a back-and-forth rather than a circular or an up-and-down motion. Their domesticated animals included the humped cow, the water-buffalo, the sheep, the dog, and the barnyard fowl. This is the earliest evidence of the domestication of a feathered animal. For a thousand years, from the time of Darius to the fall of Rome, India carried on a brisk trade with the Western world. Shiploads of linen and spices went to the Roman Empire; in payment for these products the Indians imported millions of dollars worth of silver, until in fact they depleted the Roman supply with consequent debasing of the Roman coinage and a financial debacle in the Roman Empire.

The story of early Greek contacts which can be constructed from the now available evidence has yet to be written. Greek civilization is a native growth inspired by many geniuses. Greece, however, was not an isolated culture but had many contacts with other thriving cultures in or near that nursery of civilization, the Mediterranean basin. Greek thinkers seem to have developed independently many philosophic concepts, such as that of transmigration of souls, the golden age, epochs, and cycles, which were present also in early Indian thought. They seem to have developed independently those Stoic ideas of living according to nature, of equality in men, and of a desirable world society, which are present, perhaps at an earlier date, in Confucian thought. Possibly, however, some day these similarities will be shown to be the result of the spread of ideas between these respective civilizations through the channels of trade.

Plato and Pythagoras express obligations to Egypt; Minoan ideas, crafts, and arts came to the Greek mainland; Oriental cults from Asia Minor were transplanted to Greece.

But the debt of Greece to other cultures is small compared with the debt of others to her. Under Alexander and his successors Hellenism spread throughout the Mediterranean world, into India as well as into Asia Minor, Syria, the Arabian peninsula, Egypt, Sicily, and southern Italy. The outstanding influence was in architecture and in art, particularly sculpture. Subsequently Greece exerted a powerful influence upon Roman culture, especially in philosophy, literature, art, and architecture. Through Roman civilization Greece was destined to influence Western Europe and ultimately the whole world. The spirit which actuated the Renaissance was essentially the spirit of Greece, that is, of Athens.

As the Old Testament abundantly testifies, the Jews of biblical times were influenced by many surrounding cults. The sacrifice of children, particularly the first-born, was introduced by Manasseh during the Assyrian domination when many foreign cults found lodgment in Jerusalem, as notably the cult of Tamuz. While the Assyrian dominated the Near East the cults of the conqueror spread into the conquered territory; the prestige of the powerful nation included her gods and her religious ceremonies. In the courts of the temple and on the roofs of a palace in Jerusalem altars were erected to the Host of Heaven; the horses of the chariots of the Sun were stabled within the sacred precincts of the temple.

Offerings were made to the Moon and to the signs of the zodiac; and the masses worshiped the Queen of Heaven, that is, the planet Venus. The religious calendar of the Jews which developed after the Exile contains the double New Year celebration which characterizes Babylonia; and the feast of the day of Atonement, held on the tenth of Tishri, at the autumn equinox, shows in its ritual strong Babylonian influence. After the Exile the Jews adopted the Babylonian names of the months, and also, probably, the practice of intercalation of lunar months at irregular intervals, a practice which almost certainly was derived from Babylonia. Similarly, the sundial, erected in Jerusalem in the time of Ahaz, must be attributed to Assyrian influence: there were intimate contacts with Mesopotamia, and the Chaldeans are credited with the invention of this timepiece. Judaism itself was destined at a later date to exert a powerful influence upon two cults: upon its rejected child, Christianity, and upon that hybrid faith, Mohammedanism. Jewish influence is apparent in the early development of these two cults, and frequently in their later history Judaism exerted an influence upon them, as, for example, in several of their respective messianic movements.

Mohammedanism is largely a compound of Jewish and Christian influences grafted upon a primitive superstitious Semitic cult of the desert. The *Koran* has borrowed wholesale from the Old Testament. It has taken Old Testament patriarchs and kings as saints or near-saints, and regards Jesus as second in power and sacredness to no one save Mohammed. Its tradition of the *Khidr,* or Green One, is probably an adaptation of the Elijah tradition; its concepts of *imam* and *mahdi* have been inspired by Jewish messianism.

When Mohammedanism became political and cultural, and welded religion, life, and politics into a formidable civilization, it absorbed and modified traits from other cultures and transmitted many of these to adjacent regions.

It absorbed many traits of Hellenism which it transplanted to other lands within its control, where, in many cases, they were modified. Arabian civilization is, in fact, largely a Mohammedanized Hellenism. Many of these Arabized Hellenic traits were introduced into Europe by the Mohammedans.

Among these introduced traits are the artistic *motifs* which predominated in Moorish Spain; the characteristic Moorish architecture; and contributions in nearly all the fundamental sciences and branches of learnig, as, notably, anatomy, physiology, chemistry, astronomy, Greek philosophy, geography, and history. Applied arts and crafts and agricultural products were given to Europe by Mohammedans: metallurgical refinements, irrigation, asparagus, the peach, the orange, the grapefruit.

More recently Mohammedans have again been liberal borrowers of traits. Egyptian Mohammedans have adopted the Copt's calendar, which they use in addition to their own. They are familiar with the months and seasons of the Copts and celebrate several of the Coptic festivals. Their usual charm against evil spirits in the bath, a place which is especially prone to be haunted, is a cross above the doorway. Their architecture is in many respects the result of Coptic influence. Some of the earliest and most important of the Cairo mosques were built by Copts. The Arabs in Egypt did not excel in neat or accurate workmanship and they requisitioned the careful handiwork of the Copts.

During the first half of the nineteenth century the wealthy Turks of Cairo initiated the adoption of certain Western European traits. They introduced the use of the knife and fork. Almost immediately thereafter came the custom of drinking wine openly, a custom which soon became common among a large number of high government officials. Lane, writing of these innovations during Mohammed Ali's rule, about a century ago, says:

> That a remarkable indifference to religion is indicated by this innovation is evident; and the principles of the dominant class will doubtless spread (though they have not yet done so) among the inferior members of the community. The former have begun to undermine the foundations of El-Islam: the latter as yet seem to look on with apathy, or at least with resignation to the decrees of Providence; but they will probably soon assist in the work, and the overthrow of the whole fabric may reasonably be expected to ensue at a period not

very remote. The acquisition of a powerful empire, independent of
the Porte, appears to have been the grand, and almost the sole, object
of the present Basha of Egypt. He has introduced many European
sciences, arts, and manufactures; but all in furtherance of this project; for his new manufactures have impoverished his people. He
has established a printing-office; but the works which have issued
from it are almost solely intended for the instruction of,his military,
naval, and civil servants. A newspaper is printed at another press,
in the Citadel: its paragraphs, however, are seldom on any other
subject than the affairs of the government. It is in Turkish and
Arabic. Sometimes three numbers of it appear in a week; at other
times, only one is published in a month. (p. 563)

The present century has witnessed an astoundingly rapid adoption of
Western traits by Mohammedans in Turkey, including European dress
and the Latin script; the abolition of polygamy, the discarding of the veil
by women, the granting of women's suffrage, the free mingling of women
in public gatherings; and public schools of the Western type. Lane's
prophecy has come true not only for Egypt but for Turkey, with a
suddenness which has astounded the Western world.

Renaissance and Post-Renaissance. The Renaissance is largely the
revival and diffusion of the culture traits of the ancient world. It is not
an historical accident that the revival of the classical cultures spread
north and west. The time of its onset in various parts of Western
Europe is roughly proportionate to the distance from the place of origin,
for it spread as traits diffuse, first to adjacent regions of the former
Western Roman Empire. Northern Europe received these influences only
after they had permeated the regions of Southern Europe. The story of
post-Renaissance Europe and of lands settled by Europeans is largely a
story of the spread of culture traits. The elaboration of any important
trait has almost invariably been a composite of contributions from individuals of different national cultures. The watch which we carry in our
pockets today has been invented, this part or that, by Swiss, Germans,
French, English, and Americans. A political theory is a product of the
thought of many individuals, and seldom, indeed, are all of them members
of the same national group. Thus, as Waddell (1930) says, "the in-
ventiveness which is the basis of civilization and of national advance seems
comparable in its evolution to an infection or inoculation rather than to
[the growth of] a plant; it has spread over the earth not so much as
the results of special racial physique and inheritance, but by contact and
converse of those who already possessed it with those who possessed it
not" (p. 178). It is true that only those cultures which are prepared to
receive the trait are influenced. Of cultures as of individuals it is true that

> . . . No secret can be told
> To any who divined it not before;
> None uninitiate by many a presage
> Will comprehend the language of the message
> Although proclaimed aloud for evermore.

Thus communism may spread to the countries adjacent to the U.S.S.R.,
as, notably, Poland, parts of Germany, and Central and Southeastern

Europe; but it seems improbable that it will control those countries of Western Europe which have been tolerant of the demands of the workers, unless there should be another war with disruption of Western capitalism.

The Spread of Chinese Traits into Europe. From at least the days of the Romans there were contacts between China and Europe. The Romans introduced silk from China and possibly fish culture—if they did not copy their fish ponds after those of ancient Egypt. Rhubarb and *gin-seng* came as much-prized medicaments. In post-Renaissance days many Chinese traits came into Europe, most of them, originally, by way of Arab traders. Among these were gunpowder, the compass, paper and later its manufacture, porcelain or chinaware and later its manufacture, the rococo style of architecture, the natural garden, tea and social tea-drinking, vases, water-color and landscape painting, the use of wall scrolls from which wallpaper developed, possibly movable type, which was the basis of the printing-press, playing cards, dominoes, dice, and a stimulus to gambling which in turn was a stimulus to the development of the theory of probability. The totality of the influence of these traits on eighteenth-century Western Europe was considerable; and the compass and gun-powder had already transformed Western society.

Influence of the Prestige of a Culture upon the Diffusion of Its Traits. The prestige of a culture has been an important factor in facilitating diffusion, though prior diffusion may sometimes be largely responsible for the prestige.

The prestige of Greek culture was largely responsible for its permeation of the Roman Empire in the first centuries B.C. and A.D. and subsequently. The prestige of Graeco-Roman culture was the underlying factor in the Renaissance and in the spread of the Renaissance spirit throughout Western Europe, a prestige which has survived to the present day.

In the twelfth century French architecture obtained a reputation which enabled its exponents to spread French architectural motives throughout Western Europe. From the Ile de France artists traveled into all quarters of Europe and spread French principles of design and building which were capable of continuous development and fusion with the motives prevalent in countries which desired to absorb the French inspiration. In the latter part of the twelfth century the movement permeated all of France, and during at least the next two centuries penetrated foreign lands.

A Frenchman of the period, Guillaume de Sens, was the architect of Canterbury. Eucles de Montereau, who went with Saint Louis to the Holy Land, had charge of the fortifications at Jappa. A French architect, Philippe Choniard, held a permanent post at the court of the Emperor Frederic II and probably was responsible for the greatest castle of the age, the Castel del Monte, near Andria in Apulia. In Sicily Pierre d'Agincourt worked for Charles of Anjou, and built in Naples the Castel Nuovo. In Cyprus a master-mason from Troyes built churches, convents, and commanderies. In distant parts of Hungary Villard de Nonnecourt and Martin Ragevy built churches.

A native of Avignon, Matthieu d'Arras, built the great bridge at Prague. French architects were employed in Germany, Spain, Poland, Finland, and Sweden. In the sixteenth and seventeenth centuries the grandeur of the French court and the development of court life under Louis XIV and his successors gave a prestige to French culture which has continued to the present day. French manners, French styles, and French literature were copied in many countries and the French language became and has remained an international language, particularly in diplomacy. Paris still sets the styles in women's dress, soaps, perfumes, and laces.

Meanwhile, England, thanks largely to her commercial and military successes, was attaining prestige, particularly in the eyes of her great rival, France. Especially in the eighteenth century many English traits entered France and English influence stimulated many French traits. Such were the social-political clubs, the natural garden which the English had copied from the Chinese, the respectability attained by actors, and the prevalence of amateur acting. English political institutions and political ideas influenced the ablest French thinkers, as notably Rousseau, Voltaire, and Montesquieu.

The dramatic importance attained by the United States during and immediately following the World War, when its material prosperity placed it in the forefront of the countries of Western civilization, resulted in great prestige for American culture. Many traits penetrated certain countries of Western Europe, the movie, perhaps, most extensively. Germany, for example, sent many observers to this country to learn at first hand our commercial and industrial methods. The English and the French, and doubtless citizens of other countries, expressed fears that Europe would become Americanized.

The prestige of Western civilization is largely responsible for its permeation of such countries as Japan, Turkey, parts of China, and other Asiatic lands. Frequently it has been impressive and appealing to those who have despised and resisted it.

The Diffusion of Amateur Radio in the United States.[2] The history of the radio falls into three periods. Before 1900 radio was almost entirely a problem of the scientific laboratory. From 1900 to 1921 radio was put to practical use in shipping and as a supplement to the telegraph and cable by commercial and governmental agencies. During this period radio also became a hobby. Radio amateurs made transmitting and receiving sets and found their recreation in listening in to commercial and governmental ship and land stations, in communicating among themselves, and in experimenting with reception and broadcasting. In 1921 radio broadcasting became an important commercial enterprise and radio entered the third phase of development. During these years the diffusion was

---

[2] Information furnished by Dr. Raymond V. Bowers from an unpublished Ph.D. thesis in Sociology at the University of Minnesota.

vertical as well as horizontal. In the period from 1900 to 1914 radio diffused from the scientist to the commercial, industrial, army, and navy engineer, and from them to the mechanically minded group of boys and young men. From 1914 to 1921 scientist, engineer, and radio amateur made commercial broadcasting possible and facilitated the diffusion of the radio to the masses. Viewed chronologically, the diffusion was simultaneously in two dimensions: each stage of the vertical diffusion was accompanied by diffusion to a larger and less technically trained public. From the small group of scientists working on the radio problem in 1900, the radio spread to hundreds of less technically trained commercial and government engineers. This latter group, by putting radio stations on land and sea, by designing inexpensive radio parts for mail-order supply houses, and by writing simplified articles on radio technology for newspapers, magazïnes, and supply-house catalogues, facilitated diffusion of the radio to the thousands of mechanically minded boys and young men. Factory-made sets and broadcasting by these various groups insured the adoption of the radio by millions of people. From 1900 to 1914, the period of the vertical diffusion from commercial and governmental agencies to the radio amateur, practically all commercial and governmental stations were in the seaboard states and most of them were on the coast. The ship stations, which probably were a much greater source of diffusion than the land stations, were concentrated in the great transoceanic shipping centers of the North Atlantic and Pacific states. In 1914, the first year for which there are adequate data, although horizontal diffusion was under way, 96.4 per cent of radio amateurs were in the seaboard states, though the population of those states was only 77 per cent of the population of the country; and only 3.6 per cent of the amateurs were in interior states, although the population of the latter group was 23 per cent of that of the country. The North Atlantic and Pacific states, which contained 35 per cent of the population of the country, had 80 per cent of the radio amateurs.

As long as the extension of amateur radio was dependent principally upon vertical diffusion, its geographical diffusion was confined to the areas of commercial and governmental stations. After 1914, however, when amateur radio clubs and other institutional developments had begun to weld radio amateurs into a vigorous national organization, horizontal diffusion came to play a more important rôle than vertical diffusion. From 1914 to 1930 amateur radio spread from the seaboard states to the inland states, from the North Atlantic and the Pacific states to the Middle West, Mountain, and Southern states, from large cities to small cities, and from urban to rural areas.

The Diffusion of Concepts. Concepts, too, like institutions and material traits, are diffused. As examples may be cited the spread of the messianic concept and that of the psychologically kindred belief in the return of the national hero. The messianic concept first emerges in Egypt, some fifteen hundred years before there is record of it among the Jews. Subsequently it is found in Babylonia, Judaism, Zoroastrianism, and Hinduism. The Jews carried the messianic faith with them into all Mediterranean and European lands. Christianity, paradoxical as the fact may seem, has fathered if not fostered messianic sects, and messianism, in the guise of mahdism, has permeated Mohammedanism for centuries. Buddhism carried modified Hindu messianism into farthest Asia, to Tibet, China, and Japan. The belief in the return of the national hero has had an unbroken continuity among whites for five thousand years. In ancient Egypt the belief attached to Re and Osiris and then to the pharaoh Amenemhet (Ameni, he was called by Ipuwer), who reigned about 2000 B.C. In Babylonia the return of Hammurapi, possibly contemporary with Amenemhet, was expected. Persia and India knew the belief. The Jews assigned this rôle to Elijah. Mohammedanism adopted it, probably from the Jews.

Christianity expected the return of Jesus and Christian Europe has assigned the rôle to many national heroes, among them Barbarossa, Charlemagne, Arthur, Roderick, Olaf Trygvason, Olger, Peter II, Napoleon, Nelson, Kitchener. During the present century the return of Marco Kralyevitch, of Barbarossa, and of Kitchener has been expected in Serbia, Germany, and England, respectively.

The Growth, Spread, and Local Diversification of the Christmas Complex. Many concepts, ceremonies, and institutions have undergone long and continuous modification in the course of their travels and local developments. An understanding of their present status implies an insight into their cultural history and their varied cultural environments. To illustrate the kind of modification which a culture trait may undergo in the course of its diffusion through various culture areas and its persistence in varied culture environments we shall outline the making, modifications, and travels of the Christmas complex.

The Christmas celebration has had varied local expressions, some of which have passed to contiguous regions and thence to distant lands. Thus, through diffusion, phases of the Christmas festivity which once were limited to a small locality have become characteristic of large areas and in some cases of almost all Christendom. No one phase of the Christmas celebration, however, has spread to all lands. Today, as has been the case throughout the history of Christianity, each people has a specific and often a distinctive manner of celebrating the birth of Christ. In spite of the name, Christmas is not Christian in origin but is wholly pagan, a series of rites which have been adopted by Christianity and made into a sacred celebration.

The anthropologist calls such a clustering of traits a complex. The pagan element in this complex runs concurrently with the religious, for Christmas is celebrated outside of as well as within the Church. Its celebration within the Church is comparatively recent. The Basilidians, an early Eastern Christian sect, celebrated the birth of Christ on January 5. Otherwise before the fourth century Christianity did not celebrate the Nativity. In fact, there was no agreement upon the day of Jesus' birth. Hippolytus, for example, a Christian Father of the third century, considered March 28 the date of the Nativity. In the fourth century, however, March 28 was made the day of the Conception; hence a date approximating the New Year came to be regarded as the day of Christ's birth. Finally December 25 won general acceptance in Christendom. Inasmuch as for three centuries the Christians did not celebrate the Nativity, one wonders why they introduced in the fourth century a celebration of the occasion and why they chose December 25 as the date of the Nativity.

The answer is clear: They took over the seasonal celebrations of their main rivals, Mithraism and Roman paganism.

From December 17 to 24 the pagan Romans celebrated the Saturnalia. The period was a time of joy and mirth during which the toga was laid aside, informal dress was worn, distinctions of rank were dropped, slaves dined with their masters, were waited upon by them, and enjoyed unlimited freedom of speech. Among all classes gifts were exchanged. The favorite presents were wax tapers and clay dolls. Children especially were the recipients of dolls.

Almost simultaneously with the introduction of Christianity into Rome came Mithraism, brought to the Eternal City, "the most religious city in the world," by legionaires returning from campaigns in India. During the first three centuries of Christianity, Mithraism was its most formidable foe. Like Christianity, it preached a religion of purity and righteousness, with ceremonies of rebirth, regeneration, and purification by blood.

The followers of Mithras celebrated December 25 as the "birthday of the unconquered sun," or as the "birthday of the new sun." Several of the early Christian Fathers, for example, Ambrose, Augustine, and Prudentius, refer to the advantages of celebrating Christmas on this day. A hymn by Prudentius asks: "Will the recurrent sun disappear? Is not Christ born on earth to increase the way of light?" Cyprian calls Christ the "true sun," and this metaphor, or a similar one, was much used by the early Christians. The Saturnalia and the Mithraic celebrations were the inspiration of the celebration of the Nativity and the stuff out of which the early celebrations of Christmas were made. Perhaps, too, in the fourth century came the inspiration of the *praesepe,* that is, the adoration of the cradle, or manger, of Christ. The cult of the cave in which the infant Adonis was born was adopted into Christianity by the Empress Helena, and in 335 the Emperor Constantine, who had made Christianity the official religion of the Roman Empire, richly endowed it. In the days of St. Jerome, one of the chief shrines of Tamuz, or Adonis, was in Palestine, at Bethlehem. "Bethlehem, which now belongs to our faith," says St. Jerome, "and is one of the most sacred places in the whole world, lay formerly under the shadow of a grove dedicated to Tamuz, that is to say, Adonis, and the very grotto where the infant Christ uttered his first cries resounded formerly with the lamentations over the lover of Aphrodite." If the Adonis cult was not the origin of the Christian adoration of the cradle, it is at any rate clear that the latter was merged with the Adonis cult.

The celebration of the birth of Christ on December 25 was carried by Christians into every country of Europe and later over practically the whole world. But owing to persistent pagan influences there are many local variants of the Christmas celebration. Thus a fifteenth-century treatise states that the Bohemian Christmas custom of baking white bread, cutting up and distributing apples, and wrapping fruit trees in white cloth was observed in order to insure a lucky year and a good harvest. These are doubtless old pagan practices which became attached to the Christmas celebration.

The early Teutons believed that during the twelve days between Christmas and Epiphany, Wodan's favorite animal, the horse, was endowed with the gifts of speech and prophecy. During this holy season, the Christianized Teutons declared, horses were wont to put their heads together and confidentially impart to one another the experiences and trials of the past year. This communion of equine spirits, the sole pleasure vouchsafed these noble animals, atoned in a measure for their hard lot. At the present day, it Germanic lands, including England, the peasants do not harness the horses at Christmas-tide and do not speak of them by name, but use circumlocutions and pet epithets. On Christmas night hostlers sleep in the manger, or under it. The dreams which they have there are prophetic of events during the coming year; for in their slumber they overhear the conversation of the horses.

The influence of the Saturnalia persisted in the old English custom of appointing an officer, known as the Lord of Misrule, to superintend the revels at the Court and in the houses of the wealthy. In Scotland a similar official, known as the Abbot of Unreason, was appointed until, in 1550, an Act of Parliament abolished the office. A statute of Henry VII forbade card-playing by apprentices except during the Christmas holidays; and many people who would not indulge in games of chance on any other day of the year made an exception of Christmas. The first lines of a prologue in a book on Christmas, entitled "Round about our Coal Fire, or Christmas Entertainment," published in London in 1740, indicate the pagan spirit which dominated the English celebration of Christmas.

> O You merry, merry souls
> Christmas is a coming,
> We shall have flowing Bowls,
> Dancing, piping, drumming.
>
> Delicate Minced Pies
> To feast every Virgin,
> Capon and Goose likewise,
> Brawn and a Dish of Sturgeon.
>
> The wenches with their wassall bowls
> About the streets are singing,

declares Wither in his *Christmas Carol;* and the custom of carrying "wassall bowls" from door to door, with song and merriment, in Christmas week, still is observed in certain English rural districts.

In England the spring custom of mummers' plays was transferred to Christmas, and the two became inextricably intertwined; that is, the mummers' plays became part of the Christmas complex.

In some parts of the Southern states, of this country, the people at Christmas indulge in the capers and tricks which characterize the celebration of Hallowe'en in the North. Signs on stores are exchanged, gates are removed from hinges, and ropes or wires are strung across walks to trip the unwary.

In Northern Europe, particularly in Scandinavia, at the winter solstice the old pagans celebrated the return of the sun; then, too, the spirits of the dead returned and were given food. Sacrifices were offered to insure a good crop during the coming harvest. In Denmark several of the games, rhymes, and riddles, typical of Yuletide, prognosticate the events of the coming year, such as the weather, the harvest, the matrimonial prospects of the girls, fortune, misfortune, and death. These Christmas practices are pagan traits grafted upon Christianity. As a part of the present Christmas complex they flourish as vigorously as they did in pagan days, though with modifications and ameliorations. Thus, according to a modern Danish hymn, if the angels are kindly received into the house, they will prophesy and insure a good year for the seed slumbering in the fields.

The Yule-log customs, which are limited to northern Germanic lands, are perhaps survivals of the belief that the spirits of the dead hovered about or visited the abodes of the living—a belief which prevailed in Greece, Rome, Iran, China, and many primitive cultures. Ancestral spirits were immanent in the hearth fire, and were propitiated with libations. The souls of the dead returned to their old homes at the New Year, and meat and drink were set out for them. That is why Christmas is a family festival, a season for gatherings "round the old fireside," a joyous time for the reunited household of the living and the dead. In accordance with a pagan custom, part of the Christmas log was kept to light the Yule fire on the following Christmas:

> Kindle the Christmas brand, and then
> Till sunne-set let it burne;
> Which quencht, then lay it up agen,
> Till Christmas next return.
>
> Part must be kept wherewith to teend
> The Christmas log next yeare.
> And where 'tis safely kept, the fiend
> Can do no mischiefe there.

The custom of decorating the Christmas tree with imitation apples, peaches, and pears is a survival of the popular belief that on Christmas Eve fruit trees blossomed and bore fruit; hence it is appropriate to serve fruit on Christmas day and to use a bowl of it as a decorative feature.

Christmas gifts were originally New Year's gifts—as they still are in Roman Catholic Europe—and they date from the Saturnalia. The Romans called them *strenae,* a word which survives in the French name, *étrennes,* "New Year's gifts," or, more recently, "Christmas gifts."

The use of the Christmas tree may also be of pagan origin. Virgil speaks of such a tree hung with toys; and the tree displayed in the Roman Saturnalia may be the ancestor of the Christmas tree. Possibly it was introduced into Germany by Roman legions. If, however, such was the case, the custom obtained little hold upon the people. Before the seventeenth century there is no mention of the use of the tree in Christmas celebrations, although in England in the Elizabethan period, evergreens, especially the mistletoe, which had been a sacred plant among the Celts and the early Teutons, were used liberally.

The first mention of the use of the Christmas tree appears in a work published in Strassburg in 1605, written by a citizen of that city. The next reference to the use of the tree is in a book, written also by a Strassburger, published about the middle of the seventeenth century, in which the custom of using the tree at Christmas is disparaged. By the latter half of the eighteenth century, however, the Christmas tree apparently was rather well known in Germany, for there are many references to the use of it. After the middle of the nineteenth century it was commonly used in that country.

The use of the Christmas tree was a Protestant rather than a Catholic trait and spread more rapidly among Protestants than among Roman Catholics. The well-to-do townspeople rather than the peasants were the first to adopt it. As late as 1855 it was not used in the country districts of Old Bavaria, which is mainly Catholic, and even today it is little used in that part of Germany. Its use today is much more common in Protestant North Germany than in Catholic South Germany.

In 1830 Queen Caroline introduced the Christmas tree into the Low Countries. In 1840 the Duchess Hélène of Mecklenburg introduced it into the Tuileries. The Empress Eugenie approved, but for many years the French middle classes refused to adopt it. In 1890, however, a half century after the introduction of the Christmas tree into France, thirty-five thousand Christmas trees were sold in Paris. The employment of the tree in England is first referred to in 1789, though its use in that country was not general before 1840. In 1840, the year in which the tree was introduced into Paris by a German, Queen Victoria and Prince Albert, her German consort, put up a Christmas tree. The fashion spread rapidly through England.

An English woman who was nursery governess to the infant Prince of Naples, heir to the Italian throne, introduced the Christmas tree into Rome, where many of the upper-class families adopted it. The Christmas tree was first used in Denmark and Norway about 1830. It was not introduced into Sweden proper until 1863, although the Swedish population along the coast of Finland was using it as early as 1800. In Europe outside of German-speaking countries the use of the tree is not general, but is a characteristic only of the well-to-do, whereas in North Germany every family has a Christmas tree. If a family is too poor to buy one, a tree is provided by benevolent patron or charity organization. Such, at least, was the case before the World War. With the exception of

Southern Belgium and Northern France the Christmas tree has not spread into Latin countries, either those of the Old World or those of the New. On the other hand, in France and in Spain, at Epiphany, which marks the end of the Christmas celebration, crowds of young people go from place to place to meet the magi. After much merriment, they conclude that the magi will not appear until the following year. This custom has not spread beyond Catholic countries.

The candles on the tree light the way for the Christ child. They may be a survival of the neap fires, or New Year's fires, which were kindled at about this time of the year in pagan Europe to restore the waning light and heat of the mid-winter sun. In Istamboul, Greek Orthodox Christians, probably as a result of Russian influence, use the lighted Christmas tree. In modern civilization the electric globes which have supplanted candles are appropriately candle-shaped. A recent variant is the illumination of small evergreen trees on the lawns of houses, by means of electric globes attached to an extension wire. A tree decorated in this fashion in Minneapolis on Christmas day, 1914, appears to have set the style. The custom spread rapidly through the United States and is now in use in probably all districts of this country. The community Christmas tree is found in many parts of the United States, but appears to be restricted to this country. It probably does not antedate the present century.

High-class Roman pastry cooks employed poets to write verses and mottoes to accompany holiday presents of bonbons. This custom suggests a prototype of the Christmas card, but it is not possible to establish a historical connection with the use of our present Christmas card. Even though this Roman custom may have afforded no inspiration to the originators of our present Christmas card, it nevertheless is true that the immediate forerunner of the type of card used today was not very different from these Roman prototypes. It was a small piece of cardboard to which a flower, a decoration, or an appropriate picture in colors was attached, accompanied by a printed sentiment or appropriate quotation. The development and use of the Christmas card were facilitated by the popularity of the Christmas tree in England and by the sentiments which Charles Dickens popularized. Immediately before the appearance of the Christmas card, special ornamental notepaper and envelopes were printed for use at Christmas, and also cards decorated in relief, though they carried no verbal expression of the Christmas sentiment. In the 'forties' of the last century it was also the custom for engravers' apprentices to send to friends at Christmas-tide specimens of their work. The first modern type of Christmas card, however, is credited to Sir Henry Cole, who in 1846 suggested to J. C. Horsley that the latter design a special form of greeting to send to friends at Yuletide. Sir Henry's suggestion bore fruit in the form of a card on which was displayed a decorative trellis covered with a grapevine that formed small panels on the right and left, in which were figures representing acts of charity. This original card was reprinted in 1881 and many copies were sold. In the United States, Christmas cards were first printed in 1848; but not until 1890, when the so-called "calendar houses" came into existence, were they printed in large quantities. The personal Christmas card became popular only after its exploitation by sales agencies and publishing companies.

The custom of kissing under the mistletoe is possibly a vestige of the license permitted at many folk festivals. At any rate, whatever the present rationalization of the custom, osculation under the mistletoe was not inspired by redundant religious zeal. The custom did not spread beyond English-speaking lands, although there is a roughly analogous New Year's Eve custom in Lower Austria, the Rhitian Alps, and France.

The custom of hanging up stockings on Christmas Eve was first practiced in Holland, Belgium, or Northern France, and comes to us through the New York and New Jersey Dutch. The tale that Santa Claus comes down the chimney may have had its origin in the belief that the Norse goddess Hertha descended by this route to extend her beneficient influence through the smoke arising from a fire of fir kindled on the hearth in her honor. In parts of Germany, Scandinavia, and Holland, on Christmas Eve the children offer up the chimney a petition to Kriss Kringle, beseeching him to fill their stockings on Christmas morning; and they may, in addition, voice their specific hopes for presents. One folklorist surmises that the concept of Santa Claus driving his reindeer sledge down the chimney was inspired by the older concept of the witches' flight up the chimney and away on a broomstick. We doubt it.

The name by which Santa Claus is sometimes designated, namely, Kriss Kringle, is an old form derived from the German words for Christchild, *Kris' Kind*. The name Santa Claus is the English variant of the Dutch *Santa Niklaus,* but the name is of Eastern European origin. The original Santa Claus was a Greek Bishop, later known as Saint Nicholas, a patron saint of children and sailors. The custom of giving presents to children on Saint Nicholas' day, December 6, was later transferred to Christmas, and to it was moved also the rôle of this patron saint of children. The reindeer which pull his sled are the result of influence from the North, from Lappland and Sweden. These animals appealed strongly to the imagination of the northern non-reindeer using peoples who had no nobler draught animals than dogs and horses. In the dead of winter no conveyance could compete with the reindeer teams portrayed in the descriptions of Santa Claus which were brought to the New World by the Dutch, and which spread from New Amsterdam throughout the United States, and from this country to Canada and England. In Latin countries, whether in the New World or the Old, there is no Santa Claus and children do not hang up their stockings at Christmas. He has, however, a substitute in Latin lands. In some parts of Mexico, for example, there is a *posada,* or tree (literally, "inn"), on which hang gifts which a masked impersonator of Santa Claus bestows upon the children, making, with each presentation, a speech expressing good wishes for the recipient. This custom is a modification of an earlier practice, also called *posada,* of carrying dolls on a pole and selling them to children at this time of the year.

In Italy the rôle of Santa Claus is played by *La Benfano,* an old woman who, on the night before Epiphany, gives the children dolls, trumpets, watches, marbles, or other toys, and candy. An incentive to the practice is found in the fact that the Wise Men from the East brought to the Christ-child presents of gold, frankincense, and myrrh. Such, at least, is the present rationalization. In Spain, however, it is not the custom to give presents to children at Christmas. One of the latest commercializations of the Christmas complex is the formation of the *United States Santa Claus Company,* organized in Chicago a few years ago. It offers to provide any home with a professional Santa Claus at Christmas. The *Santa Claus Company's* Santa Claus guarantees that he will remember the names of the children, deliver the appropriate seasonal remarks, and make no mistakes in distributing the gifts. In 1927 this company booked more than a hundred orders for Christmas. The next step will be the use of automata for this function.

The origin of the Christmas carol is not known. For centuries the singing of Christmas carols out-of-doors has been popular in Germany, France, Belgium, Holland, Russia, and England. Recently the custom has been introduced in various localities in the United States. Christmas carols have never been a feature of the Christmas celebration in Central Europe or in Latin America. In some countries the Christmas carol is a survival, in some it is a revival of an old custom, in most lands it is a borrowed trait.

The mince pie, which is an accompaniment of the Christmas dinner in English-speaking lands, had a religious significance; it was oblong and represented the manger of Bethlehem. The mutton in it commemorated the flocks which the shepherds tended on the first Christmas night. The spices represented the myrrh and frankincense offered by the magi to the Christ-child. During the time of Charles II, plum pudding became a part of the Christmas dinner; it carried a flavor of pagan festivity more potent than the savor of religious piety. The dishes appropriate at Christmas differ from one country to another, although practically every country has a specific Christmas menu. In France it once included chicken and liver pudding, and, in Paris, goat and donkey. Now, turkey or chicken is served by the well-to-do. The Spanish have sweet almonds and cream, followed by a course of fish broiled in front of an open fire and basted with lemon, garlic, and oil. Germans and Alsatians eat smoked or roast beef with sour sauce, black pudding, and baked apples.

The principal item on the Swiss table is goose, supplemented with confectionery, cake, fruit, nut pudding, fritters, fruitpaste, spices, marmalade, eggs, and *kirsch* (cherry brandy). Russians eat a soup consisting of beef bouillon, boiled cabbage, sour cream, the fermented juice of beet roots, and pork. At the dinner of the Italian, which is eaten in the evening, between eight o'clock and midnight, eels constitute the principal dish, each guest receiving an eel rolled in a laurel leaf. Serbians, Cubans, and Portuguese serve young pig. The turkey and cranberry sauce of the American table are the result of a transfer of the Thanksgiving menu to the Christmas holidays.

Christmas has had a variety of meanings through the centuries of Christianity, and the manner of celebrating the occasion has differed widely from region to region. From paganism have been taken practically all of the elements which have become integral portions of its celebration. The attitude toward many of the respective traits which have entered into the making of Christmas has been different in Roman Catholic Latin countries from that in Protestant Germanic lands. The Christmas tree, for example, is seldom found outside Germanic lands, and the adoration of the cradle is typical only of Catholic countries. Even within a country the methods of celebration may have limited regional distributions. Such is the case in North and South Germany. In the United States, too, there are local differences. The method of celebration typical of New England is not characteristic of the Southern States. In the South, the English type of celebration predominates, the social and festive character being the emphatic element. The Pilgrims forbade the celebration of Christmas and made it compulsory to work on that day as on any other. The Puritan hatred of Christmas celebrations persisted in New England until the end of the last century. Even today the New England celebration of Christmas does not have the abandon which characterizes the Christmas celebration in the South. The fire-crackers which enliven Christmas day south of Mason and Dixon's Line would be as much out of place in New England on Christmas Day as on Thanksgiving Day.

Christmas celebrations are still in the making, and during the last few decades have shown no signs of abatement. The form of celebration a century hence no one can predict; but, if recent trends are prophetic, a century from now Christmas will still be the most important annual celebration in Western civilization, and will retain a potent sentimental appeal.

> Yet I feel
> If some one said on Christmas Eve
> "Come let us see the oxen kneel,"
> I should go with him in the gloom
> Hoping it might be so.

V. Recent Social Changes and Trends in Europe and the United States

Recent Changes in Europe. The World War left a great part of Europe exhausted and distraught. The attitudes, organizations, and activities which had served their purposes in war time were not well adapted to the demands of a nation at peace. The ambitions which went into the building of a new order were ambitions which grew out of the old nationalistic order of rivalry, enmity, and hatred, rather than of an intelligent civic idealism attuned to the new world order which many men thought was about to dawn.

The Versailles Treaty and the treaties with the former Allies of Germany made a new political map of Europe. Old states were carved up into new ones and new political and economic frontiers were created. Most of the new post-War states adopted republican and parliamentary forms of government; Hungary alone adopted the form of a kingdom. In the three largest kingdoms the dynasties of the Romanoffs, Hohenzollerns, and Hapsburgs were swept away. Kings disappeared from Turkey, Greece, the German states, and, in 1933, Spain; in other states the power of the throne waned. None of the new states or reorganized states adopted the American form of government in which the president is the head of the executive branch of the government and independent of the legislative branch. In the main the French or the British system was adopted, in which the king or the president has little actual power and serves mainly as a figure-head, perhaps serves best if the head is empty.

The British Parliament, the "mother of Parliaments," has not functioned as satisfactorily in post-War days as previously.

Until recently there were in Great Britain only two major parties; and party control of Parliament was comparatively simple. Since the War there has been in almost every democratic European country a powerful third party. In some countries there have been several parties almost equally powerful and therefore equally powerless. Multiplicity of parties makes it difficult for a country to adhere to a consistent policy.

Thus party issues are so numerous and so many-sided that a government often finds it impossible to control a majority in parliament. The result is compromises and middle courses which satisfy no one. This was notably the case with the regime of the British Labor Party which after two elections during the decade 1920-1930 had a larger number of representatives than any other party but lacked a majority of the total membership of the House. During the post-War years there have been numerous changes in government in practically every European state. From 1918 to 1933 inclusive seven governments held office in Great Britain, fifteen in Germany, and twenty-four in France. In the last-mentioned country some of the governments survived for only a few days; and 1934 repeated the story of previous years.

In many countries parliamentary government is now made more difficult than previously by reason of the democratic device of proportional representation. Proportional representation assures the representation of all considerable minority groups and thus makes the parliament a mirror of the political sentiment of the country. Parliaments, however, are not merely representative bodies but also legislative bodies which make laws by majority vote; and increasing heterogeneity of political composition makes effective majorities so much the rarer. Apparently parliament cannot be at one and the same time both thoroughly representative and efficiently legislative. The failure of parliaments has been partly responsible for the development of forms of dictatorship which have appeared in many European countries since the War, as notably in Greece, Russia, Spain, Roumania, Hungary, Austria, Italy, Poland, Germany, and also in Turkey. These dictatorships, Russia aside, are sometimes referred to as forms of fascism. Two other forms of social-political movements have been power- ful since the War, namely, socialism and communism. The latter has been established in Russia under a form of Soviet dictatorship.

Both types of movement mark the decay of capitalist civilization; neither of them has captured the government or attained any considerable influence in countries in which the mass of the people are well fed and face life with the habitual equanimity. In every country, however, both fascism and communism are present in some form and appeal to a certain number of the people, not only in Europe but in the countries of the New World as well.

During the depression years after the War there was a considerable extension of social services, which in most countries have been continued. The workers now have votes; and no government can afford to withdraw assistance from a class whose votes are vital to that government's existence.

In those countries in which a parliamentary system prevails the pressure from the workers is to some extent effective. In those countries in which fascism has secured control the fate of the workers has been less fortunate.

In Italy fascism brought and maintained a low wage standard; in Germany Nazism has dissolved the workers' unions, appropriated their funds, and made the workers servants of the state, a status which bids fair to be interpreted as that of servants to capitalism. This so-called state socialism has nothing in common with the classical socialism which aimed at improving the status of the workers, but is in effect its negation. The only alternative for the workers in those countries in which labor is persecuted seems to be communism.

Another feature of post-War development is the strengthening of na- tionalism and the alliance of nationalism with the right rather than with the left. In the nineteenth century, as notably in Spain and in the German and Italian states, the reverse was the case: nationalism was the ally of liberalism and the foe of autocracy. In post-War Germany and Italy nationalism has been the rallying cry of conservatives and royalists rather than of liberals and democrats.

Recent Social Trends in the United States. In the autumn of 1929 the President of the United States asked a committee of social scientists to examine and report upon recent social trends in the United States. The findings of the committee were published in 1933 in a two-volume sum- mary and twelve monographs, the latter dealing at some length with special fields. The cost of the investigation ($500,000) was covered by private funds. The Chief Executive of the nation thought the enterprise sufficiently important to endorse it publicly, and to write the foreword of the published results, in which he states: "This study . . . should serve to help all of us to see where social stresses are occurring and where major efforts should be undertaken to deal with them constructively." The study undertaken by this committee was the first attempt by a group of trained students of social life to discover and describe the character and drift of our society in its manifold entirety. It remains the most comprehensive and detailed study which has been made of the social life of a people within the compass of a generation. The period covered is approximately the first three decades of the present century, with an occasional word about the closing decades of the last century. The study was scarcely under way before a financial depression had visited the country; and the writers of the respective reports realized that the trends of the first three decades of the century might be considerably modified during the next decade, were, indeed, in many instances already being modified or even reversed. The effects of the depression are another story; and one which the social sciences should secure forthwith.

The report of the President's Committee on Social Trends shows that there have been many significant changes in every phase of social life during the present century. Old enterprises have disappeared or have been greatly modified, and new ones have been substituted or have supplemented the old. During the preceding century we were busily, too busily, exploiting our natural resources. There was much utilization of raw materials and there was much waste. For example, the metals and coal were generally mined in the cheapest fashion, which sometimes involved processes that will make it more expensive in the future to secure the temporarily abandoned coal or ore than if they had been secured in the initial stages. In many cases, moreover, future mining must be done at greater expense because of greater depths or the playing-out of the rich ores or seams of coal. Timber resources have been squandered in unbelievable abandon; lands once heavily timbered are now barren and useless. The result has been not only devastated territory, but destructive floods which would not have occurred had adequate forests been spared. Only at the expense of many hundreds of millions of dollars can the wanton waste be repaired; and restoration of forests will not recompense the hundreds of thousands of citizens who have been ruined by this thoughtlessness or outright brigandage.

The population still increases, but not with the high rate of increase which characterized the last century. The immigration which had risen to the peak of a million a year before the World War dropped thereafter to a little more than a hundred thousand a year, and has since ceased almost entirely, with, in fact, in recent years an excess of emigration. There has been a decrease in the death rate and in the birth rate; if predictions are fulfiled, in less than a half century the population will be stationary.

The average length of life has been increased by a decade, due largely to the decreasing mortality rate in infancy and childhood. Owing to the drop in the birth rate and the increase in the average length of life there will be an increasingly larger percentage of the population in the adult group, including the age grades above fifty. The span of life has not increased but the percentage of the population which reaches middle age is greater. In most communities we shall not have to enlarge our school facilities for the young but we shall need greater educational facilities for adults. In some communities there are already superfluous school desks in the rooms for the lower grades of grammar school. Some of the expense which has gone toward caring for the young must soon be transferred to adults and the aged.

The development and extension of communication facilities has been an important phase of twentieth-century American civilization. The railroad appears to have reached its acme of prosperity; and already it has fallen upon hard days. Freight and passenger hauls have declined and some railroads have become defunct. Perhaps we shall see a renaissance of the railroad under new types of conveyance which are now making their appearance—gasoline or electric engines, and streamlined cars. Meanwhile the day of the automobile is at hand; and motor vehicles are doughty rivals of railroads. There is a motor vehicle for about one person in five. The airplane is playing a gradually more important rôle as a carrier of mail and passengers. The telegraph is used more than formerly and there has been a great increase in the traffic of the long-distance telephone, which now unites all parts of the country and makes this continent and Europe a telephone unit. The private telephone has become a necessity among the middle classes and is frequently an adjunct in the homes of industrial laborers. Radios are now as numerous as telephones and are found in some regions in which the telephone is not used: in Alaska beyond the Arctic circle, in Antarctica, with the Byrd expedition. In 1934 radio audiences throughout the world could hear in one evening speakers in the Explorers Club of New York City broadcasting to the Byrd expedition in Little America and the voices of Byrd and his party beyond the Antarctic circle. As a part of the radio romance, with practically every broadcast of program or event the audience is treated to an account of the virtues of some commercial article which the advertiser recommends.

Newspapers continue to have large circulations. The present century has witnessed an extension of syndicated articles and the development of chains of newspapers under one control, as notably in the Hearst and Scripps-Howard chains. The same editorial may appear simultaneously in widely separated parts of the country. Competing with the above-mentioned agencies and with theater, dance hall, and library, as well, is the movie-house, which now offers sound-motion pictures. The extent to which the sound-movie influences speech, dress, and opinion cannot be determined, but may be considerable.

Banks, and likewise their total deposits, have increased. Many small banks have been associated with at least one large bank. More people carry life insurance and they carry larger amounts than was the case a generation ago. Group insurance is a feature of this development.

Illiteracy decreases and is almost absent in the states of the Middle West which have had little immigration during the past few decades. It is highest in the South, particularly, though by no means exclusively, in the Negro population. From kindergarten to university more people go to school. Curricula of secondary schools have undergone considerable changes. There has been a decrease in the amount of Latin and Greek taught and an increase in the sciences. Comparable changes have taken place in the colleges and universities. A statistical study of enrollment in colleges and universities in 1933 shows that "liberal training maintains its hold. Young men and women in practically undiminished numbers are continuing to take liberal arts courses in the universities, almost equally in the privately controlled institutions having tuition fees and in the institutions under public control where tuition is free, with varying incidental fees. In the independent colleges of arts and sciences, which are very largely controlled with tuition fees, about 95 per cent of last year's enrollment is reported this year [1933]" (Walters, 1933). In the colleges and universities, however, as well as in the secondary schools, there has been a considerable development of vocational training. Much of the work done during the first two years of college is pre-professional, a preparation for training in medicine, dentistry, law, or other profession. In the high schools there has been a great increase in the number of courses offered in the industrial arts, including such subjects as manual training, mechanical drawing, woodwork, automobile mechanics, and almost as great an increase in the number of courses in the household arts and in physical education.

There has been enlargement of the metropolitan area, the region dominated by a large city, a consolidation created largely by the automobile and the telephone. The fine arts are given an increasing amount of attention. Sculpture, painting, decorative arts, and architecture receive recognition from municipalities and are liberally supported by private citizens. In many parts of the country there is increasing attention to the esthetic.

Public services of various kinds have increased.

Health is now a social problem, the concern of schools and communities through departments of health, clinics, hospitals, sanitariums, and visiting nurses. Typhoid and smallpox, as public scourges, have disappeared, though only unceasing vigilance keeps them in check. In spite of vigorous opposition from a portion of the medical profession, socialized medicine gains ground. The future historian may consider the twentieth century significant not only for its developments in education, science, technology, and the arts, but also for its impetus to recreation. Probably a larger number of people travel for pleasure than was ever the case before, and, thanks to the automobile, they go greater distances. Commercialized amusements have become major financial enterprises. In January, 1931, the country contained 22,731 motion-picture theaters with a total seating capacity of approximately 11,300,000. In 1930 there were more than twelve million radio sets in the country, which is about 40 per cent of the number of families in 1930. These two enterprises do not exhaust the list.

In almost every athletic sport more games are played and a larger number of people are participants than was the case a generation ago. Attendance at contests has increased. Tennis and golf have become common, whereas at the beginning of the century few people indulged in either one of these sports.

Social work has grown from a haphazard individual charitable enterprise to a profession taught in colleges and universities and supported by public as well as private agency.

Social work is now concerned with family and child welfare, medical needs, children in the public schools, probation work in the courts, welfare in industry. Much of the work is necessarily limited to an immediate response to present needs, but the professional social worker emphasizes preventive and socially constructive measures. One of the most significant trends in social work is the development of case work, the attempt to ascertain the peculiar needs of the individual or family and to adopt remedial measures suited to their respective needs.

There has been growth and extension of the social survey which describes the social needs, general or specific, and (or) the social assets of a district, community, or region. A *Bibliography of Social Surveys* published in 1928 lists 2700 such projects, completed or under way. These include surveys of schools, health, city and regional planning, industrial conditions and relations, housing, and general social conditions. A nation-wide sampling survey of the costs of medical care, begun before the depression, was completed and the results published in 1932.

There has been a small but consistently gradual increase in crime, though there have not been crime waves.

The murder rate is high and convictions for murder are few. The present century has seen the rise of gangs and the extension of their power and influence into various fields, particularly in the large cities. From 1932 to 1934 there was an increase in kidnapings and in the amounts demanded for ransom, these demands going from $50,000 to $200,000. Lynchings were decreasing, with, however, in 1933 evidences of a possible resurgence of that form of lawlessness which was publicly defended by one state governor and uncompromisingly denounced in a public statement by the Chief Executive.

Government, particularly the national government, has been participating to an increasing extent in social programs. It has given attention and funds to child welfare, care of mothers, public sanitation, and the needs of agriculture.

During the depression the national government devoted billions of dollars to relief and provided work in fields which had not been entered previously, even indirectly, by the federal government. In 1930 nearly 70 per cent of all federal aid was given to the following activities, all of them recently assumed by the federal government: vocational education and rehabilitation; water-power development; cooperative agricultural extension service; cooperative distribution of forest planting stock; highways; forest roads, trails, and highways; cooperative farm forestry; demonstration in rural sanitation. The federal government is now in the fields of banking, agriculture, commerce, highways, mail service, navigation, radio, food inspection, weights and measures, education, and health, to mention merely a portion of its services.

Among conspicuous trends in local, state, or national government Merriam (1933) includes the following:

The tendency toward organized planning in cities and latterly in other and broader situations requiring community foresight. Advancement of scientific research regarding government, and scientific research on the part of the government itself, especially as seen in Washington bureaus and in state universities. Increasing attention to the basic problems of civic education and to the scientific study of the problems. Adherence to the doctrines of liberty, equality and democracy in the face of conflicting tendencies in the economic world. Widespread abandonment of the earlier doctrines of individualism. (p. 1535)

VI. Efforts to Understand, Control, and Direct Social Life

All human groups experience social change. Everywhere men attempt, however feebly, to understand, control, and direct their social life. In these fields the efforts of the white man far surpass those of any other people. These efforts on the grand scale are recent in the white man's civilization, in fact they are recent in human civilization, and they characterize only certain Caucasoid social groups. They can be described as though they stood outside of social life proper and were not a function of social structure. Actually, however, no real separation can be made between social thought and social practice. Social theory, as embodied in law, constitution, and formal education is as inseparably a part of social structure as science is a part of technology or as diagnosis is a part of surgery. The important divisions of social life are not always territorial; for our purposes, however, we shall briefly survey the efforts which have had territorial units as their main delimiting objective.

Local Community. Western man has begun to study his community as an end and an object of interest in itself.

The results may be a social survey, a taking-stock of financial resources, or an effort to grasp the important phases of community life from several aspects. *Small Town Stuff, Tepoztlan, Middletown, Arctic Village,* are pictures of practically the whole community. Other studies describe the life of a group within the community, such as a nationality or a religious group, and some describe an institution, such as *Taxi Dance Hall.* In addition to these scientific descriptions which are not aiming *per se* to improve the community or life in the community, but rather to enrich social science itself, there are studies of the resources and liabilities of the community which serve as a bill of particulars on all counts and constitute a useful source of reference in planning for the future. City planning, which used to be the preoccupation of utopians, is now a job for at least a city engineer, an architect, and a specialist in transportation. Zoning and building ordinances help to remake the city or to insure the continuance of certain features. Even the scruples of political parties make way, here and there, for a city manager who is employed as an expert to administer the affairs of the community and who may to some extent influence its policies. Men have begun to see their community in its geographical and cultural setting and to plan in accordance with the promises or limitations of environing regions. Some who have approached these problems with vision have shown that to be locally minded is not necessarily to be small minded, for the social microcosm may be as complete as the macrocosm and have, in its own field, almost as great potentialities. Each locality can be a world to itself, though a world within a world; and the discovery and exploitation of potentialities are as important as the discovery of limitations. Gradually, boosting gives way to building.

State and Regional. Some states are taking account of their resources and planning their social and economic life. In some areas the people are becoming regionally minded. This larger territorial unit may include several states, or may include portions of states, such as "Delmarvia," the comfortable peninsula between the Chesapeake Bay and Delaware Bay, or the extensive Middle West.

National. Thinking in national terms, other than narrowly political terms, is a phenomenon of comparatively recent history. Fascism in Italy, Nazism in Germany, and Bolshevism in Russia have been religious (or anti-religious), political, social, economic, and educational movements. Since 1918 there have been comparable though less violent movements in many Western countries.

International. The present century has witnessed not only the greatest outbursts of nationalism which the world has known, but also the greatest amount of interest in internationalism and more international organizations and movements than all previous history has seen. In the last thirty years there has been published a library of books which treat of various phases of internationalism. Among these are contributions from some of the leading political thinkers and from scholars in almost every major field of endeavor. The acknowledged importance of the international field is illustrated by the fact that the current *Encyclopaedia of the Social Sciences,* in a volume published in 1932, devotes sixty-five pages to phases of that major topic. It recognizes under special articles the specific importance of the following: international advisers; international finance; international labor organization; international law; international legislation; international organization; international relations; international trade; international waterways. There are in addition in this encyclopaedia many important articles in which the international phase is treated, such as "Agreements, international," the League of Nations, the Hague Conference, Permanent Court of Arbitration.

These are not matters of mere bibliographical magnitude. On every hand there are evidences of an international mindedness which did not exist so abundantly or discriminatingly a few decades ago. One of the most significant features of the interest in international affairs is the fact that at last the practical and hard-headed man has begun to believe that internationalism is an important matter and not merely the ravings of utopians. The concept of a world society of which nations and not merely governments are constituent members is no longer regarded as a mere fantasy but as a present possibility, whatever guess one makes about the probability of its realization during the next few million years.

Concerted Disarmament. The maintenance of armaments is a costly enterprise. Peace becomes almost as expensive as war. The protection which armaments give a country would seem to be dependent upon the strength of the armaments of potential enemies; each country with fifty thousand men under arms is perhaps as well protected as each country with five hundred thousand men under arms. Thomas Paine suggested this in the eighteenth century and the principle has been reiterated in the present century. Why, then, have not the countries reduced the expenses of armaments? Beginning with the Washington Disarmament Conference of more than a decade ago several international Disarmament Conferences have been called for the purpose of reducing armaments. · At the Washington Conference a proportionate strength between the navies of England, Japan, and the United States was agreed upon, contingent upon the naval strength of other countries remaining as it then was. But the Disarmament Conferences of 1927 and of 1932, the latter still (1934) continuing formally, have accomplished nothing. The reasons for their failure are not difficult to discover. There is no agreed method of weighting the relative kinds of armaments, such as tanks, poison gas, battleships, cruisers, submarines, airplanes, men under arms, conscription. The kind of armament which furnishes the best offensive and defensive force for one country is not identical with that which affords the best defense and offense of another. No formula has been found which will insure that one nation has protection and attacking power commensurate with that of any other.

Nor, indeed, is this arrangement desired by any of the nations. Each group of delegates represents a national interest, not a world interest or an international interest, and each is jockeying for the most advantageous military position. In short, each nation hopes to secure out of an agreement upon limitation of armaments a relative advantage over every other nation. If it cannot do so, why should it limit armaments? What body of delegates would wish to return to their country with the assurance that they had effected an arrangement whereby their country in the event of war would be in no more favorable situation than would any enemy country?

The League of Nations. In 1919 the Treaty of Versailles established the League of Nations. Eventually nearly all the more important nations, and most of the smaller, except some of the very smallest, such as San Marino, Liechtenstein, and Monaco, became members of the League. The U. S. A. is the only large Power which did not eventually become a member. Subsequently some of the members withdrew, as, notably, Brazil, Japan, and Germany. The League was supposed to maintain the political lines laid down by the Versailles Treaty and to prevent war among its members through the use of economic boycott. When, however, Japan was not supported in her military aspirations in China and the League attempted to thwart her designs there, Japan (1933) notified the League of her intention to withdraw. Germany followed this example in 1933.

These withdrawals demonstrate the essential weakness of the League so far as control over the large Powers is concerned.

For this impotence the League itself is not to blame.

The constitution, or Covenant, of the League assumes that the constituent member states are sovereign bodies.

Hence the unanimity rule for Council action; and, without the consent of the Council, the Assembly is powerless.

The Council has, moreover, been ruled by the great Powers, who will not be "dictated to" by the smaller Powers.

In larger international affairs the League may have accomplished little and may have more often failed than succeeded in its efforts, but in many matters, more particularly in matters involving the backward regions of Europe, it has accomplished much that is creditable. To its credit are its efforts to suppress the international white-slave traffic and the illegal drug traffic, maintain the rights of minority peoples, and regulate interstate commerce and river traffic, as, for example, on the Danube. The International Labor Organization, the establishment of which was provided for in the Treaty of Versailles, has investigated the conditions of labor in various countries and has obtained in many countries favorable governmental action, especially in the legislation of maximum hours of work. It has no authority but functions merely as a deliberative body which makes recommendations. It has recommended, among other things, the forty-eight–hour week and insurance or other provision for the maintenance of the unemployed. Twenty-five states, including most of the leading industrial countries, have ratified this convention. Its recommendation for the establishment in each country of machinery for fixing minimum wages has been ratified by ten countries.

Propaganda. The War and post-War years witnessed the development of propaganda as a new and powerful technique. It has been said that the German army was defeated as much by paper bullets as by military strategy and superiority.

In recent years propaganda has entered every field of national and international affairs and is utilized by almost every financially powerful agency. It has employed all the major channels of communication—newspapers, magazines, radio, and movie. It parades most successfully in disguise.

Western Civilization in the Doldrums. The period from the Renaissance until, roughly, the beginning of the present century is generally regarded as the upward swing of the pendulum of Western civilization. The eighteenth century had its pains and travails, as typified especially by the revolutions in France and the American colonies; and reverberations from these revolutions ran through many other countries during the first half of the next century.

To most men who lived during the last century the optimism of eighteenth-century rationalists and early nineteenth-century environmentalists seemed to be justified. Technology was making great strides; science was overcoming every obstacle; in many countries representative government was becoming more firmly entrenched; the increasing hazards of war seemed to make war less likely because more destructive; internationalism in politics and finance was growing apace; the lot of the common man, no matter what class distinctions prevailed, was improving; the poorest in the nineteenth century enjoyed comforts which the feudal lord could not command. *Victorian* came to mean not so much a period as the smugness and satisfaction which characterized an era. Since 1918 that smugness has gone. The calm expressions of thoughtful men are more lurid than the rabid radicalism or perfervid journalism of two decades ago. Spengler contends, with the logic of the mathematician and the data of the historian, that Western civilization has reached its apogee and must needs decline. H. G. Wells—and, in all sincerity, who has been a more accurate or a farther-sighted prophet of Western civilization?—is apprehensive lest civilization destroy itself, and describes our present age as the age of frustration; Bertrand Russell, Quaker, pacifist, philosopher, mathematician, and keen observer of contemporary events, speaks of the possible overthrow of all forms of Western civilization; William Mc-Dougall characterizes our social life as *Chaos;* and Robert Briffault devotes a book to the *Breakdown* of modern civilization. Even the Sage of Northampton realized that in spite of four years of that now remote Golden Age, Coolidge Prosperity, "the country is not in a good condition." These are but a few of our contemporaries, most of them recognized as men of outstanding ability, who have published reflections of this tenor upon the course of events. Millions have read books of this character, and presumably millions have thought that the problems treated in them deserve consideration. It would be difficult to match these books by optimistic works of similar quality or quantity.

The prevalence of a conviction does not prove the pessimistic thesis, but it does show a trend of thought, an abandonment of old convictions, and the consciousness of the sad plight of modern man. Especially during the depression years following 1929 many keen students of human life have doubted that life in *Middletown* is preferable to life in *Arctic Village* or in *Tepoztlan.*

A glance at some of the changes in the social life of the white man during the present century will show that change, not to say turbulence, has characterized almost every portion of his domain. A war cost some ten million lives on the battlefield and disrupted Western civilization in unprecedented manner. In its train it left new political frontiers, new forms of government, new international alignments. Indians, Turks, Egyptians, have been in revolt against Western civilization even while they were adopting many of its traits with unprecedented rapidity. In Europe old monarchies have been swept away and monarchies which remain have been curtailed. Republican, socialist, communist, or fascist governments have sprung up. One of the most striking things in the new order has been the challenge to democracy, as seen in fascism and communism, with no common agreement upon a preferable alternative. Everywhere there is a feeling of uncertainty and of insecurity, a breakdown of morale. Certainly the world has not been made safe for democracy; rather it seems to have been made safe for Marsocracy, and unsafe for any stabilized order.

Such is the irony of affairs, the nations which are most likely to fight are so involved with all other nations that any European war is likely to become a world war comparable in magnitude with the last one. Whether we shall have war depends largely upon whether the forces of nationalism continue to hold the field or the forces of internationalism shall triumph. Certainly neither fascism nor communism is likely to break down the primary forces of nationalism. The main forces underlying nationalism have been capitalism and the jockeying for special privileges by those who would gain in money or prestige by a war—or think they would gain. In some countries the younger generation seems to be more nationalistic than the older; in some countries it is more internationalistic. There are many mutually antagonistic trends; and the wisest and most knowing of political sages cannot predict the outcome of inevitable clashes of interest groups.

VII. SUMMARY AND CONCLUSION

The white man is not a social group or an organization of groups, but a sum total of groups of white men having nothing in common save a pattern of race characteristics and, for the most part, Indo-European languages. The linguistic unity is apparent only to the grammarian, not to the users of the respective languages, most of which are so different from one another as to be mutually unintelligible. The white man has no known common history but a variety of histories, many of which have comparatively little in common. The white man has no common civilization, but a collection of types of civilization which in their entirety present almost as great variety and contrast as if all other historical civilizations had been included. At no period of history has the same type of civilization prevailed throughout the white race; and no branch of the white race has had through all periods of history the same type or degree of civilization. Membership in the white race, therefore, connotes no one type of life; and has little meaning apart from reference to physical traits. Viewed from the larger perspective of human history, and leaving aside the question of ultimate indebtedness, the white man has been in recent centuries the greatest creator of civilization and also the greatest destroyer of both human and natural resources.

The white man has destroyed natural resources, mineral, vegetable, and animal, over great areas of the world; he has annihilated native peoples so ruthlessly that in many parts of the world a few hundred years, or even less than a hundred years, of contact with whites leaves no trace of the people who were occupying the soil when the whites arrived. The last Tasmanian aborigine died a half century ago; native Australians are fast disappearing, they survive only in a few isolated spots; the Beothucks of Newfoundland were extinct before ethnology was a science; from most of the region east of the Mississippi the Indian has been exterminated or removed, and in the region west of that river the red man lingers in few places outside of arid regions from which the whites have not cared particularly to dispossess him. Such, essentially, is the story in every land to which the Anglo-Saxon has gone. The Latin, in recent centuries, has not been so destructive of natives or of native culture as has the Anglo-Saxon, but in areas which the Latin has colonized he has brought to the native little except ruin. In most lands which have been claimed by whites few natives survive to curse their destroyers; and for the most part the morale and social organization of those who remain have been so severely shattered by the whites that the native cannot effectively resist the white man's demoralizing culture. A history of the British written by Tasmanians, Australians, New Zealanders, or South Africans, and a history of European settlers and their descendants written by American Indians, would present a picture of the white man and his civilization dramatically different from that presented in the histories of European civilization written by Europeans or so-called "Americans"— to use a word appropriated by the people who appropriated the continent. Western civilization has been taken to the Chinese; and, partly by way of Japanese routing, it has, with the exception of Mongoloid invasions, introduced more chaos into their life than all the confusions of the preceding two thousand years.

And what, precisely, has European civilization to offer in compensation? Much, by way of science and technology; little, indeed, by way of a more satisfying scheme of social life than is known to other peoples. The material conditions of life in Western civilization have been greatly improved. And yet it is difficult to be sure that on the whole Western civilization has increased the comfort or the satisfaction of living. This in spite of its creation of material comforts and of spiritual satisfactions which in themselves seem to enhance life. Leonardo da Vinci had in mind the white man when he said: "The works of men's hands will become the cause of their death."

SELECTED BIBLIOGRAPHY

BREASTED, J. H. 1933. The dawn of conscience. New York: Scribner's. Pp. 4??.

CARTER, H., & MACE, A. C. 1923 & 1927. The tomb of Tut-Ankh-Amen. (2 vols., 2nd by H. Carter.) New York: Doran. Pp. 231; 277.

COLE, G. D. H., & COLE, M. 1933. The intelligent man's review of Europe today. New York: Knopf. Pp. 624.

DICKINSON, G. L. 1931. After two thousand years. A dialogue between Plato and a modern young man. New York: Norton. Pp. 213.

CRESSY, E. 1925. An outline of industrial history with special reference to problems of the present day. London & New York: Macmillan. Pp. 364.

EVANS, A. 1925. The early Nilotic, Libyan and Egyptian relations with Minoan Crete. J. Roy. Anthrop. Instit. Great Britain & Ireland, 55, 199-228.

HONATAUX, G. 1929-32. Histoire de la nation égyptienne. (3 vols.) Paris: Plon. Pp. 427; 633; 573.

HUXLEY, A. 1928. Jesting Pilate. London: Chatto & Windus. Pp. 291.

LANE, E. W. (n.d.) The modern Egyptians. London: Gardner. Pp. 595.

McDOUGALL, W. 1931. World chaos. The responsibility of science. London: Kegan Paul. Pp. 119.

MERRIAM, C. E. [Ed.] 1929. Studies in the making of citizens. (11 monographs.) Chicago: Univ. Chicago Press.

MONTESQUIEU, C. L. S. (n.d.) Spirit of the laws. (2 vols.) New York & London: Dume. Pp. 402; 282.

PARSONS, G. 1928. The stream of history. New York: Scribner's. Pp. 611.

SELIGMAN, E. R. A., & JOHNSON, A. [Eds.] 1930-. Encyclopaedia of the social sciences. New York: Macmillan.

STEFFENS, L. 1931. The autobiography of Lincoln Steffens. (2 vols.) New York: Harcourt, Brace. Pp. 884.

THOMPSON, J. M. 1929. An historical geography of Europe 800-1789. Oxford: Clarendon Press. Pp. 152.

[Various.] 1933. Recent social trends in the United States. New York: McGraw-Hill. Pp. 1568. (Also 12 monographs.)

WADDELL, L. A. 1930. Egyptian civilization: its Sumerian origin, real chronology, and Sumerian origin of Egyptian hieroglyphs. London: Luzac. Pp. 223.

WALLIS, G. A., & WALLIS, W. D. 1933. Our social world. New York: McGraw-Hill. Pp. 372.

WALLIS, W. D. 1930a. An introduction to sociology. New York: Crofts. Pp. 433.

————. 1930b. Culture and progress. New York: McGraw-Hill. Pp. 503.

WALLIS, W. D., & WILLEY, M. M. 1930. Readings in sociology. New York: Crofts. Pp. 639.

WALTERS, R. 1933. Statistics of registration in American universities and colleges. *School & Soc.*, **38**, 781-795.

WOOLF, L. 1931. After the deluge. A study of communal psychology. London: Hogarth Press. Pp. 347.

CHAPTER 10

SOCIAL HISTORY OF THE YELLOW MAN

EDWIN DEEKS HARVEY

Dartmouth College

INTRODUCTION

The most numerous portions of the human race live in Asia. Prolonged residence and observation among Mongoloid peoples gives awareness of their essential humanity in the fullest sense of the word. And judged by their cultural achievements different members of these Asiatic peoples are on a parity with the more "gifted" members of other races. An investigation of the works and thought of some of these mighty peoples reveals an extraordinary diversity of gifts and brings a realization of high accomplishment on their part. These stocks, one opines, will bear unscathed any comparisons made between them and "the best of earth's children."

Physically the yellow race seems indomitable. The Mongols under Genghiz, and his successors, began to plan, carry out, and endure those military exploits which led to the sack of Moscow, the subjugation of Europe through western Poland and to the Adriatic Sea, the opening-up of sea routes to the West and the inclusion of Persia and China, of Korea and Western Turkestan under the wide domains of their scepter. At the same epoch other vast populations of Asia deemed it an honor to pay yearly tribute to the ruling power in Peking. Of late the Japanese were engaged in foreign wars in which they were uniformly successful, showing themselves able enough to whip the "Russian bear" to a standstill, and capable of appropriating every bit of modern military technique on the field of battle and of organizing those services of supply without which the best of armies would surely go down to defeat. It is well known that the Chinese endure extremes of temperature that seem to polarize members of other races into inactivity. And anthropologists tend to believe that the yellow race will survive, partly on the basis of its physical endowment, into that dim future of the human race when its other varieties shall have become extinct.

The yellow race, often bronzed rather than yellow and statuesque in the harmony of its proportions, as well in its purity as in its commingling of racial strains, includes in Asia such diverse peoples as the paleo-Siberians, the Chinese, Manchus and Koreans, the Japanese, Mongols and Tibetans, the Turks of Central Asia and large inmixtures of the population of Burmah, Siam, Annam, Cambodia, Malaysia, and, more distantly, Polynesia. In Europe it reckons the Magyars, Finns, and Lapps, and other strains among its members. In Africa the streak is seen in Hottentot and Bushman and possibly the Malagasy of Madagascar, while all, or nearly all, Americanists substantially agree on the

Asiatic origin and kinship of the Amerindians with the yellow races of Asia.

Culturally this race can, if it will, proudly reckon the great civilizations of China and Japan, of Mexico and Peru as part of its accomplishments. Of late the world has witnessed the surging spectacle of the re-birth of ancient Japan whereby its people have taken a place in the front rank of humanity. In view of the varied resources of the Eastern Hemisphere and the proved abilities of the Chinese and Japanese, it becomes almost a truism to allege that the yellow race, and its scions, has independently invented all the material traits and non-material institutions so necessary to the expanding life of man; and which man, so to speak, places between himself and the threatening forces of the universe. Our attention will be focused naturally on the attainments and culture-services of those members of the yellow race which may be judged to have contributed to the stream of world culture. Hence the civilizations of China and Japan will be more fully dealt with; passing mention will be made of the military exploits of the Mongols and Turks of Central Asia as also the enumeration of the *material* contributions of the Aztec-Mayan and Peruvian cultures. Mexico and Peru did add such valuable material traits as cocoa, quinine, potatoes and tomatoes, and other things. But their matrilocal, communistic social organizations find their counterparts in other cultures and were of no great moment to the advancing stream of world-culture. They are, moreover, dealt with in another part of this work. The Polynesians and the mixed races of South-Eastern Asia have been recipients rather than contributors to world-culture and so they too call for nothing but passing mention as having within their veins a modicum of "yellow" blood.

The most recent advances in knowledge concerning the yellow races have considerably modified erstwhile notions on their antiquity and origin, as well as on the wideness of their dispersal and the estimation of their rank in world-culture. The discoveries associated with the name, *Homo Sinanthropus Pekinensis,* push back the antiquity of Chinese ancestry to times co-eval with that of *Eoanthropus dawsonii.* Japanese archeologists by their spade work and scientific comparisons of the finds on their own islands assure us of the presence there of paleolithic and neolithic man. Manchuria, too, has recently yielded up knowledge of neolithic man who certainly lived on the banks of the Yalu River and elsewhere in that empire. The length and breadth of Siberia has given up very numerous traces of paleolithic man within its vast confines.

Only a moment's thought is necessary to lead one to the conclusion that yellow man had his origin in Central Asia. This is further suggested by the present geographical proximity of his leading representatives to that focal point, by the above-noted archeological findings, by persistent traditions among the race; and by the reliable historical records which seem to substantiate the idea. The most numerous branches of the race which strayed outside came from there: Attila and his Huns came westward from Asia into Europe as did Genghiz Khan and his Mongols.

And Chinese tradition relates that expeditions set out eastward from the confines of their empire. And, finally, anthropologists, as just mentioned, disclosed to us the fact of the physical inmixture of Mongoloid traits in far-flung races, an inmixture which in the nature of the case must have originated in part from the Mongols of Asia.

CHINESE BEGINNINGS

Reiterated tradition points backward to the time when these peoples knew not the use of fire. The *Chinese Classics* remark that there was an age when men lived like the beasts of the forest, consuming raw whatever they collected, drinking the blood of beasts and swallowing the hair and feathers of their victims, and

> "there were no rites. The later sages then arose, and men learned to take advantage of the benefits of fire . . . They toasted, grilled, boiled and roasted. They produced vinegar and sauces . . . Thus they were able to nourish the living, and make offerings to the dead." (Quoted in Harvey, 1933, p. 36)

The thought is interesting in that it combines the origin of the physical and institutional traits in one, as well as to mention man's first genuine culture trait, that is, fire. Fire not only gave them dominion over physical nature, but it helped their institutional development as well—for with its use they went on to establish rites, to nourish the living, and to serve the dead. It is difficult to conceive what religion would have been, or indeed would yet be, without the use of fire. The element has almost everywhere been regarded as divine. Nowhere is this truer than among the yellow races. In kindred Japan the Sun-Goddess in dying gave birth to fire. Fire in the shape of the sun's globe is still almost the only religious symbol known to thousands of Chinese and Japanese. To spit on the hearth or in the fire is sacrilege to a Mongolian and the perpetrator of such an outrage would run serious risk of suffering injury in life or limb. The possession and control of fire freed the yellow race from fear of wild animals, from fear of the demons of the earth and air and sky. It cooked their food, thus releasing greater amounts of energy from the same amount of raw material. The hearth became the center and rallying-point for the family. Fire aided the process of social integration, caused them to become forethoughtful. In such ways fire molded the course of the evolving social life of the yellow races.

In summary fashion we may at this point note that the ancestors of the Chinese domesticated animals and plants; evolved shelters and tailored clothes; developed transportation and courier routes; dug and worked mineral ores; worked out exogamic marriage institutions, protective of children and regulative of the sex impulse; established an all-embracing religious ritual whereby "all under heaven" had their appointed positions and whereby no single action could be carried out under caprice; where indeed even the occupants of imperial thrones were no less subject to the prescriptions of religious and ceremonial ritual than were the commoners —probably more so, for with their higher privileges they had the greater responsibilities, as both the *Legacy of Ieyasu* and the *Chinese Classics* affirm (see Hearn, 1913, pp. 433-438). These peoples also evolved efficient educational institutions so that the many were made more or less literate; and at times their political states shook the world.

Ascending the stream of time as far as possible, ones notes the presence among the Chinese of traits that are common to the peoples of the West; "civil government, rhymed poetry, painting, trousers, wheat and barley, our common domesticated animals, and bronze and iron." Kroeber (1923 and 1933) thinks these were all invented before their ancestors left their central Asian table-lands for the marches of the East. Historical records, persistent traditions, and the very perfection of the Chow civilization itself necessitates the assumption of a lengthy pre-literate growth of culture.

The records relate stories of mythical kings and sages who are the culture heroes of the race. Some such were Pan Ku, the Hammerer of the Universe; Fu Hsi, the founder of exogamous marriage, the regulator of the hunting and fishing seasons, and the domesticator of animals; Shen Lung, the domesticator of plants, and the patron and founder of agriculture; the "emperors" Yao and Shun, familiar to every Chinese schoolboy, were prototypes of those great servants of mankind who give precision to daily toil by the invention of time-systems and political arrangements which mark the consolidation, peace, and security which accompany the political state; Yü, the Great, was the first engineer who taught the Chinese the practical control of flood-dykes and sluice-gates. Now all these were at one time men in the flesh. But their services were so supreme, marking as they did the invention and application of such important and useful culture traits, that these originators, in keeping with the cultural level of the times were naturally apotheosized.

The same early records seem to show the Chinese as immigrants, possessed of superior culture, and living in the midst of a savage aboriginal population. These savages put up a stiff opposition to the oncoming of the "black-haired" race. No less than thirty-nine wild tribes—and there were undoubtedly many more—are mentioned in the early books of Chinese history. The descendants of such peoples still exist under the names of Man-tze, Jung, I Man, Lolo, Li Miao, Ti, and others. Their folkways differ in many essentials from those of the surrounding Chinese people. But they and their ancestors were overcome and pressed back by the superiorities of advancing Chinese warriors and their culture. The records also reveal the anxiety of Chinese leaders lest their soldiers and people should revert to the ways of the savages, i.e., should "Indianize." Thus in the *Shu-ching* or *Book of History,* there is the obscure command on the part of an early general to "break communications with heaven." Chinese commentators aver that this means that the Chinese soldiery were not to contaminate themselves with savage ways of worship nor give themselves over to the seductions of aboriginal shamans.

Several more legendary centuries succeeded the events of the preceding paragraph. During this period, to judge by passages in the *Chinese*

Classics,[1] a very considerable political and social constitution was worked out, under which added increments of welfare and security were won. This was the Shang-Yin "constitution" and it became the prototype for the far more reliable ones wrought out by successive dynasties even down to the seventeenth century A.D.

The implement divided the land into nine great fiefs or provinces, the ninth at the center of them all was the "imperial" domain. The others were held by feudatories who all rendered a more or less constant loyalty to their liege lord, the "Emperor." The culture was far enough developed for these nobles to be given such titles as: *kung, hou, poh, tze,* and *lan,* meaning in order, duke, marquis, count, viscount, and baron. There were three grand-dukes who were ministers of defense, works, and administration respectively. From among the ranks of these nobles were chosen the following officials: a Grand Administrator, Chief Justice, Chief Marshal, Chief Engineer, Head Astrologer, Secretary of "Social Functions," Secretary of Agriculture, Chief Forester, Choirister, Shamaness, etc. All in all, there were about eleven hundred "imperial" functionaries together with the usual host of minor officials and servants. These all had one principal function, namely, to "pacify" the empire, that is to preserve a state of universal peace and harmony, to watch out that every individual in the state did his or her duty, and to keep the "barbarian" tribes around them in full subjection. The records, scanty as they are, nevertheless reveal periods when "all under heaven" (the Chinese) enjoyed great prosperity, and when each in his degree, according to his economic position, lived well.

The above implement gave way in course of time to that arrangement which in theory controlled Chow China. It is embodied in the *Chow Li* and the *Chow Kuan.* Both these Classics form the Chow Constitution. Together they present a picture of one of the severest arrangements that men have lived under. Fortunately for the Chinese people the rules were never enforced in all their minutiae, as they were under similar circumstances nearly two thousand years later in neighboring Japan.

A delineation of the Chow constitution will aid in an understanding of the growth of the social life of the Chinese people of that period. There were six ministries and between them the satisfaction of every possible human need was theoretically provided for. The Prime Minister, or *chung tsai,* was mayor of the palace and had immense prerogatives. He was in effect the chancellor of the "empire." He represented the empire on all important state occasions. He was commander of the palace guard

---

[1]Wieger (1916, Vol. 1, pp. 16-17, 53-57, 75-83, 209, 309-310; Vol. 2, p. 1307). Text and comments on the growth of the Chinese political constitution are given in these pages. The constitution is more than political—it is also social. The imperial constitution was completed by the time of the Tang Dynasty. No further change was made until the Revolution in 1911 A.D. and thereafter. At that time a modern democratic instrument was written on paper. It remains at this date largely a dead letter. China labors at present under a relapse to the worst of feudal conditions. The Kuomingtang leaders are making what seems to the present writer a hopeless endeavor to pacify and unify the country.

and personally responsible for the safety of the "Son of Heaven." He controlled the treasury, the state granaries, and the appointment of all officials. He governed the administration and personnel of the empire; fixed the annual budget, that is, determined the annual rate to be levied on the feudatories, and the sums to be expended annually for the upkeep and defence of the land. He audited the books of the whole realm. Some idea of the extent of his powers is seen from the fact that he controlled the emperor's harem and decided on the composition of its inmates. He made and unmade eunuchs and through them exercised rigid control over imperial household affairs. The customs of the time prescribed one empress, three wives of second rank, nine of the third, twenty-seven of the fourth, eighty-one of the fifth, and an unlimited number of maidens and women who rendered every sort of service to their imperial mistresses. Unless the "Son of Heaven" were a very strong personality it was the *chung-tsai* who decided most matters of policy.

It is evident that such arrangements would have to be supported by an adequate industrial organization. Such was the case. A whole panoply of armorers and sword-makers, experts in the fashioning of lances, bows and arrows and shields was there. Textile establishments, hand looms, dye-works, and shoe-plants furnished the apparel of the period. Clan, state, and imperial farms, intensively worked, delivered an unceasing stream of cereals and the other products of husbandry. There was a head-farmer to oversee and control the work on all farms of the whole land— one of the adjuncts of his office was to dispose of those who were *persona non grata* to the ruling powers. Such unfortunates "were not," a euphemistic term for natural or violent death! Again, there were cooks and butchers, brewers and distillers. Tea was as yet unknown and the common drink was rice-water. Fermented and distilled beverages were made from rice and millet for the ruling classes. The poor man drank his rice-water when he could obtain it. From very ancient times in China sweetened fruits were preserved; meat and the carcasses of animals were kept in cold storage; sour pickled vegetables and pickled meats were known; smoked and dried meats were also made.

Somewhat less imperious than hunger needs but equally useful and perilous are those of sex. The Chinese no less than all other peoples have provided institutional devices and safeguards to surround this interest so that it should constantly deliver to them all the satisfactions it is intended to give and at the same time shield them from its obvious perils. They very early hit upon the device of exogamy and equally early had discovered the dangers of consanguine marriage and they punished incest with the severest of sanctions. There was aptly enough a ministry or portfolio to care for these important matters.

The second Chow minister was called the *shih-to,* or the Grand Director of social relationships. His was the task of stirpiculture, or the regulation of marriage. This ministry oversaw the breeding of human beings in ways fit to please the most ardent modern eugenists. Under his guidance every bachelor under thirty years of age and every spinster under twenty would be suitably married. Then as the conditions permitted each couple would give birth to as many children as possible. He possessed heavy sanctions against the wilfully childless. The minister was set over the breeding of animals and men and over agricultural operations, with the head-farmer under him. By the aid of the astrologers he determined the beginning and the ending of seedtime and harvest. In times of public calamity his was the moral or spiritual function of issuing edicts to comfort the people and allay needless alarms and so prevent the rise and spread of panics. He told them that the government had their interests at heart and that they were to be quiet in their homes. The inspectors of fields and forests, of herbs and gardens, of water and mines, and of textile industries reported to him, as well as the priests and guardians of the Altars of the Land and Grains. Quite consonant with the above, the Grand Director controlled and administered the guardians of the civic peace. The police were his minions, and in China their duties have ever been more preventive than retributive. They, like the doctors in old China, who were paid as long as their patients kept well, were held in honor so long as they could maintain civil peace. In theory there should have been no criminals to apprehend and so their necessary apprehension was a reflection on the good conduct of these guardians of the law themselves.

Still, by far the most important of his duties were those concerned with the mating and marrying of people. His subordinates gave guidance where necessary and they could ask for proof why married couples had few or no children. He was equipped with power to enforce his decrees as to the number of children each woman should bear. It was, of course, inevitable that in spite of such laws some would remain unmarried or childless. Then on their deaths they were interred in nameless graves in a separate place as having been useless to society.

If the above official thus admirably promoted internal peace and harmony, the *ssu-wu* or Grand Marshall had the equally onerous duty of taking care, no less, of external enemies. He was the Minister of War and had charge of political and judicial executions. He was commander-in-chief of the palace guards and of the feudal levies. But he did not recruit his levies, and so his was not much more than nominal oversight, except when he was some outstanding military man. The Grand Director had charge of raising and equipping the armies, and the Grand Marshall their leadership. The rule for martial levies was two soldiers from each hearth. Each large fief was supposed to furnish 36,000 men; the next smaller, 24,000; and the smaller ones up to 12,000 men. The figures are evidently schematic and not to be taken at their face value. Army discipline was severe. Poor rustics, seized in their fields, were served with weapons, dragooned, and squadroned and sent into battle in such compact masses that flight was impossible. The carnage and slaughter in battle, even allowing for possible inaccuracies, of which Chinese annalists are rarely guilty, were terrific. The least infractions of discipline were punishable with death. The Grand Marshall was also a civil justice and heard and decided certain sorts of cases according to custom. He had to inspire awe and respect for China among the six neighboring nations and hold the thirty-nine barbarian tribes in submission. He inspected arsenals and the manufacture of arms; kept constant guard over all the military passes into the country, over their fortresses and their garrisons. He directed the imperial stud so as always to have sufficient remounts for the cavalry and changes for the war chariots. Recommendation for promotion and rewards for meritorious service always had their inception with him. He was head-archer of an empire where archery as a weapon of war endured up to 1900 A.D.! His office had charge of the night-watches which were regulated by a clepsydra, or water-clock. He had to execute such nobles as were condemned to being shot to death by bow-and-arrow, and then stand guard over their corpses and by arrow-flights prevent the vultures from desecrating their dead bodies.

The *ssu-kou* or Chief Justice was the fifth minister. He had to administer the laws of the realm, and, in theory, could render judgment only with the consent of the people as confirmed by the ruler. In practice both sanctions were frequently dispensed with. His power by prescription and assumption became wide and tyrannous. Major sentences, outside the bastinado which was regarded as curative rather than punitive, were the pillory (cangue) with written statement affixed as to the offense and its punishment. He had to see to the incarceration of youths condemned to a central house of correction; to those who had been sentenced to life servitude in the imperial studs and pasturages; to tattooing the faces of condemned prisoners who would henceforth be slaves; to the shaving of their heads; and to account for the number of those condemned to forced employment as doorkeeper or common-carrier. Additional punishments which he oversaw were nose or ear amputations with banishment to the distant frontiers accompanied with forced labor; castration for males with menial duties in the harem; amputation of both feet with forced labor in the harbors as stevedores. There were said to be five hundred offences which were punishable in this manner. But one again suspects that not every offender was as severely punished as the laws and customs permitted. Yet the offenses so liable are listed. Death was inflicted for five hundred other infractions of the law and custom and might take the following forms: boiling to death in a caldron; being sliced to death by as many as eight hundred minute slicings; being sawn asunder; being torn apart by two horses or two chariots moving in opposite directions. The offense was often, to our seeming, trivial in the extreme. One such was the dissemination of false rumors. But it may be that in those early unstable times the spreading of false reports among an untutored populace was very dangerous. And so standardized had Chow China become that it was heterodoxy, severely punishable, to introduce new folkways, strange doctrines, new forms of thought, speech, dress, utensils, instruments, or procedure. Those who so much as tampered with the written character or who introduced novelties in song or dance were severely chastised.

The Chief Engineer, or *ssu-kung,* directed public works and the arts and sciences. Makers of bows and arrows; furriers and embroiderers; basket-makers, seamstresses, and jewelers; basket-makers, potters, metal-workers, cabinet-makers, and carpenters; and all other artizans were directly under his supervision. They could not engage in any craft without license from his office.

The last grand minister of this ancient régime was the *tsung-poh,* the Grand Officer of the Cult, or the *cultus ministerium.* As the name indi-cates, all religious affairs and those of education were passed in review by this official. It is a commonplace that there is little or no privacy in Asia. Hence this ministry watched over all the behavior of all Chinese from the "son of heaven" downwards to the lowest coolie. Assistant secretaries cared for banners, music, musicians and public dancers, augurs and diviners. It was the duty of the latter to resolve the course of public action in accordance with the markings on the back of a smoked tortoise-shell and the way in which the stalk of the Achillea fell on the ground. Official astrologers were under this *ministerium* as were also the annalists, scribes, statisticians, and calendar-makers.

Such was the organization and the officialdom of the first great semi-historical period in the life of the Chinese people. All human interests were to be met and satisfied by laws and custom with the extreme meticulousness of detail which has just been described. The Chow con-stitution did bring considerable welfare and security to the "black-haired" race. Chinese idealists of later times, catching vague glimpses of its serv-ices and glories, have accounted it divine, the creation of sacrosanct ances-tors and of the great daimons of the land.

Yet "all is not gold that glistens." The stiff feudal arrangements and the folkways of the time put a numerically advancing population into a strait-jacket. No allowance was made for new political, social, moral, and economic necessities due to the very expansion of the numbers of the people. The trend was also towards the creation of ever-enlarging terri-torial groups. And it took the periodical outbreak of warfare to force the necessary political consolidations to take place. It must be recog-nized that the Chow "king" was in reality only a feudal suzerain, that oftentimes he was a *roi faineant,* and that in any event a strongly central-ized control was more a wish than a reality.

Another defect in the Chow arrangements was the lack of provision for social experimentation. The whole society was custom-bound. No possi-bility was left for variation, and for the selection and transmission of favorable variations in the mores. The lot of the common mass of the people was for centuries that of serfdom, or even actual slavery. Indeed, domestic slavery has survived from the tenth century B.C., into the China of the twentieth century A.D.[2] In Chow times the common man was in a condition of abject misery from which he has even today climbed but

---

[2]This form of slavery consists in the ownership of persons of both sexes who live in the family and do the menial work for their keep.

little. Now he has a little that he can call his own but then he had only "the crumbs which fell from his master's table," and they were scanty. The men of the lower classes were sodden, illiterate laborers and their women nothing but procreative drudges. They were but a shade removed from the contemporaneous common folk of Egypt who had no "souls." Beasts of burden, they (of Chow times) were subjected to treatment that defies adequate description but the nature of which may be gleaned from the severities of the penal code, a code which survived nearly unchanged into the twentieth century of our era!

It is also probable that the masses of the common people had not then risen to the comforts and securities of ancestor-worship. The study of early Chinese (and Japanese) records leaves a distinct impression of an aristocratic societal organization. There is genuine truth in the saying that "the rites do not descend to the common people." Of course, Chinese society is in this respect no different from all others. Rights, powers, privileges, comfort, security, the softening of manners and mores, welfare and happiness come first in large measure to the upper classes and then later to those below. And this obvious fact should be remembered in making an appraisal of the realities of growing Chinese culture.

But the Chow constitution was nevertheless a necessary instrument. A waxing population, upon that stage of culture, called for increasing regulation and got it. The Chow king, in theory, supervised all appointments and promoted and demoted as circumstances seemed to require. He received, once every six years, all revenue accounts; he made a progress through all the fiefs once every twelve years; he kept a watchful eye on all the feudatories, and when he was a strong personality this was a happy fact. The manner of all intercourse between king and subject and between subject and subject of whatever rank was minutely prescribed. The *Chow Li,* or *Ritual,* and the *I Li* specified the tone of voice and the sort of gestures of hands and feet and body postures which were suitable for every occasion. So disciplined were they that no one so much as indulged in needless glances of the eye, upon pain of censure or reprimand. Birth, deaths, marriages, all prospective undertakings and contemplated journeys had to be announced publicly in the temples of the ancestors and before the altars of the Spirits of the Land and of Grains. At first the ritual was very useful in an upbuilding culture but in the end ritual suppressed all spontaneity and made automatons out of officials and people.

However, human life is always stronger than the theoretical bonds with which man so frequently and irrationally surrounds it. Chow China moved forward to strong consolidation through almost a thousand years of feudal strife and turmoil; and, one may add, because of it. There is evidence of an expansion of population and a competition of life which forced the concentration of power into fewer and fewer hands and which in consequence enlarged the peace areas throughout the land. The numbers of rulers dwindled and the size of their fiefs increased. This shrinkage had its inception at a time earlier than the. Chow period. It well illustrates the Chinese proverb of how the big fish eat the smaller ones, of how these in turn eat the still smaller, and these the smallest, then how they eat the mosquitoes, which in turn consume the grasses and the grasses at length consume the earth.[3] At all events the diminution in numbers of independent rulers began from a theoretical 10,000 in the year 2500 B.C., to 1773 holdings in 1500 B.C., to about 300 in 1000 B.C., to 10 in 300 B.C., to none in 221 B.C., when the First Emperor, Tsin Shih Hwang, wiped out feudalism and replaced it with an all-embracing empire (Wieger, 1916, Vol. 1, p. 75).

For a thousand years previous to this event the Great Ones of China had said to their vassals, "Come here! and they came; Do this! and they executed the command." They were simply and solely the owners of land and people and the products of their labors. The "stupid" people when the sentence of tattooing was given them became slaves to live as near or as far away from their birthplace as the judge should determine. So low were they in the scale of culture that they were scarcely a proletariat in the modern sense. The sentiment of the time allotted reason and knowledge to rulers alone and their will was the law; and they handled the common man as we now handle domestic animals. Anarchy, lawlessness, treachery, arbitrary rulings were frequently the order of the day. A justly renowned story has survived from the years of Confucius' wanderings as a practical outcast from his native state of Loo. The Sage and his following once came upon a widow weeping by the roadside with her young children. The Teacher sent a disciple to ask the reason for her grief and he was told of the ravages of a tiger. Asked why she did not move away to some other place, she replied that they had good government here. "Ah!" said the Sage, "bad government is worse than tigers." Surely his own *Spring and Autumn Annals of the State of Loo* and Tso's *Commentaries* thereon are replete with stories of the tigerish governments of the epoch. But yet, amazingly enough, Chinese society moved on.

An efficient machine always runs under some sort of motive power. Such regimentation as partly described above could not have been effected without the presence of some powerful ideation. This was to be had in ancestor-worship and its dogma of filial piety. The unbroken obedience of the Chinese people to this central fact of their mental outfit explains the continuity and indestructibility of Chinese culture; makes its solidarity and homogeneity understandable; accounts for its powers of assimilability into itself of all other alien and encroaching cultures. It is, of course, a commonplace that the Chinese have to date always assimilated every other people and their civilization, making it and them part and parcel of their own polity.

Elsewhere the present writer (1933, p. 230) has thus described the place and power and dynamic beliefs of ancestor-worship.

> Devotion, fealty, unbroken sacrifice by the children to the ancestral spirits and obsequious faith in living parents are the most vital

[3]Smith, A. H. *Chinese Proverbs*, see index, under "fish."

sentiments activating Chinese society today, and is the chief amalgam which maintains whatever organic unity the nation presents. The organized cult of state worship and the magnificent public displays connected with it were unquestionably based upon the mores of the family group and the worship of ancestors.

As its most pervasive and most characteristic accumulation of mores, ancestor worship may be said to have endowed Chinese society with its form and to have given sanction to related series of societal developments and institutions. Sex-regulation is thus thoroughly of a piece with the taboos dictated by the dogma of filial piety, for the decisive rationalization of all the durable relationships of the sexes seems to lie in the general philosophy of conduct born of ancestor-worship. Large families and especially many sons to nurture and conciliate the ancestral ghosts remain the foremost ideals of sex and family existence.

We may take a little more material from the same source but continue by paraphrasing. Then, essentially, ancestor-worship is an outgrowth of the vast system of animism, fetishism, and related sciences of the occult. It derives from spirit beliefs and rests on the basic assumption that the living can communicate directly with the dead, with the souls of the remembered dead. Throughout Chinese life and thought, whether portrayed in the classical, historical, or folklore books, or in actual conversation with Chinese people of today, one repeatedly marks the assumption that the ancestors are not far away. It is an implicit article of everyday faith that the souls of ancestors are waiting to bless their filial descendants. It needs no great elaboration to drive home the fact that ancestor-worship is the very cement of Chinese society, holding men to all the advantages of association by its beliefs, doctrines, and practices.

This cementing principle has throughout the long course of Chinese experience been applied to communal activities. It has been used to buttress and support the family and the clan in the first instance and then society as a whole. As in kindred Japan, so in China, ancestor-worship has always been used primarily to yield comfort and security to the group. Throughout Asia generally it was the group which received first consideration, the individual was ever last. In so far as he conformed to the mores of his time and place, food, and shelter, and raiment, and the comforts of social life would be assured him by his group. Non-conformity brought ultimate death, but fidelity to the group, expressed by scrupulous fulfilment of ancestral rites, brought its due rewards of earthly and ghostly felicity.

Still these yields in welfare were dependent on individual initiative and upon the kind of person completing the rites. As they say, "a mere nobody in this world is not a somebody in the next." Individuals who could greatly achieve have had recognition everywhere. Genghiz and Kubilai, Confucius and Mencius, Chu Hsi and Wang Yang-ming, Tseng Koh-fan and Sun Yat-sen, all received recognition in their day, or, at worst, were apotheosized after death. Great services to the group result in China in beatification and sainthood in much the same way as they do at the hands of the present-day Roman *curia*. On the other hand, social slothfulness which so easily passes over into conscious and unconscious transgression of the ebullient ways of life has ever brought humiliation or banishment with mutilation to the far-distant frontiers of Turkestan or Yunnan. Great social turpitude, which would begin with a fundamental irreverence for the unseen spiritual powers, might even bring outlawry with or without the protecting branding of Cain. In China some chain-gangs were tatooed as literally as Cain was marked. Others, less fortunate, received the fate of having "every man's hand being against them."

The proverb that the more a thing changes the more it remains the same is not inapposite to things Chinese. The foregoing material has been selected from the very early history of China. And, while it is evident that the population and area of the Chinese peace group have tremendously expanded during the last three thousand years, it is yet true that abrupt changes in the culture have occurred only at rare intervals. The Han dynasties (210 B.C. to about 225 A.D.), for example, witnessed the setting-up of the competitive literary examination system which was destined to survive till the nineteenth century of our era. And these two dynasties also saw the introduction of Buddhism and the consequent enrichment of the thought and emotional life of the Chinese people. Taoism is nothing but crude animism which peoples the earth, the heavens, and the waters with swarming multitudes of demons, malignant for the most part. Confucianism, however elevated its ethical system may be, is somewhat too austere and ascetic to be of much comfort to the common man. But Buddhism at once completes the lacks of both of China's indigenous religious systems. Hence a social history of China would be the poorer did it not contain some reference to the services of Sakyamuni's world-philosophy.

The alien cult was particularly naturalized in China during the Tang dynasty (618-907 A.D.). In the personalities of its founder and its chief divinity, Kuan Yin, Buddhism supplied a something to the Chinese which deepened their mysticism, kindled their emotions, and set their imaginative faculties aflame, particularly in all the arts of pleasure such as painting and poetry and literature. By its very otherworldliness, Buddhism enriched the imagination of a people all too earth-bound. Multitudes of Chinese found new scope for personal expression in its sectarian duties. To a minority of the literati it even offered new light on the problems of the deeper aspects of the soul, on man's social life and his spiritual destiny. To the masses of the Chinese people it offered cult heroes and demi-gods, and rites by which the terrible dangers of everyday life might be avoided, or its pressing crises allayed. Buddhism made for idealism in action and widened popular perspectives both for this life and the next. The concept of "Nirvana" which is an abstruse, mystical doctrine, even in its vulgarizations led to an extension and deepening of popular religious thought because of its picture of an illimitable future. And it was Mahayana Buddhism which wrought the profoundest changes in Chinese thought.[4]

---

[4]Present-day Buddhism, except in Japan, has become so debased, its abbots

Its social, as well as its spiritual services, are succinctly set forth in the following from *The Mind of China:*

> This mighty church not only possessed the far-reaching moral teaching of Gautama, but its organizing genius enabled it to accommodate itself to the latent animalism of China. Through its hierarchy of divine beings—its devas, Boddhisatvas and Buddhas—Mahayana had a strong appeal to the masses who always cherished the idea that spirits of men could dwell in external objects as fetishes. (And so be available to help in case of need.) Moreover it intensified belief in the soul by enunciating a doctrine of spiritual progress . . . in its fold the individual can begin his spiritual ascent to Buddhahood, a state which in and of itself is consonant with every terrestrial and celestial harmony. Thus Mahayanism seemed to give a dynamic, growing aspect to life here, and to the life after death . . . Buddhism made the soul eternal, (a very different matter from the conditional immortality of seven generations in native Chinese thought) and able, through the good offices of its mortal descendents and through masses and prayers said for it, to rise to a devaship, an arhatship, or even to spiritual Buddhahood, that is, soul perfection, without any of the trammels of this earthly life. (pp. 270 ff.)

It is illuminating to note the definite social values of this other-world philosophy. Membership in any of the numerous Buddhist sects brought education, advances in knowledge, mutual aid, and protection to every member. Anybody could become a member and by perseverance and service rise to any grade in the society. It appealed, as we have noted, to the idealism of the individual, it made him feel that he was somebody. It filled him with love and compassion to all that breathes; it inculcated good works and mutual aid without looking for any earthly reward; the church introduced a true doctrine of salvation, aristocratic in form yet excluding no one who needed its comforts. It thus filled a great void in the hearts and emotions of the Chinese people. It nestled itself into their hearts and remains there to this day. Nor should it be forgotten that Kuan Yin is the particular patroness of childless women. She it is who comforts and aids them in securing the boon of sons, in a land where to have no son is the height of impiety! There is something essentially comforting to the female mind, the world over, in a deity of its own sex. Nowhere is this truer or more acceptable than in China.

But Buddhism's services by no means ended with what we have just delineated. Its monks and teachers came to educate the whole people and to set on fire their artistic genius so that it reached new heights in painting and other fine arts, never before attained. The Chinese have never shown any particular bent in sculpture but they did execute some remarkably beautiful figures of the Buddha in bronze. Their carvings in ivory or jade of Buddhist saints are scarcely matchable by other peoples. Who, having once gazed upon the benignant face of a carved

---

and monks almost universally so illiterate and superstitious, that the sober statement of its earlier civilizing functions may seem like the unchecked ravings of an unbridled imagination. The works of writers like Hearn, de Groot, and Wilkins do more than substantiate the presentation of Buddhism offered here—of its earlier services to the Chinese and Japanese peoples.

Boddhisatva, is ever likely to forget its radiance and peace? Who, having seen any of the best of the carved Buddhas, is likely to remain unmoved by the expression of its artistic power and the evidence of mastery of technique? However, it was from the impulse given to painting that Buddhism rendered its greatest service in quickening Chinese imagination. Some of the grandest and most beautiful paintings both in China and Japan had their inspiration from Buddhism. Thus one reads:

> Chinese painting is an art of *line*. They excelled in the ink sketch. Utmost vigor of stroke was here combined with utmost delicacy of modulation. Rich color and the use of gold are an integral part of the Buddhist pictures, though in the masterpieces of the religious painters a grand rhythm of linear design gives the fundamental character . . . "A picture is a voiceless poem," says a Chinese proverb. Loftiness of sentiment and tone are more stressed than technical qualities . . . Weak in the plastic, weak in the architectural sense, Chinese artists paint mostly in a lyric mood with a contemplative ideal. Hence the value given to space in their designs, the semi-religious passion for nature, and the supremacy of landscape. Beauty is found not only in pleasant prospects, but in wild solitudes, rain, snow and storm. The life of things is contemplated and portrayed for its own sake, not for its uses in the life of man. From this point of view the body of Chinese painting is much more modern in conception than that of Western art. Landscape was a mature and free art in China more than a thousand years ago, and her school of landscape is the loftiest yet known to the world. Nor was man ever dissociated from nature . . . in painting a certain noble character, according to Chinese thought, he must be given a fit background of lofty peaks and deep ravines . . . During the Tang dynasty the empire reached its widest limits, stretching as far as the Persian Gulf . . . the vigorous style of a great era was impressed on the Tang art . . . Buddhism, taught by numbers of Indian missionaries, became firmly established, and controlled the ideals and the imaginations of the time. (*Encyclopaedia Britannica*, 11 ed., vol. 6, pp. 213 ff., *passim*.)

Thus by an extraordinary development of their fine arts the Chinese have known how to minister to the needs of self-gratification in the widest meaning of the term. They have side-stepped the abyss of "all work and no play." In spite of the severity of the struggle for existence they have, as a group, found time to develop their porcelains, their poetry, their paintings, their music, and their literature. The pleasures of conversation are with them still a high art, a relaxation from the more pressing cares of life. We may, for example, consider how they regard music. They have said:

> In music the sages found pleasure, *and saw that it could be used to make the hearts of the people good.* Because of the deep influence which it exerts on man, and the changes which it produces in manners and customs, the ancient kings appointed it as one of the subjects of instruction . . . *music should not for a moment be neglected by anyone. When one has mastered the principles of music, and regulates his heart and mind accordingly, the natural, correct, gentle and honest heart is easily developed,* and with this development of the heart comes joy. This joy goes on to a feeling of repose. The repose is long continued. The ·man in this constant repose becomes a sort

of heaven. Heaven-like, his behavior is spirit-like. Heaven-like he is believed, though he do not speak. Spirit-like he is regarded with awe, though he display no rage. *So it is when one by his mastering of music regulates his mind and heart.*[5] (Italics in each case mine.)

Nor have there been wanting in China concrete examples of the effect of music on the making of character. It is told of Confucius that for a long time he had desired to hear the music of the Hsia dynasty. At length the occasion came and he was so profoundly impressed and filled with a deep peace that he neither ate nor spake for some days afterwards. For others the self-deprivation of this cherished form of personal cultivation during the period of mourning for deceased parents was a real self-renunciation. One celebrated character in history not only gave up all the delights of home-life on one occasion of national mourning, but added this last touch to his devotion in the abstention from all the delights of music. Confucius said of this man that he, Meng Hsien-Tze, was a shade above other men. Music was so utterly a part of the social life of the people that it was only renounced on the occasion of some great calamity, or in the bride's home on her wedding-day—for at that time she would be accounted "dead" to her own family, and there could be no music in her natal home.

The wearing of jewelry, the adornment of clothing, the outward display of rank or emolument, promotion for meritorious service now or posthumously, and prestige which brings the esteem of one's family or neighbors all enter into the social life of the Chinese people. For example, there was formerly an ancient rule whereby the successful Master of Arts candidate in either the provincial or national examinations had to display the characters for the degree over the main door of his dwelling. For his clansmen and fellow-villagers demanded the right of basking in such an effulgence of glory.

An account of the social growth of the Chinese people should include some notion of their world-philosophy. This is, as noted, largely animistic. Yet the better minds among them could not avoid the urge to dress it up in formal manner. Such minds were those of Lao-tze, Confucius and Mencius, Chwang-tze, Yang Chu, Mo Ti, Hsun-tze, Huai-nan Tzu, Chu Hsi and Wang Yang-ming, and others too numerous to mention. How did these men regard nature and the nature of man? The mysticism of Lao-tze, through his purported writing of the *Tao Teh Ching,* is chiefly noteworthy for his doctrine of inaction—"Do nothing, and all things will be done." He is also supposed to have taught men to return good for evil. The teachings of the book are highly paradoxical, as, "The weak overcomes the strong; He who knows how to bind, uses no ropes; He who knows how to shut, uses no bolts." Such contrasts as these were enough, apparently, to fire the imagination of China's most brilliant mind, Chwang-tze. Master of irony and a formidable dialectic he attacked both

---

[5]*Sacred Books of the East,* Chinese Classics, quoted in Harvey (1933, p. 224).

Confucius and Mo Ti. So cogent was his reasoning that he talked everyone else to a stand-still. His book abounds in quaint anecdotes and allegories. He was an idealist with all the contempt of such an attitude to the rationalistic leanings of the men he attacked. He was quite heterodox and so his book is anathema to the rigid Confucianist. Confucius and Mencius and Tseng-tze gave the Chinese the high expression of morals associated with their names—a canon of ethical precepts which endures in undiminished esteem to this day.

But while the preceding minds were quite content to probe into the nature of man there were others who saw man conditioned by the external environment of nature and they pushed their inquiries in the direction of finding out the ultimate causes of human behavior. There was one, Liu Ngan or Huai Nan-tze, who had his court just north of the Yangtze River and on the banks of its tributary, the Huai. Towards the end of the second century B.C., he is reputed to have taught that

> erstwhile before the heavens and the earth existed, there was only a being without appearance . . . there were born out of the chaos two spirits, the *yin* and the *yang*. Subsequently all things in heaven and earth began from them, and man also got his soul from heaven and his bodily form from earth . . . Man is also composed of two material parts, the one more subtle and from heaven, the other more gross and of the earth. In each of these parts there is a force, a motive-power, a soul, which is likewise material. This is called the *hwun*, or *shen*, or *ching-shen*, and belongs to the superior part (of man's nature). The *poh*, or *hsing-ti*, or *ku-hai* is the inferior soul. If the body is killed before its time the inferior soul, the *poh*, is not ripe enough to melt into the earth but exists as a wandering spirit. It is a *kwei*, or revenant, a specter. (Harvey, 1933, p. 60)

And it was at about this time that the Confucian classical canon was forming. Included in that body of literature is the *Yih-Ching*, or *Classic of Changes*. It states that Heaven, being composed of *yin* and *yang* substances, the earth came out of them and is composed of hard and soft substances, and that man's nature is made up of benevolence and righteousness. Here are some excerpts taken from the appendices of the *Yih*, which are in reality the body of its text:

> The *yin* and the *yang* are in their entirety what we call the course, the *Tao* of the universe . . . As there is no being or thing which is not full of Yin and Yang, so neither is there anything which does not consist of a *kuei* and a *shen*. The *shen* do not dwell in special places—they come from the unfathomable force of the Yin and the Yang. These two breaths possessed of operative energy produce the living beings, and the transmigrating *hwun* are the causes of the evolution of the phenomena of nature, and it is from the latter that we learn to understand the characteristics of the *kuei* and the *shen*. (Argument in a circle!) Confucius said, "The man who understands the ways in which such involutions and evolutions take place, comprehends the works of the *shen*." (Harvey, 1933, p. 61) [And thus it goes on at length.]

One finds here a curious commingling of descriptions of natural phenomena and the commandments of ethics, of abstruse philosophizing and the crude retelling of superstitions. Interestingly enough, from the standpoint of social history one finds man closely linked with his physical and social environments. And, in view of the social and intellectual climate of the age, there is no startling inconsistency in these earlier writings. Yet, in later times, in an era of somewhat greater sophistication they were felt to be lacking. And the writers of the Sung school supplied the need as well as they were able.

The most celebrated of all the Sung philosophers was Chu Hsi. He explored all the lore and teachings of Taoism, Buddhism, and Confucianism, finally coming to abide by a rationalization of the latter system. His central doctrine was that of a Grand Harmony, a Grand Unity, a Void or Nothingness. The last is relative since Chu Hsi taught that there never was a time when absolutely "nothing" existed, only that far beyond that which the human mind can contemplate matter is extremely tenuous and rarefied. The idea of "Unity" was never more than an outreaching after philosophical monism. The bulk of Chu's pages are given over to a consideration of the nature and functions of the duality into which the Great Unity is forever splitting up. Particularly is this the case with the speculation of Chu Hsi and his friends with regard to man, his nature, and destiny. The duality is, to them, composed of Norm and Matter, of Reason and Breath. Under the impulse of Reason, Matter evolved as the *yin* and the *yang* forces, which in turn produced the five *hsing* or elements. These latter are construed as spiritual rather than physical forces, whose objective symbols are water, fire, wood, metal, and earth.

As powers, or governors, these five elements have important bearings on the life of man. The two souls of man are condensations, products of the expansion and contraction of the *yin-yang* duality. Reason, actively creative, permeates everything through the *yang* principle, while the *yin* is controlled by Matter. The ceaseless expansion and contraction, from which all sensible things resulted, at length produced a pair of human beings. These then reproduced themselves sexually, whence "all within the four seas" were born.

The idea that the soul survives after death was, according to Chu Hsi, a Buddhistic error. Upon being pressed by anxious learners the Philosopher apparently relapsed into animistic reasoning. He replied that if the ancestor died a natural death he ceased to be; but that if he died violently he might still be living but would survive but a short while. Still hard pressed by his friends the Teacher was compelled to declare that all ceremonial rites benefitted only the celebrant.

> "But," said they, "if the dead exist no more, to whom do we sacrifice? If everything about their personality is lost and never gathered together again, of what use is it to offer oblations?" To which he replied: "One may not say of the dead that they are no more, since something of them survives in each of their descendents. As long as they have descendents they amount to something. They themselves no longer exist, it is true, but what they have given their

descendents survives. Decendents are like slips or cuttings of the deceased ancestor. They offer sacrifice to show their gratitude to those that begot them. The result of conception is no more, the ancestor is dead, but life and gratitude still remain. At times, if the ancestor is not immediately dissipated, oblations and sacrifices can profit him awhile. Still once his entity has melted into the rest of the universe, nothing of him can be revived to profit him from the offerings. And this in spite of what the Classics affirm . . . I, who am today, am but a Modality . . . He is dead but his elements remain in the *yin* and the *yang*. Since I shall myself be resolved into that Norm and Matter, I have communion of substance with him. That is the end of the matter." (Harvey, 1933, pp. 63-64)

Since the death of Chu Hsi in 1200 A.D., little advance has been made on his analysis of the soul of his cosmological theory. To be sure, educated Chinese have never been entirely content with such a presentation. But it is difficult to see, in the absence of an empirical, investigative natural science, how any advance in human knowledge could have been made by them. The majority of Chinese minds have been content with far less than honest Chu Hsi demanded. They have gone off into the debased mysticism of the Taoists in which all parts of the human body are equipped with their special motivating *shen,* or soul. Once endowed with such a philosophy, the scholars embarked upon a narrow speculation and had soon built up a totally absurd and ingrown pedantry. Critical thought, of the type of Chu Hsi's, and rational observation of nature were totally abandoned and their animistic premises won full sway and were frozen into dogmatic tenets for the consumption of the masses. Chinese culture, to the extent to which it developed along these lines, represented a hopelessly artificial and orthodox structure, out of all adjustment to the humanistic and changing needs of the times. Compare in this connection what happened in Japan. Contrast the animistic feudal Japan of 1810 with the dynamic, resurgent Japan of 1910. The difference was solely due to the presence of a fructifying body of scientific knowledge. When such knowledge shall be possessed by competent Chinese it is probable that a similar transformation will occur in China as completely as in Japan.

E pur si muove, nevertheless, the world does turn round. And modern China is beginning to move around another sun than that of her old animism. A modern temper in China is slowly commencing to dawn. What of China in the twentieth century? Perhaps the greatest change is one of attitude. The intellectual elite and the middle class now look forwards and not backwards. They have such sentiments as this—"If China is the country of rites, why should not parents be asked to do something for their children beyond the helpless years of infancy, why should parents always be expecting services from their offspring?" Then, too, their attitude to outsiders has changed. Of late a definite "Touch me not!" atmosphere surrounds all questions of policy; and Chinese control of the administrative direction of all matters is naturally sought. The Revolution and the modern publicity of the daily press has brought a new sense of national feeling which enhances the old tribal solidarity engendered by the ancient family mores. There are now literally thousands of daily newspapers in existence where seventy-five years ago there were none. Some eight thousand miles of railroads now operate where formerly their presence was a sacrilege to the very earth over which they ran. Thousands of miles of turnpike roads have been built for the tens of thousands of automobiles that are beginning to appear in China. The land is covered with a network of telegraph and telephone poles. In the latter connection, it should be noted that Chinese have a clever adaptation for the telegraphic transmission of news: they have numbered each of their ideographs and so merely have to transmit their equivalents in Arabic numerals. Foreign goods of every description are found in the remotest corner of the country. Pins, needles, electric-lighting fixtures, Standard Oil products, electric sewing-machines, power-plants, steamships, foreign cotton, silk, and woolen goods are among the varied articles for sale by Chinese shops, wholesale and retail. By peaceful access such goods are working a revolution of greater extent than the merely political could ever accomplish.

Their merchants and entrepreneurs have been quick to seize on the new folkways of commerce and industry imparted to them from the West. They have been especially forward in the erection and development of cotton mills.[6] Whereas in 1867 there were no cotton mills in the modern sense in China, in 1930 there were one hundred twenty-three in successful operation, the larger number being operated by Chinese capital and management. The history of cotton textiles is briefly as follows. The First Opium War with Great Britain in 1840 definitely opened up the northern ports of Swatow, Amoy, Ningpo, Shanghai, and Nanking to foreign intercourse. Machine-spun yarn from the West began almost at once to displace that from the old domestic handicraft spinneries. The importation of this spun yarn went through a crescendo up to 1899, after which year it ended in a diminuendo. In 1867 some 33,507 piculs (each 133 lbs.) were imported; in 1899 some 2,784,644 piculs; and in 1930 only 129,620 piculs. These figures tell the noteworthy tale of the expansion of the Chinese cotton industry. At first they depended on foreign yarn for their looms; now they spin their own. Again, in 1913 the imports of raw cotton amounted to 134,735 piculs while in 1930 the total was 3,456,494 piculs and an additional 6,641,000 piculs grown at home. That is, modern China is both importing and growing raw cotton for its textile mills. These new industries also made numerous places for a relatively large and new army of workers. Textiles absorbed 566,000 "hands"; new kinds of food, 176,000 more; clothing (Western style), 80,000; new architecture, 77,700; machinery, 65,500; education, 59,000; art, 10,000; and public utilities, 5,400. These figures are for 1930 and, taken together with some not here enumerated, it seems that well over a million and a

---

[6]Fong (1932). The statistics on pages 380-381 and the quotation on pages 381-382 have been taken from this invaluable work on the industry of a new China.

half new positions have been made for workers in the last twenty years. Conditions of labor in the new enterprises have sometimes been quite shocking to humanitarian members of the British Parliament who are blessed with short memories. Most of the mills are Chinese but three of them in Shanghai are British owned and run. Conditions in Chinese mills were confused with those in the British mills and so the matter became a subject of parliamentary questioning. As a fact, the I WO Mills are the elite of the industry and Chinese workers engage in a mad scramble for places in them. However, even the worst conditions in some of the less amply equipped Chinese mills tend to be ameliorated because, labor-turnover being so frequent, it becomes too expensive to run them and they tend to fail and close up.

No matter how humanitarian feelings may be ruffled, the fact is that the wages paid in all the new mills in China actually raise the standard of living for their beneficiaries. Compare, for example, the munificent wage of fifty cents a day with that where one works all day long for no wage at all. It is easily seen how much such pay is sought after, and that those workers come to make up the elite of the working-classes of China. Such wages bring class consciousness and all the correlated labor problems, such as strikes, lockouts, and, by no means least, the boycott.

A strike in a Japanese-owned mill in March, 1925, led to the May 30, 1925, incidents and to the formation of very strong labor unions. They were quickly formed and that year had a membership of 118,223 in Shanghai alone. In 1926 the Pan Pacific Trades Union Congress reported a grand list of fully organized workers of 3,065,000 membership. Industrial disputes, as said above, have been very frequent. There were 209 strikes in the cotton mills of Shanghai during the period 1918-1927 which involved 557,239 men and a loss of 6,721,956 man-days-labor. Unions are of all kinds, and this is socially significant. They range from jin-rickisha pullers, through farmers and peasants, up to those of the highly organized textile unions of the large cities like Shanghai and Tientsin.

Labor legislation has not lagged far behind this industrial advance. The Factory Act of 1930 includes among others the following provisions:

1. The general wage level must be raised; and, equal pay must be given for equal work, regardless of sex.
2. Hours of work must be reduced to not over 12 hours per day; (but one mill in response to this legislation, made the drastic change to a three-shift day of 7½ hours each in order to meet the requirements of the next article. Huge profits resulted from the re-organization).
3. Women may not work in any factory after 10.00 P.M. nor before 6.00 A.M. Children under 14 may not be employed, although those already employed in the factories may continue to work.
4. There shall be a constant stepping-up of the conditions favorable to workmen, such as protective covering on dangerous machinery, and the scrapping of out-moded machinery.
5. The principle of "joint-control" is hereby recognized; and is to

be put into operation as speedily as conditions in the industry will warrant.[7]

This Act of 1930 is remarkable as well for its provisions as for the fact that it was promulgated among a people who are likely to live up to and effectuate all its requirements. It has already, in part, reduced accidents and sickness; it has raised the scale of wages; it shortens the hours of work; it immeasurably mitigates the evils of child and woman labor; and presumptively grants to workmen a share in running industry. It has been called a Bill of Rights for Chinese Workers. It is always a nice question, of course, as to how far such legislation is enforceable. We are safe in saying as much as the conditions of industry will allow. Some mills have put some of its provisions into effect and others have done nothing about the matter at all.

Yet the backbone of China's economic life is not manufacturing industry but an agricultural economy. It always has been, and in view of her huge population, must continue so indefinitely. The present social and economic outlook for fully 350,000,000 rural people is one of unrelieved gloom. They are now enduring the miseries of one of China's long periods of anarchy. The Revolution of 1911 was meant to bring new hope and life to China's toiling millions of peasantry. Instead, the last twenty-two years have been filled with almost continuous internecine warfare and its losses, and the poor of the land have paid the bills. They have done so with increased rent and taxes and forced levies of goods and property; their sons and daughters have been forced into army service by the wandering hordes which have traversed the land from east to west and north to south during the period. After all these years of arson and pillage the countryside of China has almost reached the limit of destitution and poverty. In addition to the harm done the country people by all the "injustices" of misgovernment, they have had to endure an unusual number of natural calamities, such as droughts and floods, famine and earthquakes, pestilence and insect pests, cyclones and hailstorms.

Some idea of the precarious agricultural economic conditions may be gathered from such facts as that millions of people have forsaken or been driven off the land; that 50 per cent and over of the peasants are tenant farmers without land of their own. The demands of the landlords and tax-collectors must always be met. Frequently the peasants have to mortgage their future crop to the landlords before the seed is in the ground and the tax-collectors, usually accompanied by soldiers, take most of what is left by the landlords. It has been estimated that over one million four hundred thousand farmers were killed in Hunan, Hupeh, Honan, Anhui, and Kiangsi (the five central provinces around the city of Hankow) during the years 1927 to 1932. While Chinese statistics are necessarily unreliable, one estimate avers that nine and a half million people have been separated from their land. It is further alleged that the natural

---

[7]See footnote 6.

calamities of the years 1928 to 1931 brought forty million people to the verge of destitution. Total property damage is estimated at something over a billion and a half Chinese dollars, which, considering Chinese values and resources, forms an incredible loss.

The burden of militarism is very heavy and it falls on the peasant farmer in ever-increasing taxation and looting by soldier-bandits and bandit-soldiers. Out of a total governmental expenditure of thirty-one millions in November, 1932, twenty-eight went to pay soldiers and there was a deficit of twelve millions. All this ultimately returns on the rural economy. A country which grows 180,000,000 tons of rice annually had nevertheless to import some 15,000,000 tons. One cause is the forced growing of opium instead of cereals. This is chargeable to militarism. Foreign trade statistics compiled by the Chinese Maritime Customs show a serious adverse balance of international trade for 1932, and no invisible exports are discoverable to restore the balance. Such a condition is seriously alarming in official circles and of course agricultural economy has to shoulder the load.

China has known many crises like the present and the long course of her history has shown the Chinese people to possess unimaginable recuperative powers. But the situation is different at the present juncture. China has to bear the severe competition of other national groups, groups which are equipped with the high-powered technology and compact institutional organization of such an industrial life. China's chances of survival at the present are seriously debatable.

Yet the informed prophet on things Chinese is likely to speak with great reserve. He knows the latent capacity of the common people of China. He sees already the beginnings of reform in many directions. He marks the new attitude of Young China. Already, Young China seems to have begun to walk on the path of self-direction in marital affairs. And we may profitably conclude this section of the essay on China by going back for some consideration of the history and strength of the old Chinese marriage mores and how modern Chinese young people are automatically adjusting themselves to this important human interest.

Early Chinese thought on the relation of the human sexes begins very realistically as follows:

> Before there were husbands and wives there must have been simply people, living on the earth; before there were fathers and sons there must have been husbands and wives; before there were brothers and sisters there must have been parents and children. These relations between husband and wife, between parent and child, between child and child, are the principles of the family relations. From them one extends the relationship to other members of the family (i.e., to the clan, large and small) unto the ninth class of his kindred. (Su, 1922, p. 13)

Paralleling many other peoples, the Chinese believe that marriage was founded by a divine hero, or ruler. Fu Hsi is their particular personality and he is reputed to have lived in the early part of the third millenium B.C. And the regulation of the family life in earliest China was matriarchal. This is particularly striking in view of their later developed strongly patriarchal consciousness. The *Shu Ching,* at its beginning, constantly refers to people who were the sons of So-and-so, and the "So-and-so's" name is always a female one. These records also show the presence of a strong belief that regulation of the sexes in marriage brought happiness and welfare. The Great Yao appointed his co-ruler, Shun, the Regulator, to instruct the people carefully in the five relationships—that between father and son there should be affection; between sovereign and minister there should be righteousness; between husband and wife, attention to their proper functions and mutual esteem; between old and young a proper order; and between friends there should be fidelity.

The *She-ching,* or *Book of the Odes,* brings us the earliest picture of Chinese family life and they portray it as harmonious and happy. They say, "Happy union with wife and children is like the music of lutes and harps." Another Ode shows the wife of a working-man sending him from her side protesting that she will do her part in the cultivation of virtuous friendships with and for him.

> "And," she says, "I will hope to grow old with you. Your lute in your hands will emit its pleasant tones . . . When I know those whom you love, I will repay their friendships from the ornaments of my girdle." Still other poems reflect a widow's constancy, the duties of children to parents and of fraternal affection. They say, "Of all the men in the world, there are none equal to brothers. On the dreaded occasions of death and burial, it is the brothers who greatly sympathise . . . when your brothers are all present you are harmonious and happy . . . in accord with your brothers you will find lasting happiness. For the ordering of your family and your joy in your wife and child, examine this and study it. Will you not find it true?" (Su, 1922, pp. 26-30)

Nowhere are the deep and abiding satisfactions from a happy married state more vividly portrayed than in the following passage from the *Chinese Classics.* In the *Li Ki* it is said,

> "The ceremony of marriage was intended to be the bond of love between two families of different surnames, with a view in its retrospective character to secure the perpetuation of the family line. (Then minute details are given concerning the proper ways of sending proposals and gifts, all to be done in the ancestral temple of the lady and with proper reverence.) In this way was the ceremony respected and watched over, while its importance was exhibited and care taken that all its details should be correct . . . Marriage which defines the relations of the sexes eventuates in righteousness and repose." (Quoted in Harvey, 1933, p. 249)

Here we may note again the consciousness of the operative presence of the four major interests of humanity. Children in the family are necessary if adults are to be enabled to give expression to their higher personality; marriage is, moreover, a social matter—it is the bond of love uniting two stranger families; its attendant ceremonies will satisfy the deep emotional needs of prestige and controlled ostentation; and the whole is to be shot through and through with religious sanction. Through all the ages the Chinese have subjected themselves to strict regulation of their sex mores. Through hundreds of years the sex-tabus have been at work strengthening the family. Survival of human groups depends very greatly on the way in which they will make their automatic adjustments in the handling of this great interest, and the Chinese seem to have done well in this respect. European travelers and observers have reached a similar conclusion. Thus Marco Polo says of conditions in a large city in China in the middle of the thirteenth century:

> "The natives of the city are men of peaceful character, both from education and from the example of their kings, whose disposition was the same . . . and there is such a degree of goodwill and neighborly attachment among both men and women that you would take the people who live on the same street to be all of one family. And this familiar intercourse is free from all jealousy or suspicion of the conduct of their women. These they treat with the greatest respect, and man who should presume to make loose proposals to a married woman, would be regarded as an infamous rascal." There is still another bit of evidence. It is from the writing of two French abbes of the eighteenth century. They are at pains to account for the happy estate of the common people of China. They think it to lie in "the general modesty of Chinese women; in the reverence and worship paid by them to their own husbands; in their joy over the birth of sons; in their deep piety; in their religious veneration for their husband's parents; their good breeding, courteous bearing and manners, and the unexpected charm of their feminity, and so on." (Harvey, 1933, p. 251)

Chinese scholars have a saying with which observation does not entirely agree. They say that "the rites do not descend to the common man." But how, even allowing for some exaggeration, could the above be true if the culture of those self-styled elite had not deeply penetrated among the masses of the people of China? Where else in all the world, except perhaps in neighboring Japan, does one come across such uniform courtesy and genuine humanity as among the homogeneous masses of Eastern Asia?

How such high-bred character may be produced is easily gleaned from the following quotation. Concerning the inception of every important undertaking there is the general rule that

> When the day of sacrifice had come, the man wisely gave himself to the work of purification. That purification meant the production of uniformity in all thoughts till a uniform direction of all the thoughts was realized . . . when he was about to attempt a purification for a great occasion *he guarded against all things of an evil nature, and suppressed all his desires* . . . He allowed no vain thoughts in his heart but kept them in strict adherence with what is right. He allowed no reckless movement of his hands and feet, but kept them firmly in the way of propriety. Thus the superior man, in his purification, devotes himself to carrying to its utmost extent his refined and intelligent virtue . . . there was the looser ordering of the mind for seven days . . . and the complete ordering of it for three days, to effect the uniformity of all thoughts . . . The ruler

accomplished his purification in the outer apartment, and his wife
her purification in the inner. After this they met for the first time
in the grand temple. (Harvey, 1933, pp. 237-238)

Here we may catch a glimpse of how a whole vast people were so-
cietally disciplined until all their interests were not only cultivated to
a high degree of perfection but were fully served, and themselves brought
into a homogeneity of culture which is almost incomprehensible to Western
minds.

"New occasions teach new duties." Does this thought of J. R. Low-
ell's apply to modern China and in the sex mores so far studied? It
does. Conditions in modern China again enforce the thought of the unity
of all life. For example, in the writing of new state and federal political constitutions, the rights of women and sex equality are specifically
included. Young women took seats in the local and national parliaments
of China. Nor were they at all backward in claiming the emancipation
of women *in toto*. They demanded that the new folkways and mores
should everywhere cease to discriminate against women; that the right
of inheritance should be given to daughters as well as to sons; that husband and wife, son and daughter, should be equal before the law; that
males and females should be equally able to choose a career; that matrimonial problems should be resolved quite as much in favor of women as
of men; that the laws of China should fix the legal age at which young
persons may marry; that the support of a concubine shall be punished as
bigamy; that employers shall be forced to pay equal wages for equal
work regardless of sex; that child-bearing women be given a subsidy or
be paid wages ample enough to cover the disabilities of confinement; that
it shall be a crime to bind the feet of young girls and women.

These Chinese young women are much concerned about marriage.
They affirm that the purposes of marriage are not single but complex
and that, therefore, they shall be given an education so that they may
become efficient helpmeets to their mates. They demand co-education so
that the sexes may get well over their mutual shyness and come to study
and know the peculiarities of each sex and so at length come to establish
happy unions based on mutual knowledge. They remark that marriage
should bring the greatest happiness to people, yet how can it if the women
enter it as dumb brutes, uneducated, uninstructed? There are more
radical currents in which it is alleged that the old familial system is
doomed. This is either wishful or Russian thought. It may be both.
They say that the system no longer accords with modern conditions; that
it is falling to ruins spontaneously, and that, therefore, other provision
must be made for safeguarding this important human interest. The
following quotation is vividly alight with this sort of notion:

> Youth no longer permits its grandparents to mate them as shep-
> herds on the mountains mate their sheep. For, with the waxing
> importance of a developed personality, and its right of self-decision,
> they are more and more rejecting the old marriage system of China.
> Think of the old system and the place in it of the daughter-in-law!

She was chastised for twenty years by her mother-in-law; then in turn she did the same for the same length of time for her daughter-in-law; then the last twenty years of her life she spent in loathsome indolence, and the empty vanities of her boudoir. What a life program for women! But modern education is fortunately changing all that. Soon the young women of China will be free. To be sure, partisans of the old ways will eulogise wise wives and the tender mothers of the old system. But the new wives will be wiser, and as tender! So speaks a youth in one out of the hundreds of magazines and journals devoted to the cause of women in the new China. (Wieger, 1920-32, vol. 5, pp. 250-251)

Here is a new spirit and here the Russian teaching, if such it be, has surely been effective. Does present progress fit the above? It does. There are women's banks run by women; there are "schoolmarms" a-plenty; there are young Chinese business women, doctors, and even lawyers. The new day has surely dawned for the few and the promise is for many more. Of course, the movement is confined to the port-cities. The women of the great agricultural hinterlands have scarcely heard of these stirring thoughts, and if they have they disregard them. But the new day has dawned.

KOREAN CULTURE HISTORY

In view of the geographical nearness of Korea to Manchuria and China, one is not surprised to discover that her culture is in every way a faint copy of that of China. China fulfiled her civilizing mission by sending her men and arts to Korea in the twelfth century B.C. In government, law, education, manners, etiquette, social relations, her influence is supreme. "Educated men observe and practice the teachings of Confucius and Wen Wang," wrote the Korean king to his suzerain in Peking some ten years before his country was opened to foreign intercourse. It has been well said that their literature, their superstitions, their system of education, ancestral worship, and modes of thinking are Chinese. So far has this been carried that, although the Koreans showed themselves original enough to have devised an alphabet of eleven vowels and fourteen consonants, with a script called En-mun, they failed to make use of it, so great was their veneration for Chinese writing.

The Chinese Book of History, as well as early Korean books, states that Chi-tze, a counselor of the Yin dynasty who felt himself unable to give allegiance to the new Chow masters of China, betook himself in the year 1122 B.C. with several thousand immigrants to what is now Korea and proceeded to civilize the land. He found none but trogloditic inhabitants there and, having subdued them, he and his descendants, civilized and ruled the land till about the fourth century B.C. Thenceforward for almost fourteen hundred years feudalism was the order of the day. And culture went on by this means of political organization.

The fourth century A.D. witnessed the introduction of Buddhism to Korea with all its civilizing influences. It, of course, carried Chinese learning and culture to Korea as it went on to do for Japan very soon thereafter. Matters narrowed down to power being exercised by three feudal overlords, and then the king of Silla, about the tenth century A.D., unified the whole country under his personal scepter and established his capital at Songdo. He was of the surname Wang. His dynasty lasted till about the fourteenth century A.D., when Litan came to dominate the peninsula and his house lasted until 1910 A.D., when the land was annexed by Japan.

Korean abilities are highly spoken of by observers. Mrs. Bishop thinks them well up to average intelligence and keen in business. She thinks they belong to a different race from the Manchus and Chinese, cites minor physical differences, but then goes on to note and describe physical traits that are surely Mongoloid. Such are obliqueness of the eyes, high cheek bones, lank hair, etc. Anthropologically the Koreans are surely Mongoloids showing slight variations from the norm.

Mrs. Bishop notes the misrule of the House of Li and thinks that that sufficiently accounts for the squalor and backwardness of the Koreans. She says:

> I believe that the fishing industry, with every other, is paralyzed by the complete insecurity of the earnings of labor and by the exactions of officials, and that the Korean fisherman does not care to earn money of which he will surely be deprived on any or no pretence, and that, along with the members of the industrial classes generally, he seeks the protection of poverty. (Bishop, 1897, p. 158)

Her book, *Korea and Her Neighbors,* repeatedly carries the same thought of the insecurity accorded to earnings or a very slight economic surplus, of the vampire-like nature of Korean officials, of the possibilities latent in Korean men and women if they could only be given their rights to enjoy the fruits of their labor. She describes the prosperity of the Korean farmer when once he had come to enjoy the securities offered him by the Russians in Siberia. She says:

> Korean hamlets with houses of a very superior class to those in Korea were sprinkled all over the country. At one of the largest villages . . . we called at several of the peasant farmers' homes, and were made very welcome, even the women coming out to welcome the official with an air of decided pleasure. The farmers had changed the timid, suspicious, or cringing manner which is characteristic of them to a great extent at home, for an air of frankness and independence which was most pleasing . . . The houses, of strictly Korean architecture, were large, with five or six rooms, carefully thatched, and very neat within, abounding in such comforts and plenishings as would only be dreamed of by mandarins at home . . . The days of the return journey gave me a good opportunity of learning something of the condition of the Koreans under another government than their own . . . The total number of immigrants is estimated at 18,000 to 20,000. It must be remembered that several thousands of these were literally paupers, and that they subsisted for nearly a year on the charity of the Russian authorities, and after that were indebted to them for seed corn. They settled on the rich lands of the Siberian valleys mostly as squatters, but have been unmolested for years. Many have purchased the lands they occupy,

and in other cases villages have acquired community rights to their adjacent lands. It is the intention of the Government that squatting shall gradually be replaced by purchase, the purchasers receiving legal title deeds. [Mrs. Bishop goes on to show in detail how prosperous these Koreans have become and then concludes with the following graphic words.] But there is more than this. The air of the men has undergone a subtle but real change, and the women, though they nominally keep up their habit of seclusion, have lost the hangdog air which distinguishes them at home. The suspiciousness and indolent conceit, and servility to his betters, which characterize the home-bred Korean has very generally given place to an independence and manliness of manner that is rather British than Asiatic. The alacrity of movement is a change also, and has replaced the conceited swing of the *yang-ban* (leisure class) and the heartless lounge of the peasant . . . comforts and a certain appearance of wealth no longer attract the rapacious attentions of officials, but are rather a credit to a man than a source of insecurity. (Bishop, 1897, Chap. **XIX** *passim.*)

Thus speaks a writer of authority on the people who live inside and outside the country which she visited now nearly forty years ago. Since then, great changes have come over the land and people of Korea. The Japanese annexation of the year 1910 should be reckoned as among the greatest, for it gave to the common Korean man an outside power which could protect him from the ravages of the officials and the afore-mentioned *yang-ban,* or leisure classes. It is eminently to the point that a brief account of the changes in Korea since 1910 should be given, for governmental security has made possible the adequate satisfaction to the Koreans of their most intimate needs.

Korea under either Chinese or Russian sovereignty would have been a direct threat to the national existence of Japan. Accordingly, the latter country saw herself compelled to put an end to this threat and to the existence of dangerous anarchy in the Peninsula by waging the successful wars with China in 1894 and with Russia in 1904. It has been well remarked that the Japanese victories resulted for Korea in the renunciation of Chinese suzerainty and the introduction by the Japanese of many important reforms. These were either reforms in existing social agencies or the downright creation of new ways of living and new institutions. Thus large changes were carried out in the governmental departments. A measure of reform was effected in the judicial and prison systems. Taxation was placed on an equitable basis. The suffocating pressure of the trade gilds was relaxed. Postal and educational systems were introduced. An approach to a workable constitution was made. The distinction between *yang-ban* (the leisure classes) and the commoner was abolished, as were domestic slavery and the cruel beating and slicing to death of prisoners. The age of marriage for both sexes was raised. Degraded classes were enfranchised, and then, later, Koreans and Japanese were put on an equal footing before the law and in the equal ability to occupy administrative positions in the service of the state.

Previous to the advent of the Japanese both in 1905 or 1910, it may be said with much truth that Korea had no government, that the people suffered wholly from misgovernment. For example, in finance no distinction was made between the royal household revenues and those of the state. If the Korean king needed money for his personal or household use he took it wherever it was available. No attempt was made at national bookkeeping beyond recording just enough items to enable court and officials to squeeze wealth out of the common people for their own personal purposes. Perhaps it is not altogether without significance that the murdered Korean queen once said that she had never seen anything of Korea outside her palace except the broad highway which led to the ancestral temple at the time of the annual festival of the *kur-dong*. Nor did any Korean city-women know their own land beyond the limited territory with which they might be able to become acquainted between the hours of eight P.M. and midnight. During these four hours they went abroad and the men stayed at home. At all other hours they lived in the strict seclusion of their homes. This applied specially, of course, to the women of Seoul and other large towns. But the seclusion of Korean women was generally real, finding its extension even in the fact that country women there, until very recently, did not assist their men in the work of the fields.

The permanent arrival of the Japanese in the Peninsula marked a change and gave the people a real government. On October 30, 1910, the Organic Regulations of the Government-General of Chosen (Korea) were promulgated by Japanese Imperial Ordinance. It included government by a Governor-General, a Secretariat and five departments: General Affairs, Home Affairs, Finance, Justice, Agriculture, Commerce and Industry. In 1919, with the appointment of Governor-General Baron Saito, a new and liberal set of ideas was promulgated by the Imperial Japanese Government, as follows:

(1) Non-discrimination between Japanese and Korean officials;
(2) simplification of laws and regulations;
(3) prompt transaction of state business;
(4) decentralization policy;
(5) improvement of local organization;
(6) respect for native culture and customs;
(7) freedom of speech, meeting and press;
(8) spread of education and development of industry;
(9) re-organization of the police system;
(10) enlargement of medical and sanitary agencies;
(11) guidance of the people;
(12) advancement of men of talent;
(13) fostering of friendly feeling between Japanese and Koreans.
    (Ireland, 1926, p. 78)

And the Governor, in a speech introducing these measures, showed great liberality of thought and attitude. He kept his word, as a glance at his performances during the subsequent ten years of his tenure of office suffices to demonstrate. The actual loans made by Japan to finance all the reforms amount to very large sums. For example, the budgets of 1911 and 1926 were 52 and 188 million yen respectively! The paper program for local government became an accomplished fact during the years that followed 1919. So that in addition to the central government at Seoul (Keijo) there were established thirteen provincial governments, twelve municipal prefectures, two hundred eighteen rural counties and districts, and two insular districts. All these were put into running order, were financed, and remain to the present. Financing them alone was a stupendous task, for there was no fiscal system in existence in Korea on which the ruling power could build. The great educative service to the Koreans of such an organization must be obvious. They had not had anything resembling it for so many centuries that the memory of its earlier existence had been completely forgotten.

As in China, so in Korea, the administration of justice was carried on by means of a barbarian code. The Powers had accordingly secured the principle of extraterritoriality under which their nationals lived. With the coming of the Japanese and the setting-up of civilized civil and criminal codes this principle was no longer necessary and the Powers willingly yielded it. One law and one justice and one uniform internal administration of the arts of peace came to prevail. The administration of criminal law is efficient, speedy, and sure. Ninety-five per cent of the criminal cases end in the conviction of the accused. The judiciary staff to handle this is composed of Japanese and Korean judges, prosecutors, clerks, interpreters, and police.

The essential principles underlying and governing educational policy carried out by the Japanese Governor-General in Korea may be gathered from the following:

> "Be filial to your parents, affectionate to your brothers and sisters; as husbands and wives be harmonious, as friends, true; bear yourselves in modesty and moderation; extend your benevolence to all; pursue learning and cultivate the arts, and thus develop your intellectual faculties and perfect your morality; furthermore, be solicitous of the commonweal and the public interest; should occasion arise, offer yourselves courageously to the State." And in a notification to teachers in 1916 there is also the following. (1) The fostering of loyalty and filial piety are to be made the radical principles of education, and special attention is to be given to the cultivation of moral sentiments. (2) Practical utility shall always be held in view when imparting instruction. (3) Robust physical development is to be striven for. (Ireland, 1926, p. 188)

These sentiments speak for themselves as does also their fruition, namely, the large number of schools, the large public expenditures therefor, and the large number of pupils enrolled in them. In 1911 and 1924 enrollment figures were 110,789 and 542,679 respectively for one sort of school, while in kindergartens and a special kind of native school the figures for the same years were 141,604 and 256,858.

Such developments in education as well as in agriculture, sericulture, fishing, new and more equitable systems of land-holding, national finance and the new financing of the farmer, totally new ideas in medical science, public hygiene and sanitation, the renovation of irrigation canals, new afforestation, encouragement of mining and new securities for commerce, manufacturing and banking, new and incorrupt police protection—all these matters, and many more, mark a new day for the toiling people of the Hermit Nation.

Yet no one should assume that "sudden in a minute all is accomplished and the work is done." There are all sorts of obstacles to progress in Korea. The natives, with extraordinarily long memories, have not forgotten the Japanese invasion of their country under Hideyoshi in 1598 A.D. Nor will the inhuman murder of their queen in the summer of 1895 soon pass into oblivion. These events raise Korean suspicions of Japanese motives in whatever they undertake in the Peninsula. Then, too, the Japanese are aliens and imperialists, two facts that provide almost insuperable difficulties in the way of building up a common understanding. Again, the work of culture-building halts because of lags among the Korean people themselves. There one may observe the existence of many anachronisms, such as a widespread shamanism side by side with a modern and enlightened system of public-school education. Or, again, the seclusion of women beside new wide streets and roads and all manner of modern means of communication and transportation.

Debased Buddhism and passionless Confucianism hardly exist any longer in Korea and one might assume a blank slate and the opportunity to build up new emotional reactions to the whole of life without the antecedents and stereotypes of such world-philosophies as these. Yet nothing would be more inexact. The hoary animism of Northern Asia has its impregnable strongholds in the mental outfit of every Korean. And its priests are actually organized into gilds in the capital city, Seoul. Shamans are nothing more than wizards and sorcerers. They deal in the occult and its principal exponent, namely, demons. Demonology is their science and art. These men, by reason of their alleged control over demons, assure their patrons of success in new undertakings and security against the play of the aleatory element in human life. There are blind sorcerers, and other sorceresses. Each class is organized into a tight corporation. Their conjuring arts for the control of occult forces closely resemble those of ancient and modern China. Hence they are really neither specifically Korean, Chinese, or Japanese, but are Asiatic.

By a few throws of the dice or the tortoise shell the wizard will discover the name of the demon now infesting the house or troubling the person. Then by means of magic formulas, the waving of a wand and the speaking of the demon's name, he will try to dislodge him. Taking next an eastern branch of a peach-tree, as in China, he will place it vertically on a table, crooning chants the meanwhile over it. The malignant demon, quite in the manner of Mephistopheles' actions in Faust, comes at call, but tries to take vengeance on the man holding the wand. The wizard rescues him and the holder of the wand now places it over the neck of a bottle which has been previously closed with a bit of paper. The wand now touches the paper and the demon forthwith enters the bottle which is at once corked tightly. The bottle is then buried at the cross-roads exactly as in China, and elsewhere on the Asiatic mainland.

The two chapters on demonism in Bird's *Korea* can be taken as accurate descriptions of Chinese exorcism and demonology. These persons are very numerous in Korea and their fees have been estimated to reach an annual total of two million five hundred thousand dollars.

The road of culture-building is a long, steep, arduous one. Present-day Korean culture is hindered in its growth not only by such obsessions as those of demonism but also by the intractabilities of nature and human nature. Good roads are about as scarce in Korea as tigers are plentiful and production-capital scanty. However, as in China and Japan, the sunrise of a new day is at its beginning. The slow infiltration of Western knowledge which necessarily accompanies its technology is acting as a ferment to bring Koreans to desire the end of seclusion for women; to jump with avidity into new ways of making a living; to indulge in new forms of pleasure such as the phonograph; to acquire new emotional reactions to life in general in which a new element of hope is compounded. The night is far spent, the day is at hand, the faint rosy streaks of dawn are discernible on the mountain tops of their human barriers to progress.

THE MONGOLS

The Mongols were conquerors and not consolidators or statesmen, except for a brief period of about one hundred years in China. And even there it is probable that the strength of the antecedent Chinese culture and its governmental organization kept the country going. Chinese historians are inclined to pass over the ninety years of Mongol rule of their country as an interlude, but some weight must be given to the services of conquerors. They at least mix peoples and civilizations. And this cross-fertilization of racial stocks and cultures may prove to be of vast importance. As has been said, "the predatory habits of the Turkish, Mongolian and Manchu population of northern Asia, and their irruptions into other parts of the continent and into Europe have produced very remarkable results in the history of the world."

Brave and hardy the Mongols have always shown themselves to be, but the capacity for consolidating the fruits of victory, for establishing a settled government, and for gaining the allegiance of the conquered people has invariably been wanting in them. They have, except for the brief interlude of power under Genghiz and his successors, always been pastoral nomads, shepherds, hunters, herdsmen. Stocks allied to the Mongolians are the Manchus, the Turks of Central Asia, the Chinese, Japanese and Koreans, the Tibetans, slightly less so the Burmese and the Siamese, the Kachins and Shans of North East Burma, the Bhils and Kols of Central India, while the Malays surely carry the Mongol strain about with them. Physically the Mongols have yellow-brown skins, black eyes and lank black hair, are short of stature with little or no body hair, have flat noses and oblique eyes. They, and their related stocks, live in the whole of northern Asia, on the plains of Central Asia as far as the

Caspian Sea, Tibet, China and Japan, Malaysia and Indonesia, with the exception of Papua.

Both Turkish and Mongol traditions represent the two nations as descended from two brothers. Genghiz, the founder of the Mongol power, must have had large numbers of Turks in his armies. Ethnographically it is difficult to distinguish between physique or customs of allied tribes such as the Finno-Ugrians, the Mongolians, and the Manchus. Genghiz and his Mongols arose in the fertile valleys and vast expanses of three rivers in North Central Siberia: the Kerulen, Upper Nonni, and Argun Rivers. He was born on the banks of the tributary Onon River in 1162 A.D. and was named Temuchin. At the age of thirteen his father died and his vassals wished to desert from their allegiance to the young Temuchin. His mother, however, rallied those who were faithful to her son, and, after years of ceaseless warfare, Temuchin convoked the notables on the banks of the Onon in 1206 and there, at their request, he ascended the throne of the Mongol Empire with the title of Genghiz, Chinese *Cheng-tze,* or Perfect Warrior. (See *Encyclopaedia Brittanica,* 11th ed., Vol. 15, p. 316.)

In succeeding years Genghiz entered China through a pass in the Great Wall and, with three armies commanded by his sons and himself, penetrated to Shantung and Honan. He sent a message to the Kin Tatar emperor of northern China, promising to retire if the latter would send largesses to his officers and men. This ruler did so and also sent imperial princesses, 500 youths and maidens, and 3000 horses. Genghiz retired. Then later through a misunderstanding he engaged in warfare with the powerful ruler of the Kingdom of Khwarizm in West Asia. In 1219 he started from Karakorum. Two armies set out, one led by his second son, Jagatai, and the other by Juji, his eldest. Mohammed of Khwarizm led out 400,000 against Juji but was routed, leaving 160,000 dead on the field. Jagatai had meanwhile been investing Otrar on the River Jaxartes and after five months it fell. The garrison was put to the sword. A third army took Khojent and a fourth under Genghiz and his son Tulé advanced on Bokhara. On ascending the steps of the principal mosque, Genghiz said, "The hay is cut, give your horses fodder." They at once sacked the city and outraged the inhabitants. From there Genghiz advanced on Samarkand, which surrendered as did Balkh. Genghiz went no further but 70,000 men under Tulé ravaged Khorassan, and two flying columns under Chepe and Sabatai Bahadur pursued Mohammed, who fled to the Caspian Sea where he died of pleurisy. Genghiz took and sacked Merv, Nishapur, Herat, Delhi. Shah Mohammed's son, Jellaluddin, defeated at Delhi, mounted a horse and jumped twenty feet into the river below and swam ashore under Genghiz's admiring eyes, thus escaping. He, Genghiz, then ravaged the provinces of Lahore, Peshawar, and Melikpur. Herat, having rebelled, he sacked it and in that sack 1,600,000 persons are said to have perished. Genghiz then returned to Mongolia via Balkh, Bokhara, and Samarkand.

In 1222 Chepe and Sabutai had marched into Armenia and Georgia, defeating everyone whom they met until they at last reached Astrakhan.

The Russians in Kiev now made the mistake of killing the Mongolian envoys, which brought Chepe and Sabutai on them. There they "came, saw, conquered," and sacked the Russian cities and went as far as Great Bulgaria and the Adriatic Sea. Then they returned home to Mongolia. During these campaigns in the West, Genghiz himself had gone into China and had overcome the Kin emperors so that now his kingdom's boundaries were coterminous in China with those of the Southern Sung domains. On this campaign Genghiz saw the five planets in conjunction and, superstitious, he began his return to Mongolia. On his journey he was seized with an illness and died in 1227 A.D. Ogotai, his son, succeeded him. But later on his line became extinct. Juji succeeded to Khwarizm, Jagatai to Bokhara, and his youngest son, Tulé, had charge of the home country and the archives of state. From Tulé was descended Kubilai, who in 1259 became Khakhan, and emperor of China.

With the conquest of China and Kubilai's accession to that throne the Mongol power had reached its greatest extent. Its active control and influence extended from Korea to the Adriatic Sea and from Canton to the Vistula River in Western Poland. Mongol armies had been in Vienna and had destroyed Moscow and other cities of Eastern and Central Europe. Mongol power was effectively exercised through Persia, Mesopotamia, and Syria. Although Kubilai had won Korea he failed to conquer Japan and the southwestern parts of what is now regarded as China; and he failed also to consolidate the gains in Annam, Siam, and elsewhere in that region. And his dynasty lost control in China in less than a century. History records the gradual weakening of Mongol power and the absorption of its glories and prerogatives by the various empires of the Moslems in India and Persia and Central Asia. And a native dynasty in China won control there. Now the Mongols have, for some centuries, remained nothing more than roving bands of nomads in southern Siberia and northern Turkestan. They started from and have returned to a stage of culture not greatly differing from that of the Navajo Amerindians of southwestern United States. We here pass to a consideration of that other related race which Kubilai failed to assimilate, the Japanese.

JAPANESE CULTURAL HISTORY

The Japanese call their country the land of *kami,* that is, the home of the ancient gods. These were, and are, in reality the spirits of their ancestors. Japan is another of the lands of the yellow-skinned peoples whose predominant world-philosophy is ancestor-worship. So simple and so complex a fact as this goes far towards enabling one to reach an understanding of this gifted and able race. It points to the secret springs of *bushido* or loyalty of the *samurai* or *daimyo* to their liege lords. It enables one to comprehend the utter devotion of high officers to their emperor and country, as where, for instance, the lieutenant-commander of a Japanese gunboat committed *harakiri* in 1927 off Nanking because of the outrages offered to fellow-countrymen in the troubles of the time. Ancestor-worship accounts for the enduring, ordered, serried, hierarchical ranks and stratifications in Japanese society, and the high sense of duty so characteristic of the people when observed *chez soi.* This attitude of fealty and subjection is in reality offered to the ever-living, ever-watchful, and ever-rewarding gods and accounts in a large sense for the rise of Japanese culture. The average Japanese, even today, is persuaded that his own prosperity and the very welfare of his nation closely depend on the goodwill of the totality of the ancestors of the nation. Now this culture was at once solid and beautiful, satisfying and graceful. It commends itself to the thoughtful attention of mankind because it, for long ages, harmonized the interests of the individual and the group. Therein the individual, by serving and supporting and promoting its institutions, could give high expression to his own personality either by the contribution of some material invention or by molding its institutions. Examples are the services of the original makers and inventors of the celebrated Japanese swords and other artifacts; or the works of Hideyoshi and Ieyasu in the unification of Japan or the composition of such an instrument as the *Legacy of Ieyasu.*

The written records of Japanese beginnings are found in the *Kojiki,* or *Records of Ancient Matters,* and in the *Nihongi,* or *Chronicles of Japan.* There one finds pictured the culture of a prehistoric race and epoch. Archeological investigations tend to confirm the truth of much of the legendary or traditional matter in these two books. The traditions, as elsewhere, point back to primordial weakness, unregulation, and poverty of cultural beginnings. The tabu of incest and the prescription of exogamy are unknown and close consanguine marriage occurred. The mythology, which is often so close to the facts of historical growth, tells of a brother-sister divine pair, Izanagi and Izanami. They, standing on the bridge between heaven and earth, thrust a jewelled spear downwards into the brine. When withdrawn from the ocean the water-drops from it crystallized into the solid land and on that land the divine pair by processes of human generation begat the land which is now Japan.

The legend has a Pluto-Proserpine element in it for the beloved Izanami perishes from the defilements of a visit to Hades. Her spouse, Izanagi, who had gone in after her, also suffers from the defilements of his journey and is obliged to purify himself therefrom. From the droppings of the washing of his left eye, the Goddess of the Sun, Ameratsu, is born. The God of the Moon and the God of Force sprang respectively from the washings of his right eye and nose. The dying Ameratsu also gave birth to fire. Thus does the mythology reflect early Japanese consciousness of their ancestral appropriation of light, fire, and force as culture traits and their adaptation to human uses in the struggle for existence and the competition of life.

A number of other items in Japanese tradition support the idea of early indefiniteness in social relationships. There is, for example, the great prominence of women in social life and the fact that the children dwelt with their mother and not with their sire. They in fact knew only their uterine siblings, not their sire's offspring by other women. Women "dwelt apart from their husbands with their children, and so different families might have the same sire." This is perhaps indicated by one of the names for husband in Japanese, namely "night-prowler." Such a name is of large anthropological meaning. It may well account for the fact that children of the same sire might marry but not those of the same mother. For often enough they would not know their blood relationship on the male side.

One of the significant facts of early Japanese social life is just this prominence of women. Then already they were the helpmeets of their men. The *Chronicles* tell how during a dynastic crisis, and consequent social insecurity, that it was

> a girl who warns one of the "emperor's" generals of the threatening plot; it was the sovereign's aunt who interprets the warning; and it was Ata, the wife of the rebellious prince, who led the left wing of his army. (*Encyclopaedia Britannica*, 11th ed., Vol. 15, p. 253)

This inclusion of women in the corporate life is shown, further, by the fact that taxes have to be paid not only on animals' skins and game secured by men but also on "textile fabrics of women"—which incidentally reveals the stage of the arts when the report was made. All along

> women continue to figure in the story. The image of the sun-deity (a female) enshrined in Ise, is entrusted with the keeping of a princess, as are the mirror, sword, and jewels inherited from the sun-goddess; a woman, Tachibana, accompanies Prince Yamato-dake in his campaign against the Yemishi (the northern Ainu), and sacrifices her life to quell a tempest at sea; also the consort of Suinin is the heroine of a most tragic tale in which the conflict between filial piety and conjugal loyalty leads her to self-destruction; and a woman is found ruling over a large district in Kiushiu when the Emperor Keiko is engaged in his campaign against the aborigines. (*op. cit. ibid.*)

About 200 A.D. mention is made in the Chinese annals of a female Japanese sovereign old and unmarried and much addicted to magic arts, and attended by one thousand female servants. She dwelt in a palace with numerous pavilions, surrounded by a stockade, guarded by soldiers. Few saw her face, except one old soldier, who served her meals and acted as a medium of communication. This record undoubtedly refers to the Empress Jingo whose every act was prompted by divine interposition.

But with the oncoming of a severer feudal militarism women in Japan seem to have dropped into the background of social life. Now and then mention is made of some celebrated empress who contributed to the life of the nation. But henceforth Japanese woman added her most momentous contributions through the material and spiritual comforts of her home life. As she assisted her man, so she succeeded in creating that character of feminine beauty which Hearn describes so compellingly. Not so much can be said for Japanese man, and the samurai in particular, whose chief fault was faithlessness towards women.

> But the samurai lady claimed no privilege of timidity on account of her sex. She knew how to die in the cause of honor just as readily

as her husband, her father or her brother did, and conjugal fidelity did not rank as a virtue in her eyes, being regarded as simple duty (*Encyclopaedia Britannica,* 11th, ed., Vol. 15, p. 253)

These early Japanese legends need further supplementing. It is generally agreed that the mythological period in Japan extends down to 461 A.D., which is the earliest date to receive outside confirmation. But very evidently much cultural life had gone on before that date.

Archeological investigation shows a long antecedent savage stage of arrow heads, hunting-life, and lack of social cohesion. But the earliest written records reveal a people on a high barbaric level. Iron was used for the manufacture of spears, swords, knives, and more peaceable tools such as door-fasteners. Bows and arrows were in use, special mention being made of feathered arrows; pestles and mortars were known, as were also the wedge and the sickle. Fire-drills and the weaver's shuttle are mentioned. Rowing and punting and primitive coastal navigation were undertaken. House-building is frequently described with houses surrounded by stockades, in view of the relative insecurity. Rugs and garments of skin and silk were manufactured. The people lived on the banks of streams and on the seashore, indicating a somewhat sparse population. The practice of frequent bathing is alluded to, a practice which thus early became a permanent part of Japanese culture. Another trait which must have survived from very early times is the necessary building by the expectant mother of a parturition-house. Such a custom is now found only among such peoples as the Yukaghirs and Yakuts of Siberia.[8] In a windowless house, Japanese mothers gave birth unaided to their children.

The food of these early Japanese consisted of fish and the flesh of wild animals caught in the chase, and of such wild roots and fruits and nuts and seeds as could be collected. Rice is mentioned in the *Kojiki,* a sure proof of its domestication at a very early period. *Saké,* the Japanese national drink, is also mentioned, as are chopsticks for the eating of food. Pottery, and hence an upper barbarian level of culture, was present and it was used to cook with and as an eating utensil. Fire was used in the arts and for cooking but not as yet for warming. Garments were known and highly specialized into tailored trousers, upper garments, skirts, girdles, veils, and hats. The material for clothing was woven from hempen thread and from mulberry bark. The protection of the masses against rain was then what it now is, the very serviceable grass hat and widespreading cape. Singularly enough, no mention is made of sewing with needles and thread, but, since tailored garments were made, the former seem necessary for the latter. In the early days, in contradistinction to the present, adornment of the person was conspicuous with necklaces, bracelets, and head ornaments of precious stones. Agate, serpentine, steatite, crystal, glass, and jade were the raw materials for the manufacture of jewelry. Hair-dressing was an art aided by combs. The hair was bound up in two bunches by the men, one on each side of the head; young boys

---

[8]Japanese immigrants from Siberia may have brought such a trait along with them from the Asiatic mainland.

tied their hair in a top-knot; unmarried girls let theirs hang down in two braids, while the married women used a combination-dressing of the unmarried of both sexes. But these rules were not invariably followed. The hair was not cut and at times sex-distinction was hard to draw from the dressing of the hair or by the dress, since both men and women dressed alike. A scanty beard was often the only mark of the male sex. The horse was in use, but for riding and for carrying loads only; no carts were used. Barnyard fowls and the cormorant for fishing had been domesticated. Dogs and cattle are alluded to in later parts of the *Chronicles,* but sheep were unknown. Nor have the latter thriven in modern times because of the nature of native Japanese grasses which are harmful to them.

These rather numerous inventions were accompanied by some corresponding institutions, for, on the principle of "the strain to consistency and harmony in the mores," mechanical traits and mores go hand in hand. Material gains and inventions always need the buttressing, supporting frame work of protective, regulative institutions. The *Records* tell us that the people lived in stockaded houses; that women were slightly more numerous than men; that the wealthy sometimes had four or five wives, others two or three, but that pair-marriage seems to have been the rule. Women were faithful and not jealous and children were much prized and well looked after. The criminal as well as all his immediate family was extirpated for grave offenses. For lesser crimes he was executed and his women and children enslaved, and Cain-like, were tattooed. Early distinctions of rank set in under which "everybody became somebody else's man up to the sovereign who dwelt in Yamato." Religious practices were known as is shown by the presence of mourning rites and officials who were called "mourning-keepers." They saw to it that funerals were observed with all decorum and that the necessary ritual purifications were made after death and burial.

Next to fire and speech, the art of writing is highly important in a developing culture. The Japanese, having no script of their own, went across the seas and took over Chinese calligraphy. This civilizing art came into Japan via Korea about 400 A.D. But this trait could not have come singly. With its advent would come also a knowledge of many of the most salient traits of the powerful culture of China. The facts are that there was an influx of Chinese and Koreans from the Peninsula together with many of the arts and sciences of both these highly civilized lands. Thus a cross-fertilization of race and culture took place. The hybrid vigor of the one and the increased adaptations of the other could not but have been highly beneficial to the race of Yamato. The traditional conquest of Korea by Japan had the effect of settling many Koreans in the latter country either as prisoners of war or as immigrants to a less densely settled country and so to one of greater opportunity. Japan at this time obtained seamstresses from the mainland, and so learned to make tailored clothing. At about this time also they began to garner ice, using it to cool their national drink, *saké.*

One noteworthy aspect of social life began early to appear in Japanese life. This was the tendency to organize the body politic into rigidly defined class groups or bodies which followed the same callings or practiced the same arts of life. Such classes were called *bé;* hence all families in Japan were classified either as *kobétsu, shinbétsu,* or *bambétsu* (Hearn, 1913, pp. 259-260). The first was composed of the imperial "branch" or noble houses which headed up in the ruler, all claiming descent from the Sun-Goddess; the second was the "divine" branch or clans descended from other divinities; finally, the bambétsu were the "foreign" branch and it was made up of the masses of the people. Possibly the latter was so designated because it was made up of numerous and succeeding waves of craftsmen from China and Korea of which the following is but one of many instances. About 540 A.D., 7053 householders and their dependents came to Japan from China via Korea.

But fundamental to the above class-stratification, and cutting much deeper into the organization of Japanese society, is that of the family. This was, as hinted, closely tied up with ancestral worship, indeed, socially speaking, the latter was the sole *raison d'être* for the family in Japan. It will bear repeating that foremost in the mind of each of its inhabitants is the conviction that

> the welfare of the living depends upon the welfare of the dead. Under the influence of this idea, and of the cult based upon it, were developed the early organization of the family, the laws regarding property and succession, the whole structure in short of ancient [Japanese] society. (Hearn, 1913, p. 65)

From this flow important consequences. Such a family was a society in the strictest sense of the word. It was organized for the winning of subsistence and for self-perpetuation. Such a family would inevitably grow into a clan, which is a basis for all larger aggregations of society. Again, organized as they were on the patriarchal basis, it was imperative that every Japanese woman should bear a son, or as many sons as possible. For only males could carry on the family line and offer sacrifices acceptable to the ancestral spirits. It would seem almost as if the society had worked out an automatic adjustment of the highest value, one that was self-regulative and irresistible. It was of course the greatest possible calamity to die without male issue:

> to die without leaving a male heir, in the case of an elder son and successor, was a *crime* against the ancestors. In their thought the father, not the mother, was the life-giver, the duty of maintaining the cult rested on the man, not the woman. (Hearn, 1913, p. 68)

The woman shared the blessings of the cult, and as the mother of a son she would undoubtedly win a lot of influence, but she had no part in its maintenance. She might remain in her parent's home provided a husband could be found for her and he were willing to adopt her father's name. These things show the extraordinary strength, form, and tenacity of the East-Asiatic family and marriage arrangements. The family and clan did not, and does not, consist of a single married pair but of several married pairs of different age groups and their children. Thus great-grandparents, grandparents, parents and children in Japan mean one family. There, as in China, the family and clan may include the entire population of a village or small town. Thus any typical "Smithtown" may include sixty or more persons who all bear the same surname, dwelling under the same roofs around one common courtyard. The present writer knows a village in China like this which includes two thousand persons within its membership and they all bear the same surname, which is Chao.

It follows, furthermore, that marriage and the having of children is a sacrament, an offering to the divine spirits of the ancestors. In case of divorce the mother would leave the family with empty hands. Her children belonged to her man's clan and stayed behind her in its membership. Of course, the eldest male in the family had supreme autocratic power. He had, and sometimes exercised, his power to sell or even kill his children. He could compel them to marry the person of his selection who was accordingly "right." And he could prevent the marriage of those whom he thought "wrong." He could disinherit unfilial children, and prescribe to all their callings. In its extreme form this *patria potestas* meant life or death, liberty or its opposite, the right to divorce his own wife or those of his children, the right to hold office or to choose an occupation. "The family was a despotism."

The strength of this old Japanese family lay, as a fact, in its mutual aid, sanctioned by benevolent ancestral spirits. It enforced obedience but it gave comfort; every member did something for someone else, it had to give its utter protection to its every member. Hearn (1913, p. 86) says of it at its best:

> In a well-conducted household, where every act is performed according to the old forms of courtesy and kindness,—where no harsh word is ever spoken,—where the young look up to the aged with affectionate respect,—where those whom years have incapacitated for more active duty, take upon themselves the care of children, and render priceless service in teaching and training,—an ideal condition has been realized.

This sort of family-grouping is the material out of which Japan built her larger social aggregations. One may never forget that it was this sort of family which came gradually to possess the land, that its organizing might was used effectually to dominate the whole environment until it became, as nearly as may be, the possession of the whole Japanese people. With such a picture in mind one may proceed to study the further integration of advancing society in the "land of the rising sun."

Expanding numbers of the people gave rise at last to two larger forms of the ancestral family, the greater and the lesser clans. According to Hearn (1913, p. 255) the greater clans included large bodies of serfs and slaves. These had several names such as *tomobé*, i.e., bound to a place or district, serfs that could never leave the land they were born on; *yakabé*, personal slaves of a family, the menials; *kakibé*, something like the *tomobé*, narrowly bound to an estate; and *tami*, or dependents. These classes were all above the status of outcast, like the modern *eta*, but they were narrowly held and forced to productive enterprise by their masters. The surplus of their labors gave leisure to their superiors, leisure for thought and invention, and so led to a speeding-up of the culture. Thus the arts of life and the institutions would undergo strengthening and integration. Thus would they suffer variation, selection, and transmission and culture increase.

The smallest societal units thrive best under leadership. And surely every larger group will need a chieftain. Men as well as their inventions and institutions also have to pass the tests of fitness. Indeed a growing population automatically sets up such tests. They are there, even if their presence, because of their silence and invisibility and intangibility, is not directly sensed. The clans came to possess such leaders who were called *daimyo,* that is, chief. Early and growing Japanese society presents the picture of a congeries of more or less powerful clans of which one came finally to prevail over all and whose chief became the "heavenly sovereign" or Emperor. He succeeded to imperial power because of the gradual accretion of prerogative which passed into his hands. Very early one such person came to possess the right to represent all the clans before the common ancestral diety—the privileges and powers of a high priest; he next won the further right to represent them in all their "foreign" relations, he could declare war or negotiate peace in the name of all the clans, hence he came little by little to exercise supreme military authority; and, lastly, he had the right and the responsibility of settling disputes between clans, to establish new clans, or to abolish old ones whenever they threatened social peace—that is, he became arbitrator and magistrate. But his powers were none too autocratic. He had to exercise them with the consent of the governed. But no one else had equal rights and when he was a strong man, as was often the case, he drew to himself immense authority. Gradually through the centuries the worship of the Sun-Goddess became a race cult, until at last the Emperor in the Meiji period became Supreme High Pontiff and his nation a race divinely descended from Ameratsu.

But ere this last stage came to pass, the whole people underwent the long antecedent development of feudalism with the Fujiwara, Taira, Minamoto, Ashikaga, and Tokugawa shoguns as the real governors. This period of over a thousand years was marked by the rise of the military power which at first kept the country split up into a congeries of small states but with leadership and unification ultimately passing into the hands of two powerful clans, the Satsuma on the Southern Island of Kyushiu and the Choshu clan on the Main Island. And it was the threat of the military power of these two clans which at last made possible national unification at the time of the Restoration (1868 A.D.).

The holders of the great estates were, as we have just seen, called *daimyos.* During the times of the internecine warfare up to the Tokugawa era (seventeenth century A.D.) these land-owners had suffered according to the vicissitudes of the times, and their estates had frequently changed hands, one family branch succeeding to another without much continuity of policy. But the two hundred and fifty years of peace ushered in by the

Tokugawa Ieyasu's reforms gave permanence and continuity to their lines, and large powers were gradually absorbed by some of them. The Lord of Kaga, for example, had an estimated income of one million pounds sterling while the poorest of the *daimyo* would have an income of at least ten thousand pounds. There were many men of notable ability among them. For example, Ieyasu, the great founder of the Tokugawa line of shoguns, was as much distinguished for his administrative abilities as he was for his strategy and tactics in war. He, according to Hearn (1913, pp. 377-383), deliberately set out to prevent the assumption of too much power by the great feudal lords.

He, therefore, classified them in a fourfold way. They might not exercise any powers not granted to the class in which they belonged. Any passage or transfer from a lower daimyo ranking to a higher one was made difficult by Ieyasu's methods. The *Sanké* were of the Three Exalted Families from whose membership a successor, and from them only, should a new shogun be chosen. The *Kokushu* were lords of provinces with power privileges which were strictly provincial. The *Tozama* were "outside" lords of greatly diminished powers, while the *Fudai* were the "successful families" who had been rewarded for their fealty and services to Ieyasu. As a further check the heads of all four classes of the daimyo were required to reside in Yedo, in *quasi-hostage status,* and give a yearly account of themselves to the shogun. No inter-marriage might take place between members of the court and the daimyo families without the express consent of the shogun at Yedo; no daimyo might apply direct to the emperor for a new title nor might he set foot within the imperial domain of Kioto without the shogun's consent; and all entrances to the Kwanto (district around Yedo) were provided with guardhouses where everyone, of whatever rank, had to be examined, in order to prevent the wives and children of the daimyo from secretly leaving Yedo for their own province. These measures gave Japan two hundred fifty years of peace, down to 1868 A.D.

The daimyo were served by the samurai, or soldier-retainers. Up to the time of the Restoration these latter numbered two million. They were perhaps the finest body of retainers the world has ever seen. They formed a class apart in Japanese society. Their code of honor was a military one; they despised money and the earning of it, living off stipends from their lords; the name samurai has become a synonym for loyalty; they were privileged to wear one or two swords; they were well educated in Confucian learning even if sword-practice was their first duty; their code required that they should literally fulfill the saying of Confucius that a man could not live under the same heaven with the slayer of his father. It was the decay of this class in prerogative and due to a changing economic status during the middle of the nineteenth century that helped partly to make possible the Restoration of 1868. The lower samurai were getting into deeper and deeper waters and the ruling class of the time hailed the Restoration as a possible means of getting out of hot water themselves, that is, of avoiding a revolution which might be begun and carried on by a class of people made desperate by failing revenues.

Below the samurai were the *heimin,* or commoners. These were divided into three classes; husbandmen, artizans, and traders. Below these yet again were the *eta* (defiled folk) and the *hinin* (outcasts). Modern Japanese society is ranked in four classes: samurai, farmers, artizans, and traders—the *eta* and the *hinin* subclasses were given citizenship at the Restoration but, judging from reports in the newspapers quite recently, they still suffer from social stigmas. One of these *eta* not more than two or three years ago stepped from the ranks at a military review and boldly presented a list of grievances for his class to His Imperial Majesty, the present Emperor. The *eta* was immediately arrested* for breach of army discipline but was afterwards pardoned by imperial clemency. The farmers (*hyakusho*) as producers of the staff of life are most honorably ranked after the samurai, who are the protectors of the same hard-won sustenance. Farmers by warlike service might climb up into the samurai class. The emperors ever took an interest in farming, and to this day a small plot of ground is sown with rice in the Imperial Park, is tended and reaped by imperial hands. These first fruits are then offered to divine ancestors by their imperial descendant.

The artizans of all crafts ranked below the farmers. Among them the sword-smiths enjoyed the greatest respect. Their craft was surrounded by religious sanctions. The sword-maker underwent a religious purification before beginning to forge his implements. He lived alone for a month and the sacred rope of rice straw was suspended before his smithy and none of his family might enter therein. Nor did he eat of any food but that which was cooked on the sacred fire of his own smithy. The commercial class included bankers, shopkeepers, merchants, and traders of all kinds. Until the Restoration brought new opportunities for wealth-making these classes could by no means rise into the one above them. A farmer might by meritorious service become a samurai but none else. One of the greatest changes wrought by the Industrial Revolution in Japan is the partial breaking-down of this old rank and class privilege.

We have noted the repeated immigration of Chinese and Koreans into Japan. And we called attention to the fact that this meant all the advantages of heterosis, or hybrid vigor, and the cross-modification of culture traits. Along with these immigrants came a culture-complex which was destined to work a mighty revolution in the mores of Old Japan. This was the introduction in 552 A.D. of Buddhism. Its adequate adoption by the Japanese meant nothing more or less than the reception of the finest elements of Chinese civilization together with the softening and enriching traits of Buddhist world-philosophy. Japan is perhaps that country in which the tenets of Buddhism most thoroughly pervaded the general population.

As was the case in China, so now' in Japan, its religious life received larger horizons from the introduction of the faith of Gautama. Its effects were felt in literature, sculpture, in religious ritual, in education, in painting, in the rest of the arts of life and the arts of pleasure. It softened and fertilized social intercourse. "Unquestionably the influence which

Buddhism exerted upon Japanese civilization was immense, profound, multiform, incalculable." And by the end of the eighth century it had done its major work.

Conflict and religious vows ushered in the new faith. A civil war was in progress and the leaders of the one side offered to erect temples and follow the Buddha should victory be granted to their arms. It was. And the erection of Buddhist temples began apace. Korea sent Buddhist relics, priests and ascetics, architects for building Buddhist temples, and casters and bronze workers for Buddhist idols. Priests and scholars went back and forth between Japan and China and immense additions to Japanese knowledge and culture were made. Immigration kept pace with the movement to such an extent that in 814 A.D. there were 382 noble families of Chinese and Korean extraction as against 792 of purely native growth.

Buddhism spread in Japan partly because of its own inherent worth.[9] What can be said and done against a faith which promises surcease from the ills of life if once one grants its premises? Its religious ritual was a most welcome supplement to the austerities of Shintoism and Confucianism. The ethical precepts of these two latter systems are well as far as they go. But man possesses imagination and an emotional life also, which need nurture and stimulation in their own way. Buddhism brought to Japan a new evangel of tenderness which was a wide humanizing force. Moreover, in its Mahayana form it possessed a daimonology which could readily be fitted into the cruder animism of Shintoism and Confucianism—that is, grafted on to the worship of ancestral spirits and the high gods.

> Besides teaching new respect for life, the duty of kindness to animals as well as to all human beings, the consequence of present acts upon the conditions of a future existence, the duty of resignation to pain as the inevitable result of forgotten error, it actually gave to Japan the arts and the industries of China. Architecture, painting, sculpture, engraving, printing, gardening—in short, every art and industry that helped to make life beautiful—developed first in Japan under Buddhist teaching. (Hearn, 1913, p. 208)

Buddhist daimonology, as hinted above, supplemented the meagerness of Shinto world-philosophy. While acknowledging the greater gods of Shintoism, it nevertheless alleged that all worship paid them led the soul of man, ultimately, to Buddhahood, to the divine estate of Nirvana, where although living on the earth, the soul of man ceases to strive because no longer driven by restless desire. Common Buddhism identified the Goddess of the Sun with an Indian deity; the God of War with Amitabha; and the goblins and evil demons of Shintoism with the Pretas and Rakshas of India. Wicked ghosts were those souls, self-doomed through former evil deeds to an endless state of the same—they were not necessarily unhappy

---

[9]Perhaps it may be justifiable to call attention to the note of warning on page 373 above. Buddhism almost everywhere except in Japan is now so debased, or at least this is the common conception of it, that it is almost impossible for the Western mind to think of Buddhism as being a civilizing force. Such it was up to the ninth century A.D. in Japan and China—and a mighty one! Now it seems dead in China and almost moribund in Japan.

ancestral spirits. The Japanese Buddhist was bidden offer sacrifice *for* rather than *to* them. The same attitude of mind was inculcated to all the malevolent demons of disease such as small-pox, fever, dysentery, coughs, and colds. The doctrine of Pretas became a powerful ethical influence and social and family bond.

In addition, Buddhist teachers taught a new doctrine of nature, belief in which brought the soul into new and loving communion with forest and stream, with flower and shrub, and their beauties. Its universal animism gave the concept of the presence of holy life in the grasses of the fields and the blossoms of the mountain-side. The teachers taught, too, a resignation to the ills of life. Whatever misfortune or stroke of ill-luck has hit you is due to the everlasting law of Karma. Do not repine, for the evil you now suffer is not due to immediate fault on your part, but to some deed done in a former existence. (What a welcome contrast to the exact law of individual responsibility inculcated by Shintoism and the mores of the samurai!) Pray that its Karma may be exhausted in the present evil and that so you may come even now to know bliss.

The Western Paradise of Buddha was another element of transference from China and India which brought comfort to the downhearted Japanese converts to Buddhism. Its Lord of Immeasurable Light was there waiting to comfort those who should succeed in reaching those blessed shores. And was not the Ship of Salvation ready to carry those thither who by penitence and ethical and religious efforts should merit embarkation thereon? While Hell was the penalty for evil deeds its state was not irrevocable. One might by good deeds now performed on earth, and even in Hell, succeed in embarking for the Paradise of Amiba. The beggar of today might be born in the palace of the daimyo tomorrow. (Who can overestimate the comfort this might bring to the poverty-stricken? For it should ever be remembered that the great masses of Japan, below the two million samurai, lived in degradation, in the deepest misery, and that frequently they rose in bloody revolt against their masters in protest over the misfortune that was their lot.) Always the recompense would surely come and be apportioned to those who had fairly earned it. Life was hard but not impossibly so and the Good Buddha would see to it that one enjoyed bliss in the hereafter which would be proportionate to one's ethical and social behavior in the here and now. (Again, what a warm, comforting contrast this is to the coldness and austerity of Shintoism!)

Such doctrines have rarely failed to meet response. In Japan in 675 A.D. an emperor forbade the eating of "the flesh of kine, horses, dogs, monkeys, or barnyard fowls, and forbidding the use of traps and pitfalls in the taking of game." Like early Christianity, when among an illiterate people, Buddhism taught not by word of mouth only, but also by pictorial representations. By carvings, paintings, decorations and bronze castings, the story of Buddhism was fully told. Smiling Buddhas and Boddhisatvas, feminine angels, and monstrous demons kindled the imagination and stirred the emotions and charged the wills of Japanese converts for the performance of ethical and social service. Colossal temples, statues, images, and paintings "richly dight" in golden glows could scarcely have failed to become springs from which the supreme secular and religious artistry of medieval and modern Japan should gush forth.

It has been suggested that perhaps the greatest service of Buddhism to Japan was its educative one. Shinto priests did not teach literature or the arts but Buddhist priests did. By degrees the educational system of the whole nation was committed to them. Translation of the Buddhist canon was itself an immense addition to their mental furniture. It is alleged furthermore that most of what is truly admirable in Japanese character stems from the Buddhist system. These priests also became parish clerks charged with keeping the records of births, deaths, and marriages of the whole empire. It civilized and moralized the Japanese people; it introduced the higher forms of poetry, fiction, the true writing of history, and a new and more comprehensive world-philosophy. Every well-informed Japanese acknowledges his nation's debt to its cultural values. As said, its work was done by the end of the eighth century A.D., although it has since continued its beneficent work all through the ages up to the time of its disestablishment in 1868. Never quite as debased as on the mainland, Buddhism, through its many sects, is still doing much for Japan.

The details of the secular history of Japan do not much concern the present exposition and they are used only as convenient pegs upon which to hang the vital story of the growth of social life in that country. The year 1615 A.D. saw feudal Japan completely unified under the guiding hand and genius of the greatest of all the shoguns, the Tokugawa Ieyasu. This man was even greater in his peace measures than in warlike operations. He, by supreme military ability, conquered the country and then, by wisely tolerant behavior, pacified it and rendered it prosperous. His work endured from 1615 till 1868, when it was fittingly closed by the Restoration, brought about in part by the great abilities of one of his remote descendants, the last of the shoguns. During the two hundred and fifty years of the Tokugawa shogunate, Japan, except during periods of famine and food-shortage, lived under the wise provisions of Ieyasu's enactments.

The character of the greatest of all Japan's shoguns is revealed in part in the document which bears his name. It is known as the *Legacy of Ieyasu*. This was his ante-mortem will for Japan and it also reveals, as in a mirror, the subsequent social growth of the empire. It was during the more than two hundred years of peace after Ieyasu that Japanese character and culture had its fullest efflorescence. It was a time when all the arts of life had their greatest development and expansion, when Japanese humanity received its fullest expression. Their joy of life, their ingenuous kindness, their public impassiveness in the face of disaster, their social discipline, all seem to stem from the great example and precepts of Ieyasu's life and *Legacy*. Its more social aspects here follow.

The Great General and Wise Ruler declared that the people were the foundation of empire and he counseled and commanded understanding and leniency in dealing with them. He distinguished between the classes of the people not in the matter of privilege but in the matter of social responsibility and duty. He ordained that any daimyo breaking the laws to the injury of the people, no matter what his rank, should have his estates confiscated. In the matter of adultery, especially grave in a social system founded on ancestor-worship and the necessary keeping of the line pure, he confirmed the injured husband's right to kill but he must kill both the guilty ones. If he failed to kill the one or the other he would be adjudged as guilty as they were. In the case of the common people, particular attention or deliberation had to be given to this matter. He remarks on the weakness of human nature, that among the young and simple-minded peasantry momentary impulses of passion may lead to folly, whereas the parties to adultery are not really bad, and must be dealt with according to circumstances. But if the parties were of high rank no clemency was permitted, for they ought to know and to act in better wise. They are to be put to death without deliberation. The case is different with artizans and other workmen.

He had the same mind about punishments as had the ancient Chinese, saying in his ninety-first article that where they abound the ruler must be without virtue and degenerate. He worked out particular enactments to protect the peasantry from the rapacity of landlords. The private as well as the public life of the great daimyo was to be under surveillance, and they were liable to punishment for immorality. Debauchery should be examined and punished according as it constitutes a bad example to the masses. For treason and insubordination there was no pardon. He says:

> The guilt of a vassal murdering his liege lord is in principle the same as an arch traitor to the Emperor. His immediate companions,—all even to his most distant connections,—shall be cut off, hewn to atoms, root and fibre. The guilt of a vassal once lifting his hand against his master, even though he does not assassinate him is the same. (Hearn, 1913, p. 379)

Yet even here he included mercy and leniency, if circumstances permitted them.

His legislation on the relations of the sexes is nothing if not illuminating. Ancestor-worship required in the daimyo, at times, the practice of concubinage. Sons were indispensable. Yet Ieyasu says of the practice that

> "silly and ignorant men neglect their true wives for the sake of a loved mistress, and thus disturb this most important relation. . . . Men so far sunk as this may always be known as samurai without fidelity or sincerity" . . . He equally condemns celibacy, saying, "One should not live alone after sixteen years of age; all mankind recognizes marriage as the first law of nature." (Hearn, 1913, p. 380)

The childless man should adopt a son.

With regard to religion, in the thirty-first article written when he was extirpating Jesuit Christianity, Ieyasu says,

> High and low alike may follow their own inclination with repect to religious tenets which have obtained down to the present time, except as regards the false and corrupt school [of Roman Catholicism]. Religious disputes have ever proved the bane and misfortune of this empire and must be firmly suppressed. (Hearn, 1913, pp. 381-382)

The general character of the Tokugawa rule can be inferred from the preceding. The sumptuary laws, if broken, fell with great weight on the offender. What one should eat or be clothed with depended strictly on the class he was born into. The sort of house as to its style and dimensions was equally prescribed. The dowry of one's daughter was determined by one's rank in society, not by one's ability to pay. Every one's pleasures were likewise conditioned by rank. Infractions of privilege were severely dealt with. The whole country reached a condition of almost stable equilibrium which brought an irresistible aversion to change. The lower strata of the population were the ones to pay the greatest price for this stabilization. The population of something under forty million had to pay the way for some two million samurai and their following. Agriculture was not being pushed even to produce as much as it might, the arts in this respect being backward. Serious troubles, rice-riots, arose at times throughout the Tokugawa era and these were put down with bloody means. Moreover there was one force with which Ieyasu had not and could scarcely have reckoned, namely, that of an expanding population. Its law is that the numbers of the people will tend to increase up to the limits of the supporting power of the land for a given stage of the arts and for a given standard of living. But always there is observable a tendency to overpopulation. This condition is reached sooner or later. The old arts fail to meet the needs of growing numbers and then either the standard of living falls or there is a revolution, peaceful or otherwise. These forces now began to have their day. And to them there were added forces outside the empire which even Ieyasu's policy of exclusion could not control. These were the massively expanding factors of the Industrial Revolution of the West, their expanding overseas commerce, their need both for raw materials and for markets for their finished products. It was these which brought the treaties of commerce with England and Russia and other nations in 1851, and Commodore Perry's ships to Yedo in 1854.

As is apparent from the foregoing, the foundations of Japanese culture were laid in remote ages. The present mikado is the one hundred and twenty-fourth sovereign in direct line. He symbolizes the very long continuity of Japanese culture history. He rules over a gifted composite people. They are the descendants of Mongoloid, Caucasian, Malayan, and Polynesian stocks largely overlain by the Mongoloid strain. Cross-modification of both culture and physical stock brought forth a people who were to be faced with the problems of a composite culture, not their own, and based on the appropriation of mechanical and other forces, with which they had hitherto had no experience whatever. Would they be able to make the transition and survive, or would they fail? The answer is the modern transformation of Japan. It is the contrast already suggested between feudal and modern Japan. The answer is singularly enlightening and substantiating of the position of the cultural determinists. Man, allege these latter, is what his culture makes of him, or somewhat less deterministically, man is made by his cultural opportunities, placed before him for appropriation and new growth, new advancement. Modern Japan has in this respect already gone very far.

The Restoration of 1868 was made possible largely by the active support of the lower ranks of the samurai. Their economic position had been steadily growing worse during the Tokugawa era. And in addition there was the just-mentioned pressure from the outside. The facts back of the resurgence of Japan are profound. They are: the old feudal economy was breaking down; and the necessary, if gradual, emergence of a feudal country into a completely modern, industrial, financial, political, and military state of the first rank, and with its social and religious interests somewhat in arrears; this resurgence was peculiar in that a group of patriotic men in Japan were the first in history, at all events in recent history, to set about the task of a planned economy for their people.

These young men, destined to become the *Genro* or Older Statesmen, showed an extraordinary acumen in all their measures. They borrowed the best of the arts of life and institutions obtainable from all the world. They went to France for their educational system; to Germany for medical knowledge; to England for the creation of a navy and to Germany again for instructors for their new army; to England for tutoring in the founding of a new banking system; to engineers from all the world for the building of new manufactures. They ended by engaging in successful warfare with a great European power using the most approved methods of modern military science. But their victories and accomplishments in peace are infinitely greater than those of war.

The government went into business enterprise but on the basis of fixed principles, some of which meant nearly complete absorption of the businesses by the government but in other cases their gradual devolution on to the shoulders of private enterprise. At first subsidizing shipping, textiles, iron and steel, the government later withdrew. Any enterprise which it did aid was by a strictly controlled system of subventions and subsidies, with interest charges on money loaned. It has fostered sugar-growing; has controlled the price of rice; has formulated measures for stabilizing the important silk industry; has established research laboratories to promote every conceivable advance in industry such as that which has revolutionized the soy-bean industry. Contributions from the national treasury have been made to promote general social purposes, for public works, for agriculture, for fisheries, the development of transportation, public utilities, the utilization of natural resources, providing of banks and bank-credit, development of foreign trade, maintenance of financial stability, and the protection of the whole by an intelligent foreign and domestic policy.

The results have been the astonishment of the rest of the world. The population has increased from a normally stable one of 25,000,000 of the early part of the nineteenth century to one of about 64,000,000 for Japan proper at the present time. And all the while this growth of population numbers has been accompanied by a steadily rising standard of living for all its members.

The consequences for the Japanese people have been mixed. On the one hand is their undoubted increase of economic welfare, with the masses of the people enjoying the use of necessities which in Old Japan would have been luxuries for the daimyo, had they been invented at the time. Then again, the Industrial Revolution has tended to disrupt the lines of social cleavage which were fixed in the Tokugawa era. The bankers, for example, who then were a despised class may now with money buy a peerage and be received in high walks of life. Anciently, if the commoner met a feudal lord on the highway he had to knock his head in the dust. Nowadays, members of the nobility are passed on the street unnoticed. Then, the lower classes had no right of appeal from social injustice meted out to them by a superior. Now they can, if they are strong enough, carry injustice to the courts of the land. The social gains from modern industry take the concrete form of lighter taxation burdens, more equitably distributed; a cosmopolitan attitude to life, fostered by every sort of agency and especially by the widespread use of newspapers; the possession of universal compulsory education; universal male suffrage, with 10,000,000 votes cast at the last election and with adult woman suffrage in the offing; the passage of protective labor legislation; and, in connection with the insecurity of the job which is a part of the modern industrial system, there is the beginning of unemployment insurance legislation which is to do away in part with that risk. By this legislation, hours of women and children are regulated, health insurance is compulsory in some trades, and medical care must be furnished by the employer.

With increasing industrialization in Japan there seems to go increasing insecurity of the job. Unemployment problems were not serious, however, until a few years ago. This is because Japan is still more of an agricultural nation than she is industrial. In 1930, however, there were 322,-527 persons idle for whom there were apparently no jobs, and they were beginning to wear out their welcome with their relatives with whom they were staying. Increasing industrialization seems to be correlated with the necessity of welfare work and with labor unrest. Welfare work takes the form of providing for the aged and industrially disabled, for the sick and orphaned, and for foundlings, and for women both before and after childbirth.

In 1931 there was formed in Japan an All Japan Labor, Farm and Masses Party. Its objectives, according to Moulton (1931, pp. 381-382), are the following:

> enfranchisement of men and women over eighteen years of age; reform of central governmental administration; direct election of governors, mayors and village heads; abolition of secret diplomacy and elimination of military armaments and the shortening of the term of military service; the right of cooperation in the international proletarian movement; the establishment of a complete system of indemnification for false arrest and accusation; the abolition of the "peace preservation" law of the police; abolition of the existing pension system and the establishment of old age pensions; the institution of a seven hour working day and the adoption of an equal scale of wages for men and women; the reduction of prices on government monopoly products; an increase in inheritance, capital, interest, land, business profits, and income taxes; prohibition of licensed vice; extension of period of compulsory education to ten years.

Reading between these lines one discovers much accomplished and much still to be done.

The presentation here offered makes apparent with what skill and ingenuity the yellow races have manipulated the opportunities of their environment. They were able, in many ages and in varying degree, to satisfy the major human interests for a population which was always growing numerically. From conditions near to primordial destitution, we have observed the yellow races climbing up to a position of relative wealth and affluence; to a state where the individual would receive measurable security against the ills of life. He would be able to win this safety to the degree in which he made use of all the institutions developed to serve human needs. We see these peoples—women, men, and children—at first living in small groups and carrying on activities that brought them sustenance and a growth of numbers, up to at least one billion at the present day. They, by their behavior, exactly met the meaning of the word "society." They were small societies—groups composed of human beings of the two sexes and of disparate ages, engaged cooperatively in winning subsistence and for group persistence.

But eventually these groups of yellow men went far beyond the primal satisfactions of hunger and love. We may say of them that they exploited the possibilities of their own natures and their environment to the last limits. For they went on to the creation of all the fine arts, these arts of pleasure which create and minister to the higher human personality. Chinese and Japanese art, like poetry, painting, literature, and even some sculpture, will bear comparison for delicacy of feeling, profundity of insight, and power of expressing deep human emotional needs with that of any other land. Humanity has been permanently enriched by their artistry in porcelains, silks, teas, lacquers, and bronzes. Nor should the associative powers of the Japanese, Chinese, or Mongols, for example, be forgotten. A resident in the Far East receives the constant impression that sociation has been carried very far among them. All sorts of institutions have been founded and carried on by means of which men have lived well. This the examples of the preceding pages suffice to demonstrate.

But what of the future? Unavoidably every culture must contain prophetic germs within itself. It must offer some sort of control over the future. A major aspect of human society is its capacity to grow and expand. With expansion of numbers there come further needs of societal regulation and an unavoidable demand for enlargement of the arts of life, if society is not to become moribund. It is necessary for some group or portion of a group to assume the leadership in the dissemination of culture. At present the mantle of leadership in East Asia has fallen on the Japanese. They alone have made the most recent advances in human knowledge their own complete possession. They have even made original contributions to modern science and to the modern arts of life. Empires rise and fall, to be sure, but at a certain stage in the development of culture it is imperial peoples who disseminate its most useful traits. Eastern Asia is already on the up-swing into a new cycle of growth, impelled thereto by the science of the West, as mediated to its peoples in large part by the people of the "Rising Sun." The latter seem, as just remarked, to have been uniquely able to assimilate the knowledge and science and the arts of life of Western peoples; to adapt these arts to their own needs and then to pass them on with added increments to the Asiatic mainland. By the absorption of these arts they are already in the way of creating a "population-policy" which may in the end lead to the greatest per-capita return in human welfare. In the past, these three or four yellow peoples have often attained to the high level of an optimum population. In the world crisis now upon them, as upon us, it is possible that their contribution will be not only national but international in scope. The yellow races may, as in the past, make still further additions to human welfare which will aid effectively to establish a unified world-culture.

SELECTED REFERENCES

(The literature on the subjects is enormous. The references given below represent some of the more important books known and read by the present writer for the composition of the preceding chapter.)

ALLEN, G. C. 1928. Modern Japan and its problems. New York: Dutton. Pp. 226.

ANESAKI, M. 1930. History of Japan with special reference to the social and moral life of the nation. London: Kegan Paul. Pp. 423.

BALL, J. DYER. 1925. Things Chinese. (Ed. by E. T. C. Werner.) Shanghai: Kelly & Walsh. Pp. 766.

BISHOP, I. B. 1897. Korea and her neighbors. New York: Revell. Pp. 480.

BLAND, J. O. P., & BACKHOUSE, E. 1910. China under the Empress Dowager. London: Heinemann. Pp. 525.

CHAMBERLAIN, B. H. 1898. Things Japanese. London: Murray. Pp. 470.

Encyclopaedia Britannica. 11th, 12th, and 13th eds., articles on Ghengiz Khan, Japan, Korea, Mongols, Turks, and China.

FONG, H. D. 1932. The cotton industry and trade in China. (2 vols.) (Nankai Instit. Econ., Indus. Ser., Bull. No. 4.) Tientsin: Nankai Instit. Econ. Pp. 356; 116.

HARVEY, E. D. 1933. The mind of China. New Haven, Conn.: Yale Univ. Press. Pp. 321.

HEARN, L. 1913. Japan: an attempt at an interpretation. New York: Macmillan. Pp. 541.

HOOTON, E. A. 1931. Up from the ape. New York: Macmillan. Pp. 626.

IRELAND, A. 1926. The new Korea. New York: Dutton. Pp. 354.

Japan Times Year Book, Tokyo, 1928.

KNOX, G. W. 1907. The development of religion in Japan. New York: Putnam's Sons. Pp. 204.

KROEBER, A. L. 1923. Anthropology. New York: Harcourt, Brace. Pp. 528. (Rev. ed., 1933.)

LATOURETTE, K. S. 1920. The development of Japan. New York: Macmillan. Pp. 237.

LEGGE, J. 1879. Sacred books of the East, sacred books of China. (Ed. by F. M. Müller.) Vol. 3. The Shih King, etc., 1879. Pp. 492. Vol. 16. The texts of Confucianism, 1882. Pp. 448. Vol. 27. The texts of Confucianism, 1885. Pp. 484. Vol. 28. The texts of Confucianism, 1885. Pp. 496. Vol. 39. The texts of Taoism, 1891. Pp. 396. Vol. 40. The texts of Taoism, 1891. Pp. 340. Oxford: Clarendon Press.

LIPPERT, J. 1931. The evolution of culture. (Ed. and trans. by G. P. Murdock.) New York: Macmillan. Pp. 766.

MOULTON, H. G. 1931. Japan: an economic and financial appraisal. Washington, D. C.: Brookings Institution. Pp. 645.

MURRAY, D. 1900. Japan. New York: Putnam's. Pp. 431.

NITOBÉ, I. O. 1931. Japan: some phases of her problems and development. New York: Scribner's. Pp. 398.

SU, S. G. 1922. The Chinese family system. New York: Orientalia. Pp. 112.

WERNER, E. T. C. 1910. Descriptive sociology, Chinese. (Compiled and abstracted upon the plan organized by Herbert Spencer.) London: Williams. Pp. 312.

WIEGER, L. 1906. Textes philosophiques. Ho-kien-fu: Imprimerie de la Mission catholique. Pp. 552.

————. 1916. Textes historiques. (2 vols.) Hsien Hsien: Imprimerie de Hsien Hsien. Pp. 1-916; 917-1875.

————. 1921. Chine moderne. (6 vols.) Vol. I. Moralisme, 1921. Pp. 529 Vol. II. Le flot montant, 1921. Pp. 483. Vol. III. Remous et écume, 1922. Pp. 452. Vol. IV. L'outre d'eole, 1923. Pp. 474. Vol. V Nationalisme, 1924. Pp. 294. Vol. VI. Le feu aux poudres, 1925. Pp. 292. Hsien Hsien: Imprimerie de Hsien Hsien.

PART IV

ANALYSES OF RECURRING PATTERNS IN SOCIAL PHENOMENA

CHAPTER 11

LANGUAGE[1]

ERWIN A. ESPER

University of Washington

LANGUAGE AND PSYCHOLOGICAL THEORY

When the attempt is made to formulate a "psychology of language" (in the sense of an outline for relating linguistic data to psychological principles and for suggesting research by which such relationships may be discovered), the first difficulty to be met is the existence of at least two systems of discourse in contemporary psychology. Psychology as "the science of experience" differs from psychology as "the science of behavior" in technique and units of analysis as well as in the patterns and integrations which it seeks to analyze. Our treatment of language may be made to conform to either of these systems of discourse, but the study of language itself makes abundantly clear the fact that our selection of a

---

[1]The *aim* of the following discussions is a *practical* one; that is, I have attempted to present viewpoints and data which might suggest research, in the field of language, of an experimental or other controlled and objective nature during the next decade or two. If, therefore, I have permitted myself a somewhat dogmatic tone or a somewhat cavalier treatment of the writings of certain distinguished scientists and philosophers, this need not be taken too seriously by the reader, who will perhaps also make some allowances for limitations of space. For I am under no illusion of having presented here anything of the nature of metaphysical, philosophical, or other 'ultimate truth.' In part, the need for such discussions as follow arises from the mutual isolation of the literatures of linguistics and of psychology; on the historical occasions when these literatures have come in contact, as in the controversies between Delbrück (1901) and Paul (1920) on the one hand and Wundt (1901) on the other, the results have not been happy. At present, psychologists seem to be obtaining their notions about linguistics from such writers as Sir Richard Paget (1930) and J. Vendryes (1925); at most, they refer to the writings of Sapir (1921) and Jespersen (1922), who, though they are held in the highest regard by their colleagues as linguists, represent in their *general theory* viewpoints which I do not regard as especially helpful in the framing of psychological problems, and which are not universally accepted within their own profession. In some recent psychological textbooks I have found chapters on language which seem to have been based on the works of Max Müller. In part also the need for discussion arises from the dominance in both linguistics and psychology of conceptions developed in the long history of philosophy and logic; here it should be remembered that these disciplines represent highly derivative uses of language which have been almost entirely cut loose from *techniques,* such as are necessary in controlled and objective research.

Since I have not appended a bibliographical reference to every one of my statements, I wish to acknowledge my general indebtedness to the writings of Albert P. Weiss (1929a), Leonard Bloomfield (1933), Grace A. De Laguna (1927), and Frank Lorimer (1929). My presentation doubtless departs in many respects from the views of these writers; and the reader should consult their works for correction of the incompleteness and inadequacy of my account.

system of discourse will condition the nature of all of the phenomena and relationships which we observe and, perhaps still more fundamentally, our choice of research problems and of techniques.

When, during the nineteenth century, elaborate attempts were made to develop a psychology of language, these attempts were dominated by the prevailing metaphysical dualism of the times. Psychology was regarded as the study of mental life, and language was of interest as being the most important means for the "expression of ideas." The most elaborate development of this point of view was that of Wundt (1911-12). Wundt's theoretical basis is psychophysical parallelism. The fundamental assumption is that every change of psychical state is accompanied by changes in correlated physical processes. The relationship is one of regular concomitance, not a causal one. An important class of such correlated physical processes consists in the "expressive movements," which are externally observable indicators of inner mental states or contents. Not only the original psychical elements, but also the fact of the correspondence to these of specific bodily movements, must be treated as "givens" incapable of further analysis. Thus, "Every emotion, in consequence of that natural unity of the psychophysical organization which must be regarded as the empirically ultimate basis (*die nicht weiter empirisch abzuleitende Voraussetzung*) of the physical as well as the psychical life processes, is accompanied by movements which correspond to its character" (1911-12, Vol. 1, p. 65). In their most primitive manifestations, as exemplified in animals and in human infants, the expressive movements are most immediately correlated with the affective processes, particularly those which accompany simple sensory experiences such as the gustatory. Such expressive movements, in origin correlated more immediately with specific types of sensory experience, may then come associatively to accompany other and more complex experiences of similar feeling tone. Each of these experiences includes, however, in addition to the affective processes, ideational elements, and the expressive movements are therefore in some degree indicators of the latter. But the further psychical developments which proceed from this accessory feature of emotional expression are the basis for the entire further development of actual gesture-language. It is above all as an expression of *ideas* that the expressive movement is able to arouse in others the same emotions, since it is through the effects of corresponding ideas that corresponding emotions can be aroused. The *affective* expressions can always indicate and induce only the same basic types of affective processes. But through the *ideational* contents and the movements expressing them both the emotion itself and its arousal in others gain a definite basis. The ideational expression arouses in others further ideas, related to those communicated by the gestures, either as a continuation of them or, if antagonistic emotions are aroused, entering into opposition to them. But now the gestures of the second person are no longer mere repetitions of those of the first; the *imitative* movement has become an *answering* movement. Thus the individual emotion has become a common one, continually changing with the continual gestural interaction; intercommunication has been established. But for Wundt the primary function of speech remains not *communication* but *expression* of ideas. For speech may express feelings as well as ideas, and it may occur as an expression of thought even under conditions where communication is neither possible nor intended.

Wundt has written very extensively on the subject of language, and his discussions in this field require for their adequate interpretation a consideration of his voluminous contributions in other fields. The above summary statements can therefore give only a very general notion of the theoretical basis and scientific motivation from which his treatment of language proceeds. But without for the present following this treatment farther, we must consider the question as to whether, in the light of recent physiological, psychological, linguistic, and sociological concepts and research, this theoretical basis or any similar one is likely to be heuristically justified. This question is here raised only as it bears on progress in the study of language; the larger question as to the relative validity of the various "systems" of psychology need not be entered upon. So far as concerns language, however, the matter is all the more important in view of the fact that, until recently, a majority of the works on language, written by psychologists, philosophers, linguists, and sociologists, have been dominated by more or less similar mentalistic prepossessions. De Laguna (1927), in connection with an excellent summary and critique of the Wundtian views, gives illustrative extracts from the works of Sweet, Sapir, Paul, Wissler, and others. To these may now be added Pillsbury and Meader (1928), who define language as "a means or instrument for the communication of thought, including ideas and emotions."

In the first place, it is obvious that to Wundt language was of interest not as a research field in its own right but as an indirect source of information concerning conscious processes. This was true also for the other fields which he included in his *Völkerpsychologie*. Boring (1929) has stated Wundt's position in this respect as follows: "The goal of psychology is the analysis of mind into simple qualities and the determination of the form of their ordered multiplicity. The method, Wundt thought, is adequate to the problem except in the case of the higher processes, where analysis fails and we are reduced to the comparative observation of social phenomena, as when we use the study of language as the key to the psychology of thought" (p. 328). Thus the study of language not only took its departure from the individual consciousness of the psychological laboratory, but the intention was that it should return thither, for the purpose of casting light on that consciousness. Here we see how preexistent concepts and categories can restrict a research field. Wundt started from a narrowly defined basis: the conscious processes of the normal, adult individual (or even the adult trained in a certain type and terminology of introspection), and he had analyzed these conscious processes into certain elements. When now he turned to social phenomena, though he did so for the avowed purpose of gaining information not directly obtainable in the laboratory, he tended nevertheless to analyze these social phenomena one by one in terms of the laboratory processes. Thus, whether he deals with animals, with children, or with 'primitive man,' the sequence is predetermined: first expressive movements primarily indicating feelings, then a growing ideational content, then associative interconnections, and, finally, in man, a full blooming of volitional and apperceptive processes. The phenomena under observation thus afford not so much new information concerning the laws of conscious life as evidence confirming and exemplifying the original individual analyses.

To the student who takes for his problem not the nature of individual consciousness but that of language, a quite different approach suggests itself. This approach consists in an inquiry into the functional relationships into which language enters and a survey looking toward an empirical analysis of the conditions which determine its characteristics and forms. Categories, classifications, and techniques of research will then be determined by a consideration of the object itself rather than by the pattern established in the study of another problem. Illustrations of such fresh approach are to be found in recent writings of authors of varied professional backgrounds: philosophers, psychologists, sociologists, linguists; and these independent writings show a considerable agreement in their analyses of the factors entering into the language problem and in their criticisms of the traditional mentalistic approach.

Thus Dewey (1926, pp. 166-207) holds that "the heart of language is not 'expression' of something antecedent, much less expression of antecedent thought. It is communication; the establishment of coöperation in an activity in which there are partners and in which the activity of each is modified and regulated by partnership." Animal gestures and cries are not primarily means of expression but rather modes of organic behavior like locomotion; they "became language only when used within a context of mutual assistance and direction." Ogden and Richards (1927, pp. 1-23) believe that a theory of signs should be developed from an observation of other people rather than from introspection, the latter being a "special and deceptive case." The exclusive preoccupation with 'ideas' which are held to be 'expressed' by speech leads to a neglect of the behavior and concrete environment to which the speech is related. Weiss (1925; 1929a, pp. 307-327) points out that psychologists have regarded language "as a 'gift' to report the character of so-called mental states, rather than as a form of behavior." For Weiss the prime significance of language consists in its *substitutive* and *dual* stimulus-response rôle which makes possible 'biosocial' integration. Speech as stimulus may serve as a functional substitute for environmental situations; speech as response may serve as a functional substitute for overt behavior. Thus the practical situations which act upon the sense-organs of one individual may *indirectly* result in appropriate overt activity in other individuals by the mediation of speech response and speech stimulus. Air waves thus secure an integration in the activities of the members of a group which is comparable to the integration dependent upon nerve impulses in the individual organism. Specialization of sensitivities and skills in the different members of the group can thus be utilized in the development of a group efficiency in adaptation which far transcends the efficiency attainable by the isolated individual. Allport (1924, pp. 169-199) traces the phylogenetic and ontogenetic development of language in terms of processes of conditioning, whereby oral responses become conditioned to situations, and vocal sounds become conditioned stimuli for behavior. The primary 'drive' which leads to the acquisition of language is the 'need' to control others. "This, rather than the desire to communicate, 'instinct to express,' or other alleged social instinct, has been the guiding principle." Secondarily, language came to be used in controlling the *non-social* environment, that is, in elaborating, in substitutive form, modes of adaptation and analysis—'thinking.' In conversation, language remains fairly close to its original social foundation, but upon this foundation have developed many derivative, traditionally cumulative, and 'institutionalized' patterns; those of education, public opinion, government, etc. De Laguna (1927) believes that "what is needed for the successful study of the psychology of speech is a deliberate setting aside, if not an abandonment, of the metaphysical dualism which can conceive speech only as an external physical manifestation of inner psychical processes. What is needed is a fresh conception of speech as an essential activity of human life, fulfilling an indispensable function in the economy of life." This function is the mediation of human cooperation, whereby "the diverse activities of men are coordinated and correlated with each other for the attainment of common and reciprocal ends." Moreover, language plays an essential part in the development of cognition, the 'objectification' of the environment, the 'conceptualizing' of perception. Whereas behavior consists primitively of a limited number of relatively invariable and immediate type-responses to concrete environmental wholes, the development of language makes possible the attachment of highly specific responses to specific objects and properties, which can only thus emerge from their contexts, give rise to more mediate and indirect adaptations, and enter into combinations other than the primitive concrete wholes. And, finally, behavior gains a new unity and coherence because the final outcome, as well as subordinate goals in an indirect path to the final outcome of a behavior sequence, is represented far more efficiently and specifically in verbal form than in the form of 'tentative movements' or general 'motor set.' Lorimer (1929), though the subtitle of his book is *A Study of the Rôle of Verbal Activity in the Growth of the Structure of the Human Mind,* seems to reject the notion that language is primarily a means of expressing psychical contents and emphasizes the functional relationships of language to other modes of social as well as implicit behavior. His description of the genesis of speech in the child and race is quite similar to that of Allport. He states his central thesis as follows (p. 4): "The processes and organization of communication are continuous with other physiological and social processes, and the evolving structure of intellectual activity (including the *forms* discovered by logical analysis) is a function of the total growth of life prior to and including the growth of verbal activity; the structure and processes of intellectual activity, at all stages, are capable of systematic and genetic interpretation." Markey (1928) holds that speech reactions must be analyzed according to the function which they perform in social behavior. He defines a symbol as "an act which is a stimulus-substitute for another act often not present, and at the same time is a stimulus for a response to—something to be done about—this other act, while the stimulus substitute is also marked off by behavior as distinct from the other act and the response to it."

LANGUAGE AND LINGUISTIC SCIENCE

Thus far we have been considering the views of certain philosophers, psychologists, and sociologists who have had occasion to devote especial attention to the problem of language. We may now mention certain contemporary linguists and ethnologists who have taken more than usual interest in the fundamental nature of language. It may probably be said with truth that most linguists are preoccupied with descriptive, historical, and comparative details of the grammar of those languages which constitute their specialty, and that when they do turn their attention to the problem of the general nature of language, or for some reason feel it necessary to offer extralinguistic ('psychological') explanations of certain special features or processes, they very often construct theories of a naïve and *ad hoc* nature, which however they present and defend with great dogmatism.[2] Much of Wundt's work on language is taken up with combating such theories, which he classes under *'Reflexionspsychologie'* and *'Vulgärpsychologie.'* The linguist not infrequently puts himself in the place of the speaker of a language and considers why or how *he* would have uttered, preserved, or altered speech forms, *had he been reflecting or introspecting* upon the matter. Or, alternatively, he places great emphasis upon the view that speech processes are 'unconscious.' Having said this, we should also note that psychologists write fluent paragraphs and chapters on language (and phonetics!) without being in the least aware of the existence of a vast literature of scientific linguistics.

The critical problem which has been chiefly responsible for the interest of linguists in psychology is the problem of 'meaning.' The problems which fall within the special province of linguistic science are those of the description, classification, comparison, and historical tracing of *linguistic forms.* A linguistic form is defined by Bloomfield (1933) as "a recurrent vocal feature which has meaning." Thus, in English, any sentence, phrase, or word, or a syllable such as *writ-* or *-ing* in *writing,* or a sound such as the final *s* of the plural noun, is a linguistic form. On the side

[2]For the history of linguistic theory, see Pedersen (1931) and Chapter 1 of Bloomfield (1933).

of sound, these forms can be analyzed into *phonemes,* which are minimum recurrent sames of vocal feature. Thus the difference between *man* and *men* is a difference in the medial phoneme, but the pitch on which these words are pronounced is not phonemic in English, though it would be in Chinese; moreover, other acoustic variations, demonstrable by instrumental recording (or even by ear), are not 'distinctive.' The number of distinctive sounds (phonemes) of a language is strictly limited.[3] Thus, on the side of sound, linguistic science deals only with recurrent sames constituting a fairly stable and conventional system and neglects nondistinctive individual variants. This practice of the linguist is of course in agreement with the very nature of language, since the fact of recurrent sames alone makes possible its use in social interaction. Now in dealing with phonology the linguist need appeal to no other science, with the exception perhaps of experimental phonetics. But the other aspect of linguistic forms, that of semantics, raises a serious question. In what terms and by what methods are *meanings* to be defined? The answer in terms of traditional mentalistic psychology was all too easy: to each morpheme there corresponds an 'idea,' and that idea is the 'meaning' of the morpheme; the morpheme 'expresses' the idea.

---

[3]The phonemic nature of linguistic sound patterns has escaped the notice of most of the psychologists who have constructed 'nonsense syllables' for experimental use. These psychologists have also made the ancient error of confusing phonemes with letters of the alphabet. Thus Glaze (1928), whose tabulation of the "associative value of non-sense syllables" has been taken very seriously by subsequent writers, lists among the "syllables" of very low "associative value," which he would especially recommend for experiments on memorizing, the letter sequences *ZYW, QOC, JIQ, GIC, JYC.* Glaze reproaches Cason for eliminating "the best non-sense material," because Cason "did not use syllables that were difficult to pronounce." Presumably, Glaze's "syllables" (apparently he uses the linguistic term *syllable* in some non-linguistic sense) could only be presented visually. But what implicit or other response is the subject to make when he sees *ZYW* or *QOC?* If it is meant that he should not vocalize at all, the material is poorly chosen, since it has the appearance of linguistic material; if he does vocalize (as he will), his vocalization will be highly individual and variable. Will he pronounce the last three of the above examples in identical or different manner? Unless E and S are agreed on the phonemic values of the letters used, I do not see how such material can reasonably be used *visually.* In constructing syllables for *auditory-vocal* use, the experimenter will need to inform himself concerning the *phonemes* (not the *letters*) occurring in his language, the sequences in which these phonemes can occur, and what phonemes can constitute a syllable (unless of course sequences and syllable divisions which do not occur in the subject's language are to be among the experimental variables; even in this case, the experimenter will have to operate with phonemes and will need to know in what manner his material departs from the habits of the native language). Recognition of all of these facts would have made unnecessary most of the work on the 'reliability' of nonsense syllables. For examples of syllables constructed on phonemic principles and also selected on the basis of "associative value," see Esper (1933). These syllables were selected from a list of 200 which had been presented to 48 individuals, and this list of 200 had been selected by two persons from a list of all the possible monosyllabic combinations of the phonemes of Middle-Western American English. This work was done in 1925; the original tabulation will be made available on request.

In recent years certain linguists have shown an increasing dissatisfaction with this solution of the problem. In the first edition of his *Study of Language* (1914), Bloomfield accepted the psychological basis provided by Wundt. By 1926 he had come to believe that this sort of basis is irrelevant to the science of linguistics, and formulated a set of postulates by which he sought to delimit the field and bring to light the essential assumptions of this science. He takes the view that the linguist, though he may use the terminology of mental process, in practice defines meanings in terms of speaker's situation and hearer's response, since these alone constitute the data accessible to the observation of the recorder of a language. In the revised version of his *Study of Language* (1933), Bloomfield gives a lucid and illuminating account of meaning in these terms.[4] He bases this account on the fundamental linguistic situation, that of cooperative action involving two or more individuals. He points out that when an isolated individual is in the presence of a stimulus situation involving, for example, hunger contractions and visible food, adaptive response depends upon the skill of that individual; but that in the case of two speaking individuals a similar situation acting on A may elicit in him a speech response, which, acting as a stimulus on B, may in turn elicit in B an overt response which is adaptive with respect to A. The advantage of this complication is that B may be more capable of the adaptive act because of strength, training, or spatial position. This paradigm enables us to distinguish the special problem of linguistics from non-linguistic problems, and to arrive at a usable definition of 'meaning.' The speech link in the sequence is the concern of linguistics; the *meaning* of the linguistic act must be stated in terms of the situation which gave rise to it and the responses for which it became the stimulus. But the analysis of environmental situations (including intra-organic conditions of the speaker) and of non-linguistic behavior is not the business of linguistics; hence for his definitions the linguist must appeal to other sciences, or, failing such scientific analyses, must appeal to 'common knowledge.' However, just as in the case of phonemes, so here in the case of *sememes*, i.e., features of meaning, the linguist must make the assumption of *recurrent sames*. Just as there is an infinite number of non-significant variations in the acoustic character of phonemes, so too the concrete situations in which linguistic forms are appropriately used show endless differences (including differences in the history and present physiological condition of the speaker and hearer), and these differences enter into the momentary 'meaning' of the form [Paul's *okkasionelle Bedeutung* as contrasted with *usuelle Bedeutung;* see particularly Gardiner (1932), who gives the matter especial attention]. Nevertheless, there may be distinguished a *distinctive* or *linguistic* meaning, which is common to all of the situations in which the form occurs, and it is this meaning which is of primary concern to the

---

[4] This book contains an excellent and extensive bibliography of linguistics and related sciences. For a criticism of 'popular psychology' as it makes its appearance in linguistics, see Bloomfield (1932).

linguist in his usual business of describing languages. This delimitation of the problem of linguistics had also been attempted by the eminent linguist de Saussure, who has had considerable influence on contemporary linguistics. He distinguishes between *le langage,* which comprises the speech acts of individuals in concrete social situations, and *la langue,* which is the *conventional* system of a language. However, de Saussure makes the phonemes correspond to 'ideas' stored in the individuals of a speech community and proceeds in terms of an almost fantastic mentalism; he thus neglects the consideration of meaning in terms of situation. For this he has been severely criticized by Ogden and Richards (1927) and by Gardiner (1932). And yet the distinction which he makes, when shorn of its mentalistic terminology, would seem to be necessary for linguistic science, as suggested in our discussion above, and it is therefore possible that the critics mentioned have missed the point. We may probably assume that no linguist in his right mind would deny that the meaning of an utterance is determined partly by the conventional sememes corresponding to its morphemes, and partly (in many cases *chiefly*) by concrete features of situation and preceding events. But in his usual business of outlining the skeleton of a language, its phonemes, morphology, and syntax, the linguist can utilize only the conventional and generalized ('dictionary') features of meaning.

LANGUAGE AND ETHNOLOGY

Although, as we have just seen, a delimitation of the problem of meaning is justifiable for the purposes of linguistic science, and although the analysis and description of the formal mechanisms of a language constitute an essential foundation for an understanding of the social and intellectual functions of that language, yet all this is not to deny the necessity of further study, by other sciences, of such functions. The ethnologist, for example, who studies the language of a 'primitive' group will be concerned not 'only with strictly linguistic analyses but also with the relationships of language to the mode of life and behavior patterns, and to the aspects of environment which the mode of life has selected and made important. Moreover, as Malinowski (1927) has pointed out, even 'linguistic' or 'dictionary' meanings may be accessible only by way of ethnographic studies of the culture and traditions of a community when this culture departs widely from that of the student. Malinowski's discussion of the relationship of language to other aspects of life (the problem of *meaning* again!) deserves to rank as a classic in this field. From it we may draw the following principles:

1. The language of a group must be studied against the background of its general culture, its mode of life and customs, and each utterance must be interpreted in relation to its context—not merely its linguistic context, but the whole situation in which it is uttered.

2. Speech must be treated as a *mode of action,* an indispensable element of concerted human action, rather than as a *countersign of thought.*

The basic linguistic situation would be one in which a number of individuals are engaged in joint activity, and the utterances of the various individuals control and guide the actions of their fellows. Thus, during a fishing expedition, "Short telling exclamations fly about, which might be rendered by such words as: 'Pull in,' 'Let go,' 'Shift further,' 'Lift the net'; or again technical expressions completely untranslatable except by minute description of the instruments used, and the mode of action. . . . The structure of all this linguistic material is inextricably mixed up with, and dependent upon, the course of the activity in which the utterances are embedded."

3. Inasmuch as speech utterances are, primitively at least, modes of action, their *meaning* is defined primarily by the effects which they produce. This is true for the development of meaningful utterances in the child; his *mama,* etc., are reactions to certain stimulating conditions, and result in a change in these stimulating conditions; in the young infant vocalization is practically the only means of action on the surrounding world. The situation seems to be similar in many of the uses of speech among primitive peoples. "A word, signifying an important utensil, is used in action, not to comment on its nature or reflect on its properties, but to make it appear, be handed over to the speaker, or to direct another man to its proper use."

4. The basic grammatical structure and fundamental grammatical categories are an expression of real categories, and these real categories correspond to man's modes of behavior, his practical ways of dealing with the environment. Since the basic linguistic structures and classifications develop in a prescientific era of practical dealings with the environment, it is futile to look for a correspondence to 'logical' categories. The aspects of environment which are singled out in language, and the manner in which these aspects are related and classified in linguistic categories, depend upon the behavior patterns, practical concerns, and historical accidents of the total culture.

The 'Signaling' Behavior of Animals

An important part of the environment of most animals consists of other animals, particularly other animals of the same species. These other animals are the source of visual, auditory, olfactory, and other kinds of stimuli which may play a very considerable rôle in determining and controlling the behavior of the individual. The mere presence of other animals, or the size, plumage, odor, or other bodily features characteristic of species, the sexes, or of individuals may function as important determinants of individual or group behavior. But of more interest to us is the rôle of various forms of *behavior* in this control of others. Such forms of behavior have been termed 'signaling reflexes' by Max Meyer (1922), who points out that the responses of animals in certain situations are not *directly* adaptive but as stimuli do serve to elicit characteristic responses of, e.g., the sexual, protective, or food-finding type in other animals. The older writers, for example, Darwin, Spencer, and Wundt, treated these modes of behavior as 'expressions of the emotions,' and interpreted them largely in terms of the individual organism. The views of recent writers, notably De Laguna, concerning the so-called expressive movements show a considerable shift in emphasis. The main points involved may be summarized as follows:

1. In the first place, it is recognized that animals of a given species exhibit more or less definite *pattern-responses;* that is, complexes of movements which occur from time to time, and in relation to certain classes of stimulus-situations, in a more or less uniform temporal and spatial configuration. In general, the simpler the organization of the animal, the fewer in number are the varieties of pattern-responses, and the simpler and more invariable and unmodifiable are those responses which occur. Thus the responses of the unicellular animals consist chiefly in locomotion toward certain stimulating conditions and away from others. As we ascend through the animal series wr find an ever increasing number of stimulus-situations to which the animal can make appropriate pattern-responses which are more or less specific to the stimulus-situation in question, and we find also a greater variability and individual adaptability in these responses; in othpr words, the pattern-responses come more and more to be built up, by learning, to fit the particular conditions of the individual's environment. The various movements of which the animal is capable are less and less bound together into invariable patterns and sequences which can occur only as wholes characteristic of the species. Behavior becomes more variable, more plastic.

2. The pattern-response as a whole is usually directly *adaptive;* that is, it so adjusts the relations between organism and environment as to result in the intake of food, the escape from danger, etc. The overt components of these responses may also stimulate other animals and modify their behavior. But of greatest interest are certain by-products of the pattern-responses; namely, the sounds which may be uttered. The patterns of response of course usually include certain visceral components, such as those of respiration. If as a result of these actions air is drawn in or forced out of the respiratory organs under pressure, sounds will result whose acoustic character will be determined by the positions or movements of the throat and mouth parts, these positions or movements being also in some degree characteristic of the general response pattern. The resulting sounds will of course stimulate the organism which emits them, and probably reinforce its response; but of greater significance is the fact that if other animals are present possessing auditory sense-organs, these sounds will in some degree modify and control their activity. It is to be noted that the sounds themselves are *by-products* of respiratory activity. The respiratory organs are not primarily vocalizing mechanisms but rather devices for gaseous interchange. They belong to the visceral apparatus, as do also the throat and mouth. Most of the visceral processes are fortunately silent and imperceptible to others; by what might be termed an accident of nature, one set of these processes produces an audible

by-product. And thus, phylogenetically, these respiratory phenomena belong to the same class of activities as do digestion and glandular secretion; all of the functions of this class do not directly adjust the organism to external conditions, but rather adjust internal physiological conditions to the energy requirements of the overt behavior of the moment. But with the development of auditory sense-organs, these respiratory sounds have become stimuli. *In so far as the respiratory, throat, and mouth innervations are characteristic of the pattern-responses of which they are components, the resulting sounds will also be characteristic of the pattern-responses and hence of the stimulating conditions capable of eliciting these pattern-responses.*

3. As for the responses elicited in other animals by these characteristic sounds, these may possibly be to some extent determined by inherited mechanisms. But it is probable that to a large extent the connection between certain animal cries and the responses elicited by these cries is a result of conditioning. A loud cry occurring as a part of a fear or rage response might elicit flight in other animals without previous learning, just as a loud sound is said to elicit a fear pattern in young infants; a cry of moderate intensity might elicit orientation toward the source of the sound and thereafter response to the animal emitting the sound or to the situation of which that animal forms a part. Thus the clucking of the hen might result in orientation of the chicks toward the hen, and this might then be followed by response to food uncovered by the hen. But in many, perhaps in most cases, responses appropriate to various cries involve considerable learning. In the cases considered above, the specificity of correlation between cries and responses hardly consisted of more than an eliciting of flight by loud sounds and of orientation or approach by moderate sounds. For a specificity of responses depending not merely on such differences in intensity but rather upon qualitative difference in cries, considerable conditioning is probably required. It is very doubtful whether there are inherited mechanisms which provide a basis for specificity of response correlated with qualitative differences in auditory stimuli. And indeed the conditions are not lacking among most of the higher animals whereby such conditioning may occur; for from birth animals encounter various situations while at the same time their ears are stimulated by characteristic cries uttered by themselves and their fellows. But whether the connections between the cries of one animal and the responses of others have as a basis inherited or acquired mechanisms, it is in any event obvious that the variety and specificity of the responses which can be elicited by the cries as such are not great. The situations to which animals have to respond and the responses which they make are far more stereotyped than is the case with human beings. Hence the cries occur as parts of a rather limited number of what De Laguna (1927) has called *type-responses,* and in other animals they in turn elicit type-responses.

4. The responses made by others when a cry is uttered by a member of a group are only in part determined by the cry itself; in many cases

the other parts of the situation, the total context, determine the specific form which the response takes. This is of course also true of language, particularly of spoken language, but it is far more true of animal cries. For the cry itself merely tends to elicit a type-response, such as flight; the direction and manner of flight are determined by the situation. Language, on the other hand, may serve as a substitute for the various features of a concrete situation; it provides independently variable symbols for the independently variable elements of environment; at least it does so within certain limits and in certain of its uses.

5. The great biological significance of animal cries, as of speech also, lies in their providing a means for the coordination of the activities of two or more individuals. They provide a means whereby the stimuli acting upon one individual may indirectly act upon other individuals, so that, as Weiss has expressed it, the sense-organs and motor organs of one individual are in some sense placed at the disposal of other individuals. This is a function by the side of which the alleged function of the 'expression of feelings' pales into biological insignificance. We may best realize this by considering some typical type-responses which are coordinated among the members of a group by means of cries.

a. *Flight.* Certain sights, smells, etc., result in the flight of the individuals so stimulated, and also, as part of the response-pattern, in the utterance of a cry; other animals not so stimulated respond to the cry with flight, whose direction and manner are determined by the situation as a whole. In herds or flocks certain individuals are observed to stand erect, gazing about, sniffing, etc., while the others feed. Stimuli acting on the sense-organs of these individuals indirectly control the behavior of the group as a whole.

b. *Feeding.* The cry of one individual who has found food or sighted prey brings the other members of the group.

c. *Sex-behavior.* The cries, gesturings, etc., of one animal prepare another animal for sex-responses, and in the long train of associated activities, as in the courtship, copulation, nest-building, brooding, etc., of birds, the behavior of the partners is coordinated and synchronized by such means.

d. *Aggressive behavior.* In many animal species cries and gesturings are preliminaries or even *substitutes* for actual combat; the cry of rage of one member of a group may initiate rage responses in the other members, or may establish social attitudes of submission in others.[5]

In all of these cases, as has been mentioned, the cry can successfully control and direct behavior only as part of a total stimulus situation; that is, it merely initiates behavior or produces orientation in a certain direction; it cannot serve as a substitute for absent concrete situations.

Owing to the researches of Whitman and of Craig, we have some

---

[5]Other examples, together with a summary and bibliography of the literature, may be found in Alverdes (1927), who especially emphasizes the importance of cries in maintaining the cohesion of a herd or flock.

knowledge concerning the rôle of cries and gestures in social control among pigeons. The observations pertain particularly to the blond ring-dove. In general, Craig (1908) states that the behavior of doves in normal life among their fellows cannot be adequately treated by studying the birds as individuals and attributing their social interactions entirely to inborn 'social instincts.' The individual must adapt himself to the endlessly diverse and changing activities of his fellows: parents, mate, neighbors, strangers. Such adaptation requires delicate social control. "The means of social control are various, including much more than the voice, not to speak of the song. The different utterances of the voice, the varying inflections of each of these utterances, the form and color of the body, the bowing, strutting, bristling of feathers, and all the expressions of emotion are agencies potent to rouse and direct the activities of other birds." For the rest, Craig's observations afford detailed illustrations of the points which were listed above. Of particular interest is his description of the sequence of behavior in mating, which shows how the effects produced by cries and gestures are dependent upon the organic state of the socially stimulated individual and upon the features of the concrete situation. In general, then, the importance of the cries consists in their coordinating function. As auditory stimuli they are particularly effective, since they can act at a distance without special orientation of the sense-organs; they may then lead to such orientation as permits the stimulating conditions surrounding and including the other individual to become effective.

Of all subhuman animals, the anthropoid apes would seem to be of greatest interest for the study of primitive social control, particularly with respect to the possible rôle of vocalization in such control. In physical structure, in type of nervous system, in behavior plasticity, and in social grouping and mode of life these apes would seem to be very close to primitive man. The chimpanzees are said to live usually in groups of from ten to thirty individuals; according to some writers, these are usually kinship groups. Thus the opportunities for the development of social interaction would seem to be similar to those which existed in the most primitive stages of the human race. Unfortunately, our knowledge about the social life and particularly the rôle of vocalization among these apes is scanty, and in the observations which have been published the difficulty of distinguishing between facts and interpretations is very great. The very similarity in organization of the apes to human beings tends to induce in the observers an anthropomorphizing and sentimental attitude. These statements are illustrated by Garner's well-known book (1900), in which we find illustrated the uselessness of data gathered by an uncritical and scientifically untrained observer. Garner reported that apes have a "language" consisting of about twelve sounds, which they use to indicate definite situations such as danger, food, sex play, water, etc. Others have reported definite sex "words" in use by monkeys; sometimes the sound is like that of smacking the lips; at other times "a gentle 'ee-ah'." The

vocal stimulus in these cases is generally accompanied by the assumption
of a posture "inviting sexual union." It is not unlikely that all of the
alleged "words" of apes are sounds uttered as parts of pattern-responses,
and that the responses of other individuals are determined by the total
behavior in its environmental context, so that there would be no question
of 'symbolic' speech utterances in the sense of *conventional, arbitrary,* and
specific substitutes for situations which could be effective in eliciting behavior specifically appropriate to those situations even in the absence of
the situations, or, what amounts to the same thing, in the absence of
orientation of the vocally stimulated animal toward the relevant environmental feature. This view is borne out by the statements of Köhler
(1925), who had excellent opportunities for observing chimpanzees in a
group, although the group was living in confinement and hence could not
engage in the normal communal activities of free animals. Köhler states
that chimpanzees are capable of uttering a wide variety of sounds, so that
their lack of articulate speech cannot be attributed to glosso-labial limitations. They exhibit also a wide variety of facial and general bodily activity
of the sort which has traditionally been designated as 'gestural.' But both
sounds and gestures, Köhler reports, can only express emotions and never
designate or describe objects. Köhler states that he was able to identify
the expressions of "rage, terror, despair, grief, pleading desire, and also
playfulness and pleasure," and that the chimpanzees themselves "understood" such expressions on the part of their fellows even more perfectly.
So far as vocalization and gesture are concerned, I do not find in Köhler's
account of social control among chimpanzees that any great advance over
the state of affairs described for pigeons is suggested. But though
language seems to be lacking, group life in many respects resembling
that of primitive peoples is possible. There seems to be a good deal of
what Malinowski (1927) has called 'phatic communion'; that is, gesture
and vocalization which merely establish rapport between individuals.
Among animals such behavior can perhaps be genetically interpreted in
terms of 'abbreviated response' or 'tentative movements' (the genetic
aspect of behavior is however conspicuously lacking in Köhler's writings);
in human speech it is doubtless a derivative and secondary use of language,
and as such will be discussed in our final section. It does not seem to be
true, as some writers have alleged, that language is essential to the use of
simple tools. The use of digging-sticks, of sticks for reaching objects, of
box 'constructions' for reaching objects overhead, and even the 'making'
of a simple tool, as by thrusting one stick into the hollow end of another
to make a longer stick, have all been observed among these apes by Köhler,
Yerkes, and others. Nevertheless, the absence of language imposes two
limitations of utmost importance: first, cooperation in communal undertakings is radically limited; and second, social tradition, the accumulation
of useful techniques and discoveries, is possible in only a very slight degree.
So far also as individual behavior is concerned, the absence of verbal
substitutes for absent objects (and for aspects of objects to which visual

fixation is not at the moment directed), together with the inability to plan actions verbally, tends to limit the ape in the solution of a problem situation to those features which are simultaneously within sensory range.

The book by Yerkes and Learned, *Chimpanzee Intelligence and Its Vocal Expressions* (1925), is, particularly in view of the title, very disappointing. Mrs. Learned's recordings of vocal sounds are of doubtful significance phonetically, and the relationships between these sounds, the situations in which they were uttered, the accompanying behavior of the animal, and particularly the behavior, if any, elicited in the other animals are far from clear. Indeed, the whole study, so far as vocalization is concerned, was carried out in such a way, and the results so loosely interpreted, that little that is significant or reliable for our purposes emerges, beyond an indication that chimpanzees utter a considerable variety of sounds. Examples of alleged "words," printed in letters whose values as phonetic symbols are not defined, are as follows: *gak, gahk, ngak, nkak,* reported as variants of a "food-word," and said to have been uttered when the animal was eating or waiting for his food; *m,* "sound emitted with lips closed"—reported as occurring in relation to fruit; *ho-oh,* "uttered with prolonged vowel in first syllable, voice dropping very low in the second"—reported as a cry of alarm. For all of the sounds listed the melody is indicated in conventional musical notation (the recorder is a musician). The melody is said to be the characteristic feature of the sound recorded as *m,* when uttered in relation to fruit. Learned writes, "The term *fruit motive* is applied to a group of purely tonal phrases which are thoroughly distinctive in character and which were uttered by Chim and Panzee very frequently in connection with the eating of oranges, apples, and bananas." Yerkes' chapter on "Anthropoid Speech and Its Significance," in his book *Almost Human* (1925), also strikes me as being uncritical and as revealing a totally inadequate conception of the nature of language. At most, these studies suggest that it might be possible to demonstrate a tendency for certain laryngeal and oral positions and actions to be characteristic of certain pattern-responses, and particularly of tentative or preparatory responses which precede feeding, flight, sex-behavior, etc. Further suggestions in this direction are to be found in the writings of Pfungst (1912) and Boutan (1913). Such a demonstration, however, would need to proceed in quite objective fashion, and the experimenter would need to rid himself of preconceptions derived from traditional notions about human language and to abandon the attempt to record animal sounds in terms of the phonemes of his own particular language. If among the members of an animal group any sounds are to be found which function in a genuinely substitutive fashion (actual linguistic forms), this also will need to be objectively demonstrated in terms of speaker's situation and hearer's response, where both speaker and hearer are animals; "sympathetic insight" on the part of the human observer means only, in such cases, the implicit operation of analogies with human behavior. And, finally, it is unlikely that data relevant to these problems will be obtained as by-products of investigations of 'ideation,' 'reasoning,' or 'rational processes' among animals.

A number of persons have attempted to teach sounds of human speech to apes. Thus Yerkes (1925) arranged various forms of apparatus by means of which bits of banana could be caused to appear when the experimenter pronounced certain sounds, such as *baba* or *nana*. The hope was that the chimpanzee would learn to imitate these sounds as a means of causing the fruit to appear. The experiment was unsuccessful; at most the ape might make some lip movements, possibly in imitation of those of the experimenter. Yerkes concludes that there is slight, if any, tendency to imitate sounds, and that this is the chief reason for the chimpanzee's failure to develop speech. Furness (1916) claims to have had better success in teaching apes to produce articulate sounds. He reports that he was able to teach a young orang-utan to pronounce the words 'papa' and 'cup,' and that when he showed her the cup "and asked 'what is this?' she would say cup very plainly." With a chimpanzee Furness reports that he had little success in similar efforts. How much in Furness' article is cold fact and how much is interpretation, it is impossible to say. There is much internal evidence of a sentimental attitude, and little intimation of the application of the controls so essential in work with animals. Thus Furness remarks, in passing, that the animal "understood almost everything that it was necessary for me to say." Investigations of alleged "understanding" of speech by dogs, horses, monkeys, and apes have repeatedly shown the necessity of the most rigorous and objective controls; with the data at present available, nothing further can profitably be said about this matter.[6]

THE ACQUISITION OF LANGUAGE BY THE CHILD

Screaming. In the newborn infant, the air that for the first time enters the lungs is forced out with a strong expiration which produces the 'birth-cry.' Thereafter, various stimulating conditions, such as stomach contractions, wetness, fatigue, pain, etc., also release the screaming reaction. This screaming is during the first days relatively undifferentiated. Attempts to represent by conventional symbols the sounds uttered are of very doubtful validity or value, although such attempts have been made by many writers in terms of the phonemes of the languages spoken by these writers. It appears that the screaming is usually with wide-open

[6]A summary of the literature of anthropoid life and behavior is provided in the recent comprehensive survey by R. M. and A. W. Yerkes (1929). In their discussion of "Vocalization, Speech, and Language" of the chimpanzee, they take in general a negative position with respect to the ability of this animal to use or acquire "true language," but state that "with ability to understand sounds and to react appropriately, the case is far different, for the evidence is abundant and convincing that much that the captive chimpanzee hears from human lips is meaningful and may under favorable circumstances acquire association with appropriate response." But the evidence which they cite in support of this statement is of anecdotal nature.

mouth, though the tone thus produced may be rhythmically interrupted by glottal or oral changes. After a few weeks there may develop a certain amount of differentiation in the screaming or crying sounds uttered under the different stimulating conditions, so that mothers claim to be able to distinguish, e.g., between the cry of hunger and that of a pin-prick.

Reference has been made in a previous section to the biological and social significance of the infant's crying. The human infant is in its early days not much more than a vegetative organism; it is dependent for its food, cleanliness, comfort, and everything else involving manipulation of the environment upon others. The activities of these others in relation to the infant are largely controlled by his vocalizations. This function of social control has been discussed, on the basis of objective observations under controlled conditions, by Weiss (1929b) and by Irwin (1930). There is no advantage to be gained by referring to the infant's cries as 'expressing' various emotions or inner ('mental') states, as is done by most writers. When an observer reports that he can distinguish between an infant's cry of 'anger' and his 'sorrowful' cry, he is merely reporting that a cry of a certain acoustic quality accompanies a certain set of other bodily responses, such as flushing of the face, slashing with arms and legs, etc., and that this whole pattern of responses characteristically occurs under certain stimulating conditions, as when the child's movements are hampered; similarly, he has observed that a cry of a different acoustic quality occurs as part of a different response-pattern under different stimulating conditions. In neither case have any 'inner states' been observed, and the assumption of such inner states only leads the observer to neglect his real business, which consists in accurately and objectively describing the cry, the accompanying behavior, and the stimulating situation. Such descriptions will be improved by the omission of affectionate diminutives and question-begging adjectives. Recognition of these facts has appeared in the literature only in recent years. A brief account of the change in points of view, together with a bibliography of the subject of infant vocalizations, is given by McCarthy (1929). The older literature was impressionistic and more or less sentimental, based usually on casual observations under uncontrolled conditions. The birth-cry was frequently interpreted as expressing the infant's wrath or joy at entering the world. Crying was held to become differentiated to express various emotional states. All such observations are of course based merely upon the subjective interpretations of the observers; they are 'intuitive' observations in which there is no question of controlled analysis of physiological, environmental, or social factors.

The birth-cry is regarded by more recent writers as reflex activity, being an incidental result of the blood-oxygenation mechanism, in which air is "pulled rapidly over the vocal bands causing them to vibrate" (Blanton and Blanton, 1927). Major (1906) characterizes the first stage of vocal activity as "reflexive crying" and holds that this crying has no intellectual or emotional significance, being "produced ·as well by a child without a cerebrum as by a child with one. . . . What one means then, by saying that language has its beginnings in these reflexive cries is that much of the physical apparatus which is used in later speech activities is involved in the early reflexive cries." Fenton (1925) writes: "During this early period sounds are reflex in character; when the vocal muscles chance to contract, sounds arise, but they are uttered without intent, and are not to be thought of as indicating particular meanings. Variations in sound are more often indicative of differences in intensity than anything else. The greater tension of muscles under stress of excitement flattens the sound and makes it more shrill in extreme hunger or pain." Blanton (1917) carried out an observational study of twenty-five infants during the first thirty days of life. Of the birth-cry she says: "It differed in no way in timbre, pitch, etc. from other cries of the first few days. The birth-cries of different infants were not alike, ranging from simple *a* (as in *at*) to *u* (as in *cut*)." And further, "In the subjects with which I worked I did not find the cries of hunger, to noxious stimuli, to fatigue, etc., uniform. There were differences of vowels and consonants, of timbre and degree, but no one was used as response to one set of circumstances that was not at the same time used to others. . . . The cry of colic was the one exception. . . . The 'hunger cry' has generally a well marked rhythm." Elsewhere (1927) she writes, "During the first months of life, the cries of the infant are in response to hunger and pain and cold, and differ from each other only in intensity." Sherman (1927) investigated "the ability of observers to judge the emotional characteristics of the crying of infants." The results indicate that "there was very little success in judging the emotional accompaniment of the cry when the stimuli were not known. When the stimuli were known to the observers, they named the emotions which were usually expected to result from such stimuli." McCarthy (1929) observes, "This result is very interesting because of the light it throws on the previous studies which have given all the various interpretations of these early cries. It must be remembered that the observers in these early studies always knew the stimuli for the cries, and hence were unduly influenced in their interpretations by the knowledge of the situation, rather than by any peculiar characteristic of the cries."

Babbling. Within the first three months, on the average probably toward the end of the second month (Stern and Stern, 1922), babbling begins. It may, however, begin as early as the third week. Attempts have been made to represent babbling sounds by linguistic symbols, but in the first place most of the writers have little or no knowledge of phonetics, so that they merely record the sounds of their own language (French, German, English, etc.) which seem to them (with their specialized and fixed adult habits of perception) most like the child's sounds; and in the second place even a trained phonetician would have extreme difficulty in describing or representing the sounds; even the range of sounds represented by the International Phonetic Alphabet could give only an approximate representation of the inspiratory clicks, the crowing, gurgling, squeaking, and the wide variety of vocalic sounds uttered by the infant. Furthermore, because of the difference in the size of the mouth cavity and other parts in the infant as compared with the adult, the range of sounds must be qualitatively different in the infant. This latter point has been discussed by Jespersen (1922, p. 104).

Investigation, with or without the aid of apparatus, of the manners of articulation must of course be much more difficult in the infant than in the adult. McCarthy (1929) discusses the technical difficulties in the way of recording the sounds of infants either by means of written symbols or by means of apparatus, coming to the conclusion that no adequate method is as yet available. One of the chief difficulties in dealing with infant speech sounds is that these sounds are not members of a fixed phonetic pattern [concerning such phonetic patterns in actual language, see Sapir (1925)] and that there is no linguistically meaningful context to guide the observer. A number of experiments have demonstrated the errors which are made when nonsense syllables are recorded by hearers; the situation is much worse for infant sounds, since the nonsense syllables are at least series of sounds which are members of the conventional adult phonetic pattern. Unfortunately, most of the observers of infant sounds seem to have been not even aware of these difficulties, so that their reports are bizarre and of little value.

While the sounds produced in screaming are almost entirely of a vowel character, in *babbling* consonantal sounds occur; that is, the vowel sound is preceded, interrupted, or terminated by an obstruction somewhere in the oral or laryngeal cavities which has usually a stop, but sometimes a fricative character. The consonantal sounds which are most frequently reported in the literature as being the earliest to occur are labials (p, b, m) and velars (k, g, x, etc.) [For the significance of these symbols and a general discussion of speech sounds, see Bloomfield (1933, pp. 74-138, 547-549).] Such sounds are reported by Stern, Preyer, Strümpell, Vierordt, Lindner, Idelberger, Friedman, von Taube, Oltuszewski, Deville, Schultze [bibliography in Stern and Stern (1922); Tracy (1893), who reports similar sounds as being among the earliest to appear, also summarizes the earlier accounts]. Blanton (1917), listing all of the sounds made by twenty-five infants in the first thirty days, gives the consonants m, η, g, h, w, r, j; and the vowel sounds aw, ij, uw, ϵ, a (I have substituted phonetic symbols for the "o as in owl" form of records given by Blanton). On the basis of these reports it would appear that in the early babbling period the most frequent obstruction in the oral cavity to the expiratory stream occurs in the region of the uvula and soft palate and that obstruction by the lips is next most frequent; obstructions produced by tongue-tip and blade seem much less frequent.

During the course of the first year, the variety of babbling sounds increases rapidly and comes to include a multiplicity of sounds greater than that of any individual language; many sounds are produced which do not occur in the language of the adult community. Sounds also occur in a great variety of sequences and combinations, many of which are not found in the adult language. These facts are illustrated in the observations of Preyer (1905) and of Fenton (1925). This variety in vocal sound production has an important bearing on the question whether any special racial heredity facilitates the acquisition by, e.g., a German child of the speech of his community. So far as we know, any human infant could acquire with approximately equal facility the speech sounds of any language.

As time goes on, the infant may continuously babble for many minutes at a time, sometimes repeating the same sounds over and over. Gesell (1925), on the basis of a complete 24-hour record of the vocal activities of a six-months-old child, calculated that 3 per cent of the waking time of the child was expended in some form of vocal activity; at nine months, 6.66 per cent was so expended. Other observers have reported a greater amount of vocalization than this. The stimuli which release the babbling reactions are perhaps largely internal. Thus Stern and Stern (1922) report that babbling occurs especially after meals, after sleep, etc. Irwin (1930), on the basis of carefully controlled observations, has also come to the conclusion that most of the early activity of the infant is to be related to intra-organic stimulation. Whether we ought to speak here of definite reflexes, in the sense that definite receptors are functionally connected with definite effectors, seems doubtful; perhaps it would be a truer picture of the physiological conditions if we supposed that the neural energy released by the internal and external stimulating conditions ramifies over relatively low neural levels to be distributed to various motor points, resulting in movements not only of the jaws, tongue, soft palate, etc., but also of the arms, hands, legs, etc. All of this activity appears 'random' in character, in the sense that the actual movements going on at any instant do not seem to be specifically correlated with or an adjustment to any specific stimulating conditions. This random character of the vocalizing activities has led to their being described as a form of 'play,' and much writing of a sentimental nature has had for its theme the 'joy' and 'pleasure' which the infant takes in 'playing' with its vocal organs. Moreover, since the babbling vocalization is a less intense form of activity than the early screaming, occurs under conditions in which painful stimuli are absent, and develops at a time when smiling, laughing, crowing, etc., appear, it has frequently been held to be expressive of 'pleasant emotions.' Such interpretations are of very doubtful explanatory value.

Sound Imitation. During the second six months of life usually, but sometimes earlier, the child begins to imitate some of the sounds which stimulate its ears. To account for this an "instinct of auditory imitation" is often assumed, but this assumption is unnecessary and does not seem to accord with the observed facts. As soon as the child begins to babble, it stimulates its own ears, and there is consequently an inevitable and invariable concomitance of a pattern of motor activity and the specific pattern of auditory stimuli produced by this activity, the auditory pattern differing in quality according to the nature of the vocalizing movements.

The human nervous system having the functional properties that it appears to have, it must of course gradually come about that the auditory stimuli become adequate for releasing the vocalizing movements with which they have been temporally associated.[7] The child, then, by virtue of the fact that its own babbling restimulates its own ears, sets up in itself a series of auditory-vocalizing habits. The establishment of such habits is perhaps evidenced by the increasing repetition of the same syllable for many minutes at a time; we see here a characteristic 'circular reaction,' in which the reaction provides the stimulus for its own repetition. But the presence of such habits is more certainly established when the child begins to respond to sounds pronounced by others with more or less similar sounds. According to Stern and Stern (1922), the child reproduces at first only those syllables which it has itself been producing in its babbling; this supports the assumption that we are here dealing with fairly specific habits and not with a general "instinct of auditory imitation." These findings of Stern, according to which a babbling period must precede any imitation of sounds, are confirmed by other observers. Of interest in this connection is the fact that deaf children do not learn to talk unless special methods of training, by means of vision or touch, are employed. This matter is discussed by Allport (1924), whose account of language acquisition by the child seems to have had a wide influence. Moreover, according to Gutzmann (1902), the deaf child does not babble so much or in so modulated a manner as does the hearing child.

At the age of eight to nine months, according to the Sterns' observations, there occur the first cases of imitation of sound-sequences which had not previously occurred in babbling. The component elements of these sound-sequences we may assume to have previously occurred in babbling, although this point is not made clear. Furthermore, there would appear to be a considerable margin of error in determining whether a particular sound-sequence had or had not occurred at some time during babbling. Stern distinguishes between *echolalia* and *metalalia*. Echolalia is imitation of sounds immediately after they are heard; metalalia is the reproduction of sounds which have been repeatedly heard in the past but which have not stimulated the child's ears immediately previous to his first production of them. Thus the Sterns' Hilde, at age 1:10, had heard every evening for some time the words *gute Nacht,* without imitating them; one evening, before others had pronounced the words, she suddenly said *Nacht.* No

---

[7]The concept of conditioning, association, or redintegration to which I am here appealing is not to be identified with that frequently indicated by the term *conditioned reflex.* I do not consider it worth while to make any assumptions about 'reflex arcs' or other specific neural mechanisms. But the concept of conditioning, as it has been presented by Rexroad (1932), and particularly by Guthrie (1930, 1935), appears to me to have sufficient factual basis to justify its use, at least for the present, as a guiding principle. Guthrie states the general principle of conditioning thus: *"Stimuli acting at a given instant tend to acquire some effectiveness toward the eliciting of concurrent responses, and this effectiveness tends to last indefinitely."*

evidence is given that the word was not implicitly repeated on the earlier occasions. Stern gives other examples and believes that such mediate imitation of the adult speech which the child is continually hearing is of great importance in the acquisition of speech. Further, and carefully controlled, research on this matter is desirable.

There have been conflicting views on the question as to whether there is a distinct stage of sound imitation preceding the stage of speech understanding. Meumann, Compayré, and Sully held that a distinct period of meaningless sound-imitation precedes the acquisition of true language, while Preyer denied that any imitation occurs before the beginning of language comprehension. Stern holds that while imitation of speech sounds occurs long before spoken utterances begin to be understood, yet it enters upon its greatest development in the first half of the second year, when the child is already learning to understand (i.e., to respond appropriately to) many words. During the first three-quarters of the first year, imitation of specific articulated sound-sequences is less frequent than imitation of gestures (e.g., hand-clapping), of unarticulated sounds (e.g., clicking of the tongue), and of the modulation of the voice. Only somewhat later does "articulated imitation first begin to emerge from chaotic imitation." Thus the imitation of sounds and sound-sequences is not a development which runs its full course before the initiation of the following stages; the formation of habits of this type and of the two types to be described below together enter upon their most rapid development toward the end of the first year and the beginning of the second.

If the imitation by the child of the sounds and sound-sequences of adults depends upon previously occurring circular conditionings of the child in the course of his own vocalizing activity, we should not expect the early imitations to be perfect; phenomena similar to the 'irradiation' observed under laboratory conditions would be expected, so that an adult sound which is not identical with any of the infant's conditioned sounds would yet evoke one of these sounds; the infant's vocalization would then be classed by the adult as a "mistake in imitation." Jespersen (1922) has compiled a list of the sound-substitutions of children in which he finds certain similarities and regularities. These 'mistakes' of course mean that the specific ear-vocal mechanisms have not been perfected. Thus suppose that an adult pronounces the word *cat*. The correct reproduction of this word requires that a very definite sequence of complex muscle contractions take place in specific combinations and in a specific order. It may happen, however, that the impulses from the ear tend to set off simultaneously almost all of the muscular contractions involved in the whole utterance; the result is a set of antagonistic contractions and a failure of articulation. Similar results might be due to the fact that the adult's sounds do not correspond exactly to any of the infant's, so that tendencies toward incompatible articulations might be set up. Some evidence of such occurrences is afforded by Stern's description of the strong effort which appears to accompany the first "voluntary" sound imitations; according to Stern,

"Die Anstrengung treibt dem Kinde Röte ins Gesicht." The inaccuracies in the ear-vocalizing mechanisms may also result in the reversing or jumbling of sound-sequences; e.g., *efelant, waps;* also in 'assimilations,' such as *goggie* (doggie), *kekl* (kettle). During this period of learning, and afterwards as well, repetitions of the same sound are extremely likely to occur. (We may *conjecture* that when a sound has just been produced the neural and motor mechanisms involved remain in a functionally active condition for some moments and are likely to be reactivated by impulses from the kinesthetic and auditory receptors stimulated by the vocalization.) Many observers have noticed this tendency toward repetition, and some have pointed out its possible linguistic significance as a basis for the reduplications so common in nursery speech, such as *papa, mama, dada,* etc. Some of the cases of 'assimilation' mentioned above also belong here. Those linguists who attribute great importance to the transmission of a language from one generation to the next as a factor in phonetic change would see in such tendencies toward assimilation, dissimilation, metathesis, and haplology an important source of sound-changes of these types. Similar phenomena of course occur when languages are 'borrowed' by one people from another, as when conquered people adopt the language of their conquerors, or vice versa, and sound-changes of the above-mentioned types may thus result. Such phenomena of course are not in themselves adequate for an explanation of phonetic change in the strict sense; in the sense, that is, of modification of a specific phoneme or set of phonemes in all linguistic forms in which they occur under the same phonetic conditions. For phonetic change in this sense the evidence is not adequate to justify an explanation in terms of children's 'mistakes' in imitation.

Verbal Understanding. In the last months of the first year the child may begin to 'understand' a few utterances of others. This means that he begins to respond with specific bodily movements (which from a social point of view may be termed 'appropriate') to certain words or phrases pronounced by others. Thus, to take an example reported by Stern and Stern (1922), suppose the child to be in its bath. Its chief motor activity during some minutes may consist in slashing movements of the arms. The adult classifies these movements, in view of the situation, as 'splashing,' and may consequently say *splash, splash.* We have then a situation similar to that described in the preceding section; while certain motor activity is going on, a definite sound-pattern acts on the child's ears, and, as such things go, this concomitance is likely to be repeated on many occasions. Hence the sound-pattern is likely "to acquire some effectiveness toward the eliciting of the response with which it was concurrent" on these occasions; it becomes possible to elicit the 'splashing' movements by pronouncing the word, regardless of whether the child has or has not been making the movements just previously. A very important type of such conditioned responses consists in the child's orientation toward an object when the name of that object is pronounced; the procedure of course consists in the adult's providing that such orientation shall occur while the name is heard. A related example, also given by Stern, is as follows: the child's hand was lifted to its nose by the parent, who said, "Da hat das Kind die *Nase.*" After sufficient repetition, the child would perform the appropriate movement when the parent said, "Wo hat denn das Kind die *Nase?*" Schäfer (1922) experimentally established in his ten-months-old son conditioned responses to eight specific verbal stimuli. Thus the child learned to clap his hands, look toward a stuffed dog or toward a metronome, shake his rattle, etc., in response to the specific verbal stimuli. In each case Schäfer selected movements which had been observed previous to the verbal conditioning. The learning occupied only a few days; forty-five days later the child responded correctly to four of the words. Thus the general situation necessary for this type of learning is that the child be performing some specific activity, whether 'randomly,' or in response to gestures, or under an adult's manual guidance, at the same time that certain sound-sequences stimulate his ears. We may describe this learning as *the establishment of conventionalized speech sounds as adequate stimuli for releasing bodily movements or postures.*

Returning to the example of a (German) child in its bath, let us suppose that the child has been conditioned as described and that on a later occasion the parent says not merely *patsch, patsch,* but uses these words in an imperative sentence: *Mache mal patsch patsch.* The splashing movement is likely to occur simply because the sounds *patsch patsch* have occurred in this utterance; the rest of what we call the sentence has no specific influence on the reaction. In other words, the child is at this stage merely learning to react to relatively short sound-complexes with differential bodily movements. Syntax and grammar are as yet of no significance in the child's behavior. It may of course happen that the parent from the beginning utters the complete sentence, and it is conceivable that the arm response comes to be elicited by this complex sound-pattern as a whole; but the principle remains exactly the same; measured by the child's response the 'sentence' functions in exactly the same way as the shorter utterance; there is no more grammar or analysis in the one case than in the other. This fact has not been obvious to many observers, and many marvels of infantile understanding have been reported; just as in the anecdotal literature of animal behavior it has frequently been reported that an animal "understands" sentences because he does different more or less appropriate things when different word-sequences are pronounced.

Verbal Utterance. This stage of language development, which is the beginning of speech in the ordinary sense, begins usually during the first half of the second year, though it may begin as early as nine months or as late as two years. The learning process may be exemplified as follows: Suppose that auditory-vocal mechanisms have been established such that when the auditory receptors are stimulated by the sound-sequence *wau wau* the appropriate respiratory and oral contractions occur whereby similar sounds are produced. If on a sufficient number of occasions the visual receptors are simultaneously stimulated by the light pattern of a toy dog, this visual pattern becomes adequate to set off the specific vocal response. This type of learning may be described in general as *the establishment of conventionalized speech reactions as specific responses to socially presented stimulus patterns.* Watson (1925) gives an account of the experimental establishment of such a response in an infant of about six months. The infant's bottle was taken from him and held before him while the adult said *da.* This procedure was repeated once a day for three weeks; after this number of joint presentations the infant repeated the word after the adult when the bottle was held before him, and thereafter produced the word when the bottle was presented without accompanying auditory stimulation from the adult. "Thereafter for several weeks it was as easy to touch off this response as to call out any other bodily reflex. The verbal response was confined almost exclusively to this one stimulus. On a few occasions he said it when his rabbit was held in front of him but not when other things were shown him." Presumably, however, the effective stimulus-pattern consisted in the total situation, including the intra-organic condition of hunger and anticipatory feeding reactions attributable to the fact that this situation had on previous occasions been followed by actual feeding. This functional relationship of verbal utterance to total concrete context and to patterns of relevant non-linguistic behavior is probably characteristic of language in its primitive form, in the race as in the child. The utterance occurs as part of an anticipatory adjustment to a practical situation.

The observational literature of children's speech development consists in large part of vocabulary lists at various ages, and particularly of tabulations of 'first words,' by which are meant usually the first occurrences of 'meaningful' utterances of the kind described above. [For references to articles and books in which these tabulations are summarized, see McCarthy (1929); also Markey (1928), and Lorimer (1929).] Unfortunately, few of the writers have seen the necessity of controlling their observations or of giving adequate reports of the specific environmental situations and non-linguistic behavior patterns which would together constitute the 'meaning' of the utterances. I have selected from the Sterns' summary (1922) the records of fourteen children of different nationalities for whose early 'words' fairly adequate data are given, and have made a tabulation based on the first four words recorded for each child. This tabulation may be summarized in terms of the percentages of the children who had learned definite sound-sequences in relation to

father, mother, other persons	50.0%
food, toys, other objects	93.0%
reaching, orientation, other actions	78.5%

The fact that all but one of the children had words in relation to food, toys, or other objects is of considerable interest. Markey (1928) found in Bateman's list of thirty-five 'first words' only three belonging to this class, and emphatically contrasts this small number with the large number of words for persons. This result, however, seems to be an artifact;

many of the entries in Bateman's list consist of only one word, and parents notoriously concentrate at first on teaching the child to say *mama, papa,* etc. Moreover, it is very difficult to demonstrate that these utterances are specifically elicited by the persons in question (and that they are not merely babbled or imitated). I do not find convincing the *arguments* by which Markey seeks to establish the 'personal reference' and 'action content' of words, although I believe his *thesis* to be valid, with certain modifications. The points involved might be summarized as follows:

1. There are probably very few utterances (if any) in the published lists which were not "associated with persons," in the sense that these persons played an essential part in attaching the utterances to given situations or actions. Thus the words for food obviously occurred in interaction with adults, and most of the others reveal adult tutelage by their conventional forms and were probably established in play with adults.

2. It is equally obvious that most of the words accompany some sort of action, whether manipulation, locomotion, reaching, or merely orientation, and that these actions will consequently constitute a part of the 'meaning' of these words.

3. Nevertheless, it is clear that objects other than persons play a much greater part in the child's earliest speech than Markey supposes. It is true that the connection between many of these utterances and definite objects does not appear to be very specific, but this lack of specificity is characteristic of nearly all of the 'words' of this period. But the published accounts at any rate indicate the sorts of objects and actions in relation to which verbal activity is chiefly developing. The *objects* are the ones with which children come most in contact, which they have most opportunity to manipulate, and which the parents most assiduously emphasize; they are chiefly recurrent visual patterns which move against an indifferent background, which emit sounds, or which are sufficiently small to be manipulated; of the latter, the most certain to occur are those connected with feeding. The *actions* are chiefly reaching and orientation (which in the young child who does not yet walk must be very frequent); eating; gestures of the 'bye-bye' type; manipulations of toys; and playful activities, largely invented by the parent, of the 'peek-a-boo' type. And all of the utterances are established in relation to visual and auditory patterns on the one hand, and to patterns of response on the other.

The Rôle of Language in Behavior Organization and Control

The Integration of the Vocal Responses with Other Behavior. A number of writers have of late been emphasizing the 'behavior content' of linguistic utterances. By this they mean that these utterances are not merely themselves forms of behavior, but that they have become integrated with and also surrogates for various more or less specific modes of non-linguistic action. In the presence of objects and situations, of various patterns of visual, auditory, and other forms of stimulation, there occur certain patterns of activity, of 'dominance' and 'subordination' in the nervous system, and certain resulting patterns of tension and relaxation in the visceral and skeletal musculature of the body. Parts of these latter patterns may be implicit, other parts explicit. In the young infant, these patterns, in their relations to environmental stimulus patterns, are not very specific, but they become more and more so in the course of the child's continual manipulations of small objects and orientations toward larger moving and sounding objects. Indeed, objects *become* objects for the child precisely to the degree that specific neural and muscular patterns come to be elicited by specific stimulus patterns. Moreover, not only do objects thus come to release behavior patterns in the child, but the objects themselves exhibit certain modes of behavior. The mother, who smiles, talks, feeds the infant, handles him in various ways; the father, who handles him in somewhat different ways; the dog who walks about and barks—all of these not only constitute visual, auditory, and tactual patterns, but also such patterns in movement and action; the behavior patterns of the child therefore come to include adjustments to these movement factors. Now these behavior patterns are of course built up in relation to situations which vary considerably from time to time. Certain features of situations which are usually or frequently present are sometimes absent; likewise, the neural and general physiological states in which these situations find the child from one time to another are subject to considerable variation. But the more thoroughly the behavior patterns have become established and the more integrated their organization, the more certain will it become that the occurrence of parts of situations or of parts of behavior patterns will activate, at least implicitly, the entire integrated patterns. Thus the sight of the mother comes to elicit pursing of the lips and incipient nursing movements which were originally elicited by tactual and other stimulation; the sight of the father may elicit incipient play activities which have formed part of the 'father-situation' on past occasions. These examples also illustrate how the child comes to show 'expectation' of certain behavior on the part of persons and objects; that is, since the behavior pattern of the child as it has been built up in these situations has included adjustments to the usual behavior of these persons and objects, when now this integrated behavior pattern is set off by certain visual or auditory components of the total situation, it includes these adjustments in incipient or anticipatory form. Now, as we have seen, a certain number of continually recurring situations in the infant's life include as more or less constant components the sound-sequences pronounced by adults and frequently repeated by the infant. The consequences of this fact are twofold. In the first place, the sounds, as features of recurring situations, become capable of activating the total behavior pattern established in relation to the total situation; and in the second place, the utterance, being imitated by the child, becomes an added component in his total behavior pattern; as such a component, it becomes capable of *re*activating or maintaining in action the entire pattern of which it forms a part. Words thus become components both of stimulus-situations and of response-patterns. As has been pointed out, other components of response-patterns may also occur on occasions when the rest of the pattern is not elicited and may then reactivate the whole pattern. But these other components are not so well adapted to the dual stimulus-response function and to social interaction. Gestures come nearest to meeting the requirements, but gestures interfere with manual responses to situations; they are less effective as stimuli, since they require special orientation, and as responses they require much more muscular energy than do vocal responses. The latter are adapted to the production of sounds of greatly varying quality and intensity by means of very slight muscular changes. And, finally, and most important, so far as the child is concerned, it is the vocal stimuli and responses which have received conventional, social development for this function in the history of the adult group in which he finds himself; hence words constitute the uniform and constant accompaniments of various complexes of situation and of behavior. As compared with utterances, other components of behavior patterns are much more variable and are also less conventionalized, more individual in their rôle. The pattern of non-verbal responses to articles of food or to the household cat may vary greatly in a given child from one time to another, and the variation among different children may be still greater; the vocal utterance, however, remains constant, because it is a social affair. Thus the vocal utterance becomes one of the many ways of responding to a situation, and it is of especial importance because it becomes a *focus* or *center* around which all of these ways of responding become organized, and by which they can all be activated. To speak the word *dog* before a child is to set him in readiness to engage in the behavior appropriate in dealing with dogs. And this preparation for response is initiated whether the child himself or someone else utters the word. An interesting illustration is given by Lorimer (1929, p. 81). A girl (age 1:4) was sitting in her high chair. Suddenly she said "ball!" although no ball was in sight. Upon being let down from her chair, she went to the sideboard under which the ball was apt to roll, got down on hands and knees, and looked for it. Not finding it, she went to the couch, under which she found it. Throughout this whole process she kept repeating the word "ball." What were the conditions which set off the verbal activity is not clear; probably the general situation, including the sideboard, the floor, etc. At any rate, once this response occurred, it was followed by a series of acts which had on previous occasions been among the responses to this situation. A verbal response-stimulus can thus maintain a pattern and train of actions, and it can do so more precisely than can a general 'set'; for it is a far more precise surrogate for both 'goal-object' and 'consummatory response.' When an adult 'forgets what he was looking for,' the general 'set' of seeking something is still present; what has failed is perhaps in many cases the verbal surrogate; at any rate, the supplying of this surrogate will again set him in appropriate action.

The relationships between verbal and manual behavior offer a rich field for experimental investigation, the results of which might well be of great theoretical as well as practical (pedagogical) importance. Many experimenters (e.g., Warden, 1924; Carr, 1930; Husband, 1928) have reported that the learning of manual tasks of the maze type takes place most efficiently when the movement sequence is verbalized. Experimental work suggests that the effectiveness of such verbalization depends upon two factors among others. First, this effectiveness depends upon the ease with which *unit movements* making up the patterns or sequences can be verbalized. In the usual types of stylus and finger mazes, the movements are up, down, right, left. The subject's previously established verbal-manual habits make it an easy matter to learn sequences of such movements in verbal form, and such learning may be more efficient than 'kinesthetic-tactual' learning for two reasons: (1) greater temporal overlap of responses is possible; that is, while the second movement cannot be carried out until the first has been completed, nothing prevents the subject from saying *up, right* while he is making either the first or the second of these movements; (2) the verbal sequences can be rehearsed between trials and between practice periods. The more readily such verbalizations occur, the more does the so-called *manual* learning become in actuality *verbal* learning, and this fact should be borne in mind in evaluating the studies of relative learning and retention efficiency in manual as compared with verbal tasks (cf., e.g., the experiments of McGeoch and Melton, 1929). At the same time, I have found, in unpublished experiments, that the verbalizations may occur more readily and accurately when accompanied by the manual movements, and that, when subjects are asked to recite verbally (in the absence of the apparatus) a learned manual sequence involving the use of the fingers in push-button fashion, many of them make the finger movements in abbreviated form while reciting (to some, however, it never occurs to do this; they rattle off the recitation in purely verbal fashion). This of course merely points to the fact that the verbal-manual relation is not one-sided; the stimuli associated with each type of response are among the conditioned elicitors of the other.

As distinguished from movement sequences of the above types, there are probably many types of skill which, as Renshaw and Postle (1928) have suggested, "have components for which there are no communicable language equivalents," and the acquisition of such skills, as these experimenters have shown, is not facilitated by preliminary verbal instruction. Renshaw has elsewhere (1928) suggested, on the basis of experimental study, that such tasks are not 'serial' in nature, but that the learning "consists solely in acquiring skill in reacting to each local situation as it is presented in the present," on the basis of verbally unanalyzed visual-tactual-kinesthetic cues. It is undoubtedly true that much manual behavior is extremely complex and variable, and it would follow from our discussion of linguistic forms as 'recurrent sames' that a one-to-one relationship between manual movements (analyzed on a physical or physiological basis) and verbal utterances is not to be expected. Two observations should, however, be made: First, the degree to which manual behavior is functionally analyzed into units to which correspond verbal surrogates will depend in some degree upon the historical and practical conditions of this behavior, in the individual as well as in the group; just as the conditions of life of an individual or a group may be reflected in the utterance of different specific linguistic forms in relation, e.g., to each of a hundred different kinds of birds or plants, or to many different parts of a tool, so the components of a very complex manual act may be verbalized in very detailed fashion where individual or cultural factors favor this. Even if pursuit learning as it ordinarily occurs is not of true serial character, but consists of a multitude of momentary adjustments, it is not inconceivable that these momentary adjustments might be verbalized up to some limit of precision, and that the possibility would then be present of true serial learning, again within certain limits. Though the efficiency might actually be less under these conditions, the possibility of *social control* would be present. (Consider, however, the fragmentary and incomplete nature of verbal control as it is developed by an individual, a matter to be discussed presently.) Secondly, in cases where individual movements and short sequences are not under verbal control, larger [and of course biosocial; see Renshaw (1928)] units of behavior may be under such control, as when we request an expert marksman to hit the target one inch below the bull's eye; such control is usually all that is required for social and practical purposes [though perhaps not for *pedagogical* purposes; concerning the difficulties here, see Carr (1930)]. Watson (1924a) has called attention to the fact that an enormous multiplicity of bodily habits is established in the child before linguistic development is adequate for any specific verbal control. In some degree, striped-muscle components of these habits may later be verbalized, but *most of the visceral* ('emotional') *components remain unverbalized throughout life,* though a great deal of visceral organization "is constantly forming without verbal organization." The obvious reason for the unverbalized state of visceral organization is its non-social and private nature; at most verbalizations may be established "when the acts of belching, elimination, releasing of gas, masturbation, sex intercourse and the like are exhibited in the presence of elders." Another source of verbal conditioning is of course the medical; the child learns to report 'a pain in his stomach,' or even a 'pylorospasm.'[8] He also learns to verbalize the complex conditions associated with accept-

---

[8] I owe this example to Dr. Homer Wheelon, who was the original demonstrator, by fluoroscopic technique, of many of these conditions of the digestive tract. Previous to such demonstrations, the patient could of course have only a 'stomach ache'; the fluoroscope 'socializes' the specific internal conditions and thus brings them within range of physician-patient pedagogy. As for verbal *control* of visceral processes, this is of course limited by their visual and social inaccessibility, so that pedagogy usually develops only in relation to the impingement of these processes on the external environment. The establishment of such control is, however, not impossible; bladder control is an example, and experimental conditioning to verbal stimulus has been demonstrated for the pupillary reflex; in the latter case, dualistic psychology would say that a previously 'involuntary' process has become 'voluntary.'

ance or rejection of objects or of simple stimuli by reporting that he experiences 'pleasantness' or 'unpleasantness'; later, if he is trained in certain psychological laboratories, he may report that he experiences 'bright-pressure' or 'dull-pressure.'[9] But obviously nothing approaching the precision of environmental-verbal-manual correlations is possible in the case of visceral stimulus-response relations, a fact which is the source of great difficulties for physicians and much profit for 'psychoanalysts.'

A second factor which affects the efficiency of verbal control of manual tasks is the degree to which a single brief verbalization may determine a whole series or complex of movements. Thus Heron (1924) found that certain of his mazes could be 'correctly' traversed if the subject verbalized as follows: "Always go as far as possible and press firmly against each succeeding side which interrupts progress." Once such a verbalization had occurred, no further 'errors' would be made. There are some tasks which apparently cannot be adequately performed at all unless brief generalized verbalizations have been formulated, although the tasks involve manual movements; in these cases the adaptive behavior must be elaborated, the problem solved, in verbal terms, often of the *counting* type. After the verbalization has been perfected, the manual movements *may* occur without error, even though the specific nature of the problem offered is varied within certain limits. Such a task has been studied by Waters (1928) and discussed by Carr (1930). The latter also discusses the relation between tuition and learning. Thus, for example, to what extent can the acquisition of manual skill be hastened by providing the learner with verbalizations? The studies of Carr and his students indicate that the efficacy of such guidance is strictly limited. The suggestion might be made that the verbal guidance which individuals ordinarily use in their acquisition of skill consists in extremely fragmentary and individualistic 'tags' *derived* from the forms of ordinary language, and that these 'tags' occur in combination with other fragmentary cues (eye movements, local muscular tensions, unverbalized environmental factors, etc.), so that the behavior is by no means guided throughout or exclusively by verbal cues, and so that the individual is not able to give precise verbal description or instruction to others. In the social control of behavior, the topic here being discussed is of course of great importance, and not only in the pedagogy of manual skills. Consider for example the attempts which all societies make to insure 'moral' or 'socialized' behavior by means of maxims, commandments, and slogans. The difficulty here is in integrating these verbalizations with all of the varied concrete situations and specific modes of behavior which the censors of a society regard as coming under the head, e.g., of 'honesty' or of 'modesty.' Hence it fre-

_____

[9]On this topic, see P. T. Young (1930), who discusses the difficulties of 'affective psychology.' The matters which we are here discussing are presumably of fundamental importance for 'experiential psychology,' since an important *instrument of research* (language) of this type of psychology is in question (at least from the point of view of the *experimenter* in the observer-experimenter relation). For a critical discussion, see Lashley (1923).

quently happens that the teachers content themselves with establishing the verbalizations in relation to a standard situation such as the school-room or church; economic and other factors may also lead to the divorce-ment of practical behavior from the traditional verbalizations, although the utterance of the verbalizations is still enforced.

Categories. Linguistic forms are members of *form-classes* (Bloomfield, 1933, pp. 264 ff.). The class of a form may be determined (1) by its structure and constituents, e.g., certain morphological features such as suffixes, or certain syntactic features as in prepositional phrases; (2) by a special constituent or *marker,* e.g., the preposition *to* in *to go;* (3) by the syntactic position and construction in which it occurs, e.g., *goose, man, he* may all occur in the appropriate position of the actor-action con-struction. Here we have an enormously complex system of habits which every speaker of a language must acquire. These habits are cultural 'givens,' socially transmitted through the ages. The two kinds of genetic approach which might seem to be open to us do not take us far. The acquisition of syntactic and morphologic habits in the child has been studied, but such studies, though important in other connections, show only by what stages and with what errors a socially pre-formed behavior pattern is built up. Historical linguistics takes us back to earlier pat-terns which are just as complex and just as much 'givens' as are our present patterns. Presumably these categories and form-classes developed as progressive modifications of linguistic forms in relation to the environ-ment and practical concerns of the countless generations of speakers, but a speculative reconstruction of these factors is likely to lead to nonsense.[10] What we *can* do (the linguist having provided an analysis of the form-classes and syntax) is to investigate the influence of these form-classes on the behavior organization of the speakers of a given language. Thus, if in a given language the name for a certain class of persons belonged to the same linguistic form-class as forms which we would translate *skunk, rat,* and particularly if this form-class were small, presumably a reference to that class of persons would carry with it, in speaker and hearer, rather specialized attitudes and behavior patterns, and these atti-tudes and patterns would seem to the speakers (if the question were raised) natural, inevitable, and inherent in both word and object; for the ordinary speaker, the object *is* what its name says it is. This is an expression of the degree to which utterances become integrated with other behavior. The existent form-classes thus impose restrictions on the or-ganization of behavior, which restrictions are all the more effective because

---

[10]Perhaps this is an appropriate place to introduce the perennially necessary statement that there are no known peoples or 'tribes,' primitive or otherwise, who lack or have lacked a language, or who have a language of such limited vocabulary that it must be eked out by gestures, or have a language lacking in both morphologic and syntactic complexity. Some languages lean more heavily on syntactic construction, others on morphology, but all languages are highly com-plex affairs and adequate to the organization of complex behavior and the trans-mission of elaborate cultural patterns.

these classes are 'givens' acquired in each speaker's infancy, and are universal in the community.[11] All this may cause serious mischief even in sophisticated uses of language. To quote from Bloomfield (1933, p. 270):

> The categories of a language, especially those which affect morphology (book : books, he : she), are so pervasive that anyone who reflects upon his language at all, is sure to notice them. In the ordinary case, this person, knowing only his native language, or perhaps some others closely akin to it, may mistake his categories for universal forms of speech, or of "human thought," or of the universe itself. This is why a good deal of what passes for "logic" or "metaphysics" is merely an incompetent restating of the chief categories of the philosopher's language.

To exemplify the fact that linguistic classes must be treated as cultural 'givens' behind which we cannot go, the following is quoted (Bloomfield, 1933, pp. 271 f.):

> The gender-categories of most Indo-European languages, such as the two of French or the three of German, do not agree with anything in the practical world, and this is true of most such cases. In the Algonquian languages, all persons and animals belong to one category, an "animate" gender, but so do some other objects, such as "raspberry," "kettle," and "knee"; all other objects (including, for instance, "strawberry," "bowl," "elbow") belong to the other, "inanimate" gender.

Much organization of behavior in relation to environment is thus imposed by the categoric patterns of a language. An enormous amount of additional organization is imposed by linguistic classifications which are not categoric (in the technical sense) but are rather of the type usually discussed in psychology under the heads of association, abstraction, and generalization. Thus we have, in English, the class *tree*, which includes *maple*, *fir*, etc.; or *evergreen*, which includes *fir*, *spruce*, etc. *Color* includes *red*, *blue*, etc.[12] The significance of this for behavior organization has been discussed by Weiss (1929a). In relation to very many objects and conditions the speaker learns to utter a number of different forms. Both the stimulus and the response patterns to which these forms are related will differ in range of variability. Thus the patterns which on various occasions accompany the utterance of *cat* are less varied than are those which accompany the utterance of *animal*. In so far as an object or situation can elicit utterances of different degrees of specificity, whole systems of related techniques and attitudes can be made available in addition to those which are relatively specific. If the appearance of new adaptations (particularly in cases where a critical degree of novelty in

---

[11]For a discussion of such limitations, see Sapir (1933).

[12]What is categoric in one language may not be so in another, a very important point frequently misunderstood; see Bloomfield (1933, pp. 277 ff.). Perhaps it might be convenient to use the terms *categoric* and *non-categoric* form-classes, the latter term being used for groups of the *tree: maple, fir* sort; although this would necessitate a re-definition of *form-class*.

environmental pattern renders the usual specific responses inadequate) depends upon the possibility of variability in response, we have here an obvious source of varied reactions. Frequently, of course, a situation elicits at first a less specialized utterance, correlated with a wider variety of stimulus-response patterns, and this utterance (or the whole situation, or a changed aspect of the situation) associatively elicits a more specialized utterance which determines the adaptation. Moreover, linguistic organization is not only hierarchical; the existence of what might be called 'horizontally associated' forms such as *cat, dog, horse* also helps to bring the related behavior patterns into interaction. Stimulus-response patterns thus become organized in systems and hierarchies, and tremendous abbreviation is made possible in the techniques of social control and of pedagogy. However, while linguistic organization is thus the basis for much variability in adaptation, it also imposes restrictions of a sort similar to that mentioned above in our discussion of categoric classes. Thus, e.g., if an *utterance* is, for a given psychologist, also a *psychophysical act,* while for another psychologist it is also a *biosocial response,* the further procedures will be limited to those which have been integrated with these respective class-names. The techniques and hence the resulting data and conclusions will in the one case as in the other be incapable of variation beyond certain limits; this is a universal characteristic of linguistically organized behavior, and it is not possible for a human being to shed his language and nakedly to view the world in its nakedness, though the attempt is often made. At most, in our example, we might say that an utterance is *both* a biosocial response *and* a psychophysical act and try to proceed with the two sets of technique simultaneously; sometimes such ventures are productive of more adequate and highly integrated techniques and verbalizations; sometimes they are productive of complete befuddlement. At best, we would still be restricted by a finite and peculiar type of organization, just as we were before.

Experimentally, the organization of linguistic forms has been studied by means of the association technique, e.g., by Thumb and Marbe (1901) and by Esper (1918). Such experiments show that, in such languages as German and English, word-stimuli elicit predominantly word-responses which belong to the same grammatical category. In addition, they may belong to the same more restricted non-categoric class; thus in the stimulus-response pair *rose—violet,* both words are substantives, and they are both likewise names of flowers, a class which is not categoric in English. Presumably the stimulus-word *rose* elicits the response-word *violet* because both words have frequently been heard and uttered in common contexts (i.e., in temporal contiguity). But the chief reason for such joint occurrence comes out more precisely, as I believe, in another type of experiment. This type of experiment (Esper, 1925, 1933; see also Wolfle, 1932) involves the establishment in individuals of a set of 'artificial linguistic forms.' The subject learns to respond to each of a number of 'nonsense objects' with a specific 'nonsense name' (whereby the name of course ceases to be nonsense). Various degrees of similarity in the objects and various degrees of phonemic alternation or of suppletion in the forms are among the variables studied in the various experiments. It is thus possible to study under somewhat controlled conditions some of the factors which affect linguistic organization.[13] When subjects have been thoroughly practiced in such a 'system' over a period of many months, it is found that the 'words,' when presented as stimuli in an association test, elicit definite other 'words' of the system. Thus, if to object A corresponds name a, and to object B, name b, and if, in the association test, a elicits b, then it is regularly true that during the previous months of practice it was b which occurred most frequently as a momentary 'error' in naming A, and frequently it is true that the stimulus-response relation B—b was unstable; that is, B frequently elicited names of the other objects. What suggests itself then is as follows: No linguistic form has an absolutely specific and constant relation to an absolutely specific and constant stimulus-pattern. Consider for example the relation of *names* to *objects*. "When we say that a certain response is the specific response to an object, we are really stating a statistical probability; given numerous occurrences of this object, this response is the one which will occur most frequently" (Esper, 1933). On various occasions, then, the object will elicit, not the name most specific to it, but the names relatively specific to similar or related objects, and these various responses will have various frequencies of occurrence.[14] On many occasions also there will be a tendency for the object to elicit *both* a less specific *and* a more specific response. This 'multiple response tendency,' as I have called it, is a characteristic occurrence in the experiments, and I take it to be the same tendency as gives rise to *lapsus linguae* and to linguistic *adaptation* and *contamination*; it might even be supposed that a good deal of the morphology of language has arisen through this tendency. The fact that verbal associations exist (*gravis—levis*, etc.), I take then to be not a primary phenomenon which can explain the above processes (as was supposed by Thumb and Marbe), but rather a result and none-too-reliable indicator of the frequent occurrence of such 'multiple responses.' I say none-too-reliable, because I by no means believe that verbal associations cannot arise in other ways (i.e., they may result from *any* temporal contiguity of the utterances). *This lack of specificity in the relations between linguistic forms and stimulus-response patterns is the chief cause of the difficulty in defining 'meanings';* in formulating definitions, we have to treat as recurrent sames a system of continually shifting relations.

---

[13]I say *linguistic organization*, but whether conclusions drawn from such experiments have any importance for linguistic science must be determined by linguists. Professor P. Kretschmer has told me that he regards such experiments as *Spielerei*.

[14]I am not appealing here to similarity as a 'principle of learning'; what variations in a given stimulus-pattern may occur without a failure of a given response must be regarded as an experimental problem; we can, however, predict that if a given stimulus-pattern elicits a given response, there will be other patterns which will also elicit it. Thus arise 'biosocial equivalences.'

An experimental technique for studying the factors influencing the establishment of 'abstract' and 'generalized' verbal responses has been devised by Hull (1920). This technique consists in teaching the subject to respond with the name of the 'radical' to a series of complex Chinese characters in which this 'radical' is embedded ('abstracting'), and thereafter testing his ability to make this response to other complex characters in which this 'radical' is also embedded ('generalizing'). Among the important results of this study is the finding that, if the desired skill consists in making a 'generalized' response to a number of previously unseen characters having one feature (the 'radical') in common, no reliable difference in efficiency appears between the methods of (a) presenting the common feature in isolation during training and (b) presenting it embedded in complex characters. However, definitely greater efficiency resulted from making the common feature, during training, especially prominent (as by printing it in red) in the concrete context of complex characters.

DERIVATIVE USES OF LANGUAGE

Non-social Speech. We have said that utterances are primitively both substitutes for situations, in that they become capable of eliciting the behavior appropriate to these situations, and also substitute responses, in that they may constitute on occasion almost the sole responses to situations. Originally, of course, situations usually elicit in the child not only the utterances but also other behavior; but as he grows older the responses to many situations are more and more reduced to the verbal components, whereby orientation, manipulation, locomotion, or utterances are elicited in others. Thus the verbal components begin as *additions* to the response patterns and become more and more *substitutes* for them, in both their stimulus and their response aspects. At the same time, the verbal behavior is being reduced in increasing degree to implicit forms. The early establishment of speech occurs, as we have seen, under the tuition of adults, and necessarily in an overt manner. But the general principle of conditioning would not lead us to expect that utterances established in relation to persons *and* other stimulus-response patterns would fail to be elicited in relation to these patterns in the absence of persons. *Non-social* speech thus develops, and plays a guiding rôle in individual activity and adaptations (as in the 'constructive' manipulation of objects). It is favored in this rôle by the speed with which it can occur (as compared with a sequence of gross manual and locomotor acts), so that it is peculiarly adapted to the function of *tentative* or *anticipatory* adjustment. It may occur even when the practical acts are prevented by accompanying circumstances. Moreover, it may be continually repeated during a sequence of manual and locomotor acts (thus serving to guide and maintain these acts) without interference with the overt behavior. And, finally, painful consequences of manual responses may inhibit such responses without terminating the speech activity. But in the absence of other persons much variation in degree of overtness of the utterances will occur, since no factor is present to enforce overtness. Much abbreviation of utterance and a gradual reduction to implicit form is therefore likely to occur. But *social* situations may also favor such reduction; situations may be present which tend to elicit utterance on the part of the child, but the adults on many occasions suppress such utterance. Moreover, in situations of the 'game' type the child learns to run through a preliminary speech series in implicit form before making a final and resultant utterance. [For an interesting discussion of this, see Lorimer, (1929, p. 69).] In these ways, speech, which in its origin is a *social* affair, becomes in addition and in increasing degree a method for the elaboration of *individual* adaptations and for the guidance of individual trains of behavior. A new method of 'trial-and-error' adaptation is thus substituted for or added to the manipulative type of 'trial-and-error' adaptation, and it has the following advantages: (1) greater speed; (2) smaller energy expenditure; (3) less serious consequences resulting from 'errors'; (4) availability of a greater range of behavior through the control of related systems of response by the patterns of linguistic organization; (5) the fact that it can occur when practical behavior is prevented by context or by absence of the situation (for speech having to do with absent situations can be elicited by factors, extra-organic or intra-organic, which have on occasion been components of such situations; such speech then serves as a stimulus-substitute for the entire absent situation and may then initiate a sequence of verbal dealings with it). In the development of such individual speech activity, much abbreviation and many modifications of linguistic forms and of syntax will occur, so that even if an individual has elaborated a solution of a problem in such terms he may find great difficulty in 'translating' his verbal sequence into social speech. This is all the more true because the implicit speech 'tags' often (perhaps usually) occur merely as components in a complex sequence which also includes incipient gestures, local muscle tensions, visceral tensions, etc.; many of the essential links in the sequence may consist solely in the latter sort of activity. About the nature of such individualized speech activity we have no precise knowledge; suggestive examples are given by Watson (1920) and by Lashley (1923), and the general topic is discussed by Watson (1924b). That tongue movements occur during 'thinking' has been shown by Thorson (1925), who found, as was to be expected, great individual variation in such movements. To her negative finding that 'thought' may occur without the registration of tongue movements by her particular apparatus I attach no importance. Jacobson (1932) has recently demonstrated action currents in tongue and lips during 'thought'; this method is of course far more sensitive than Thorson's system of levers. All such methods, however, can demonstrate only the occurrence of laryngeal or oral activity and the varying intensities and physiological patterns of such activity during 'thinking.' They can reveal nothing concerning the *nature* of individualistic speech, i.e., concerning its linguistic forms, its deviations from social speech, its sequences, and its relation to the elaboration of adaptations and to the organization of behavior.

The problem with which objective investigation must deal is not efficiently stated by the question, "Is thinking merely the action of language mechanisms?"[15] I propose that the discussion of 'thinking' be left to experiential psychology and that objective investigation take for its topic the genesis, characteristics, conditions, and functional relations of *the implicit elaboration and organization of adaptive behavior.*

Conversation. The fact that utterances may function both as responses and as stimuli has other consequences. The 'speaker's situation' may be reduced to the presence, facial expressions, and utterances of other persons, and the 'hearer's response' may be reduced to further utterances, gestures, and facial expressions. Such reduction occurs in conversation, the telling of tales, the instruction of others, and the planning of future action. Verbal interaction may thus occur in the absence of practical situations and of manual-locomotor adjustment to such situations. There is thus in a sense a cutting-loose of speech from immediate practical concerns and concrete environment.[16] The course of such speech is in part determined by individual implicit elaborations in the intervals occupied by the utterances of others. These facts must have had a considerable influence on the development of language. A great number of linguistic forms cannot be defined in terms of any concrete 'speaker's situations' or 'hearer's responses,' but only in terms of other forms; that is, both of these aspects of the 'meaning' of such utterances consist in other utterances. Presumably the patterns of syntax were determined chiefly in such 'autonomous' uses of language. There is thus created an entire artificial environment, which is in touch with the concrete environment only at certain points or only indirectly. Collaborative organization of practical techniques and planned manual-locomotor action are of course mediated by such speech, but many of the steps in such planning are very remotely related to concrete situations; they are almost purely verbal, and have no other rôle than to determine further utterances leading toward the final verbalization which actually guides the practical behavior. An excellent illustration of this use of language is given by Bloomfield (1933, p. 28).

In relation to many features of the environment, the only relatively

---

[15]See the papers read at a 'symposium' on this subject, published in the *British Journal of Psychology*, 1920, vol. 11; particularly the article by Watson.

[16]This derivative type of speech, together with the literary type, was probably the basis for the traditional definition of language as a method for the communication of ideas; linguists who occupy themselves with the recording of narratives or the study of written documents might well fail to see the primary relation of speech to practical situations and to behavior. Similar factors would affect the viewpoints of philosophers. For our fundamental linguistic theory we are concerned not so much with *derivative* as with *primary* uses of language, as is evidenced by the oft-repeated and obviously true assertion that the real, living language which changes and develops is the spoken language of the people; it is evidenced also by the interest which has always been taken in the problem of the origin of language, a problem whose insolubility has perhaps been due in part to our preoccupation with highly derivative uses of language.

specific response acquired is a verbal one; the 'hearer's response' to such utterances consists chiefly in orientation or further utterances. Thus we learn to call the moon by its name, but this name is integrated, for most persons in our society, with no behavior other than 'looking' and the utterance of related speech. Such almost exclusively verbal responses have been discussed in psychology under the head of *'discrimination.'* In the case of such environmental features to which no specific *non-verbal* responses have been attached, it is not surprising that they are 'discriminated' if a *verbal* response is attached to them, and not 'discriminated' otherwise. The classical experiment is that of Lehmann (1888), who showed that if subjects were taught numbers for each of a set of nine shades of gray they could identify these grays with considerable accuracy, whereas in the absence of such verbalizations their success was but little better than chance.

Finally, we have that form of purely social speech in which linguistic meaning plays almost no part. This is 'phatic communion' (Malinowski); it is exemplified by such utterances as greetings and 'polite' or 'sympathetic' murmurs. From time to time astonishment is aroused by independent discoveries of the fact that the most inappropriate and outrageous utterances can be inserted in the stream of 'phatic communion' (as at a 'reception' or 'tea') without disturbance of this stream, provided only that the appropriate facial expressions and non-phonemic 'tones of voice' are maintained.

Literary, Philosophical, and Scientific Language. Between this and the preceding type of language transitional forms of course occur, as in oral narrative. The criterion which might be said to differentiate literary language is its enforced conformity to explicitly formulated and arbitrary rules, which are quite different in nature from the 'rules' of ordinary language; the latter are *ex postfacto* generalizations formulated by linguists in somewhat the manner in which psychologists attempt to determine the 'laws' of human behavior. In literary language, the rules govern subject-matter, vocabulary, syntax, rhythm, etc., and may in addition require phonemic features which differ from those of ordinary language (as, e.g., in stage and ceremonial speech). Such arbitrary regulation antedates the origin of writing; in illiterate communities, the rules are orally transmitted, and deviations from them in ceremonial narrative or epic recitation are readily detected by the hearers. For written language, the rules are formulated in books such as the ancient 'rhetorics' or the recent *Modern English Usage* of H. W. Fowler. While such rules govern formal, ceremonial, and written language, and while writers expend great labor in ascertaining the 'correct' forms and syntactic constructions, the speech activity which constitutes the preparation for such formal uses is of the type discussed above under the heads of *non-social speech* and *conversation.* A startling illustration of this fact was afforded a few years ago by a group of scientists who were so incautious as to publish a stenographic record of a 'symposium' in which they took part; the illustration is startling because of the contrast between their symposiac utterances and their published writings. Equally startling are the 'lapses' which are to be found embedded in formal writing; examples will undoubtedly be found in abundance in the present chapter. Such lapses may be regarded as reprehensible by connoisseurs, but their occurrence is not surprising in view of the fact that from childhood to death we are almost continuously engaged in conversational and in non-social speech activity, whereas we have to learn the formal language in somewhat the fashion in which we learn to play bridge.

In literary and philosophical writing we see the final stages in the development of an almost purely linguistic environment and of almost exclusively linguistic behavior.[17] The limits of such development are reached in mathematics and in logic. For human adaptation, the significance of such language consists in the fact that certain of its forms, arrived at by purely verbal sequences, may by indirection impinge upon the world of practical concerns and be the occasion for new adaptive techniques and integrations.[18]

BIBLIOGRAPHY

ADAMS, S., & POWERS, F. F. 1929. The psychology of language. *Psychol. Bull.*, **26**, 241-260.

ALLPORT, F. H. 1924. Social psychology. Boston: Houghton Mifflin. Pp. xiv+453.

ALVERDES, F. 1927. Social life in the animal world. New York: Harcourt, Brace. Pp. ix+216.

BLANTON, M. G. 1917. The behavior of the human infant during the first thirty days of life. *Psychol. Rev.*, **24**, 456-483.

BLANTON, S., & BLANTON, M. G. 1927. Child guidance. New York: Century. Pp. xviii+301.

BLOOMFIELD, L. 1914. An introduction to the study of language. New York: Holt. Pp. 335.

————. 1926. A set of postulates for the science of language. *Language*, **2**, 153-164.

————. 1932. Review of *Lautgesetz und Analogie*, by E. Hermann. *Language*, **8**, 220-233.

————. 1933. Language. New York: Holt. Pp. ix+564.

BORING, E. G. 1929. A history of experimental psychology. New York: Century. Pp. xvi+699.

---

[17] Philosophical and scientific discourse is subject, at least in theory, to the rules of logic and of scientific method, as well as to those of rhetoric. However, were these rules to be religiously observed by writers or rigidly enforced by editors, the volume of such discourse would be enormously reduced. For a critical discussion of 'lapses' from the rules, as exemplified in psychological writings, see Johnson (1932).

[18] For reviews and bibliographies of the literatures of the psychological, pedagogical, philosophical, physiological, pathological, and physical aspects of speech and language, see Adams and Powers (1929), Powers (1929), Travis (1929), Metfessel (1929), Urban (1929), Buchanan and MacPhee (1928). The two articles on linguistic development by Latif (1934) appeared too late to be utilized in this chapter.

BOUTAN, L. 1913. Le pseudo-langage. Observations effectuées sur un anthropoïde: le gibbon (*Hylobates Leucogenys* Ogilby). *Actes de la Soc. Linéenne de Bordeaux*, **67**, 5-80.

BUCHANAN, M. E., & MACPHEE, E. D. 1928. An annotated bibliography of modern language methodology. Toronto: Univ. Toronto Press. Pp. 428.

CARR, H. 1930. Teaching and learning. *J. Genet. Psychol.*, **37**, 189-219.

CRAIG, W. 1908. The voices of pigeons regarded as a means of social control. *Amer. J. Sociol.*, **14**, 86-100.

DE LAGUNA, G. A. 1927. Speech: its function and development. New Haven, Conn.: Yale Univ. Press. Pp. xii+363.

DELBRÜCK, B. 1901. Grundfragen der Sprachforschung. Strassburg: Trübner. Pp. vii+180.

DEWEY, J. 1926. Experience and nature. Chicago: Open Court. Pp. 443.

ESPER, E. A. 1918. A contribution to the experimental study of analogy. *Psychol. Rev.*, **25**, 468-487.

————. 1925. A technique for the experimental investigation of associative interference in artificial linguistic material. *Linguistic Soc. Amer., Lang. Monog.*, No. 1. Pp. 47.

————. 1933. Studies in linguistic behavior organization: I. Characteristics of unstable verbal reactions. *J. Gen. Psychol.*, **8**, 346-381.

FENTON, J. C. 1925. A practical psychology of babyhood. Boston: Houghton Mifflin. Pp. xvi+348.

FURNESS, W. H. 1916. Observations on the mentality of chimpanzees and orang-utans. *Proc. Amer. Phil. Soc.*, **55**, 281-290.

GARDINER, A. H. 1932. The theory of speech and language. London: Oxford Univ. Press. Pp. x+327.

GARNER, R. L. 1900. Apes and monkeys: their life and language. Boston: Ginn. Pp. xii+284.

GESELL, A. 1925. Mental growth of the pre-school child: a psychological outline of normal development from birth to the sixth year, including a system of developmental diagnosis. New York: Macmillan. Pp. 447.

GLAZE, J. A. 1928. The association value of non-sense syllables. *J. Genet. Psychol.*, **35**, 255-267.

GUTHRIE, E. R. 1930. Conditioning as a principle of ·learning. *Psychol. Rev.*, **37**, 412-428.

————. 1935. The psychology of learning. New York: Harper. Pp. 258.

GUTZMANN, H. 1902. Die Sprachentwicklung des Kindes und ihre Hemmungen. *Zsch. f. Kinderforsch.*, **7**, 193-216.

HERON, W. T. 1924. Individual differences in ability versus chance in the learning of the stylus maze. *Comp. Psychol. Monog.*, **2**, No. 8. Pp. 60.

HULL, C. L. 1920. Quantitative aspects of the evolution of concepts. *Psychol. Monog.*, **28**, No. 123. Pp. 85.

HUSBAND, R. W. 1928. Human learning on a four-section, elevated, finger maze. *J. Gen. Psychol.*, **1**, 15-28.

IRWIN, O. C. 1930. The amount and nature of activities of newborn infants under constant external stimulating conditions during the first ten days of life. *Genet. Psychol. Monog.*, **8**, 1-91.

JACOBSON, E. 1932. Electrophysiology of mental activities. *Amer. J. Psychol.*, **44**, 677-694.

JESPERSEN, O. 1922. Language. New York: Holt. Pp. 448.

JOHNSON, H. M. 1932. Some follies of 'emancipated' psychology. *Psychol. Rev.*, **39**, 293-323.

KÖHLER, W. 1925. The mentality of apes. New York: Harcourt, Brace. Pp. 342.

LASHLEY, K. S. 1923. The behavioristic interpretation of consciousness. *Psychol. Rev.*, **30**, 237-272, 329-353.

LATIF, I. 1934. The physiological basis of linguistic development and of the ontogeny of meaning. *Psychol. Rev.*, **41**, 55-85, 153-176, 246-264.

LEHMANN, A. 1888. Ueber Wiedererkennen. *Phil. Stud.*, **5**, 96-156.

LORIMER, F. 1929. The growth of reason. New York: Harcourt, Brace. Pp. xii+231.

MAJOR, D. R. 1906. First steps in mental growth. New York: Macmillan. Pp. xiv+360.

MALINOWSKI, B. 1927. The problem of meaning in primitive languages. In *The meaning of meaning*, by C. K. Ogden and I. A. Richards. London: Harcourt, Brace. Pp. 451-510.

MARKEY, J. F. 1928. The symbolic process and its integration in children. New York: Harcourt, Brace. Pp. xii+192.

McCARTHY, D. 1929. The vocalizations of infants. *Psychol. Bull.*, **26**, 625-651.

McGEOCH, J. A., & MELTON, A. W. 1929. The comparative retention values of maze habits and of nonsense syllables. *J. Exper. Psychol.*, **12**, 392-414.

METFESSEL, M. 1929. Experimental phonetics. *Psychol. Bull.*, **26**, 305-323.

MEYER, M. F. 1922. Psychology of the other-one. Columbia: Missouri Book Co. Pp. 439.

OGDEN, C. K., & RICHARDS, I. A. 1927. The meaning of meaning. New York: Harcourt, Brace. Pp. xxii+363.

PAGET, R. 1930. Human speech. London: Harcourt, Brace. Pp. xiv+360.

PAUL, H. 1920. Prinzipien der Sprachgeschichte. Halle: Niemeyer. Pp. xiv+428.

PEDERSEN, H. 1931. Linguistic science in the nineteenth century. (Trans. by J. Spargo.) Cambridge, Mass.: Harvard Univ. Press. Pp. x+360.

PFUNGST, O. 1912. Zur Psychologie der Affen. *Ber. ü. d. V. Kong. f. exper. Psychol.*, 200-205.

PILLSBURY, W. B., & MEADER, C. L. 1928. The psychology of language. New York: Appleton. Pp. vii+306.

POWERS, F. F. 1929. Psychology of language learning. *Psychol. Bull.*, **26**, 261-274.

PREYER, W. 1905. Die Seele des Kindes. (6th ed., ed. by K. L. Schaefer.) Leipzig: Fernau. Pp. 462.

RENSHAW, S. 1928. An experimental test of the serial character of a case of pursuit learning. *J. Gen. Psychol.*, **1**, 520-531.

RENSHAW, S., & POSTLE, D. K. 1928. Pursuit learning under three types of instruction. *J. Gen. Psychol.*, **1**, 360-367.

REXROAD, C. N. 1932. Outline of the conditions under which learning occurs. *Psychol. Rev.*, **39**, 174-183.

SAPIR, E. 1921. Language. New York: Harcourt, Brace. Pp. vii+258.

————. 1925. Sound patterns in language. *Language*, **1**, 37-51.

————. 1933. Language. In Vol. 9 of *Encyclopaedia of the social sciences*, ed. by E. R. A. Seligman and A. Johnson. New York: Macmillan. Pp. 155-169.

SCHÄFER, P. 1922. Beobachtungen und Versuche an einem Kinde in der Entwicklungsperiode des reinen Sprachverständnisses. *Zsch. f. päd. Psychol.*, **23**, 269-289.

SHERMAN, M. 1927. The differentiation of emotional responses in infants. *J. Comp. Psychol.*, **7**, 265-284, 335-351.

STERN, C., & STERN, W. 1922. Die Kindersprache. Leipzig: Barth. Pp. xii+434.

THORSON, A. M. 1925. The relation of tongue movements to internal speech. *J. Exper. Psychol.*, 8, 1-32.

THUMB, A., & MARBE, K. 1901. Experimentelle Untersuchungen über die psychologischen Grundlagen der sprachlichen Analogiebildung. Leipzig: Engelmann. Pp. 87.

TRACY, F. 1893. The language of childhood. *Amer. J. Psychol.*, 6, 107-138.

TRAVIS, L. E. 1929. Recent research in speech pathology. *Psychol. Bull.*, 26, 275-304.

URBAN, W. M. 1929. The philosophy of language. *Psychol. Bull.*, 26, 324-334.

VENDRYES, J. 1925. Language: a linguistic introduction to history. New York: Knopf. Pp. 378.

WARDEN, C. J. 1924. The relative economy of various modes of attack in the mastery of a stylus maze. *J. Exper. Psychol.*, 7, 243-275.

WATERS, R. H. 1928. The influence of tuition upon ideational learning. *J. Gen. Psychol.*, 1, 534-549.

WATSON, J. B. 1920. Is thinking merely the action of language mechanisms? (V.) *Brit. J. Psychol.*, 11, 87-104.

―――. 1924a. The unverbalized in human behavior. *Psychol. Rev.*, 31, 273-280.

―――. 1924b. The place of kinaesthetic, visceral, and laryngeal organization in thinking. *Psychol. Rev.*, 31, 339-347.

―――. 1925. Behaviorism. New York: People's Instit. Publ. Co. Pp. 248.

WEISS, A. P. 1925. Linguistics and psychology. *Language*, 1, 52-57.

―――. 1929a. A theoretical basis of human behavior. Columbus, Ohio: Adams. Pp. xvii+479.

―――. 1929b. The measurement of infant behavior. *Psychol. Rev.*, 36, 453-471.

WOLFLE, D. L. 1932. The relation between linguistic structure and associative interference in artificial linguistic material. *Linguistic Soc. Amer., Lang. Monog.*, No. 11. Pp. 55.

WUNDT, W. 1901. Sprachgeschichte und Sprachpsychologie. Leipzig: Engelmann. Pp. 110.

―――. 1911-12. Völkerpsychologie. Vol. I: Die Sprache. (3rd ed., two parts.) Leipzig: Engelmann (Kroener). Pp. 695; 678.

YERKES, R. M. 1925. Almost human. New York: Century. Pp. 278.

YERKES, R. M., & LEARNED, B. W. 1925. Chimpanzee intelligence and its vocal expressions. Baltimore, Md.: Williams & Wilkins. Pp. 156.

YERKES, R. M., & YERKES, A. W. 1929. The great apes. New Haven, Conn.: Yale Univ. Press. Pp. xix+652.

YOUNG, P. T. 1930. Studies in affective psychology. *Amer. J. Psychol.*, 42, 17-37.

CHAPTER 12

MAGIC AND COGNATE PHENOMENA: AN HYPOTHESIS

RAYMOND ROYCE WILLOUGHBY

Clark University

INTRODUCTORY

The subject-matter of this chapter, in common with many other topics of undoubted social importance, has remained on the anecdotal and speculative level for a very long period indeed. It is not difficult to understand why this is so; in most branches at least of psychological endeavor the feasibility of a method is in direct proportion to the probability of the conclusions to be derived from its use and in inverse proportion to the significance of those conclusions. Thus we have on the one hand a body of well-attested information on matters concerning which nobody but experts has any interest, and on the other hand a body of poorly attested information on matters of very great importance. Acceptance of the task of writing about the subject-matter here treated more or less automatically places the writer in the position of arriving at a result which belongs in the latter category, for there are no practicable methods for crucially testing hypotheses in this field—the best observations either are made in pseudo-experimental situations, from analogies of varying cogency, or are more or less critical, statistically controlled (or not!) observations made by persons of varying clinical astuteness.

Confronted with these facts, then, the present writer must reconcile himself as speedily as may be to the necessity of using the time-worn method of previous writers: citation, inference, speculation. He may be supported, however, in this necessity by two or three considerations. The first of these is the vast importance of the topic. On any reasonable ethical theory of the place of science in life or of knowledge in conduct, there are matters of such far-reaching meaningfulness that any knowledge about them with any degree of probability exceeding .5 is a more valuable possession for mankind than knowledge of a very high degree of probability about certain other matters. Examples are the source of the improved mental hygiene that has been observed to accompany or follow the practice of prayer, as contrasted with the problem of whether or not the retina of a rat is capable of reacting to a given color. The total importance may be thought of crudely as a sort of product of probability by meaningfulness. We should naturally prefer generalizations high in both, but we should not fail to give some weight to examples low in probability provided they are very highly meaningful.

A second consideration is that it may not be necessary at this stage, pre-scientific as it is, to go over again exactly the same ground covered by

Frazer (1925) and Tylor (1888). *The Golden Bough* settled for all time the problem of amassing an adequate sampling of data; twelve more volumes—or twelve hundred—of additional magical curiosa would hardly manufacture additional comprehension. There is no need for mere encyclopedic "completeness," and no attempt has been made here to "canvass the literature." An attempt has been made instead to' present selected instances brought to bear upon an hypothesis. This tactic, too, is nothing new; it may be said that one more hypothesis piled upon the legion already proposed will hardly further our knowledge, and in the long run this may be true. However, a certain number of new insights have been won since the nineteenth century, and by their help it appears to the writer that we may be standing on the brink of some sort of synthesis of a number of heretofore more or less isolated phenomena into some single, rather far-reaching point of view. An attempt at such a synthesis is the excuse for this chapter. It has probably not been extensively noted, for example, that the processes of shamanistic divination are much like those of the obsessional neurotic; and day-by-day observation of the latter has revealed that the burdened but essentially normal person may evolve out of his attempts to resolve his tensions a magical system in all respects similar to that of the primitive, but "pure" from the kind of cultural contagion and social transmission which a generation ago were taken as self-evident in any discussion of the subject. Continued reflection upon the range of data accessible is likely to show that there are no very sharp boundaries of the sort that so exercised our grandfathers. The most reasonable answer to their crowning problem, "What is the essential difference between Magic and Religion?" is probably that there is none, and the exact criterion of demarcation between the subjective experiences of mystical ecstasy and febrile delirium will probably never be found.

The phenomena to be reviewed, therefore, will be considered as a more or less continuous series, and the assumption of this form constitutes part of the hypothesis presented. The other part is that they are to be regarded as defensive efforts of the organism to neutralize or resolve tension or "anxiety." Stating the case in these terms suggests a consideration of the possible nature of anxiety-tension, and the main discussion is therefore begun in these terms, but more with the intent of presenting a reasonably well-rounded picture than with that of formulating a serious neurophysiological hypothesis. Following this, a collection, so far as possible from original sources, of examples of the phenomena in question will be presented; these will be arranged in the presumable order of intensity of the anxiety requiring control, as judged by the strength of the controls; and accompanying notations will endeavor to make clear the structure and function of each item of behavior cited. In a section on the social significance of anxiety and its control an endeavor will be made to summarize the prevalence, sources, and effects of anxiety in relation to culture-type, to estimate the efficacy and desirability of the control methods enumerated, and to consider whether or not practical improvements can be devised. A brief final section will present the limited number of points of view which have been advanced on the subject.

THE NATURE OF ANXIETY

Phenomena Manifested Clinically. Externally, the victim of an anxiety attack presents a fairly characteristic group of symptoms, for the enumeration of which we may draw upon the treatise of Stekel (1908) : the pulse rate is increased, the amplitude diminished; the face is blanched; dyspnea appears; there may be cold sweat; the pupils are enlarged, and the eyes may protrude; the muscles of the face and body may display heightened tonus; the blood pressure may be increased; there is dryness of the mouth and excessive hunger and thirst; there may be heightened pressure in the bladder and rectum and loss of sphincter control; there may be screaming or mutism; vomiting, weakness, dizziness, trembling, paresthesias, cramps, and insomnia may be a part of the picture. The degree to which the phenomena exhibited are disturbances of the functions under sympathetic control is striking, and is made more so by the later work of Richter (1927), who found that in a unilaterally sympathectomized patient both sweating and galvanic reactions to "emotional" stimuli were present on the intact side only, and by that of Kling (1934), who found in a population of over 800 students a marked association between psychoneurotic, gastro-intestinal, and allergic symptoms.

Subjectively, the patient experiences great distress. He may complain directly of anxiety, or his attention may be concentrated on symptoms of suffocation, pressure or pounding of the heart, etc. He frequently fears imminent dissolution; dreams in which some horrible fate is about to befall him are typical; sometimes he is unable to assign any adequate cause for his condition, but often he has projected and rationalized it to his own satisfaction. The whole picture on the psychic side, in short, is one of an experience of an imminent and tremendously hostile and powerful mysterious force, before which the patient is completely disorganized and seeks only to escape or find help; in extreme cases, he is unable even to do that.

The chronic anxiety state, of course, lacks the cataclysmic aspects of the attack; in it the symptoms are modified to the point where the patient can support them, or almost support them, for protracted periods, succumbing to an attack only if and when additional stress is encountered. The most noticeable external symptoms of the chronic anxiety state are hyperkinesis and hyperloquacity, often of a strained sort, hypochondriac trends, over-solicitousness, distrust (including self-distrust), over-reaction to danger situations, lapses and obscure self-punishments, and, in general, a state of anxious expectation which in all but the most sophisticated constantly seeks to find or create external situations adequate to justify it. Subjectively, the anxiety dream and the misfortune fantasy, and preoccupation with catastrophe, are characteristic.

Temporally, the onset of the attack appears to coincide with (1) a weakening of the controlling forces or (2) a strengthening of the sources or increase in the volume of anxiety. Thus Stekel mentions the emergence of acute anxiety states after acute intoxications with atropin, hyoscine, cocaine, etc., and in the course of chronic toxic conditions like alcoholism (as in delirium tremens, a typical anxiety attack with specific content) ; anxiety may also appear as a concomitant of deprivation in these conditions. These phenomena are presumably to be thought of as conditioned on chemical alterations, possibly in the direction of greater permeability, in the state of the sympathetic nervous system. More commonly, however, the attack seems to be dependent on a sudden increase in the amount of anxiety to be controlled. Thus in a case reported by Stekel a young widow who felt that her remarriage was impossible because of her child succumbed to a typical anxiety-attack while reading aloud to her family an erotic passage from a romance.

The recession of anxiety, either acute or chronic, appears to coincide with the reestablishment of a connection between the imaginal and at least the implicit sectors of the motor system [in which connection Watson's (1928) restatement of "the unconscious" as "the unverbalized" appears to be extremely pertinent]. In the case cited above, the anxiety receded completely when the young woman disregarded the admonitions of her counselors and married the man of her choice. In another case of Stekel's (typical of successful psychotherapy in general) an anxiety-attack subsided immediately when he enabled the patient to complete a crucial sentence which had been obstructed by a (psychogenic) lingual cramp.

In summary, then, the phenomena of anxiety as manifested clinically are objectively those of disturbance of the systems under sympathetic control, and subjectively those of great distress and impending catastrophe; they may be concentrated in an attack or constitute a more or less chronic condition of the organism. Their irruption usually coincides either with a sudden increase of tension due to conflicting impulses or with a decrease of capacity (usually organic and environmental) to tolerate such tension ; and their recession with resolution of this tension and consequent reestablishment of a connection between the imaginal and motor systems.

Pavlov's "Neurotic" Dog. Pavlov (1927) found that his dogs could be divided into two broad types, which he regards as the two poles of a continuum. The first, which he calls the excitable type, is characterized by great motor activity, but forms conditioned reflexes only under special conditions (formation of several concurrently in order to avoid drowsiness, etc.) ; the second or inhibitable type behaves cautiously and with marked "reserve," but forms exceedingly stable conditioned reflexes without any particular difficulty. Special experimental set-ups lead to disturbances easily recognized as pathological in both these types, and the types of disturbances are, as might be expected, different in a manner paralleling the types of dogs. These differences appear to represent essentially the reactions of congenitally different nervous systems to the same neurophysiological insult, and this insult is, in Pavlov's words, "a conflict between the processes of excitation and inhibition which the cortex finds difficult to resolve."

In one excitable dog a conditioned alimentary reflex was established to an electrical stimulus of a sort which would normally elicit strong defense reactions. Upon attempting to generalize it by applying the stimulus to a number of cutaneous areas, a point was suddenly reached at which the conditioned elementary reaction already established was lost and was replaced by the normal defense reaction, and a number of months did not suffice to remove the supervening restlessness and irritability. In another series differentiations were set up between a circle and an ellipse, and upon successive approximations of the ellipse to the circle a similar threshold was reached where the responses already established abruptly disappeared, and "the hitherto quiet dog began to squeal in its stand, kept wriggling about, tore off with its teeth the apparatus for mechanical stimulation of the skin, and bit through the tubes connecting the animal's room with the observer, a behavior which never happened before; on being taken into the experimental room the dog now barked violently, which was also contrary to its usual custom."

In a further excitable dog progressive delay of the response led, at two minutes, to the same general breakdown of organized behavior: "and with a further prolongation of the delay to three minutes the animal became quite crazy, unceasingly and violently moving all parts of its body, howling, barking, and squealing intolerably; all this was accompanied by an unceasing flow of saliva [the response was in terms of salivary reflex], so that although the secretion increased during the action of the conditioned stimuli all traces of the delay completely disappeared." The inhibitable dog solved this problem without difficulty, probably due to the fact that it was not necessary to present it with several conditioned responses at once to prevent it from falling asleep. But an inhibitable dog in which the establishment of normal conditioned responses was followed by the electric-stimulus problem described above lost its normal responses under the same conditions that had initiated the anxiety outburst in the excitable one, and "started at this time to lose weight and became very dull."

In still another series of experiments it was observed that, while the dogs remained externally healthy, the following of a stimulus at a positive rate by one at a negative rate without any intervening interval resulted in the extinction of the reflexes already established, i.e., a change in the direction of inhibition. Experiments made after a flood, the consequences of which had involved the dogs, showed also that many of the established reflexes had been lost, and in one of these animals a small trickle of water into the experimental room elicited defense reactions and immediate interruption of a series of uniformly positive responses. The similarity of these results to those reported by child-guidance workers (e.g., Blanchard, 1929) for children with specific mental disabilities will be evident.

Recovery from these pathological states was not very uniform or complete. Among those conditions which exercised a favorable influence, however, were reestablishment of the simpler response and the presence of the experimenter. Thus in the ellipse-versus-circle experiment, "a fresh development of the latter differentiation [circle versus 2:1 ellipse] up to its previous exactness progressed twice as slowly as at first," but during the reestablishment of this crude differentiation the animal gradually became quieter, returning finally to its normal state. In the post-flood experiments "the experimenter now remained in the same room. . . . All the reflexes showed an immediate restoration in the first experiment and the animal took the food with avidity, but it was sufficient for the experimenter to leave the animal alone for all the abnormal symptoms to recur." In the case of one dog the presence of the experimenter's clothes within olfactory range was sufficient for maintenance of the normal state.

The similarities between the behavior of the dogs and that of the anxiety patients are so striking as not to require extensive summarization. In both cases the initiation of antagonism between strong excitatory and strong inhibitory nervous excitation throws the organism into a condition of generalized activity, as if a general nervous irradiation or overflow were in process (in the congenitally excitable type of nervous system). The establishment of connections allowing the discharge of the excitatory impulses through motor pathways (reestablishment of the simpler reflexes, praxitherapy for neurotics) or the associative "promise" of such establishment (presence of the experimenter, dependence on the physician) will to some extent bring about recession of such general irradiation. In passing, it may be noted that response in Pavlov's experiments was always in terms of the salivary reflex, which is under the control of the sympathetic system.

Similar but less extreme results are reported for children from four Russian experimenters by Krasnogorski (1925). They suggest that the organism when subjected to conflicting stimuli may defend itself by (1) generalization of excitation, which we are suggesting should be equated with anxiety, or (2) generalization of inhibition, also clinically observable in children with this type of stimulation history.

Kapustnik (1930) has reported that conditioned responses formed to real stimuli were generalized to their spoken or printed symbols, and conversely; also that extinction of the responses to the real stimuli was accompanied by extinction of the responses to the corresponding symbols. No mention is made in the abstract of the important case converse to the latter; but there is strong presumption that all successful psychoanalysis is describable as extinction of conditioned responses to real and second-order stimuli consequent upon extinction of the responses to the corresponding verbal symbols; and this formulation is obviously extensible also to magic and the major part of the series of cognate symbolic phenomena here treated.

Ovsiankina's Interrupted-Action Experiments. In Ovsiankina's (1928) experiments the subjects were set a variety of tasks (mechanical puzzles, geometrical puzzles, formboard problems, copying, sorting, bead stringing, paper-chain making, modeling, tower building, drawing, folding, etc.) and at various points (near the beginning, in the middle, three-fourths done, near the end) were interrupted in a number of ways, classifiable as apparently accidental interruptions and interruptions obviously due to the experimenter's will. In the former type of interruption resumption of the interrupted activity occurred in all the cases (47); in the latter, it occurred in 224 and tended to recur in 27 more (83 per cent of all interruptions, for the two categories). It is, however, the experiences and modes of reaction of the subjects with which we shall be most concerned here.

There was a very high incidence of conflict behavior immediately following the interruption; there were protests, anger, and discomfort; when another task had been substituted, it was performed with only partial attention, the subject being conscious that something was hanging over him, that the second task was a diversion from the main work, etc. In one case there was, subsequently, at first amnesia for the interruption and then a transposition of the (actually) interposed second task to the end of the first one. In those cases where interruption had been by the experimenter's verbal prohibition, there was in some cases a furtive resumption of the task. There was a fairly high incidence of *"spielerische"* and *"Ersatz"* resumptions and completions, in which a gesture or symbol of the full solution appeared to resolve the tension to a tolerable degree. In some cases the idea of the uncompleted task disappeared from consciousness, while the affect of discomfort remained. After resumption of the original task subjects often worked more intensively, as if to forestall a second interruption, and one subject drew away from the experimenter for this purpose. There were attempts to solve interrupted problems imaginally while working at the second task. The resumption tendency operated as well in the case of unpleasant as in that of pleasant tasks. Different degrees of tension were of course observed.

In almost all cases actual completion, even by a symbolic or partial route, brought marked relief from the generated tension.

The author's comments upon a protocol from the series in which furtive resumption followed the experimenter's express prohibition might well serve to summarize the aspects of the material which are relevant here:

> Hier kämpfen zwei Kräfte: Das Quasibedürfnis drängt auf Vollendung der unfertigen Arbeit, andererseits möchte die Vp. sich doch nach dem Vl. richten und vor allem sich selbst nicht zu sehr gehen lassen.

That is, we have here a condition of true anxiety (of low degree, on account of the frankly experimental and unreal nature of the set-up) generated by setting into action nervous impulses freely discharging through the motor system and then suddenly opposing to them, as in the neurotic patients and in Pavlov's dogs, counter-impulses which do not permit discharge of the still generating excitation; the anxiety, as before, is presumably to be equated with the overflowing or irradiating excitation.

A virtual repetition of the Ovsiankina experiment has been reported by Freeman (1930). Although the findings are fully confirmatory of those of Ovsiankina and Lewin ("Initiation of a task does set up an organic disturbance which is normally equilibrated by completion. Tasks once initiated tend to be continued in spite of interruption. The experimental facts indicate that these interrupted task-sets never completely lose their directive influence on behavior") a "reinterpretation" is offered which differs from that of Lewin apparently as the American language differs from the German. Lewin's "psychic tensions" become "increase in muscular tension" and "competition for the final common path," much as Freud's "unconscious," is better understood on cisatlantic shores as "subliminal"; but the essential difference seems to be highly tenuous. The important finding is the demonstration of some sort of tension, conflict, or competing excitation, and this appears to be the physiological substrate of what is referred to psychologically as anxiety.

Luria's Disorganization Experiments. The experiments of Luria (1932) were made by his method of synchronizing verbal association-responses with voluntary motions of the right hand, record being kept meanwhile of the involuntary motions of the left hand. Auxiliary data, such as reaction-times, respiratory and vasomotor phenomena, utterances, general motility, etc., were also recorded. The particular significance of the work from our point of view lies in the fact that it dealt with persons under the most powerful natural or artificial anxiety; the former were students facing peculiarly significant general examinations and defendants in murder and other felony cases; the latter, persons in whom, under hypnosis, profound conflicts had been implanted. Full citation of records is presented by the author to support his inferences; space will permit only the latter here.

The most outstanding finding immediately suggests those of the other authors we have examined: The entire behavior of the subjects is disorganized, as if by a general overflow or irradiation of excitation grown too great to be contained in the normal pathways. The activity proceeds, says Luria, directly to its terminus without being able to tolerate any inhibition whatever; and when the experimental reaction has been completed, disorganization (of a somewhat lower degree) still persists, as if this reaction were insufficient to resolve the great amount of tension present. A more complete reaction, however, such as actually passing through the examination or confessing the crime, markedly reduces the anxiety and the motor disorganization as shown by the experiment. In certain criminal cases the adoption of a stereotyped reaction is sufficient to free the record and to some extent the behavior from the more prominent traces of disorganization. The author points out that there is still another way to prevent the emergence of symptoms of disorganization, namely, to isolate the impulse from the motor system, in which case the experimental record shows a concentration of affect at associated points; this is clearly the mechanism made famous by Freud under the name of repression, and we might expect from the observations of that author what Luria finds, viz., that such an isolated impulse continues to press for motor expression, often in apparently quite inadequate ways, as in Ovsiankina's *Ersatzbefriedigungen.* The case of the widow reported by Stekel is well described in the following formulation by Luria: "The removal or the insulation of the affect from the consciousness and its overt appearance [or, we may add, its threatened overt appearance] is followed by an acute motor storm." We have indicated in passing the significance of Ovsiankina's *Ersatzbefriedigungen* for the study of magic; they appear again in even more unmistakable form in certain cognitive *"Kurzschlüsse"* noted by Luria:

> Those Kurzschlüsse which are so typical of affective thinking have precisely this neurodynamical base: the constant preparedness to re-actions, the inability to inhibit the process in the preliminary stage [due, we may suppose, to the excessive amount of excitation to be mastered], not allowing its manifestation, and finally the impulsive judgment made suddenly and under the influence of external stimuli—these are the fundamental signs characterising the thinking of the person during the state of affect and the partial thinking of the hysteric. (pp. 181-182)

A final quotation will serve to summarize this most important series of results:

> Some fairly powerful (and usually connected with the subcortical apparatus) system of activity falls under the sway of the inhibition. The conflict arising is the more intense the more imperative is the arrested tendency and the more categorical the inhibition; the tension produced in the neurodynamic system strives to escape along the path of inadequate innervation, the adequate exit being closed, and there is thus created the symptoms of an intense diffuse excitation, charac-teristic of the affect.

Freud's Hypotheses on the Anxiety-Neuroses. In 1894 Freud was led by the accumulation of clinical experience to separate from neurasthenia a syndrome which he called the anxiety-neurosis, and in the following year (1895) he developed this concept further, particularly on the etiologi-cal side, in the course of a reply to criticisms directed at his hypothesis by Löwenfeld. We have already noted the principal features of the syndrome itself in our consideration of the remarks of Stekel, who, in fact, took them as a basis for parts of his discussion; we have in addition to note here that Freud enunciated at this time an hypothesis as to the etiology of this neurosis which deserves our attention. This hypothesis stated, briefly, that somatic [nervous?] sexual excitation is more or less continuously generated by the stimulation of certain end-organs (in the male in the seminal vesicles), which upon accumulating to a certain degree is able to overcome the resistance to conduction in the pathways leading to the cortex and thus to express itself ideationally. Still further excitation will demand psychical relief, the completely adequate form of which is normal sexual intercourse. Under certain circumstances, however, the excitation may be deflected from the "mind," and "expended subcortically in quite inadequate reactions," thus preventing "the somatic sexual excitation from being assimilated psychically." The characteristic syndrome of anxiety thereupon follows, and "the symptoms of anxiety-neurosis [are shown] to be in some measure surrogates for the specific activity which should follow upon sexual excitation but has not done so." Further, "the psyche develops the affect of anxiety when it feels itself incapable of dealing (by an adequate reaction) with a task (danger) approaching it externally; it develops the neurosis of anxiety when it feels itself unequal to the task of mastering (sexual) excitation arising endogenously." As to the symptom of anxious expectation, the following is particularly pertinent in connection with the problem of magic: "There is here a quantum of anxiety in a free-floating condition, which in any state of expectation controls the selection of ideas, and is ever ready to attach itself to any suitable ideational content."

Freud has expressed this theory in terms of sexual reactions, which is perhaps not surprising if it be considered that this is the overwhelmingly preponderant source of maladjustment of sufficient degree to bring about anxiety attacks and neurosis; and he has also spoken somewhat obscurely about "mastery" by the "mind." The hypothesis would appear to be entirely compatible, however, with those we have previously considered, viz., that anxiety arises from the interposition of an obstacle in the path of free motor expression of nervous excitation, and represents a more or less generalized overflow or irradiation of the blocked discharge.

Neuro-physiological Work. Although pure physiology has little to say about the nature of excitation and particularly of counter-excitation or inhibition in the nervous system, it is important that a physiologically based hypothesis as to the nature of anxiety be not in conflict with anything that is known. We shall consider the findings of Bayliss and of Sherrington.

In Bayliss' (1931) summary of inhibition we read that inhibition is to be regarded as the converse of excitation, that the morphology in many cases is such as to suggest strongly that excitatory and inhibitory impulses impinge in the same way upon the same motor organ (muscle) from two different nerve structures, and that by suitable experimental precautions it is possible to set up an exact balance between them. The author also points out that in the hypothetical case where neuron A (motor) is inhibited by neuron B, the action of a third inhibiting neuron C upon B would have the apparent effect of exciting A although its action was really confined to B.

Sherrington (1906), in his famous formulation of the final common path, stresses the fact that antagonistic reflexes have successive but not simultaneous control of the effector neuron and draws attention to the experimental finding that cessation of inhibition may permit the original excitation to take effect. He points out further that reflexes may be arranged in order of prepotency and that there is a correlation between the prepotency of a reaction and its habitual intensity. In this connection, those reflexes "initiated in receptors which considered as sense organs excite sensations of strong affective quality" are the most prepotent in their power to usurp the final common path, while those concerned with bodily tonus, posture, etc., are among the least so.

It is plain that the neurophysiological findings make little relevant contribution of a positive nature to the problem of the nature of anxiety; but it is also evident that they offer no definite evidence against our hypothesis. One reason for the indecisiveness of this result appears to lie in the remark last quoted from Sherrington: the strictly physiological evidence has been gathered from animals sometimes as low in the phyletic scale as the frog, and has been concerned largely with electric and mechanical stimulation, with responses in terms of those tonic and muscular reflexes which Sherrington cites as most susceptible to displacement by others. It is to be supposed that conflicting excitations via the normal pathways of reflexes or more complex physiological units "initiated in receptors which considered as sense organs excite sensations of strong affective quality" would result in clearer evidence on the genesis of disorganization of behavior.

Summary of the Data on Anxiety. From clinical, physiological, and psychological data it has been shown that throwing into conflict powerful excitations toward and against motor reaction regularly results in disorganization of behavior, subjective distress, and persistent drive toward relief. This syndrome has been called variously "affect," "tension," "anxiety," and "neurosis."

In three instances it has been shown that the drive toward relief tends to set into operation implicit or explicit forms of behavior, the principal characteristic of which is their abbreviated or condensed or symbolic character and their relative indifference and impermeability (because of the necessity of attaining relief as quickly as possible) to the ordinary checks, delays, and inhibitions imposed by objective reality; thus they are objectively non-adaptive, but are subjectively adaptive to the extent that the relief aimed at is actually effected. It is suggested that these *"Kurzschlüsse"* and *"Ersatzbefriedigungen"* form a more or less graded series, according to the vigor and overtness of the reaction and presumably to the imminence and strength of the anxiety to be controlled, of which magic is a particularly striking and representative member. In the next section we shall consider the members of this series in more detail.

THE SERIES OF ANXIETY-CONTROLS

The entire series of anxiety-controls proper may be presented in two sections, viz., controls involving implicit reactions (imagery, belief, etc.) and controls involving explicit (motor) reactions; to these may be added a section on sublimation, not strictly continuous with the others inasmuch as it seems to represent rather modes of permanently dissipating anxiety than modes of keeping it neutralized.

Reactions Implicit

Among the implicit reactions we may distinguish two subdivisions, one in which the normally present criticism from the sense of reality is still present, but abeyant, and one in which this reality-check is completely lapsed; we may interpolate between these a third subdivision dealing with aids to lapse of the reality-check. It should be noted that, just as explicit reactions involve more of the psychic organization than implicit reactions, controls in which the reality-check is totally lapsed involve more of the psychic organization than controls in which the reality-check is only abeyant; the suggestion is, of course, that the tensions to be kept in bounds are stronger in those instances involving more of the total personality.

Reality Abeyant Only

Fantasy. One of the commonest forms of the phenomena under discussion is the spontaneous play of imagery known as fantasy, revery, or day-dream. It has been studied by Varendonck (1921), and we cite an example from his collection:

> To whom will Major H. transmit my report? either to the chief medical officer or to the gestionnaire; not to Countess V. Still, the latter will have her say in the matter. What if I warned her so as to dispose her in my favor and arouse her feelings against the culprit? I begin to compose the letter which I intend to write to her with this purpose, but am interrupted by the idea: What if I enclosed my visiting-card (with my academic title)? What if I asked Captain Y. to send his corporal with the letter to the hospital? And I might add a copy of my report to it. But what a loss of time to copy that long report! Still, I might enclose my own copy and tear the sheet from my field notebook. However, I might still want that copy. I could ask her to return it to me after perusal. But what if I went to see her myself? I shall have to put on my best uniform. I'll send the orderly to ask her for an interview and tell him to give her my visiting-card. (Acting:) I am talking to Lady V., and relate the events. Perhaps she will offer to send the man back to his regiment. I shall simply require a slight disciplinary measure. [Etc.] (pp. 64-65)

It is easily to be seen that the genesis of the association chain is closely connected with a condition of tension (aroused by the aggression of a soldier), and that it proceeds in the general direction of the relief of this tension; in the course of the association process, problem after problem arises, for each of which solutions are proposed until one arises to which no further problem is associated, i.e., one which leaves no check on action and permits tension partially to be relieved. The comparative slightness of the transition between verbal and visual-kinesthetic or even general associating ("acting") is especially to be noted.

Hypnagogic imagery. Meyerson (1929) reports a phenomenon called by him *images-éclairs,* which he divides into *images-heures* and *images-pays.* In the former

> In the course of a task, most often an absorbing intellectual task, more rarely during rest or in the course of a walk, I have a sudden experience like a vision of a clock face with two hands and a precise notion of the time. . . . I could not give any precise details of the form, color, or size. . . . I am obliged to say that the clock which I see has neither size nor form. . . . It seems to me that I grasp directly a moment of time, of duration, and that it is a matter not of any time, but of *my* time, *my* duration. . . . I might say: This clock is a little bit of myself.

The *images-pays* occur under similar conditions. In them

> I suddenly have a vision of a landscape with the principal characteristics of its geographical conformation, its flora, sometimes its fauna, and always its inhabitants. . . . It is most often a landscape

of some other time, seen at some other time, as during childhood or adolescence, or at least an image which calls up a landscape seen at some other time. . . . I am in this landscape. . . . I do not see myself, nevertheless I am certain of my presence. It is indefinable. It is a little as if I were everywhere, or even as if the landscape were I.

The similarities with the mystical state are outstanding and are commented upon by the author himself, who cites Delacroix (1922, pp. 256 ff.) and Woodworth's comment (1915, p. 16) that the effect of a scene added to the emotional value of an image and to a certain personal attitude is sufficient to give an impression of reality. He also inquires whether the certainty attaching to certain hallucinations may not be similarly derived. The discussion following the paper brought out the more or less general nature of the phenomenon, and the remarks of Delacroix indicated that a symbolic significance is ordinarily not difficult to demonstrate.

A letter in *Nature,* dated March 17, 1923, by M. E. J. Gheury de Bray elicited the publication of further experiences of this sort in the 1926 volume of that journal (Bostwick, Gheury de Bray, Kenneth). These observers were interested primarily in the structural rather than in the dynamic aspects of the phenomena, but the latter appear to have been the same form of imagery noted by Meyerson:

> I had exchanged a few words on the weather with the person who had awakened me, and I was therefore *quite awake;* I had closed my eyes for a few minutes before getting up, when, to my surprise and delight, an image at an *absolute standstill* appeared suddenly. The image represented a grassy rising slope with outcropping rocks, the details being so clear that, had time permitted, I could have counted the rocks; it lasted some eight or ten seconds before vanishing, and during that time it remained quite motionless. While observing its details I was fully realising that I was witnessing the process of unconscious mind-picture forming at the hitherto unobserved zero end of the scale. . . . A hypnopompic image appears as a whole, in all its intricacy of wonderful details, without any volition whatever.

Ferretti (1926) has presented a short series of hypnagogic images experienced by him which are unique in that they are accompanied by associations. Although this author finds himself greatly at odds with Freud as to interpretation (more greatly, it may be suspected, than would Freud), he regards it as clear that the hypnagogic image is in the same continuum as the dream and differs from it only in the lack of suspension of the critical faculties; and his examples appear to demonstrate this point adequately, as well as to indicate relationships to such phenomena as apparitions.

> I awoke from a dream in which, while knowing that I was dreaming, I had cut into the flesh of a live baby in the arms of a woman whom I had deceived as to my intentions, in order to study its behavior; and I awoke while seeing another woman with a baby, whom I also wished to deceive. With my eyes still closed, I was fully conscious of lying prone in my bed, with an oppressed feeling

in my chest, and a feeling of visceral weight. Meanwhile the course of the dream, representative and plastic in a lively fashion, continued.

Persisting in keeping my eyes closed in order to remain, if possible, a spectator of the process which was going on, I saw the baby, which was dead, and which now occupied the whole of my field of vision, at a distance of some half a meter from my eyes, transform itself—like a flowing rosy-white mass—into the head of my wife, cut off, and with her lips pointed as if about to give a kiss. The features were very pallid, the lineaments rigid, but they remained so only an instant; while I perceived her by intuition as pure representation, without emotion, she changed ceaselessly— just as flowed before me as a child images of stripes and curves and other chaotic masses from which could emerge forms.

Thereupon her nose became similar to that of her mother, and from her temples to her neck the changing mass formed itself as if in stone, in a plaster cast, rounded, and so the head and neck became a vase in the shape of an egg broken in half, and the color became that of a red terracotta with very primitive inscriptions.

At this point my intellectual curiosity became more active. Why, then, this terracotta?—And the whole image disappeared.

The author's associations begin with his interest in the "analysis" of child behavior, symbolized by the picture of the cutting-apart of the child. But a child cut is a child killed, and the shock of this realization leads him to the comforting, yet "killed" figure of his wife; then to a conversation which he had had with her about her mother; but the mother is dead ("rigid") and the statuesque quality in which this fact is expressed brings a conversation with a student about the psychological principles of primitive art as exemplified in a certain primitive terracotta vase. The author has withheld (presumably for the very good reason that one hesitates to publish his most intimate motives) the deeper associations which any person with psychoanalytic experience would certainly suppose to be present; the structure, however, exhibits clearly its relationships to material like that of Varendonck, which is somewhat more verbalized, and that of the unnamed pseudo-hallucinated patient reported by Nolan (see below); these internal images are evidently thought processes which proceed in terms of sensory excitation. The author reports a second experience as follows:

I awoke early in the morning, not completely rested. With eyes closed, I saw at a distance of about 20 cm. from my head, a little toward the right side, a raised arm, with the fingers somewhat closed; it gave me a disturbed feeling, as if from a threat, but not appearing real.

I understood that such an apparition might be the point of departure of a terrifying delusion in a naïve consciousness. But suddenly taking control of myself, and, observing it attentively without changing my situation, I tried, but with my consciousness somewhat heavy and serious, to propose to myself what other things could be seen in the same fashion. I said inside myself:—Let a foot appear!

There appeared a moment later something wrapped up as if in a white cloth, which might have the approximate size of a foot.

I said:—That would be a foot in a sheet. Let a head appear!

But there reappeared after the foot had disappeared, the same form as at first, which disappeared before I had time to turn my eyeball so as to see whether it corresponded to an entoptic image.

The author associates with this experience the fact that he had suffered an injury to his hand some two months before, which made it necessary for him to sleep with the fingers slightly folded; he supposes that the normal warning to himself, "Be careful that the hand is properly adjusted!" has been expressed, in the imagery peculiar to sleep, in the image plus the feeling of an imminent danger. Two factors are of special interest in our survey: (1) the adequacy of the experience to initiate a magical system—noted by the author in somewhat different terms; and (2) the fact that the unconsciously motivated image was only slightly amenable to change by the intellectual consciousness. The author presents also further images in which sentiments, demands, or warnings seemed to be expressed in sensory rather than in logical terms; in one instance a critical comment on the part of the conscious levels resulted in the disappearance, but present reappearance, of the image.

Pseudo-hallucination. The best characterization I have been able to find for pseudo-hallucination, or hallucination with insight, is that of a patient reported at second hand by Nolan (1928):

> The patient declared, "My ideas appear to me as voices, but I know they are [not] voices. They are not imperative to me, and they have no more influence upon my conduct than the ideas which pass through your mind have upon your conduct."

That is, the pseudo-hallucination is a fantasy in process of passing over into a true hallucination; it is not surprising, therefore, that it is a comparatively transitory state and thus one not frequently reported in the literature. Although investigations of its function in the mental economy of the patient are not to be expected from psychiatrists of the orthodox persuasion, there seems no reason to distinguish its function either from that of the fantasy on the one hand or the hallucination on the other; all, evidently, serve to elaborate material which can minimize anxiety pressures.

An example of pseudo-hallucination in a mystical setting may be found in St. Teresa; it should be observed that the subject saw the vision neither "with the eyes of the body" nor "with the eyes of the soul"—in contrast to occasional visions of her times in which the "eyes of the body" were involved—i.e., in which the reality-check had lapsed and the tension had drawn the perceptive system into its gratification.

> I was in prayer one day—it was the feast of the glorious St. Peter—when I saw Christ by me, or, to speak more correctly, felt him; for I saw nothing with the eyes of the body, nothing with the eyes of the soul. He seemed to me to be close beside me; and I saw too, as I believe, that it was he who was speaking to me. As I was utterly ignorant that such a vision was possible, I was extremely afraid at first, and did nothing but weep; however, when he spoke to me but one word to reassure me, I recovered myself and was, as usual, calm and comforted, without any fear whatever. Jesus Christ seemed to be by my side continually, and as the vision was not

imaginary [i.e., imaginal], I saw no form; but I had a most distinct feeling that he was always on my right hand, a witness of all I did; and never at any time, if I was but slightly recollected, or not too much distracted, could I be ignorant of his near presence. (Underhill, 1911, p. 341)

Aids to Lapse of Reality-Check

Auto-hypnosis. Hypnosis is an ancient method of avoiding the reality-check; the following from an experiment by Young (1926) emphasizes the subjective aspect:

> The hypnosis met with in these experiments seems to be self-hypnosis. S19 in normal life exhibits powers of concentration bordering on deep abstraction; S20 often goes into a reverie amounting sometimes to an ecstasy, while, as priest, he is counting his beads; S's 13 and 14 can put themselves into natural sleep almost at will; S21 has several times hypnotized himself; S22 invariably goes to sleep while riding home on the train, and wakes up just when the train gets to the stop before his own. All that E added to these men was a better chance to concentrate than usual. (p. 356)

Drug effects. The effects of various drugs as an escape from the reality-check are very widely known. From a recent study by Fernberger (1932) we quote two passages which show the striking effects of mescal or peyote.

> Observer 9. . . . there was . . . . evident exhilaration in spite of marked nausea. This observer remarked that he had "never felt worse or had a better time." . . . the designs could be brought to consciousness or eliminated by suggestion. For example, in one case, he had a brilliant vision and said to himself "This would look nice as a peacock feather" and at once the form changed to that of a peacock feather. These visions were apparently unaffected by the drum and rattle rhythms. For example, he reports the whole field covered with an unsaturated colored film which breaks up into intensive points of the same color at each sound of the drum or rattle. A marked slowing of time is reported. When listening to the report of another observer, this subject reported that his visions changed continually to correspond with the report. At another time he tried to suggest visions to another observer and found that he himself was having the visions he was attempting to suggest. . . . There was a very marked anti-aphrodisiac effect which continued for over 24 hours. The anti-fatigue effect persisted for 18 hours. (pp. 373-374)
>
> . . . . All of the observers note, in one way or another, what may be called a condition which approximates a split personality. At no time did the visual effects have reality. In every case the situation was described as apparently a rational self (probably largely verbal in its imaginal background) alongside and distinct from the sensory and concrete visual imaginal self. The two did not mix—the visions remained more or less as abstractions. . . . An Indian reported to Petrullo: "I am not shaking this rattle—God is shaking this rattle—I have nothing to do with it." Observer 1 volunteered the information: "I am not shaking this rattle—my arm is doing it—my ego has nothing to do with the control of the rhythm." The difference between these two statements is one solely in interpretation. It is easy to imagine, on such a basis of split personality, in which the rational self becomes detached and different from the sensory self, how a mystical religious interpretation of approach to the Godhead may be so readily built up. (pp. 376-377)

The following brief quotation from Mead (1932) furnishes another example of the effects of this drug:

> One woman told me that she saw the skies open and Jesus come right down and kiss her feet. The young men tell me that they see white women come to them.

Thus drug and trauma may be regarded as actual interference with the physical mechanism underlying striving and its satisfaction—interference of a sort whose mechanisms, in the present state of knowledge, must necessarily be obscure, but which may be thought of as of such a sort as to inhibit the operation of the critical, reality-testing function and throw into operation over a wider range of the total personality the processes resulting in direct satisfaction of the more insistent needs through perceptual illusion. That such an effect can be brought about by such means may, regardless of whatever hypothesis may be invoked to account for the mechanisms, be taken as evidence for a proposition familiar to observers of "abnormal" phenomena, but not particularly stressed by others, viz., that the critical reality-testing function so easily thrown out of gear by these means (it may be observed that autistic and affective functions such as rage often survive relatively unimpaired even after severe organic damage) is an extremely delicate and presumably recently evolved and unstable form of adjustment. These general mechanisms are presumably biological, common to all individuals of the human species; the Indian, the European, and the African under the influence of narcotic or inanition will suffer invasion of his perceptive system in such a manner as to support the hypothesis that his needs have somehow short-circuited to an illusory satisfaction. But the innumerable bison and the lush green meadows of the starved and fainting Oglala, the thousand-dollar orders of the tipsy salesman, and the field hand's celestial fish-fry with the Lord Himself in attendance are manifestly the cultural versions of the desiderata nearest the individual human needs.

Traumatic experience. The following much-mutilated account of the experience of Black Elk, an Oglala Dakota, may serve as an example of the lapse of the reality-check by traumatic (in this case febrile) experience. Very similar Indian apocalypses were often sought and achieved by earnest young men through inanition and self-torture.

> It was the summer when I was nine years old. . . . I rode in a pony drag, for I was very sick. . . . When we had camped again, I was lying in our tipi and my mother and father were sitting beside me. I could see out through the opening, and there two men were coming from the clouds, head-first like arrows slanting down, and I knew they were the same I had seen before. Each now carried a long spear, and from the points of these a jagged lightning flashed. They came clear down to the ground this time and stood a little way off and looked at me and said: "Hurry! Come! Your Grandfathers are calling you!" . . . . yonder where the men with flaming spears were going, a little cloud was coming very fast. It came and stooped and took me and turned back to where it came from, flying fast. And when I looked down I could see my mother and my father yonder, and I felt sorry to be leaving them. . . . I looked and saw a bay horse

standing there, and he began to speak: "Behold me!" he said, "my life-history you shall see." Then he wheeled about to where the sun goes down, and said, "Behold them! Their history you shall know." I looked, and there were twelve black horses yonder all abreast with necklaces of bison hoofs. . . . Then the bay horse wheeled to where the great white giant lives [the north] and said, "Behold!" And yonder there were twelve white horses all abreast. . . . Then the bay wheeled round to where the sun shines continually [the east] and bade me look; and there twelve sorrel horses, with necklaces of elks' teeth, stood abreast with eyes that glimmered like the daybreak star and manes of morning light. Then the bay wheeled once again to look upon the place where you are always facing [the south], and yonder stood twelve buckskins all abreast with horns upon their heads and manes that lived and grew like trees and grasses . . . . suddenly the dancing horses without number changed into animals of every kind and into all the fowls that are, and these fled back to the four quarters of the world from whence the horses came, and vanished. Then as we walked, there was a heaped up cloud ahead that changed into a tipi, and a rainbow was the open door of it; and through the door I saw six old men sitting in a row. The two men with the spears now stood beside me, one on either hand, and the horses took their places in their quarters, looking inward, four by four. And the oldest of the Grandfathers spoke with a kind voice and said: "Come right in and do not fear." And as he spoke, all the horses of the four quarters neighed to cheer me. So I went in and stood before the six, and they looked older than men can ever be—old like hills, like stars. The oldest spoke again: "Your Grandfathers all over the world are having a council, and they have called you here to teach you." His voice was very kind, but I shook all over with fear now, for I knew that these were not old men, but the Powers of the World. . . . Now there was a wooden cup in his hand and it was full of water and in the water was the sky. "Take this," he said, "It is the power to make live, and it is yours." Now he had a bowl in his hands. "Take this," he said. "It is the power to destroy, and it is yours." Then he pointed to himself and said: "Look close at him who is your spirit now, for you are his body and his name is Eagle Wing Stretches." And saying this, he got up very tall and started running toward where the sun goes down; and suddenly he was a black horse that stopped and turned and looked at me, and the horse was very poor and sick; his ribs stood out. Then the second Grandfather, he of the North, arose with an herb of power in his hand, and said: "Take this and hurry." I took and held it toward the black horse yonder. He fattened and was happy and came prancing to his place again and was the first Grandfather sitting there. . . . . "With this pipe," the Grandfather said, "you shall walk upon the earth, and whatever sickens there you shall make well." . . . And now the fourth Grandfather spoke. "Younger Brother," he said, "with the powers of the four quarters you shall walk, a relative. Behold, the living center of a nation I shall give you, and with it many you shall save." And I saw that he was holding in his hand a bright red stick that was alive, and as I looked it sprouted branches at the top and sent forth, and on the branches many leaves came out and murmured and in the leaves the birds began to sing. And then for just a little while I thought I saw beneath it in the shade the circled villages of people and every living thing with roots or legs or wings, and all were happy. "It shall stand in the center of the nation's circle," said the Grandfather, "a cane to walk with and a people's heart; and by your powers you shall make it blossom." . . . And as we went the Voice behind me said: "Behold a good nation walking in a sacred manner in a good land!" Then I looked up and saw that there were four ascents ahead, and these were generations I should know. Now we were on the first ascent, and all the land was green. And as the long line climbed, all the old men and women raised their hands, palms forward, to the far sky yonder and began to croon a song together, and the sky ahead was filled with clouds of baby faces. . . . And when we reached the summit of the third ascent and camped, the nation's hoop was broken like a ring of smoke that spreads and scatters and the holy tree seemed dying and all its birds were gone. And when I looked ahead I saw that the fourth ascent would be terrible. . . . As I rode in through the rainbow door, there were cheering voices from all over the universe, and I saw the six Grandfathers sitting in a row, with their arms held toward me and their hands, palms out; and behind them in the cloud were faces thronging, without number, of the people yet to be. "He has triumphed!" cried the six together, making thunder. . . . I looked below and saw my people there, and all were well and happy except one, and he was lying like the dead—and that one was myself. . . . I was all alone on a broad plain now with my feet upon the earth, alone but for the spotted eagle guarding me. I could see my people's village far ahead, and I walked very fast, for I was homesick now. Then I saw my own tipi, and inside I saw my mother and my father bending over a sick boy that was myself. And as I entered the tipi, some one was saying: "The boy is coming to; you had better give him some water." . . . as I lay there thinking of my vision, I could see it all again and feel the meaning with a part of me like a strange power glowing in my body; but when the part of me that talks would try to make words for the meaning, it would be like fog and get away from me. (Neihardt, 1932, pp. 20-47)

Crystal-gazing. As an example of this aid to the lapse of the reality-check we quote the following from Underhill (1911):

> Jacob Boehme, the "Teutonic theosopher," having one day as he sat in his room "gazed fixedly upon a burnished pewter dish which reflected the sunshine with great brilliance," fell into an ecstasy, and it seemed to him as if he could look into the principles and deepest foundations of things. The contemplation of running water had the same effect on St. Ignatius Loyola. Sitting on the bank of a river one day, and facing the stream, which was running deep, "the eyes of his mind were opened, not so as to see any kind of vision, but so as to understand and comprehend spiritual things . . . and this with such clearness that for him all these things were made new." (pp. 69-70)

We quote a further example from Erickson (1933). Erickson's subject had asked him for assistance in recalling the identity of a Christmas gift which she had made to a young man of her acquaintance.

> Because of the subject's affective state, another change in technique was made by asking her to attempt crystal-gazing. In the crystal she saw herself walking down the street, entering a jewelry store in which she inspected cigarette cases, and then continuing down the street and entering a department store, whereupon she immediately lost sight of herself in the crowd. She saw herself next leaving the store with a small package under her arm which she took to her room and placed in a bureau drawer. In response to further sug-

gestions she watched herself prepare the gift for mailing, but each time that she was about to catch sight of the gift, her crystal image would turn in such fashion as to occlude her line of vision. All suggestions to the contrary were without effect other than that she was able to give the rough dimensions of the article, which had not been possible previously. Further variations of the crystal-gazing were without results.

Leucoscopy differs from narcosis and trauma chiefly in its thorough-going psychological nature. Instead of deliberately damaging the physiological machinery through which the check from reality-testing is maintained, the crystal-gazer seeks to throw that process out of gear by giving it an altered and non-effective direction, by dispelling it and draining it away. This effect seems to be in some manner a function of the disposition of attention, and to operate in a way that indicates a suggestion effect through the ocular muscles. Just as repeated gentle motion of a monotonous nature is almost as efficacious in hypnosis as verbal repetition, and as counting sheep tends to induce sleep through the repeated identical motion involved, so the repeated "slipping" of the regard down the opposite curves of the crystal and their repeated recovery tends to absorb just that low degree of attention necessary to maintain contact with reality, and so to release the stratum normally kept in check—which promptly, in a susceptible subject, takes command of the visual imagery. An unexplored field for quantitative investigation probably lies in this region; how much monotonous stimulation is necessary just to remove the reality-check in subjects of various degrees of critical control, and how much more than this is necessary to restore it again? If, for example, the simple crystal will not suffice in a given subject to release the autistic activity, will the addition of a peripherally seen pendulum be sufficient? Or the faint tick of a metronome? The striking of a church bell will presumably destroy the revery and restore critical control; but at what upper threshold of loudness will the autistic activity still persist? In the meantime, however, it is sufficient for us to observe that with these aids the autistic activity can be observed at its ancient task of furnishing perceptive substitute satisfactions in lieu of motor ones; and that, in fact, historically this mode of furnishing them has been much in demand by those capable of its exercise by reason of the additional advantage that the suspension of the critical faculty is not ordinarily noticed; so it is a simple matter to project the visions upon anything handy—the "future," the "spirits," the companion, etc.—thus furnishing a complete sop to any possible lingering fragments of the critical function.

Divination. Randolph (1931) gives us a number of illustrations of divination:

> If the fire which a man kindles burns brightly, he knows that his sweetheart is true to him, but if it smoulders, she is likely to prove unfaithful. As a further test, he may go into a clearing and bend down a mullein stalk which points toward her cabin; if she loves him the stalk grows up again, but if she loves another it will die.

> The girl has only to put a bit of dodder or love-vine on a growing weed; if it flourishes, her lover is faithful, and if it withers he is not. Or she may pluck a hair from her head and draw it between her fingers—if it curls he loves her, if it remains straight he does not.

Divination has in the course of ages attracted to itself some exceedingly potent meanings. This result appears to have come about by reason of the unique avenue afforded the projection mechanisms—which in divination is nothing so immediate and temporary as the companion, or society, or even the vague but more or less harmless "future"; it is the whole of Nature, or the minds of the gods themselves, which is being interrogated; thus a positively cosmic quality is imparted to the wishes of the particular priest or other interrogator when these are read back to him from the entrails or the bird-flight formation or the fall of the arrow; and we have seen, in the case of more personal wishes of individual, private interrogators, the half-understood motivation, transparent to the more humorous and irreverent observers, involved in "correcting fortune" —as in the tales of the student who will study if his tossed coin stands on edge, the man who had to cut the cards five times before they came out right, etc. An interesting variant is dowsing for water or precious metals, wherein, as appears from an uncertain literature, the rod reflects not differentially the wishes (since the desire is spread over the whole area equally) but chiefly the unconscious knowledge of the operator—the sum total, for example, of his experience of the correlations of underground water with surface signs. The problem of the causes of the decay of public divination (by comparison, e.g., with public invocation, which flourishes undiminished) is an exceedingly knotty one; but, whatever the causes, it would appear that divination in a serious form (as distinguished, for instance, from survivals in Hallowe'en peerings into mirrors in search of future husbands and the like) survives in civilized societies only in the form of numerological fads and in the privately elaborated systems of maladjusted persons, chiefly obsessionals; wherein it fulfils with fair efficacy their chronic need for reassurance that their important wishes are yet attainable, since the universe, being questioned, gives assent.

"*Superstition.*" As an example of the practices popularly grouped as "superstition," a bit of material contributed by a psychoanalytic subject of the writer's may be considered, as being both simple and "pure." This young woman, a nurse, is a graduate of a well-known college for women and understands perfectly the irrational nature of the behavior reported, which in fact she has occasionally observed in psychotic patients.

> This is so much a matter of habit with me that I had almost forgotten to speak of it; I have always been very superstitious, and one of the commonest things I do is to count everything. For instance, I will count the stairs I have to go up or down, and if the number is odd it will mean good luck, if even, bad—incidentally, odd is male, even female. At a certain period when I wanted very much to have a certain man ask to call on me, I couldn't stop counting—if it turned out right I would feel relieved for a few minutes, but soon I

would feel the need for reassurance again; while if it turned out wrong I immediately had to count something else until it turned out right. The only part of my college course in philosophy that really stirred anything in me was the part about the beliefs of the Pythagoreans in numbers.

The extravagances of numerology will immediately be suggested (see Bell, 1933), and it will be observed also that these phenomena are very close to omen and divination; that is, all have the common root that they constitute an appeal to the external world for evidence negating the content of an anxiety.

Astrology. Astrology may be regarded as a special variety of divination. A brief example of its characteristic thought processes is cited under our treatment of points of view (page 511). Its *modus operandi* is very simple, and illustrates admirably the fact that the important point is the provision of substitute outlets for unresolved tension; a standard device for the accomplishment of this end is the general statement, applicable by any probable subject to his own case; another is the fairly common provision for repetition in case the first results are "unsatisfactory" or inapplicable; thus the situation is arranged so that (given the necessary absence or abeyance of the critical function) adequate resolution of tension is assured.

Mediumship. Mediumship presents the double problem of the phenomena of the medium and those of the sitter. Excluding cases of fraud, the former may be described with fair adequacy as the naïve projection of "free associations" or ideas arising spontaneously under the influence of whatever motivation may be present; thus an amateur medium of the writer's acquaintance reported, after several minutes of group silence, that the name "Stephen" kept presenting itself to him—an occurrence which he clearly regarded as evidence of supernormal communication, without, apparently, having noticed that the stream of consciousness is rarely quite free from images. From the sitter's point of view, mediumship may be considered as divination doubly insured against failure; for not only will the tension in himself seek to attach meaning to the objective phenomena, as in divination from natural events, but the phenomena produced by the medium, even in the absence of fraud, will hardly be devoid of special tension-releasing significance. Thus in the many published reports of sittings (of which those in the *Journal of the American Society for Psychic Research* may be cited as particularly free from contamination by the critical function) the matters dealt with are chiefly those imbricated around the principal tension-producing concern of the characteristically elderly sitters, namely, death. The connections with religion are of course obvious; spiritualism is often called a religion, and most religions are deeply concerned with the task of negating (by magic means) death and its attendant tensions. Mediumship may then be thought of as both a method of anesthetizing the critical function and a magic technique for denying death and resolving the tensions engendered by its contemplation.

Reality-Check Lapsed

Dream. From Freud (1899) we take the following examples of this very common phenomenon.

> Another dream with which the picturesque beauty of the Aussee inspired my daughter, at that time three and a quarter years of age, is equally straightforward. The little girl had crossed the lake for the first time, and the trip had passed too quickly for her. She did not want to leave the boat at the landing, and cried bitterly. The next morning she told us: "Last night I was sailing. on the lake." Let us hope that the duration of this dream-voyage was more satisfactory to her.
>
> My eldest boy, at that time eight years of age, was already dreaming of the realization of his fancies. He had ridden in a chariot with Achilles, with Diomedes as charioteer. On the previous day he had shown a lively interest in a book on the myths of Greece which had been given to his elder sister.
>
> . . . My nephew, twenty-two months of age, had been instructed to congratulate me on my birthday, and to give me a present of a small basket of cherries, which at that time of the year were scarce, being hardly in season. He seemed to find the task a difficult one, for he repeated again and again: "Cherries in it," and could not be induced to let the little basket go out of his hands. But he knew how to indemnify himself. He had, until then, been in the habit of telling his mother every morning that he had dreamed of the "white soldier," an officer of the guard in a white cloak, whom he had once admired on the street. On the day after the sacrifice on my birthday he woke up joyfully with the announcement, which could have referred only to a dream: "He(r)man eaten all the cherries!"
>
> It seems that dreams of an infantile type reappear with especial frequency in adults who are transferred into the midst of unfamiliar conditions. Thus Otto Nordenskjöld, in his book *Antarctic* (1904, vol. 1, p. 336), writes as follows of the crew who spent the winter with him: ". . . An especially characteristic dream was that in which one of our comrades believed himself back at school, where the task was assigned to him of skinning miniature seals, which were manufactured especially for purposes of instruction. Eating and drinking constituted the pivot around which most of our dreams revolved. . . . Another dreamed of tobacco, whole mountains of tobacco; yet another dreamed of a ship approaching on the open sea under full sail. . . . one can readily understand how we longed for sleep. That alone could afford us everything that we all most ardently desired." (p. 136)

These are examples, of course, of the famous wish-fulfilment hypothesis of Freud. The latter himself attempted no very penetrating analysis of the bases of the phenomenon, being content with the very considerable achievement of postulating a useful generalization on the basis of the dream itself. We may, however, observe that the wish or motive fulfilment may be regarded as a special case of the *Ersatzhandlungen* we have been discussing; the critical function having been somewhat relaxed by the onset of sleep (as in the other instances mentioned by drugs, fever, or inanition), the blocked tension seeks release through the central portions of the sensory (and probably also the motor) system which has been temporarily taken over. The present writer (1929) has previously suggested that the attainment of desired resolutions of tension in dreams is not without occasional important therapeutic results, and that such phenomena as recurrent dreams are probably to be thought of as repeated "attempts" to achieve a substitute solution on this level. Thus the principal difference between dream and magic may be regarded as that between the imaginal and the motor spheres: The magician acts out in the real world, through his peripheral motor system, what the dreamer elaborates only centrally.

Hallucination. In Gardner's *St. Catherine of Siena* (1907) we find an excellent example of an hallucinatory experience:

> We have already seen that Catherine, who was subject from childhood to imaginary visions and interior words, had long been conscious of a voice reiterating the promise of this sacred betrothal; and that on the last day of the Carnival, A.D. 1366, it said to her, "I will this day celebrate solemnly with thee the feast of the betrothal of thy soul, and even as I promised I will espouse thee to Myself in faith." "Then," says her legend, "whilst the Lord was yet speaking, there appeared the most glorious Virgin His Mother, the most blessed John, Evangelist, the glorious apostle Paul, and the most holy Dominic, father of her order; and with these the prophet David, who had the psaltery set to music in his hands; and while he played with most sweet melody the Virgin Mother of God took the right hand of Catherine with her most sacred hand, and, holding out her fingers toward the Son, besought Him to deign to espouse her to Himself in faith. To which graciously consenting the Only Begotten of God drew out a ring of gold, . . . Then the vision disappeared, but that ring ever remained on her finger, not indeed to the sight of others, but only to the sight of the virgin herself; for she often, albeit with bashfulness, confessed to me that she always saw that ring on her finger, nor was there any time when she did not see it." (p. 25)

Apparition. For a description of a typical example of this member of our anxiety-control series we again turn to Underhill (1911) and quote from the religious experience of St. Teresa:

> I saw an angel close by me, on my left side, in bodily form. This I am not accustomed to see unless very rarely. Though I have visions of angels frequently, yet I see them only by an intellectual vision, such as I have spoken of before. It was our Lord's will that in this vision I should see the angel in this wise. He was not large, but small of stature, and most beautiful—his face burning, as if he were one of the highest angels, who seem to be all of fire: they must be those whom we call Cherubim. . . I saw in his hand a long spear of gold, and at the iron's point there seemed to be a little fire. He appeared to me to be thrusting it at times into my heart, and to pierce my very entrails; when he drew it out, he seemed to draw them out also and to leave me all on fire with a great love of God. The pain was so great that it made me moan; and yet so surpassing was the sweetness of this excessive pain that I could not wish to be rid of it. The soul is satisfied now with nothing less than God. (pp. 350-351)

Though cited here as an illustration of apparitions [see also a paper by Hornell Hart and his wife (1933) and one by the writer (1934)], the above famous passage has an obvious sexual significance, which indeed must have escaped the notice of the subject only by the most heroic feats of repression. In this light it may serve also as an excellent example of symbolism, i.e., the preservation of relations through replacement of content, as well as (in so far as relates to the ascription of the subject's own motives to external entities) of the familiar device of projection. The demarcation between such a phenomenon and the hallucinations previously mentioned is of course nominal; and ordinary psychiatric delusions appear to be only rational structures elaborated in the manner of a dream (as here the theological setting) as an explanation to the self of perceptual experience. These dynamisms are to be regarded as the rules or tactics of the game, the particular devices by which the major strategy of anxiety-control takes place.

Omnipotence of thought. Omnipotence of thought, very close in structure to ritual and incantational magic in the classical sense, is a frequent component of the obsessive character; in fact, magic of this strict type may be regarded as genuine institutionalized obsession, not only in respect to the similarity of external form and rite and to the common presence of omnipotence of thought, but more fundamentally to the ritual negation of anxiety clearly to be inferred from both. An example of omnipotence of thought with definite incantational-magic characteristics is, in fact, included in the quotation from Helene Deutsch (1932) illustrating obsession (page 492 of this chapter).

Omen. Rank (1932) quotes Damm and Berkusky in pointing out the major rôle played by omen in certain activities of primitive peoples:

> More important . . . is the conclusion of Damm that most primitive games are really questions set to fate—an idea to which Berkusky first gave expression in the case of the tug of war, a ceremonial rain-magic. He assumes that the tug originally set destiny the question whether the rain-bearing monsoon would come soon or not. "But as all such questions of the future which man himself has to answer, because external factors are beyond his influence, tend to develop into a magic activity, it looks as if here also we have an attempt at forecasting the future, preceded by rain-magic." The same is true of a ceremonial wrestling-match which the Batak of Sumatra carry through each year with reference to the sacrifice to the "common father of their race"; a bull is killed, and according to the manner of his fall, whether with the wound above or below, so will the tribe's fate be; and the wrestlers belonging to the various tribes try to influence the fall of the beast in accordance with their wishes and by their own strength—which really amounts to "correcting fortune" in connection with the question put to destiny.

This type of behavior indicates clearly the relationship between some of the magic ceremonials to the outstanding "group anxieties" of particular primitive groups. In the attempts overtly to influence "fate" by influencing the manner in which the bull falls, we find a direct attack on the problem of anxiety-control, which really brings us to the next major category in the series of controls, viz., explicit reactions. Before proceeding to this category, however, the portent, a phenomenon closely related to the omen, should be mentioned.

Portent. Randolph's (1931) description of customs among certain groups of peoples makes clear the character of this rather common form of control:

> Many mountain damsels carry love charms consisting of some pinkish, soap-like material, the composition of which I have been unable to discover; the thing is usually enclosed in a carved peach-stone or cherry pit, and worn on a string around the neck.
> When a girl's apron is unfastened accidentally, or her skirt turns up, or her stocking falls down, or her shoe comes untied, she knows that her lover is thinking of her. If she stubs her toe against a stone she kisses her thumb, and rests happy in the knowledge that she will see her sweetheart within twenty-four hours. By cleaning her finger-nails on Saturday she can force her lover to visit her on the following day, and if a redbird flies across her path she is sure to be kissed twice before nightfall.

Reactions Explicit

Among the explicit or motor reactions we may distinguish three continuous and ascending types, which we may call negative control (control by avoidance), verbal control, and positive (motor) control.

Negative Control

Phobia. From Deutsch (1932) we quote the following discussion, which affords both illustration and explanation of this phenomenon:

> The patient I am going to speak about is particularly instructive for two reasons. On the one hand she is overwhelmed by anxiety feelings which are diffused in their nature, attached to no particular ideas, and not amenable to phobic precautionary measures. But on the other hand, under certain conditions, which are felt as a danger and have to be avoided in order to escape the anxiety, her anxiety feelings are intensified and do acquire a more specific character. This part of her anxiety avails itself of a mechanism which we call phobia and which evolves protective measures for removing the anxiety. We shall learn from our patient's case how this phobic defence measure arose, and especially from what motives the patient, who had been for all practical purposes healthy up to a given moment, suddenly became subject to anxiety-states. . . . Similarly this patient was a "fate-neurotic," for her life too was a continuous compulsive repetition of certain situations. . . . She suffered from an almost continuous feeling of oppression; and in addition to this diffused anxiety she began to be subject to more definite forms of anxiety, e.g., dread of heights, ships, and cats. These anxieties were really only intensifications of a continuous anxiety-state, even tho the most recent of her symptoms, the dread of cats, had the character of an animal phobia. . . . For the last few years she had lived in a *menage à trois,* i.e., she had a relationship with her friend's husband. . . . When I said at the start that the patient's life was an example of a fate-neurosis, I was referring to the fact that our patient's entire psychical life, from earliest childhood to the love-relationships of later years, represented such a triangular constellation as I have described. But it was only in her last experience that this erotic condition of the triangular relationship acquired a real nature. Hitherto these triangular friendships had always been platonic. . . . When she was four years old the mother gave birth to a little girl, . . . She was discontented that the mother, and not she, had got the child from the father. This

trauma gave rise to strong aggressive reactions against the mother and the new-born child. But such mental situations are typical, and burden most girls with the severest sense of guilt for the rest of their lives . . . the girl often condemns herself to permanent—psychically conditioned—childlessness or to death-fears during pregnancy and all manner of renunciations in her own motherhood. Sometimes the original wish for a child remains attached to the child of the "other woman," and is satisfied there, i.e., she renounces the wish to have a child of her own and expresses the longing for the other woman's child in various forms. . . . In the present situation she found fulfilment of her infantile wish, to be loved by the man who belonged to another woman. And in this case she was able to elude the super-ego and appease the sense of guilt by, so to speak, purchasing this wish with a simultaneous renunciation; for she leaves the man his rightful wife and suffers every day the painful renunciation in the other's favor, thus being enabled to possess him in common without feeling guilt. . . . Now while she was having the relationship to the husband the friend again became pregnant and gave birth to a daughter. And this birth reawakened all those reactions in our patient's psyche which she had experienced at the time of her little sister's birth. The other, and not she, had got the "present." Everything which had so far been held in balance by successful repression on the one hand and by reaction-formations and disguised acts of penitence on the other now broke down. . . . Soon after the child's birth, but quite unconscious of the connection, the patient began to suffer from fears and anxieties of various kinds. She gladly took charge of the child, but frequently felt afraid that she or someone else might let the child fall. The harmony of the home was not disturbed, but the patient's condition assumed more and more the nature of an anxiety-hysteria. . . . The analysis was able to throw a particularly interesting light on the meaning of our patient's cat phobia. In the sense of the old fairy-tale symbol, in which the cat is always the companion and double of the wicked witch, the animal represented the patient's own wicked feelings against the woman. The witch herself, the counterpart of the good fairy, represents the "wicked mother" for all of us and serves to embody our own wicked attitude in these primordial ambivalence conflicts. And to this she owes her immortality in the fairy tale. Our patient's phobia had the same meaning as the fairy tales. The anxiety she felt related to the danger with which the "wicked woman" within her threatened her. But this danger from her own emotional attitude consisted not only in the guilt-producing aggression against the woman; it was also conditioned by her former life, in which these aggressions had already played a part. . . . Thus as well as fearing to be punished for her death-wishes directed against the friend, the patient was at the same time afraid of her libidinal relation to her, for the masochistic character of this relationship constituted a serious danger. She attempted to escape these dangers by transferring them on to the symbolized animal. The cat became the representative of both her dangerous ambivalent impulses towards the woman. By avoiding the animal she tried to escape the internal dangers that threatened her. This .is indeed usually the goal of the phobic mechanism. But our patient could not reach this goal, for the mechanism only managed to absorb a part of her diffused anxiety; the greater part was not to be disposed of through phobic anti-cathexes. Why this should be so we cannot say with certainty . . . a hostile impulse, intensified to a death-wish, against her girl friend was repressed and displaced on to a suitable animal-object. Every encounter with a cat mobilized the old hatred in the patient, and at the same time the reaction to this hatred; a threat, namely, on the part of the super-ego and thereby a danger for the ego, represented by the cat, which now assumed the rôle of the punishing mother. But we saw too that the projection-object, the cat, was at the same time the representative of the homosexual, positive-libidinal impulse, and that the whole process clearly signified a compromise between this impulse and the punishing agency. This compromise would seem to be a favorable one for the ego, for it possesses in the phobic symptom a warning signal to protect it against anxiety. It is as if a severe preceptor were to threaten a child with punishment in order to rouse anxiety, but were to promise him at the same time not to punish him, provided he refrained from doing some particular thing. (pp. 113 ff.)

Tabu. Tabu is one of the most potent forces in group control. From the customs of primitive peoples, among whom it plays a peculiarly effective rôle, Frazer (1925) has gleaned numerous interesting descriptions of this type of phenomena, and from him we quote the following:

> In the first place we may observe that the awful sanctity of kings naturally leads to a prohibition to touch their sacred persons. Thus it was unlawful to lay hands on the person of a Spartan king; no one might touch the body of the king or queen of Tahiti; it is forbidden to touch the person of the King of Siam under pain of death; and no one may touch the king of Cambodia, for any purpose whatever, without his express command. . . . Formerly no one might touch the king of Corea. . . . Above all, no iron might touch the king's body. In 1800 King Tieng-tsong-tai-oang died of a tumor in the back, no one dreaming of employing the lancet, which would probably have saved his life. It is said that one king suffered terribly from an abscess in the lip, till his physician called in a jester, whose pranks made the king laugh heartily, and so the abscess burst. Roman and Sabine priests might not be shaved with iron but only with bronze razors or shears; and whenever an iron graving-tool was brought into the sacred grove of the Arval Brothers at Rome for the purpose of cutting an inscription in stone, an expiatory sacrifice of a lamb and a pig must be offered, which was repeated when the graving-tool was removed from the grove. . . .
>
> There is a priestly king to the north of Zengwih in Burma, revered by the Sotih as the highest spiritual and temporal authority, into whose house no weapon or cutting instrument may be brought. This rule may perhaps be explained by a custom observed by various peoples after a death; they refrain from the use of sharp instruments so long as the ghost of the deceased is supposed to be near, lest they should wound it. . . .
>
> We have seen that the Flamen Dialis was forbidden to touch or even name raw flesh. At certain times a Brahman teacher is enjoined not to look on raw flesh, blood, or persons whose hands have been cut off. In Uganda the father of twins is in a state of taboo for some time after the birth; among other rules he is forbidden to kill anything or to see blood. In the Pelew Islands when a raid has been made and a head carried off, the relatives of the slain man are tabooed and have to submit to certain observances in order to escape the wrath of his ghost. They are shut up in the house, touch no raw flesh, and chew betel over which an incantation has been uttered by the exorcist. (p. 224)

Verbal Control

Verbal magic. Verbal magic plays an important rôle in the religious rites of many primitive peoples. We quote from Fortune's (1932) discussion of the use of incantations in the Trobriands and in Dobu:

> In the Trobriands, incantations are chanted aloud. It is not feared that the right to use an incantation may be stolen by an underprivileged overhearer. Right of possession is socially acknowledged and not tampered with by non-possessors. In Dobu, on the contrary, anyone overhearing another charming aloud can memorize the incantation and use it himself. Eavesdroppers on one man teaching another an incantation aloud, can by successful eavesdropping steal the magical power. In practice, precautions against eavesdroppers are rigidly maintained. Dobu has a pattern of possible theft that is not known in the Trobriands. The above native statement is a rationalization of this fact in terms of the yams liking soft speech, underbreath, rather than speech aloud. (p. 107)

The prayer of the more highly sophisticated religions is more subtle, but the primitive idea of direct influence over natural phenomena by verbal magic is by no means extinct. Public prayers for rain and prosperity are frequently resorted to in the most "civilized" countries, and days of fasting and prayer in the presence of emergency are almost a part of our official social structure. The additional element appears to be a recognition of the mental-hygiene value of externalization and motor (at least speech) expression of anxiety tensions, preferably in personal terms; and it is at this point that the anxiety basis becomes clearest—in the more uncritical forms and uses of incantation it is more effectively controlled by the unquestioned, "natural" organization of the universe in terms of forces subject to control by keys in the hands of the magician. This technique for the control of anxiety (prayer) appears to be one of the most promising for utilization in sophisticated cultures, but as yet nothing has been worked out to deal successfully with the disregard of reality involved in the projection. A short discussion on this point will follow in a later section.

Mysticism. Another phenomenon which we may place in the category of verbal control is so-called mysticism. Again we illustrate from the field of religion, with a quotation from St. Bernard of Clairvaux in his *Cantica Canticorum* (Sermon, lxxiv), translated by Eales in 1895:

> The Word has visited me, and even very often. But, though He has frequently entered my soul, I have never at any time been sensible of the precise moment of His coming. I have felt that He was present, I remember that He has been with me; I have sometimes been able even to have a presentiment that He would come; but never to feel His coming nor His departure. For whence He came to enter my soul, or whither He went on quitting it, by what means He has made entrance or departure, I confess that I know not even to this day. . . . It is not by the eyes that He enters, for He is without form or color that they can discern; nor by the ears, for His coming is without sound; nor by the nostrils, for it is not with the air but with the mind that He is blended. . . . By what

avenue then has He entered? Or perhaps the fact may be that He has not entered at all, nor indeed come at all from outside: for not one of these things belongs to outside. Yet it has not come from within me, for it is good, and I know that in me dwelleth no good thing. I have ascended higher than myself, and lo! I have found the Word above me still. (Underhill, 1911, p. 293)

Myth. Mythology has long been an interesting and popular field and many collections of the myths and folklore of various peoples have been made. In these we find material which is clearly related to our hypothesis. The quotations here presented are from Fortune's *Sorcerers of Dobu* (1932).

> We have already seen that legend in certain cases is closely implicated with ritual. Four generations of human ancestors are known to the native. The generation before that is the generation of Creation by metamorphosis. Its reality is vouched for in legend. The occurrences of Creation do not live in legend alone, however, as events divided strictly from the present by an intervening gulf of time. There is a firm belief in continuity. Although a lengendary scene is laid in the time of Creation, its actors still live, their influences still prevail. Thus an underwater moving rock called Nuakekepaki still menaces and often overturns canoes on the open seas. Legend tells how Nuakekepaki is a deep sea moving rock-man, who, to pay for a wife taken from the land-dwellers, overturned canoes to obtain the valuables they contained, which he duly paid to his mothers-in-law and their brothers as the *kwesi* or bride price. All that can be made of this character is that he is a rock in one aspect, a man in another, and that as a rock he has supernatural qualities. He still overturns canoes to obtain the valuables they contain, apart from his former duty to his parents-in-law in the time of the first ancestors.
>
> Tobwaliton and Tobebeso are two sea monsters that appeared at the creation of the sea and indirectly played a part in connection with its creation. When I was in the field they were credited with counteracting the attempts of the local rain-maker, an old woman, to break a long drought which occurred. A monstrous dog called Weniogwegwe, that dates from the Creation, still roams in the forest at night, and many men have seen his great red eyes; one I met had even given his flank a resounding whack with a paddle. He is as big as a house and his eyes are like fires. In the time of the first ancestors men ate food uncooked until a woman took fire from her pubes and cooked food with it. Still a *kaiana* fire issues from the pubes of women, and there is not a man who has not seen the fire flooding the night with light, or hovering to and fro in the air—and not slept for hours after, but huddled about the fire in fear of witchcraft and death consequent upon it. Kasabwaibwaileta, Bunelala, Nemwadole, Wanoge and many other characters among the first ancestors still exist, and exert the same influence that legend vouches for their having exerted some five generations ago when existence first came into being and natural history began. (pp. 98-99)

Positive Control

Magic (rite). For an illustration of this type of positive control we again turn to Frazer's *The Golden Bough:*

> Among the many beneficent uses to which a mistaken ingenuity has applied the principle of homoeopathic or imitative magic, is that

of causing trees and plants to bear fruit in due season. In Thü-
ringen the man who sows flax carries the seed in a long bag which
reaches from his shoulders to his knees, and he walks with long
strides, so that the bag sways to and fro on his back. It is believed
that this will cause the flax to wave in the wind. In the interior
of Sumatra rice is sown by women who, in sowing, let their hair
hang loose down their backs, in order that the rice may grow
luxuriantly and have long stalks. Similarly, in ancient Mexico a
festival was held in honor of the goddess of maize, or "the long-
haired mother," as she was called. It began at the time "when the
plant had attained its full growth, and fibers shooting forth from
the top of the green ear indicated that the grain was fully formed.
During this festival the women wore their long hair unbound, shak-
ing and tossing it in the dances which were the chief feature in the
ceremonial, in order that the tassel of the maize might grow in like
profusion, that the grain might be correspondingly large and flat,
and that the people might have abundance." In many parts of Europe dancing or leaping high in the air are approved homoeopathic
modes of making the crops grow high. Thus in Franche-Comte they
say that you should dance at the Carnival in order to make the hemp
grow tall. (p. 28)

Religion (*rite*). Religious rite, like the *Ersatzbefriedigung,* may be
thought of as a kind of therapy, which operates by reestablishing an unobstructed pathway from impulse to overt action discharging it. That
due to the exigencies of the external situation important sections of this
pathway must remain on the symbolic level need not greatly interfere
with the therapeutic effect, since the external purposes served are thera-
peutically irrelevant; this consideration points, on the contrary, to a
mental-hygiene weapon which has been insufficiently exploited on the
conscious level.

Coe (1916) points out this therapeutic effect of certain religious rites:

By suggestion from the priest the worshipers are assured, for
example, that the god is present in the wine-cup that their eyes
behold, or that some new relation to God is effected by a touch or
by baptismal water. . . . In sacerdotal worship the sacrament is
reinforced by other parts of the ritual. Here the priest works upon
the people by suggestion through what is recognized by them as
partly, though not exclusively, symbolical. Pictures and statues, processions, kneeling, bowing, crossing one's self, the Latin of the Mass,
intoned psalms and prayers, the repetition of ancient creeds—these
are one and all instruments of suggestion. They are not used because
they promote reflection and deliberate action, but because they bring
attention back repeatedly to the same point, thus renewing control
by what is already authoritatively fixed. Tendencies toward sacerdotal grouping can sometimes be discerned in a change from "saying" to intoning the Lord's Prayer, the Prayer of Confession, and the
Creed; perhaps also in singing, instead of reading, the psalms. Here
the content, which was at first an expression of discriminative thinking, not only ceases to awaken like thoughts, but becomes an instrument of suggestion whereby the worshiper's mind is bent to the
ideas of the ecclesiastical authorities. . . .
Many religious reactions use the expansor muscles, as processions
and dances, song, laughter, the lightened step that follows prayer,
the friendlier relations between men.
Many of the retractations mentioned by Marshall have acquired

psychic connotations different from the original ones. It is no uncommon thing for meanings to flow faster than external forms. Think how the meaning of the following terms used in letter-writing has been transformed: "sir," "madam," "your obedient servant," "yours." Just so the bow, which was originally, perhaps, a sign of submission, is now something entirely different. So it comes to pass that kneeling, which may have originated as abasement before a conqueror, has become with many persons the posture of prayer in general, even the joyful prayer of thanksgiving.

Anyone who will take the trouble to watch persons who, withdrawing from the activities and from the sensory stimuli of our hurly-burly life, enter a church and assume the postures of meditation and prayer, will be convinced that the whole constitutes, on the muscular side, relaxation of strains. These strains are not the same as the contractions essential for muscular work, but rather contractions of muscles that have no work to do, or contractions beyond the requirements of the work in hand. They constitute on the physical side obstructions and wastes, and their mental correlate is hurry, worry, distraction, and general discomfort. The act of merely "letting go" these tense muscles brings relief, an immediate satisfaction. There are probably several reasons for this satisfaction, but one of them is certainly contained in the general law that obstructed motor activity is disagreeable, but harmonious, unobstructed activity agreeable. Of much worship at least we can say that it is an organizing of the individual, and therefore agreeable. And the result is not merely increased confidence, but also actual increase of effectiveness through focalization of attention. In other words, postures that may have originated in repression are now means for releasing the individual and increasing his capacity for self assertion. (pp. 127 ff.)

Obsession. Deutsch's (1932) discussion of the obsessional neurotic is both illustrative and explanatory of the position of obsession in our series of anxiety-controls:

Very characteristic for the obsessional neurotic are his reports about all those peculiar and uncanny happenings which seem to pursue him. If he thinks of somebody, then the person in question promptly appears; if he feels affectionately towards somebody, then the person in question is sure to die in consequence; if he utters a curse on someone, then this is realized in the most terrible form. All these events are described by these unhappy people to prove the "omnipotence" of their wishes—especially the bad ones—and their thoughts. This behavior has its psychological motivation in the fact that through the severance of the inner connections between the repressed unconscious wish-impulses and the sense of guilt which attaches to these impulses a tension arises in the ego for which a rationalization is eagerly sought. Thus where it is not possible to ward off the sense of guilt through character traits which we have learned to recognize as reaction-formations, we find along with the symptoms or even without their formation expressions of the sense of guilt which are characteristic for the personality of the obsessional neurotic.

Thus despite what is sometimes a very high intellectual level, and in full consciousness of the absurdity of his behavior, the obsessional neurotic can be so influenced by blind superstition in his relation to the outer world that he is continually dominated by it in all his actions. The cause of this lies partly in the fact that the patient attains to a certain inner perception of his unconscious impulses and thru the strength of his aggressive tendencies becomes liable to overestimate psychical processes in relation to reality, and partly in the fact that the warning voice of his sense of guilt makes him responsible for the results of his wishes in the outer world. This superstitious belief of the obsessional neurotic that his thoughts find their realization in the outer world has a certain affinity with the projection-mechanism of the paranoic, who projects the inner perception of a psychical process on to the outer world, on to his persecutor. . . .

Another typical character trait of the obsessional neurotic is distrust. In this case the suppressed hate-impulses are displaced on to the outer world. The individual behaves as if the hostility did not lie in him, but as if it was directed against him from without. Here, too, the effect of the sense of guilt seems to be that its victim can expect only bad from others.

Another obsessional neurotic patient of mine showed this sort of projection very clearly in her symptoms. She was obsessed by the thought that she was an object of envy to her younger sister. Her life was filled with protective measures against this envy. She dared not please anyone, have nice clothes, or betray any sort of accomplishment, lest she should provoke it. She could not love anyone, become engaged or have children, in a word she must give up everything which seemed to her worth having in life, for otherwise she might rouse her sister's envy. At the same time she had to utter all sorts of magic words, perform certain tasks, carry out wearisome obsessional activities, all in order to paralyze the effect of this envy.

Again it is her own hatred and envy of the sister which has turned so cruelly against herself. She attempts to project outwards the inner perception of these feelings, and she behaves as though they would flow in the reverse direction from her sister to her. Thus in order to save herself from the sense of guilt and the self-punishing tendency, she leads a life of complete renunciation of all she desires and subjects her whole existence to a masochistic punishment ceremonial. (pp. 206 ff.)

Sorcery. The following extraordinary description of an instance of the practice of sorcery we take from Fortune's *Sorcerers of Dobu* (1932):

Christopher was one night alone with me in my hut. He let fall a hint of a piece of work in the black art quite accidentally. I followed it up and with some pressure got it out of him. He began with reluctance, but soon his eyes were half starting from his head and he was rolling and writhing on the floor of my hut in active description of a thing too vigorous for words to do justice to—obviously re-living the scene he described with a thoroly ugly intensity.

A man had said to his wife's mother's brother, a noted sorcerer: "You are always on the sea and without new garden food."

Any such statement derogatory to a man's garden is as great an insult as can be hurled. The garden is knit up with the ceremonial of the sacred—any impugning of it is to blaspheme against a man's gods.

The wife's mother's brother (whom we may call Y) said nothing. Within himself he said "Later on." Later he spoke to Christopher. "You will not betray me." "How should I—I who have married your sister's daughter."

Y drank a great quantity of salt water to parch his throat and keep himself safe from swallowing his own black spells with his saliva. He chewed great quantities of ginger and *gau* to make his body hot and heat up the spells to an effective killing temperature.

The intended victim, all unknowing, went alone to his garden in the early morning. Y and Christopher set out, the sorcerer with his assistant and watch-dog. The two performed the *logau*, a charm which is believed to make the man who utters it invisible. Christopher circled three times round the foot of a convenient coconut palm while he did the *logau*. Y and Christopher could see each other, being both charmed together. Others could not see them. Nevertheless, Christopher climbed the palm to keep watch against possible intruders. From this height he also directed the movements of Y by signs towards the unconscious solitary gardener.

Y moved in concealment, charming with spells towards the gardener and charming his sorcerer's lime spatula. Then with the gardener facing him, and nearby where he crouched concealed, he burst forth with the sorcerer's screaming shout. Christopher saw the gardener fall to the ground and lie writhing convulsively under the sorcerer's attentions. (Christopher had a painful filarial swelling in his groin approaching bursting point—but here he hurled himself down on the floor of my hut, groaning horribly—re-living the scene in his excitement.)

The sorcerer feinted to rap his victim gently over the body with his lime spatula. The body lay still. He cut open the body with the charmed spatula, removed entrails, heart, and lungs, and tapped the body again with the spatula, restoring its appearance to apparent wholeness (here my informant speaks from what he apparently believes his own eyes saw in the cleared garden space below). The sorcerer's attentions here left the body of the victim, and transferred to charming the lime spatula anew. The body rose. Y said, "You name me." The body mumbled incoherently and received a feint at a gentle rap on the temples from the spatula. Again "You name me" aggressively. Again an incoherent mumble, and another feinted rap. So a third time. Y said "You go." The man went to the village, and arrived raving, leaving his personal goods and tools in the garden. His children went to bring them. The man lay down writhing, groaning, and calling on his abstracted vital parts by name—by this time it was midday. So he lay that day and night. Next day the sun climbed to its zenith and he lay dead.

Such is the account of the watch-dog in the case. At one stage he informed me that the lime spatula did not actually strike the body of the victim, but threatened striking and approached the skin closely only. At another stage he said it cut the skin. Other informants later confirmed the view that it did not strike the skin in such sorcerer's procedure, nevertheless it cut the skin. On subsequent questioning Christopher clung to the view that the spatula did not strike the skin, but it was evident that he had some magical striking, magical cutting, and later magical restoring of skin in mind. He was not vacillating between opposing views in his own mind, but only struggling for words to express his conception. So firm was his belief that he used the language of an eye witness of the removal of the entrails, heart, and lungs of the victim.

It is clear that the sorcerer's procedure is hypnotic in nature, the fear apparently being paralyzing. I have seen a man blanch—get ready to run and threaten death in reprisal at the threat of sorcery, fear that lasted until the threat was proved otherwise directed, despite my expressed intention to deal with the threatener. The fear of the sorcerer is tremendous in its strength.

I believe that Christopher's account of his adventure as his wife's mother's brother's watch-dog was no fabrication. He had no need to implicate himself so closely if he was spinning a tale. I have never seen a human being so possessed with emotion as my informant, yet retaining his sanity. He appeared to see everything that he described once again, and I felt towards him much as I did towards a man that ran amuck with a spear in my village and raved, threatening to cut my throat and eat me, stuffing rubbish into his mouth to illustrate his intention, after I got him disarmed and was proceeding to truss him up. My informant was equally ugly in manner, and more powerfully so in that he was not in any pathological state. He was, however, so strongly excited that I would be inclined to connect the running amuck, which is a well-known occurrence and which I witnessed three times during my stay, with the state of mind engendered by witchcraft and sorcery. During his recital with much bodily imitation I kept my attention closely on him and on a possible weapon in case he went out of all reason. (pp. 161-163)

Witchcraft. Witchcraft is essentially sorcery practiced by females, usually old. Thus Randolph (1931):

> Many of the old folk still believe that certain women can call up the Devil by repeating the Lord's Prayer backward, and obtain supernatural powers by selling their souls to Satan. . . . An old woman . . . "put a spell" on her neighbor's tomato plants simply by drawing a circle in the dust, marking a cross in the center of the circle, and spitting in the center of the cross. I have been told of another Ozark witch who killed several of her enemies by means of a "hair ball"—just a little bunch of black hair mixed with beeswax and rolled into a hard pellet. The old woman tossed this thing at the persons whom she wished to eliminate, and they fell dead a few hours later.

The problem, following Jones (1931), is divisible into that of the motives of the witches themselves and those of their putative victims. The former he is inclined to believe center upon lack of adequate sexual gratification or regret for its cessation, converted into hostility. When the victims were women, he supposes that they found in the witch a too adequate symbolization of the punishing mother; and when men, either that they represented the father or that their unsatisfaction represented a threat to potency, that is, a castration threat.

Sublimation

Underlying the above discussion of techniques of anxiety-control has been the conception of overexcitation as the basis of anxiety. It is natural, however, to think of the possibility that overexcitation may be avoided by regular motor discharge of energy before demoralization due to anxiety-pressure becomes imminent. Such a pattern of habitual, normal energy discharge may be given the psychoanalytic name "sublimation" without great distortion of the original meaning; and this sublimation may be relatively partial, as in art, which still preserves something of the magic mechanisms, or relatively total, as in science and construction, in which inner tension and outer accomplishment are integrated in the closest possible manner.

Partial Sublimation

Psychotherapy. First, however, a special technique should be considered whose function is deliberately and in a manner artificially to bridge the gap between the magical technique for dispelling anxiety and the thoroughly externalized art of preventing its accumulation. This is psychotherapy, and while a short adequate summary statement of its presuppositions is difficult to procure the following brief quotation from Rank (1932) will indicate with fair clearness its linkages with the illusional side:

> I have . . . . emphasized the therapeutic and indeed absolutely vital character of illusions . . . . everything that is consoling in life—that is, everything therapeutical in the broader sense—can only be illusional, and even the therapeutic effect of analysis I have tried to explain in my latest technical work by the unreality of the analytical situation.

Art. From Rank (1932) we have also taken the following discussion of art.

> The neurotic, no matter whether productive or obstructed, suffers fundamentally from the fact that he cannot or will not accept himself, his own individuality, his own personality. On the one hand he criticizes himself to excess, on the other he idealizes himself to excess, which means that he makes too great demands on himself and his completeness, so that failing to attain leads only to more self-criticism. If we take this thwarted type, as we may do for our purposes, and compare him to the artist, it is at once clear that the artist is in a sense the antithesis to the self-critical neurotic type. Not that the artist does not criticize himself, but by accepting his personality he not only fulfils that for which the neurotic is striving in vain, but goes far beyond it. . . .
>
> I suggest that the internal threatening of the individual through the sexual impulse of the species is at the root of all conflict. Side by side with this self-imposed internal check, which is taken to be what prevents or lessens the development of fear, there stands the will as a positive factor. The various controls which it exercises enable the impulses to work themselves out partially without the individual's falling completely under their influence or having to check them completely by too drastic repression. . . . If we compare the neurotic with the productive type, it is evident that the former suffers from an excessive check on his impulsive life, and, according to whether this neurotic checking of the instincts is effected through fear or through will, the picture presented is one of fear-neurosis or compulsion-neurosis. With the productive type the will dominates, and exercises a far-reaching control over (but not check upon) the instincts, which are pressed into service to bring about creatively a social relief of fear. Finally, the instincts appear relatively unchecked in the so-called psychopathic subject, in whom the will affirms the impulse instead of controlling it. . . . And here we reach the essential point of difference between the productive type who creates and the thwarted neurotic; what is more, it is also the point from which we get back to our individual artist-type. Both are distinguished fundamentally from the average type, who accepts himself as he is, by their tendency to exercise their volition in reshaping themselves. There is, however, this difference: that the neurotic, in this voluntary remaking of his ego, does not get beyond the destructive preliminary work and is therefore unable to detach the whole creative process from his own person and transfer it to an ideological abstraction. The productive artist also begins (as a satisfactory psychological understanding of the "will-to-style" has obliged us to conclude) with that re-creation of himself which results in an

ideologically constructed ego; this ego is then in a position to shift the creative will-power from his own person to ideological representations of that person and thus to render it objective. It must be admitted that this process is in a measure limited to within the individual himself, and that not only in its constructive, but also in its destructive, aspects. This explains why hardly any productive work gets through without morbid crises of a "neurotic" nature. . . .

The artistic reaction is thus distinguishable from the neurotic by an *overcoming of the trauma* or of the potentiality of inhibition resulting therefrom, no matter whether this is achieved by a single effort or is spread over the whole life-work. This overcoming, however . . . . is only possible—or at any rate only psychologically explicable—in one way, and this, as we have learned from the therapy which helps to overcome these development-inhibitions, is through volitional affirmation of the obligatory, which in every case not only works usefully, but is also definitely creative. . . .

It is this very fact of the ideologization of purely psychical conflicts that marks the difference between the productive and unproductive types, the artist and the neurotic; for the neurotic's creative power, like the most primitive artist's, is always tied to his own self and exhausts itself in it, whereas the productive type succeeds in changing this purely subjective creative process into an objective one, which means that through ideologizing it he transfers it from his own self to his work. . . .

Two fundamental tendencies . . . . are in continual conflict: the one which wishes to eternalize itself in artistic creation, the other which wants to spend itself in ordinary life. . . . This universal human conflict, which was resolved through many thousands of years by religion and the art which rested upon its ideology, has become more and more acute and difficult with the growth of individual art, until with modern artists it has taken on a form very like that of a neurosis. The conflict was always particularly intense in the artist, and this of course is one of the reasons why he was obliged to seize hold of ideological means for its settlement. For because of its "totality-tendency" the creative type is inclined, in this struggle between life and creation, to give up the one wholly in favor of the other, and this naturally intensifies the conflict rather than solves it. . . .

Whereas the average man largely subordinates himself, both socially and biologically, to the collective, and the neurotic shuts himself off deliberately from both, the productive type finds a middle way, which is expressed in ideological experience and personal creativity. . . . In this sense the general problem of the artist . . . . is contained in the two notions of deprivation and renunciation. The psychological point of view, as it culminates in psychoanalysis, always emphasizes only the deprivation, from which artists seem to suffer most in themselves; the philosophical view, to which a few artists like Goethe or Ibsen attained at the height of their achievement, emphasizes renunciation. But the aspects are complementary, like outer and inner, society and ego, collectivity and individuality. The great artist and great work are only born from the reconciliation of the two—the victory of a philosophy of renunciation over an ideology of deprivation.

We often see the artist, and the neurotic, who vacillates in a similar conflict, manufacturing the conflict (or intensifying it if it already exists) just so that he may resolve it. For the neurotic this is a test which he fails; he remains neurotic and proves to himself that he must do so. For the artist these self-created conflicts are also ultimately tests, but, in contradistinction to the neurotic, they prove his capacity to create, since he masters the conflict, in form and content, by giving it esthetic shape.

Full Sublimation

Construction and science. Concerning construction and science we need say little save that they represent the most completely externalized and most successful preventives of anxiety, and so constitute the logical end terms of the series whose lower and middle terms we have been considering. If any distinction between them is worth making, it is that, while construction, or the immediate externalization and satisfaction of needs (as when a child who desires a toy walks across the room and grasps it, or a man who is cold builds a fire), sluices away energy as fast as it is generated, scientific endeavor is capable of going one step beyond this and tolerating the accumulation of energy (anxiety) for a time before resolution becomes possible; thus the undertaking of a scientific problem implies the existence of a certain degree of tension, and the organization and carrying through of the more or less complicated procedures necessary to yield an unequivocal answer necessitate the ability deliberately to tolerate and increase that tension. This appears to be a principal reason why the scientific method was developed very late and by individuals who were both somewhat detached in outlook and thoroughly disciplined, and why even yet it cannot be applied by undisciplined individuals to any problems or by any individuals to problems engendering an unusual amount of tension, such as social problems. The necessity to "do something about it" in these instances is so imperative that it is not possible to withstand the tension. From this viewpoint, then, we may visualize ourselves as part way along a long, hard road on which the obstacles are forms and degrees of anxiety; the column is spread out over a considerable distance, with the more backward members of the groups still struggling to neutralize primitive anxieties by means of charms and rituals, and the advance guard entrenched before the more complicated types engendered by the problems of living together in harmony, but using for weapons artistic, psychotherapeutic, constructional, and scientific techniques rather than the old magical ones.

The Social Significance of Anxiety-Control

The Prevalence and Sources of Anxiety. Anxiety is the most prominent mental characteristic of Occidental civilization.[1] Evidence for this statement, which would probably meet with little objection from most competent observers, is perhaps best drawn from the statistics of those forms of social pathology which may reasonably be regarded as reactions to it, such as suicide, divorce, and the functional forms of mental disorder; the observations of Alexander and Staub (1931) in conjunction with those of a large number of child-clinic workers, of whom Hartwell (1931)

---

[1]To which, however, it is not confined; cf. e.g., Mead (1930).

TABLE 1

SUICIDES PER 100,000 INHABITANTS FOR VARIOUS COUNTRIES*

(Data taken from Cavan, 1928)

	United States	Sweden	Norway	Netherlands	Denmark	German Empire	Austria	Hungary Kingdom	Belgium	France	Spain	Italy	Switzerland	England and Wales	Australia	Japan
1816-20	...	4.8	...	...	...	...	...	...	...	...	...	...	...	...	...	...
1826-30	...	...	10.9	...	...	...	...	...	...	5.4	...	...	...	...	...	...
1836-40	...	6.6	11.0	...	21.3	...	...	...	4.6	7.6	...	...	...	(6.2)	...	...
1846-50	...	6.7	9.4	...	25.8	...	...	...	6.0	9.7	...	...	...	...	...	...
1856-60	...	5.7	...	...	27.6	...	...	...	5.5	11.0	...	...	...	(6.5)	...	...
1866-70	...	8.5	7.6	...	27.7	...	...	...	6.6	13.5	...	3.0	...	6.7	...	...
1876-80	...	9.2	7.2	4.4	26.7	...	16.2	...	9.4	16.8	...	4.1	22.7	7.4	10.6	(11.0)
1886-90	...	11.8	6.6	5.6	26.1	20.5	16.0	(10.2)	11.9	21.6	...	5.0	22.1	7.9	11.6	15.9
1896-1900	...	11.9	5.5	5.5	22.1	20.2	15.8	16.3	11.9	23.2	...	6.3	22.2	8.9	12.4	18.5
1905-10	15.1	16.1	4.9	6.7	19.2	21.4	18.2	18.5	12.7	21.7	2.8	7.9	22.3	10.2	11.6	17.3
1915	16.2	15.1	5.9	6.2	17.6	...	16.1	16.1	...	17.1	6.1	8.1	21.5	7.8	13.3	18.6
1920	10.2	...	...	...	14.3	...	...	...	13.2	20.7	...	...	22.5	...	11.8	...
1924	12.1	...	...	...	...	21.7	...	...	...	...	...	...	...	...	11.6	...

*Rates for European countries, Australia, and Japan from J. R. Miner, "Suicide and Its Relation to Climatic and Other Factors," *American Journal of Hygiene*, Monographic Series, No. 2, pp. 2-3, and for recent years from the official yearbooks of the various countries. Regarding the sources of his data, Miner states, "the rates prior to 1871 are from Morselli's Table II (p. 22), except for the English rates, which are calculated from material in the reports of the Registrar General. From 1871 the rates are quoted from Knibbs ("Suicide in Australia: A Statistical Analysis of the Facts," *J. Royal Soc. New South Wales*, XLV, 1912), with additions from the official publications of the various countries."

Parentheses indicate that the rate is based on fewer than five years' experience.

may be taken as representative, suggest strongly that crime may also in part represent a type of breakdown reaction initiated by over-anxiety, but it appears certain that there are additional factors of large and unknown magnitude, so that it does not seem best to use crime statistics for this purpose.

Suicide rates for the last 75-100 years, drawn from sources such as those usefully compiled by Cavan (1928) (see Table 1), indicate for the majority of the countries of continental Europe a steady increase, punctuated in the case of some countries by short-time peaks. The exceptions and differences are of special interest (e.g., Switzerland is fairly stable at about 22 per 100,000, Australia and the United States at half that; Denmark shows a consistent decrease from the middle 20's to 14, and Spain's typical increase—figures for 15 years only—is only from 2 to 6); it would probably be especially instructive to bring them into relationship with local changes in environment affecting mental hygiene, but to our knowledge this has never been done. These figures may be regarded from one point of view as representing the incidence of an extreme degree of anxiety; from another, assuming the population to be congenitally of approximately the same powers of resistance from year to year, they may be thought of as a measure of the degree and fluctuations of the severity of pressure.

The divorce rates, as collected by Lichtenberger (1931) (see Table 2) show in every country reported (except Japan) a consistent upward

TABLE 2

DIVORCES PER 100,000 POPULATION

(From J. P. Lichtenberger's *Divorce: a Social Interpretation,* 1931, by permission of the publishers, McGraw-Hill Book Co., New York.)

Country	1920	1910	1900	1890	1880	1870
United States	139	92	73	53	38	29
Japan	94	113	143	269		
France	71	37	25	17		
Germany	63	24	15	13		
Switzerland	51	43	32	30	33	
Belgium	49	14	11	6	3	1
Denmark	42	27	17		20	18
New Zealand	38		12	3		
Holland	29	16	10	8	4	3
Sweden	21	11	8	6	5	3
Australia	19	12	10	6		
England and Wales	17	3	2	1	1	1

trend; differences between countries, though marked, are difficult to evaluate because of conspicuous differences in the mores, both within and without the law. The figures may be regarded as a measure of inability to tolerate the additional stress of the critical marital adjustment; an important fact may be observed in the United States figures (see Table 3) —divorces for "cruelty" are solely responsible for the increase of total divorce rate, since divorces for all other causes listed are steadily declining. "Cruelty," of course, is in a large proportion of cases a matter of

TABLE 3

PERCENTAGE DISTRIBUTION BY CAUSE OF DIVORCES GRANTED TO HUSBAND
AND WIFE, RESPECTIVELY, FOR YEARS SPECIFIED*

(From J. P. Lichtenberger's *Divorce: a Social Interpretation*, 1931, by permission of
the publishers, McGraw-Hill Book Co., New York.)

Cause and party to whom granted	1929	1922	1916	1887-1906
Total divorces:				
All causes	100.0	100.0	100.0	100.0
Adultery	8.3	10.9	11.5	16.3
Cruelty	40.8	34.5	28.3	21.8
Desertion	29.6	32.8	36.8	38.9
Drunkenness	1.8	1.0	3.4	3.9
Neglect to provide	3.9	4.2	4.7	3.7
Combination of causes	6.8	8.7	8.6	9.4
All other causes	8.8	7.8	6.8	6.1
Granted to husband:				
All causes	100.0	100.0	100.0	100.0
Adultery	12.7	17.6	20.3	28.7
Cruelty	32.4	25.0	17.4	10.5
Desertion	43.2	44.3	50.0	49.4
Drunkenness	0.4	0.3	0.8	1.1
Neglect to provide				
Combination of causes	3.2	4.6	4.3	4.5
All other causes	8.1	8.3	7.2	5.7
Granted to wife:				
All causes	100.0	100.0	100.0	100.0
Adultery	6.5	7.7	7.5	10.0
Cruelty	44.1	39.0	33.2	27.5
Desertion	24.2	27.4	30.8	33.6
Drunkenness	2.4	1.4	4.5	5.3
Neglect to provide	5.4	6.2	4.6	5.5
Combination of causes	8.3	10.6	10.5	11.8
All other causes	9.1	7.6	6.5	6.4

*From report of 1929, p. 24.

projection—if the conduct of the spouse is such as to exacerbate anxiety,
it is "cruel"; objectively determinable causes—desertion, adultery, drunkenness—are proportionately declining.   Some idea, incidentally, of the degree
of difference between the severity of anxiety of total and marital situations may be gained from the fact that divorce rates range from 17 to
139 per 100,000 (1920) while the suicide rates range from 9 to 22.

Corresponding rates for mental disease would also be a useful index to
the prevalence of intolerable anxiety, but lack of diagnostic equivalence
is so extreme even within the same region that comparison of rates for
different regions and different periods would be quite unreliable.   It
seems probable, however, that there is a real rise in incidence of mental
disease even when the greatest reasonable allowance is made for increasing
facilities for hospitalization and insight in diagnosis.   Predictions containing an increase factor have, for example, been verified in commitments
—while, interestingly enough, mental hospitals in Russia, planned on the

basis of the same facts but neglecting the deliberate political-sociological attempt to decrease anxiety, are reported by Williams (1934) to have remained largely unfilled. The entire thesis of this observer, in fact, is that the major indices of anxiety (crime, divorce, psychosis, suicide, maladjustment) are actually in process of sharp decline in Russia as a consequence of the attempt to set up a social system in which conative processes are encouraged to go through smoothly and without frustration from impulse to final product.

Such evidence seems clearly to uphold the common-sense proposition that there is in our civilization a large and increasing incidence of anxiety. While we have little evidence on other civilizations, there is reason to think that the great Oriental ones have suffered much less in this way; good statistical evidence (which probably does not exist) bridging the gap between the old and the new regime in Japan would be of special interest here. There is also the important testimony of Margaret Mead (1928) to the effect that cultures do exist which are characterized by almost no anxiety, as well as that comparatively simple ones exist under similar conditions which nevertheless support a considerable weight of it.

There is little to offer also on the distribution of anxiety. Perhaps the most definite evidence is that secured for a number of populations with personality inventories of the Thurstone type, which consistently yield the result that women are more "neurotic" than men; there is also some material due to the present writer indicating that the married population as a whole is more neurotic than the unmarried (the excess for women being greater than that for men), and that there may be a paraboloid trend with age for women with perhaps a very slight decline for men. Thurstone (1930) has found that anxiety as measured by his scale is uncorrelated with test intelligence, but that whatever social pressures are due to Jewishness result in increased anxiety. It may be conjectured that the anxiety burden lies heaviest upon the "middle" class, who remain bound by difficult standards without important material support.

Among the sources of anxiety we must pay homage to heredity as to a sort of integration constant. The well-known formulation of Freud (1896) is difficult to improve as a working concept; if the mathematical formulation can be taken as a usefully concise metaphor, it may be expressed as

$$A = f(CS)$$

where A represents quantity of anxiety; C, constitutional weakness; and S, environmental stress. That is, in a personality constitutionally weak (a state of affairs which is presumably to be correlated with a deficiency in neural structure such that inhibition is ineffective against either of mutually opposed excitations) the anxiety burden may nevertheless be well within the capacity for toleration if the environmental stress is slight; while even a personality constitutionally strong may not be safe against disaster if the environmental stress is extraordinarily great. While the occasional reports of identical twins reared apart (e.g., Martinez and Ciampi, 1933) falling mentally ill at the same time have some-times implied an almost exclusive rôle for heredity, it seems more con-servative to suppose that these cases (which of course are greatly out-numbered by those implying the opposite) represent the rare extremes in which the hereditary burden was so great that the accumulation of stresses or reactions to stresses from any average environment would eventually and more or less simultaneously reach a breakdown point.

The last consideration leads naturally to that of age as a possible source of anxiety. The comparative serenity of the aged in the face of physiologi-cal deterioration and other trials is a matter of observation which appears only recently to be breaking down; on the other hand, it has been strik-ingly stated that the fantasies and terrors of early childhood constitute a real psychosis, which is normal in the sense that it must be universally passed through. These observations fall into a single picture when it is observed that in normal middle and later life there is a steadily decreas-ing number of conflicting drives which must be resolved, while in early childhood nearly all drives conflict and must be resolved without adequate possibilities for resolution—which should be considered in relation to the great influence of magic upon the young child. The interpretation of intermediate stages seems to offer no discrepancy with either the facts from the use of the neuroticism inventories reported above or the expectations from theory.

The excitations and inhibitions of sex are notoriously fertile in anxiety. The matter must be considered, of course, in the light of the cultural pattern which inculcates or does not inculcate the inhibitions which are to conflict with the normal drive. There are few societies, however, in which unlimited sex expression is permitted, and in many, including our own, the cultural restrictions bear more heavily upon women than upon men, quite apart from the probably somewhat heavier physiological de-mands upon the female. This may be related to the finding noted above that women are more subject to anxiety than men and that the burden of women is increased by marriage.

This should be considered in connection with the general problem of which it is a phase, viz., that of the proportionality between level of civilization and inhibitional burden. That a rough correspondence exists has been pointed out several times, most recently by Sherman (1933) in his study of five Virginia "hollows" of increasing level; at about the third level conflicts began to appear, and these increased up to the normal incidence on the highest level. Freud's *Civilization and Its Discontents* (1930) is a speculative study of this problem, or rather of the aspect of it constituted by the necessity of inhibiting aggressive impulses; to a large extent the rest of this investigator's work constitutes evidence of the same mechanism with respect to the libidinal impulses. We may briefly sum-marize the argument by saying that strength and number of restrictions will not give rise to severe anxiety while avenues for adequate expression remain open; but the closing of these can be expected to generate it, unless the organism concerned is one of extreme adaptive ability. Thus in the libidinal field there is little conflict so long as full sex expression is possible; but it appears in chronic form when the sex drive is brought into conflict with the fear of discovery or of pregnancy, especially when, as in coitus interruptus, this is expressed in definite and conflicting motor activity.   In the field of the aggressive impulses, there is little anxiety in groups accustomed to settling differences immediately and definitely, as by a passing exchange of blows; it arises most characteristically in individuals overtrained to a standard of forbearance which makes any expression of resentment impossible.   The bearing of this upon our own civilization is obvious; a situation has arisen, largely without having been foreseen, in which almost every circumstance of an individual's life is surrounded by formidable inhibitions which collectively form a net so tight that only the most capable may break or elude it; anxiety is therefore the most characteristic mental trait of Western civilization, and magic of one sort or another its most characteristic mental preoccupation.

   The Social Effects of Anxiety. It is obvious that anxiety considered as an individual phenomenon acts to increase in proportion to its severity the amount of energy necessary to reach a given goal and to decrease proportionately the pleasure of both the attainment and the process of attaining.   It is also reasonably clear, however, that without some degree of anxiety (specifically that degree known as ambition) there is ordinarily little motive for attainment, a situation which may be reflected socially in a low cultural level.   It will be worth while to consider these phenomena also from the group viewpoint.

   We may divide the social effects of anxiety into those which operate to increase the general anxiety load, those which engender friction in the group and make more difficult the attainment of its objectives, those which maintain dynamic tensions sufficient to cause redistributions, etc., and finally those which incapacitate individuals.   These divisions are obviously neither exhaustive nor exclusive.

   Of those which increase the anxiety load of the community in general, the most unfortunate are those which act more or less directly upon children.   A large part of the processes of character formation in the child are pretty certainly linked with the characters of the adults closest to him, particularly his parents; and the presence of anxiety in these may operate in a number of ways to reproduce and multiply it in children.   Thus anxiety may be picked up by identification, if the character of the parent is such that identification can be effected; if it is otherwise, e.g., hostile and unassimilable, anxiety may be generated through the impossibility of finding adequate protection through the period when this is needed.   The influence of teachers is only somewhat less, in that their influence is exerted a little later and somewhat less intimately and forcefully; and that of the community in general, while weaker still, may yet be sufficient to determine whether the adolescent will approach adulthood with timidity or with resolution.

   Of the effects engendering friction within groups, those affecting economic and industrial life are most conspicuous. They include effects on the individual worker through the requirement of expending undue amounts of energy to perform a given task; friction between worker and employer, and between supervisors and their organizations; and the curious general anxiety which seems in large part to have been the basis of the recent depression. Chronic anxieties forming character components in husbands and wives are responsible for most unhappinesses in marriage, and, indirectly but most seriously, for reverberations upon children; the similar effect of anxiety in teachers upon children has been referred to above.

The positive effects of low-degree anxieties or anxieties mastered or assimilated in certain ways, as by aggression, are socially extremely effective. The mild anxiety of the north and west European nations, combined with their adaptability, appears to have been chiefly responsible for their steady aggrandizement throughout the last three centuries; but within the group there have developed islands of people with practically no anxiety, such as the mountaineers of the southern United States, and these have been characteristically "backward." The same differentiation is occurring on a non-geographical basis (it has been greatly accelerated by public relief during the depression) by the "giving-up" and "floating with the tide" of individuals solving their difficulties on a catatonoid basis. The constant generation of small amounts of anxiety which are relieved in action before attaining any considerable "head" is perhaps as good a definition as we have of "normal" emotional life, but it depends upon a very delicate balance of source, external resources, and internal fertility, and so is not, by and large, a particularly frequent phenomenon in human history.

Of the effects of anxiety in totally incapacitating certain probably congenitally inadequate individuals there is little need to remark, except to say that their care is an enormous burden upon the remainder of the population. In addition to this, those individuals who are not completely incapacitated demand and *faute de mieux* usually receive attentions and services far in excess of the normal expenditure for non-affected individuals. Here should probably also be mentioned the immense army of criminals; it is unlikely that anything like a majority of them are reacting so as to minimize anxiety, but the studies of researchers like Alexander and Staub (1931), Karpman (1929), and Stekel (1924) appear to indicate that there is a fairly distinctive subclass which is so motivated.

Prospects for the Reduction of Anxiety. A distinction may usefully be made between the likelihood that the sources and active generation of anxiety may be controlled and that, once generated, it may be more or less continuously neutralized.

On the first point there seems little reason for optimism, at least concerning the near future. Although a number of societies (notably those of the Melanesian area) have been studied in which a comparatively low degree of material culture coexists with a high degree of anxiety, it seems reasonable to regard this as due to a sort of accidental incrustation of cultural patterns of a nature such as to increase enormously what might be thought of as the "natural" anxiety load of the community; it is conceivable that such a condition might be considerably ameliorated, were it worth anybody's while to undertake it, by, say, a sort of psychoanalytic modification of the better accepted educational methods. The data from the American occupation of the Philippines are perhaps the nearest we have on this point, but are not quite relevant partly because the anxiety load seems never to have been great (Jenks, 1905) and because the teaching personnel, when not religious, appears to have operated only on the conscious level, being concerned largely with such items as hygiene and English grammar (see, e.g., the files of *Philippine Public Schools*). In the more complex cultures the existence of a correspondingly greater anxiety load appears to be the rule; and such a state of affairs might be anticipated, as has been stated elsewhere in this chapter, from the consideration that in general the complex cultures will be those in which more demands are made upon the individual and more inhibitions laid upon the expression of his impulses. Thus the agricultural economy of the eighteenth century in New England, while it demanded hard work, offered reasonably prompt and sanctioned gratification for most of the basic impulses; the industrial economy of the twentieth century in the same area, however, requires of the same social stratum less physical work, but demands that the individual function in a situation which is fundamentally insecure in that the satisfaction of his simplest needs may be withdrawn by circumstances not under his control; further, he is equipped to function at all only after extensive preparation, during which he may be required to inhibit the entire gamut of sexual impulses over the period in which these are most strongly functional. This state of affairs is perhaps most highly developed in America, but evidences of similar tension are apparent over most of Western civilization, as well as in civilizations which are in process of being Westernized.

A number of factors are capable of modifying the situation; in the first place, the ecology of populations is relevant, for it is clear that density of population constitutes a direct load upon the individual constitution (Pearl, 1925; Plant, 1930). Birth and death rates may be modified from within the population, so to speak; and there seems abundant evidence that in all complex cultures both are decreasing—the former due probably to contraception and the latter to improved medical knowledge—but that the resultant is a gradual deceleration. There is to be considered here also the curious and somewhat desperate phenomenon of inverse fertility-quality relationship, which appears to be general or nearly so, and which, while little understood, may reflect the inability of the more able groups to tolerate the anxiety burden of child-rearing when means of escaping it are known to them. There is also the possibility of redistribution, which depends principally upon a complex of geographical and political factors such as the absorption or elimination of the weaker races, the decay of nationalism, the unification of government, the adaptation of types to exceptional climatic conditions, and the adaptation of physical features in limited areas to human uses, etc. In general it appears that any lessening of anxiety through redistribution is remote, but possible; and that, while the trend of population numbers is toward a mitigation more directly of anxiety-producing conditions, this is likely to occur partly by selection of more resistant types (which resistance, it is to be feared, is correlated with other less desirable traits) and partly by processes (contraception and medical care) which are ultimately complicating and so anxiety-generating.

Internal complication is much more serious. Political and social life tend to become more inextricably entangled with and overlaid by economic complications, and the effect of all these is increasingly to regiment the individual and make the free expression of his impulses more and more an incident of slight importance in the smooth functioning of the external institutions of the group. The recent widespread breakdown of the democratic idea may be regarded as a short-cut (and therefore a magic) attempt at a solution of the growing burden of anxiety imposed by the unlimited functioning of the *laissez-faire* economic system. The tendency of economic anxiety to absorb the whole of social life, which is a matter of common observation everywhere, is well described in the Lynds' *Middletown* (1929) where also short-cut solutions which have evolved out of religion, recreation, education, and particularly the automobile are also documented; this use of the automobile as a magic wand, conferring short-cuts to power upon its possessor, is an excellent example of a complication of a higher order, inasmuch as it is shown to initiate widespread disorganization in social, family, and economic life, thus raising instead of lowering the tension.

All in all, then, the picture is not a hopeful one. We may grant theoretically, perhaps, that institutions probably tend to an equilibrium in which tension is at a minimum; but there is no assurance that the resolution of a present tension, since it is not a conscious rational process, will not give rise to further and more serious tensions. And there is the constant danger that the magic or short circuiting process may escape its ordinary bounds and cast off all tensions, thereby eliminating civilization itself. This result in individuals, of course, is psychosis, and in individuals of a fairly high degree of culture is frequently initiated by a neurosis or period of attempting to master the anxiety without completely surrendering the tensions. There are probably examples of racial psychosis, as in the Maya or the contemporary North American Indian, caught between cultures and unable to maintain either.

The significance of magic and its cognate processes, therefore, is that it eases the strains in the structure. It is in effect a social neurosis, and it has of course been pointed out that obsessive and phobic magic is common in individual neurosis. What likelihood is there that the burden of anxiety can be more or less continuously neutralized by magic or similar processes which can be kept socially responsible? The outlook seems not to be especially hopeful here either. The trend of the times is predominantly rationalistic, with a strong tendency to repress any acknowledgment not only of the validity but even of the existence of non-conscious mental processes. Thus fantasy, one of the most common psychic elements, is for the most part unrecognized except in persons, such as adolescents, too unsophisticated to conceal it, and in these it is very widely condemned; the dream is acknowledged because of the possibility of disclaiming responsibility, but significance is steadfastly denied it; and magic and folklore are widely attacked as culturally subversive elements. The only considerable opposing tendency is that of organized religion, which is to a considerable extent culturally accepted, but is as naïve in its confusion of subjective and objective fact as its opponents are in their denial of the former. On this basis it appears to be losing ground as the increase in objective knowledge progressively shows that its contentions cannot be objectively supported. There remains the possibility, which, however, achieves reality only in rare personalities and by routes little understood, of the elaboration of symbolic or short-cut techniques for the amelioration of anxiety on a sophisticated basis, which should include (1) the reality of the subjective processes involved, and (2) the use of methods and material which shall be recognized for what they are rather than assigned a spurious objective reality. Without great elaboration we may indicate these as the function most nearly, among the crafts at present recognized, of the psychiatrist and the pastor (but with important modifications), and enumerate them in order of satisfactoriness as (1) prayer, (2) rite, (3) art, and (4) socialized achievement. Of these at least the first three are symbolic, and their effectiveness will be dependent upon the psychological accuracy of the symbolism, a topic discussed elsewhere; the fourth is increasingly difficult to realize, for the reasons given above; and, in general, their effective use in the neutralization of anxiety already engendered is a decidedly difficult problem in socio-psychological engineering, and one for whose proximate solution we probably have no great reason to hope.

Adequacy and Preferability of Modes of Anxiety-Control. We may consider the desirability of the various methods of control enumerated in the order of their original enumeration.

Of the modes in which contact with reality is only abeyant, fantasy of course is the great common fact of all mental life; in it the organism attempts implicitly to resolve conflicts which are as yet implicit, and in the event of a solution consonant with reality requirements the conflict is resolved by the carrying-through of a course of action. This is the fundamental fact of all achievement as well as of all reverie, and as such it must be reckoned as one of the most adequate and one of the most preferable modes in those cases in which it applies. If, however, no solution consonant with reality requirements is reached, a substitute solution incapable of being externalized may be reached which is capable of diverting so much energy from external pursuits as to interfere seriously with adjustment. It must be granted that such a result is often successful in mitigating anxiety, but it is hardly a method of preference; here we may class the motion picture, which provides the content of the fantasy for individuals with too slight creative powers to furnish their own. Hypnagogic imagery is apparently fantasy facilitated by a special bodily state, and so belongs with the class of phenomena considered in the next paragraph; and pseudo-hallucination is a phenomenon so rare and so little under conscious control that it need hardly be considered as an available mode.

Of the aids to the lapse of reality relations, the drugs, especially alcohol, are by far the most important practically. It appears to be the universal testimony that alcohol releases inhibition, thus making expression of impulse possible; but the channel of expression and the impulses expressed are pretty clearly a function of the experience and present needs of the individual. The narcotic drugs appear to block off the entire conflict, perhaps by raising the threshold of conductivity itself. The mescal practices of the American Indians, which are significantly associated with religion, show clearly the mechanism of exaltation to a condition wherein conflicts have been resolved and the usual sensory phenomena of life have been superseded by far more glamorous ones. The drugs as a whole are evidently entirely effective as means of neutralizing anxiety, but their undesirable effects are well known; they must be classed with the modes which, while temporarily palliative, easily become permanently maladjustive. Traumatic practices, such as those of the Plains Indians, avoid the same stigma by reason of the fortitude involved, but are not a real issue in present Western civilization.

The divination practices, including the observation of omens, astrology, and the consultation of mediums and clairvoyants—possibly also the practices of dowsing and scrying—are less pernicious, but probably also less effective. It is they to which the somewhat loose popular term "superstition" is most frequently applied, and since this word and its associations are in cultural disrepute the methods are available only to the extremely naïve or to those socially so placed as to avoid contact with the cultural disapprobation. Further, it is in the nature of these methods that they are completely subject to chance, and this requires for successful application further naïveté in the case of self-applied methods like omens or a degree of skilful fraud in the case of methods applied by others, as mediumship and astrology. If these are great enough, there is little to be said against the methods except that they are best adapted to the unintelligent and unsophisticated; they can be regarded as definitely adjustive in that they assist the individuals to externalize and resolve conflict.

In the case of the series of implicit reactions in which relation to reality has definitely lapsed, the adequacy of the modes of anxiety-control can hardly be doubted. A person in a thoroughgoing wish-fulfilment dream has clearly solved his problem, for the moment at least; and the prolongation of this moment in a delusional system is evidently no less final and satisfactory. But the price of solution has been the surrender of the real world and the complete loss of adjustment, at least in the most illustrative cases. The occasional existence of an individual in whom a delusion affecting external adjustment but little is combined with a tolerant or indifferent environment (as when the approach of the millennium is made to hinge upon a patient's running an elevator faithfully) need not modify essentially our common-sense judgment that this class of control modes is adequate but entirely undesirable.

The negative modes of explicit anxiety-control, phobia and tabu, are ordinarily maintained at the cost of constant affective expenditure. That is, they are unstable and only partially successful attempts to lock up anxiety, and they are constantly breaking down; thus phobi ; not infrequently extend to wider and wider spheres of activity, eventually almost paralyzing the victim, and tabus ordinarily have appended to them a provision for their ritual violation as a sort of safety valve—in spite of which they may "leak," as in the case of the body tabu in contemporary Western civilization. They therefore fail to meet the first requirement, that of adequacy. This is what we should expect on the ground that effective controls should release, not inhibit.

Verbal control modes, however, are in much better case. These are the lower grade of *Ersatzbefriedigung* or true magic, in which a partial or symbolic action discharges by displacement or substitution a conflict of excitations. On account of the peculiarly symbolic nature of the speech mechanisms, which combine on occasion strong affective content with relatively slight overt interaction with the environment, they are especially fitted to act as channels for the discharge of anxiety. And their effectiveness has been recognized throughout history; katharsis or "talking it out" is an ancient form of psychotherapy, of which modern forms, including psychoanalysis, are merely technical modifications. The leader of public worship is close in function to the psychotherapist, and both have much in common with the pronouncer of incantations, the individual at prayer, and even the invoker of negative prayer, the curse. Mysticism is evidently prayer in which the verbal element has been eliminated, being replaced by almost pure organic sensation with very general ideational content. Folklore and myth are peculiarly desirable in that they are the most socialized of all modes, but except in the naïve state in which they are regarded as historical they seem not to be especially effective.

The full positive control methods are the most representative of the series. There is little to distinguish magic rites from religious rites; both are among the most effective of the control modes in that they most completely carry through into action a definite motor impulse. Their desirability is peculiarly a function of the social environment; in a favorable setting they are both powerful and acceptable. Sorcery and witchcraft seem to represent the sadistic aspects of magic, standing in the same relation to it as the curse does to the prayer; they engender anxiety in all societies naïve enough to accept them, and so fall clearly among the self-defeating modes. Obsession is in similar case; it appears to be closely related to phobia, and to have the same character of endeavoring unsuccessfully to lock up anxiety that continually increases; it may also progress until it paralyzes the personality, and in consequence is both ineffective and undesirable.

Art as a mode of anxiety control is evidently not in the magic series; it is a creative process which externalizes fantasy and thus, so to speak, socializes it; thus it stands halfway between fantasy and reality. It may be highly adequate in achieving its goal of mitigating anxiety, and, given a receptive milieu, may also contribute greatly to the social adjustment of the artist and others; but the fantasy element may absorb the reality elements, with catastrophe as a result.

Control through full manipulation of reality is achieved by construction, and on the more abstract levels by the symbolic construction of science and particularly of technology. It is hardly necessary to say that of all controls it is the one which yields the greatest success in the mastery of anxiety, accompanied by the greatest acceptability from the ethical and social standpoints. It requires, however, special conditions of native ability and training which are prohibitive for all but a minority of individuals.

POINTS OF VIEW

Naïve. It is obvious that the most unsophisticated attitudes toward phenomena of the order we are considering will be formed on the popular levels. While the most transparent instances are probably rarely found in print, the following from the *Society Dream Book* (1925) is relatively uncontaminated by scholarly influence:

> What you dreamed last night may affect your life and undertakings for a long time to come. . . . Dreams and forewarnings have influenced the lives of individuals and nations since history began. . . . Dreams, their causes and influences, are now studied in many hospitals and colleges. This in itself is proof that the ancients were right in giving so much attention to dreams. . . . Certain dreams were found to be followed by certain events, and when so found in repeated instances, these explanations became valuable and were preserved and consulted. This happened in the long ago and still happens today. . . . Not only do we all have dreams, but many dreams are in the nature of warnings. Such should be interpreted before they are forgotten. . . . The Society Dream Book has been compiled from the most reliable sources. Some of it dates back to antiquity, and some conclusions are the results of recent studies and observations. Old truths have been verified by modern experience, and new light is shed on phases of the subject that were puzzling in the past. . . . *Look under the heading most likely to apply to your case. Look under all three headings to be better satisfied. And if the first word you consult does not satisfy, look for a word of similar meaning.*

It is evident that even at this level the critical apparatus must be approximately appeased, i.e., anxiety which is normally neutralized by the consciousness of being rational must not be liberated by the removal of its controls. But the crux of the matter, the psychic economy effected by the maneuver of appeal to the short-cut, magic *Ersatzbefriedigung,* is in the italicized directions: If the principal anxiety is not neutralized at the first contact, authority is expressly given (thus avoiding possible further anxiety about the legitimacy of such a proceeding) to permute the materials until it is, always within the frame of rationality. Thus this humble document proves to be a powerful, if crude, *Arzneimittel* in the service of folk mental hygiene. And the attitude toward magic, of course, is incorporated into the system itself, and emerges as a sort of resultant of the strength of the principal anxiety to be neutralized and the astuteness of the critical apparatus which neutralizes the secondary anxiety.

More remarkable, however, is the emergence of the naïve viewpoint in a scholar of obviously broad and deep erudition; although the author to be quoted indicates that his is the accepted position of his Church, we have not found any other example of this coincidence of attitudes. The Reverend Montague Summers, M.A. of Trinity College, Oxford, and evidently an historian of great competence, is evidently convinced of the veridical nature of at least a modicum of the phenomena of witchcraft. We quote passim from his volume, *The History of Witchcraft and Demonology*:

> In imitation of God, moreover, the Devil will have his miracles, although these are θαύματα, mere delusive wonders which neither profit nor convince. . . . To this source we can confidently refer many tricks of Oriental jugglers (p. 59). . . . Those who have seen this hideous spectacle [illusion of mutilation] assure us that it cannot be explained by any hallucination or legerdemain, and the only solution which remains is to attribute it to the glamour cast over the deluded crowd by the power of discarnate evil intelligence (p. 60). All these particulars [spiritistic phenomena] unmistakably point to demoniac intervention and deceit (p. 61). . . . It is not enough quite sincerely to claim magical powers to possess them in reality (p. 63). . . . But when every allowance has been made as we examine in detail the long and bloody history of witchcraft . . . . we cannot but recognize that there remain innumerable and important cases which are not to be covered by any ordinary explanation, which fall within no normal category (p. 64). . . . It may not impertinently be inquired how demons or evil intelligences, since they are pure spiritual beings, can not only assume human flesh but perform the peculiarly carnal act of coition. . . . Can we not look to the phenomena observed in connexion with ectoplasm as an adequate explanation of this? (p. 95). . . . When every allowance has been made . . . . there will yet remain a very considerable quota [of cases of demoniacal possession] which it seems impossible to account for and explain save on the score of possession by some evil and hostile intelligence. (p. 220)

While this viewpoint is difficult to evaluate apart from the great interest aroused by its rarity, we may venture the comment that it exemplifies most instructively the degree to which habitual emotional attachment to a principle or institution may press into its service bodily even an elaborate and smoothly functioning logical apparatus. If this be just, the viewpoint obeys (as from a rationalistic point of view we should expect) the same laws as the magic itself, which constantly negates or distorts perceived reality in the service of the resolution of anxiety-tensions. We have commented on this above in connection with the social significance of anxiety control.

Pseudo-sophisticated Point of View. Not unnaturally the next advance in the scale of sophistication is marked by the failure of the proffered resolution to meet the demands of the critical system; that is, presumably through a strengthening of the latter, no saving is now possible unless the short-cut solution becomes correspondingly more subtle, since there is nothing to choose between equal amounts of primary anxiety and the secondary anxiety due to a consciousness of being "ridiculous." The critical system is completely dominant, and magic becomes trivial, lawless, and unworthy the attention of a serious person. As a result this point of view is rarely committed to print (although it is the common contemporary one of the bourgeois levels); the following anecdote concerning Chesterfield, however, with Tylor's epigrammatic comment, does it approximate justice (1888, p. 119):

> The clever Lord Chesterfield, *too clever to understand folly*, ... relates in one of his letters that the King had been ill, and that people generally expected the illness to be fatal, because the oldest lion in the Tower, about the King's age, had just died. "So wild and capricious is the human mind," he exclaims, by way of comment.

A fairly close derivative of this repressive point of view, perhaps not too surprisingly, is fairly widespread among American schoolmen. It is expressed in a small but persistent group of studies attempting to determine (1) the incidence of "superstitious beliefs" among the school population at various age levels, and (2) the effect on this incidence of "remedial" teaching, chiefly in science. The recent study of Caldwell and Lundeen (1932) is thoroughgoing and probably representative of the best studies of this sort.

> It is often said that human life will increase in efficiency as there is increase in the use of workable truth and decrease in use of things not soundly supported. One aspect of this whole problem relates to adherence to superstitions and other unfounded beliefs. An unfounded belief implies a causal relationship between objects, phenomena or events where such a relationship does not exist. A correct connection between cause and effect is the essence of scientific thinking. In order to develop desirable and scientific attitudes of mind it is one function of science to offer remedial instruction regarding influential unfounded beliefs. (p. 1)
>
> .   .   .   .   .   .
>
> Unfounded beliefs include all beliefs that have no scientific basis or support by facts. The term refers to superstitions as well as other beliefs having no scientific foundation. Some unfounded ideas which were included for remedial instruction may be considered as superstitions while others may be regarded as misconceptions. Misconceptions and superstitions are alike in that they do not have scientific support. A superstition, while being unfounded by facts, also involves an element of fear. Many misconceptions have more appearance of scientific approval than do superstitions. The fact that a cause and effect relationship does not exist with reference to superstitions is usually obvious. This non-causal relationship regarding misconceptions is not always so evident. (p. 2)

It is of course the presupposition rather than the results which interest us here, although it is clear that the latter are strongly influenced by the former. It is difficult to know what significance is to be attached to an increase after instruction of say 30 per cent in "desirable" responses to the item "Is fish a brain food?" in the absence of any knowledge as to (1) the degree to which this is (*a*) a matter of simple information on such items as phosphorus metabolism, or (b) a magic item designed to allay anxiety by the reassurance that a solution exists for the problem of personal mental inadequacy; and (2) the degree to which the responses correspond with the (magic) attitudes. It is to be presumed that fear of unorthodoxy will always be a potent influence in the direction (in the school situation) of "desirable" answers, whatever the state of the attitudes beneath. Thus in a matter of sheer factual information, such as a date of no special significance, an increase of 30 per cent objectively correct answers, indicates an addition of that amount in the mnemonic furniture of the individuals concerned; but in the case of an item of affective value, such as the objective efficacy of a magic act, an increase may signify nothing beyond a mere learning of the "correct" external response, the underlying magic attitude (i.e., need for mitigation of anxiety) remaining unchanged, although perhaps repressed or attached to another act.[2]   In the case of many of the more transparent magical acts, in fact, the "desirable" answer is known already by a large proportion of persons, who would nevertheless "feel funny" if compelled to act accordingly; the avertive formula "I'm not superstitious, but . . . ." is of special interest here.   The social significance of repressive educative measures of this kind can hardly be so obviously salutary as supposed by their worthy proponents; but this has been considered in the appropriate section.

Naturalistic Point of View. A far more developed and genuinely sophisticated point of view is to be found in the writings of the great Victorian students, Tylor and Frazer. So well considered is this viewpoint, in fact, that the only adverse criticism that can be brought against it even at the present day is that it reflects the thought of its period in placing relatively great emphasis upon the intellectual and relatively little upon the emotional aspects of mind; it probably represents as close to a liberation from the tyranny of anxiety in the determination of attitudes as we have achieved so far. It is essentially the doctrine that while magic is "delusion" and "farrago" it is the result of a quite understandable error, viz., the confusion between mental, associative relations and physical, causative relations.   Thus Tylor in *Primitive Culture* (1888):

> The principal key to the understanding of Occult Science is to consider it as based on the Association of Ideas, a faculty which lies at the very foundation of human reason, but in no small degree of human unreason also.   Man, as yet in a low intellectual condition, having come to associate in thought those things which he found by experience to be connected in fact, proceeded erroneously to invert this action, and to conclude that association in thought must involve similar connexion in reality.   He thus attempted to discover, to foretell, and to cause events by means of processes which we can now see to have only an ideal significance.   By a vast mass of evidence from savage, barbaric, and civilized life, magic arts which have resulted from thus mistaking an ideal for a real connexion, may be clearly traced from the lower

---

[2] The highly significant fact that many children and some adults individually evolve systems of true magic in the absence of supporting cultural patterns, or even in the face of sophisticated pressure, is regularly overlooked by the proponents of the viewpoint here criticized.

culture which they are of, to the higher culture which they are in. (pp. 115-116)

Thus also Frazer in *The Golden Bough* (1925):

> If we analyze the principles of thought on which magic is based, they will probably be found to resolve themselves into two: first, that like produces like, or that an effect resembles its cause; and second, that things which have once been in contact with each other continue to act on each other at a distance after the physical contact has been severed. The former principle may be called the Law of Similarity, the latter the Law of Contact or Contagion. . . . Charms based on the Law of Similarity may be called Homoeopathic or Imitative Magic. Charms based on the Law of Contact or Contagion may be called Contagious Magic. . . . If my analysis of the Magician's logic is correct, its two great principles turn out to be merely two different misapplications of the association of ideas. Homoeopathic magic is founded on the association of ideas by similarity; contagious magic is founded on the association of ideas by contiguity. (p. 11)

It would be difficult to improve on these formulations, so far as they go; the theory involved satisfactorily accounts for a great many otherwise puzzling phenomena, and to my knowledge no evidence against it has been produced in the half century since it was enunciated. It leaves as ultimate, however, the analogical or associative principle, in accordance with the emphasis of its time upon rational elements in explanation; whereas the more recent developments in clinical psychology induce us to ask what are the determinants of the associative principle itself—why, i.e., an analogical solution is emotionally satisfying, while one on different principles is not.

Naturalistic-psychoanalytic Point of View. Before noting the addition of this final step, we may observe the emergence of a slightly different viewpoint in virtually the same field—that of the newer field anthropologist of the "functional" school. Whereas the older investigators, as Frazer and Tylor, employed almost exclusively the secondary method of collecting accounts of travelers and correspondents, thus amassing enormous bodies of data, the newer ones, as Malinowski, Mead, and Fortune, themselves proceed to the field and collect primary data by standard methods on a single culture at a time. The difference is important in relation to the matter of point of view as well as in other ways. The primary source for the older writer can hardly have had as naturalistic a point of view as the writer himself, on the average. The newer writer is his own source, and in addition he controls the language error by learning the language himself; most important, he consciously cultivates objectivity, and he is the better able to effect this in that he has given himself opportunities to study the phenomena professionally and comparatively.

It is probably not without significance that the founder of the functional school of anthropology, Malinowski, was for a time greatly impressed by the psychoanalytic findings, and that a leading psychoanalyst, Róheim, has recently reported valuable field observation on primitive belief and ritual. Observations by Deutsch and by Freud on what may be called the laboratory form of magic—that of phobiacs and obsessives— may be taken, however, as representative of the most thoroughly natural- istic point of view yet enunciated. The quotation from Deutsch's *Psy- choanalysis of the Neuroses* (1932) which is given in our series of anxiety-controls under *Obsession* illustrates this point of view.

* * * * *

Thus we have a roughly continuous evolution of attitudes from com- plete absence of sophistication, as in, say, the unquestioning regard for spirits on the part of most primitives, through an effort to reconcile faith with regard for rationality, to an apparent reversal wherein all magic is simple fraud and all sympathetic consideration credulity; then an at- tempt to explain the phenomena on a .rational, conscious basis, without regard for impulses, unconscious phenomena, or emotions; and, finally, an effort to understand them in terms of a dynamic explanation, with due regard for motivation and the functions served in the mental economy of the individual by events which may be thought of as adaptive though irrational. Whether additional stages of insight are to be awaited is at the present moment anyone's guess; a verification of the hypotheses herein put forward by rigorous statistical or even experimental neuro- physiological procedures might possibly be regarded as such an additional stage.

Bibliography

ALEXANDER, F., & STAUB, H. 1931. The criminal, the judge, and the public: a psychological analysis. (Trans. by G. Zilboorg.) New York: Mac- millan. Pp. 258.

BAYLISS, W. M. 1931. Principles of general physiology. (4th ed.) New York & London: Longmans, Green. Pp. xviii+882.

BELL, E. T. 1933. Numerology. Baltimore, Md.: Williams & Wilkins. Pp. viii+187.

BLANCHARD, P. 1929. Attitude and educational disabilities. *Ment. Hygiene,* **13**, 550-563.

BOSTWICK, A. E. 1926. Spatial and time relations in dreams. *Nature,* **118**, 627.

CALDWELL, O. W., & LUNDEEN, G. E. 1932. An experimental study of super- stitions and other unfounded beliefs. New York: Teach. Coll. Pp. 138.

CAVAN, R. S. 1928. Suicide. Chicago: Univ. Chicago Press. Pp. xxviii+359.

COE, G. A. 1916. The psychology of religion. Chicago: Univ. Chicago Press, Pp. xvii+365.

DELACROIX, H. 1922. La religion et la foi. Paris: Alcan. Pp. 462.

DEUTSCH, H. 1932. Psychoanalysis of the neuroses. (Trans. by W. D. Robson- Scott.) London: Hogarth Press & Instit. Psycho-Anal. Pp. vii+239.

ERICKSON, M. H. 1933. The investigation of a specific amnesia. *Brit. J. Med. Psychol.,* **13**, 143-150.

FERNBERGER, S. W. 1932. Further observations on peyote intoxication. *J. Abn. & Soc. Psychol.,* **26**, 367-378.

FERRETTI, G. 1926. Sogni e immagini ipnagogiche. *Riv. di psicol.,* **22**, 102-122.

FORTUNE, R. F. 1932. Sorcerers of Dobu. New York: Dutton. Pp. 346.

FRAZER, J. G. 1925. The golden bough; a study in magic and religion. (Abridged ed.) London & New York: Macmillan. Pp. xiv+756.

FREEMAN, G. L. 1930. Changes in tonus during completed and interrupted mental work. *J. Gen. Psychol.*, **4**, 309-334.

FREUD, S. 1894. Ueber die Berechtigung, von der Neurasthenie einen bestimmten Symptomenkomplex als "Angstneurose" abzutrennen. *Neur. Zentbl.*, **14**, 50-66.
English: 1924. The justification for detaching from neurasthenia a particular syndrome: the anxiety-neurosis. (Trans. by A. A. Brill.) In Vol. 1 of *Collected Papers*. London: Hogarth Press & Instit. Psycho-Anal. Pp. 76-106.

————. 1895. Zur Kritik der "Angstneurose." *Wien. klin. Rund.*, **9**, 417, 435, 451.
English: 1924. A reply to criticisms on the anxiety-neurosis. (Trans. by J. Rickman.) In Vol. 1 of *Collected Papers*. London: Hogarth Press & Instit. Psycho-Anal. Pp. 107-127.

————. 1896. L'hérédité et l'étiologie des névroses. *Rev. neur.*, **4**, 161-170.
English: 1924. Heredity and the aetiology of the neuroses. (Trans. by M. Meyer.) In Vol. 1 of *Collected Papers*. London: Hogarth Press & Instit. Psycho-Anal. Pp. 138-154.

————. 1899. Die Traumdeutung. Leipzig & Vienna: Deuticke. Pp. 375.
English: 1913. The interpretation of dreams. (Trans. by A. A. Brill.) London: Allen; New York: Macmillan. Pp. x+510.

————. 1930. Das Unbehagen in der Kultur. Leipzig, Vienna, & Zurich: Int. psychoanal. Verlag. Pp. 136.
English: 1930. Civilization and its discontents. (Trans. by J. Riviere.) London: Hogarth Press & Instit. Psycho-Anal. Pp. 144.

GARDNER, E. 1907. St. Catherine of Siena. London.

GHEURY DE BRAY, M. E. J. 1923. Time relations in a dream. (Letter.) *Nature*, **11**, 361.

————. 1926. Spatial and time relations in dreams. *Nature*, **118**, 372.

GREAT AIM SOCIETY. 1925. Society dream book. New York: Great Aim Soc.

HART, H., & HART, E. B. 1933. Visions and apparitions collectively and reciprocally perceived. *Proc. Soc. Psych. Res.*, **41**, 205-249.

HARTWELL, S. W. 1931. Fifty-five "bad" boys. New York: Knopf. Pp. xvii+359.

JENKS, A. 1905. The Bontoc Igorot. (*Philippine Is. Ethnol. Survey Publ.*, Vol. 1.) Manila: Bur. Publ. Print. Pp. 266.

JONES, E. 1931. Nightmares, witches, and devils. New York: Norton. Pp. 374.

KAPUSTNIK, O. P. 1930. Vzaimootnosheniya mezhdu neprosredstvennymi uslovnymi razdrazhiteliami i slovesnymi ikh symbolami. *Trudi lab. fiziol. Instit. Gertzena*, **2**, 11-22. (*Psychol. Abstr.*, 1934, **8**, No.153.)

KARPMAN, B. 1929. Psychoses in criminals: clinical studies in the psychopathology of crime: II. Clinical and casuistic material (IV). *J. Nerv. & Ment. Dis.*, **70**, 520-534, 622-641.

KENNETH, J. H. 1926. Spatial relation in a dream. *Nature*, **118**, 194.

KLING, C. 1934. A statistical study of the relations of neurasthenic, dyspeptic, and allergic symptoms. *J. Gen. Psychol.*, **10**, 328-343.

KRASNOGORSKI, N. I. 1925. The conditioned reflex and children's neuroses. *Amer. J. Dis. Child.*, **30**, 754-768.

LICHTENBERGER, J. P. 1931. Divorce: a social interpretation. New York: Whittlesey House (McGraw-Hill). Pp. xii+472.

LURIA, A. R. 1932. The nature of human conflicts. (Trans. and ed. by W. H. Gantt.) New York: Liveright. Pp. xvii+431.

LYND, R. S., & LYND, H. M. 1929. Middletown. New York: Harcourt, Brace. Pp. x+550.

MARTINEZ, A., & CIAMPI, L. 1933. La psicosis simultánea en la época evolutiva. Bol. instit. psiquiat., 4, 91-104.

MEAD, M. 1928. Coming of age in Samoa. New York: Morrow. Pp. 297.

———. 1930. Growing up in New Guinea. New York: Morrow. Pp. xii+372.

———. 1932. The changing culture of an Indian tribe. New York: Columbia Univ. Press. Pp. xiv+313.

MEYERSON, I. 1929. Images-éclairs. J. de psychol., 26, 569-576.

NEIHARDT, J. G. 1932. Black Elk speaks. New York: Morrow.

NOLAN, M. J. 1928. Hallucinations and sanity. J. Ment. Sci., 74, 49-58.

OVSIANKINA, M. 1928. Die Wiederaufnahme unterbrochener Handlungen. Pt. VI of "Untersuchungen zur Handlungs- und Affektpsychologie," ed. by K. Lewin. Psychol. Forsch., 11, 302-379.

PAVLOV, I. P. 1927. Conditioned reflexes: an investigation of the physiological activity of the cerebral cortex. (Trans. and ed. by G. V. Anrep.) London: Oxford Univ. Press. Pp. xv+430.

PEARL, R. 1925. The biology of population growth. New York: Knopf. Pp. xiv+260.

PLANT, J. S. 1930. Some psychiatric aspects of crowded living conditions. Amer. J. Psychiat., 9, 849-860.

RANDOLPH, V. 1931. The Ozarks; an American survival of primitive society. New York: Vanguard. Pp. 319.

RANK, O. 1932. Art and the artist; creative urge and personality development. (Trans. by C. F. Atkinson.) New York: Knopf. Pp. xlix+431.

RICHTER, C. P. 1927. A study of the electrical skin resistance and the psychogalvanic reflex in the case of unilateral sweating. Brain, 50, 216-235.

SHERMAN, M., & HENRY, T. R. 1933. Hollow folk. New York: Crowell. Pp. viii+215.

SHERRINGTON, C. S. 1906. The integrative action of the nervous system. New York: Scribner's. Pp. xvi+411.

STEKEL, W. 1908. Nervöse Angstzustände und ihre Behandlung. Vienna: Urban & Schwarzenberg. Pp. 315.

———. 1924. Peculiarities of behavior; wandering mania, dipsomania, cleptomania, pyromania and allied impulsive acts. (Trans. by J. S. van Teslaar.) London: Williams & Norgate; New York: Boni & Liveright. Pp. xiv+341; 351.

SUMMERS, M. 1927. The history of witchcraft and demonology. New York: Knopf. Pp. x+368.

THURSTONE, L. L., & THURSTONE, T. G. 1930. A neurotic inventory. J. Soc. Psychol., 1, 3-30.

TYLOR, E. B. 1888. Primitive culture. (2 vols.) New York: Holt. Pp. xii +502; viii+470.

UNDERHILL, E. 1911. Mysticism. A study in the nature and development of man's spiritual consciousness. New York: Dutton. Pp. xv+600.

VARENDONCK, J. 1921. The psychology of day-dreams. London: Allen & Unwin. Pp. 367.

WATSON, J. B. 1928. The unconscious of the behaviorist. In The unconscious; a symposium, ed. by Mrs. E. S. Dummer. New York: Knopf.

WILLIAMS, F. E. 1934. Russia, youth, and the present-day world: further studies in mental hygiene. New York: Farrar. Pp. xxii+270.

WILLOUGHBY, R. R. 1929. An adaptive aspect of dreams. *J. Abn. & Soc. Psychol.*, **24**, 104-107.

————. 1934. Ghosts of the sophisticated. *J. Soc. Psychol.*, **5**, 508-515.

WOODWORTH, R. S. 1915. Imageless thought—a revision. *Psychol. Rev.*, **22**, 1-27.

YOUNG, P. C. 1926. An experimental study of mental and physical functions in the normal and hypnotic states. Additional results. *Amer. J. Psychol.*, **37**, 345-356.

CHAPTER 13

MATERIAL CULTURE

CLARK WISSLER

Yale University

Every culture operates with a material equipment. We conceive such equipment as comprising natural materials modified by labor, mechanical devices, and all useful and ornamental objects produced by labor. The population involved in a culture looks upon this equipment as synonymous with material property. The point of view we take in this chapter is that material culture is concerned with the material possessions of man, savage and civilized.

The preceding chapter headings—"Language," and "Magic and Cognate Phenomena"—can be considered quite apart from these material things and with slight changes in terminology will apply to all mankind, civilized or savage. They are subjects of wide interest and appeal, occupying places of honor in the academic world. Material Culture in less fortunate. The historian takes some note of it, but usually puts emphasis upon such subjects as politics and war, though basing the very existence of his subject upon record in the form of materials. The social sciences ignore materials, in the main, concealing them under such formulae as production, trade, prices, etc. Even the cultural anthropologist takes far greater interest in folklore, magic, and family and social organization than in material culture. We are therefore in the unenviable position of dealing with a large subject which is more or less side-stepped by scholars.

Turning now to our task, it appears, first, that the difficulties encountered in distinguishing between men and other creatures decrease when attention is fixed upon the materials of culture. The most despised savage carries about with him a material equipment that puts all other creatures to shame; nothing like it exists anywhere. This may not be the most significant difference between man and other living creatures, but you can lay hands upon this equipment, put it into a cabinet, and have no fear that a logical expert can explain it out of existence, as he may do with such concepts as insight, instinct, intelligence, etc. It is the stubborn reality in anthropology. We mention this merely as a reminder of the distinctive place material artifacts occupy in human affairs. We can no more conceive of society without this equipment than we can imagine it without men, women, and children.

Research in material culture is, for the most part, housed in museums of anthropology, industry, history, and art. The first notable attempt to use museum collections in the study of material culture is credited to

A. H. Pitt-Rivers (1827-1900).[1] In modern textbooks he is often held up to scorn as a "social evolutionist," with little recognition given to his place in history. Primarily a museum builder, his vision of a museum as the "common man's university" was prophetic: an ideal now universally recognized. He believed that from the study of artifacts themselves the past history of the race would be revealed, but that to this end such artifacts must be carefully collected and documented.

Closely following Pitt-Rivers, Edward Tylor (1832-1917) studied fire-making appliances, wheeled vehicles, agricultural implements, etc. His conception was that fabricated objects, by their form and structure, would reveal the progressive steps in their historical development. If one views a series of lamps in the order of their dates of origin, a sequence of changes is observed, seemingly coordinated with time intervals. Archeologists have proposed similar sequences in pottery, stone work, etc., many of which have been checked by stratigraphic data and so stand proven. But there was more to the idea of Tylor, since the concept of survival entered into the picture. Thus in our day many backward peoples are breaking ground with sticks, others with crude wooden plows, while elsewhere tractors and great steel plows tear up the soil. All these are contemporary, but it is assumed that they must have come into existence in a time sequence, the earlier forms having survived to the present. Granting this, a large collection of the material equipment for cultures, great and small, should reveal history. A glance through Tylor's *Anthropology* (1893) will reveal the concept of survivals as he applied it to artifacts and the associated techniques. Both Tylor and Pitt-Rivers recognized that the forms of simple artifacts survived in their more elaborate successors. Thus the early railway carriages were like stage coaches; the first automobiles, like buggies, etc. Yet what Tylor had in mind was a pattern for invention. In the above-mentioned work he seeks to show that in every phase of culture equipment man adds to his store of artifacts by modifications and additions to those he already has. Savage or civilized, there is an urge toward a more efficient, or at least a changed, artifact. Many present-day writers in social science would have us believe that improvement is an illusion and that the shift from horse to automobile is merely a change. The claim is that the concept of change is scientific because it commits one to nothing. Yet either term will do as a name, for it is the reality of behavior that is important. Thus Tylor's view is that artifacts and techniques change and that, in the long run, man comes to use more numerous and intricate forms of both. Data in support of this belief are to be found in the documentary history of artifacts, and, while we lack a history for most of the artifacts shown in an ethnographical museum, we still believe that if and when that history is known the process of change will be, in general, the same, or conform to the invention pattern. This is the contribution of Tylor, Pitt-Rivers, and their associates. What have been rejected in part by many modern scholars are some of the specific

---

[1]See Pitt-Rivers (1906).

attempts to recover the history of certain artifacts by comparing their structures, as, for example, deriving the wheel from a roller thus: (*a*) a simple roller; (*b*) a roller hollowed out like a spool; (*c*) a section of the roller mounted as a wheel; (*d*) a spoked wheel; etc. It is true that the zoologist relates his species in this way, arriving at primitive forms, but many anthropologists refuse to believe that artifacts can be safely treated in like manner until check data are available.

Looking at this matter in historical perspective, it seems clear that with the realization that carefully collected artifacts were objective data on culture, past or present, came the urge to study artifacts and to formulate problems concerning them. Further, the formulation of problems is the necessary step looking toward a solution. Rejecting proposed solutions does not dispose of the problem.

In the United States the pioneer in the study of material culture was O. T. Mason (1838-1908). He was even more than a pioneer for he set standards in technology, best known in his classic work on basketry (1904). He made the study of basketry respectable. His method in general was to subject artifacts to structural analysis and upon this basis to work out systems of classification. Thus he defined the two main types of basketry: hand-woven and sewed or coiled. Under these heads a number of classes with their observed varieties were set up. For example, under coiled basketry we find the following classes:

a.	coil without foundation	*f.*	two-rod–and–splint foundation
b.	simple interlocking coils	*g.*	three-rod foundation
c.	single-rod foundation	*h.*	splint foundation
d.	two-rod foundation	*i.*	grass-coil foundation
e.	rod-and-welt foundation	*j.*	Fuegian coil

Mason's complete scheme of classification for basketry included the botanical identification of the weaving materials, the identification of dye materials, the technique of decoration, etc. This classification, with slight modifications and enlargements, is the basis for the description of baskets in every museum, and it is largely due to this lead that basketry, matting, and weaving in general are treated with more precision in anthropological literature than most other artifacts. Yet with Mason the structural classification of basketry was not an end in itself, since the classification was used to determine the tribal and regional distributions of types. He did not confine his studies to structure, form, and textile materials, but in every case sought tribal and regional information. Although he did not use the term "culture area," he may be said to have laid the foundation for the development of that concept.

One of the most recent special studies in material culture is by Professor Buck (1930). His publication treats of Samoa and follows the usual topical outline—as housing, cooking, foods, baskets, mats, cord, bark cloth, clothing, dyes, stone work, tools, canoes, fishing, hunting, agriculture, games, musical instruments, weapons, religious objects, personal adornment, and tattooing. Yet it differs from many other discussions of the subject in that the artifacts of the culture are not merely described, but attention is also given to the associated social settings and values. Since artifacts are in large part the product of labor, it seems strange that the literature of material cultures should have ignored this important matter; but Professor Buck regards labor as one of the vital aspects of the subject and has much to tell us of the activities from which artifacts result.

Though regarded as a primitive people, the Samoans had specialized in many crafts. A man was no longer his own boat-builder but, just as we call in a contractor, the would-be boat-owner called on a master builder. "Guilds," as organizations of builders, existed and, like others of their kind in primitive society, were ritualized and their activities surrounded with ceremonialism. For an account of the relations between the laborers and boat-owner the reader should consult the text (pp. 84-97). The following may serve as an illustration of the author's method:

The person desiring a better class of canoe had to approach a master builder with all the ceremonial preliminaries observed in house building. The canoe and the house were on the same level. The chief, therefore, mobilized his family and his resources beforehand. He planted food crops and collected fine mats for he had to feed and pay the master builder and his associates. Everything being ready, he approached the desired builder with a fine mat and over the ceremonial bowl of kava made his request and proffered his mat. The builder replied and if he accepted the mat, the contract was sealed. If he refused, the chief sought another expert with the rejected mat.

The builder on an appointed day arrived with his party, selected the timber and did the preliminary shaping whilst the chief's family did the rough work in transporting the timber from the forest to the village. The wood was allowed to season while the builders returned home. The wood sufficiently seasoned, the builders returned and dwelt on the hospitality of the chief and his family. All the general observances described in house building were carried out in canoe building. The builders had to be fed on the best of food with variety in delicacies or they abandoned the work which no one else would take up. A member of the chief's family had to be in constant attendance to show the respect evinced by an active interest in the work, as well as to anticipate the material wants of the builders. Interim payments had to be made and if they proved unsatisfactory to the builders, they left on the pretext that they had not been treated with sufficient respect. . . .

The chief's family sat within the guest house and the builders sat outside in the open space before it. Women wearing the fine mats went out and then laid them before the builders. If not enough, the builders coaxed and threatened, saying the payment was inadequate and not what they considered in keeping with the rank of their employer. The chief pleaded poverty. The builders replied by asking why, if poor, he had presumed to employ them. If the chief produced some more mats, the builders were extravagant in their praise; if not, they were equally loud in their vituperation. However, the chief was at last in a commanding position for the canoe was finished and no strike could affect him. All that the builders could do was to return home and broadcast accounts of the chief's parsimony to all and sundry.

During the building of the canoe, however, the builders could adopt a rather mean way of venting their spite on a chief when it was not deemed advisable to go on strike. They could make the canoe, if it were a fishing canoe, unlucky. There were two ways of doing this. The lashings of the topsides or gunwale to the side pieces in a bonito canoe are called the *pu fangota*. The correct number of lashings as already stated are 15 on the right and 16 on the left. All the builders had to do was to change that number and the canoe would never catch more than ten bonito. This may apply only to Tutuila where it was told to me but it gives an idea of how simply a disaster could be brought on the man who was sparing of food and fine mats. The man who had reason to suspect the builders probably watched the drilling of the topsides very carefully. Even so, there was another method easily overlooked. In the temporary fitting of the side pieces, small wooden wedges, *tina* or *mata lafi*, were driven under the lashings to tighten them. In permanent lashings, these wedges were of course removed. All the dissatisfied builder had to do was to leave a temporary lashing with the wedge under it, and the finest bonito hook could not overcome the evil influence of that one wedge. The wedge was left in a lashing under the bow or stern narrow part. When the bow or stern cover was lashed, the keenest-sighted owner could not locate the wedge. He found out afterwards from results or rather from lack of results. (Buck, 1930, pp. 415-416)

We are not to understand that Professor Buck is the only contemporary writer to conceive his task in this way, but rather that he gives us one of the most exhaustive studies of a single culture. There are other notable examples, as G. L. Wilson's discussions of agriculture and the domestication of the horse and dog as observed among the Hidatsa Indians of the Missouri (see Wilson, 1917, 1924). Wilson makes his accounts of material culture realistic by introducing the native laborer as a narrator and expositor of his own tribal culture. The advantage of such data is that one comes into a fuller realization of what primitive labor is, as a reality, and that a good account of what is called "material culture" must, of necessity, give not only the framework but much of the enmeshed substance of culture. The objective descriptions of artifacts are essential, but we cannot stop there, for the tools upon the workman's bench, though eloquent, present only the initial groundwork for a comprehension of culture.

Interesting information in regard to the material cultures of particular peoples may be found in the following references: Jenks (1900), Bogoras (1904), Roth (1924), Nordenskiöld (1919, 1920), Wilson (1917, 1924), and Buck (1930).

ARCHEOLOGY

The archeologist is, in a way, the master in material cultures. While it is true that his eye is fixed upon time perspective and boundaries for extinct peoples and cultures, he must nevertheless deal with artifacts. He has accumulated for himself a store of information as to how stone tools were fashioned, their many regional forms, etc. Ceramics is another industry well represented in the materials of archeology. Pottery proves to be one of the best indices to culture change, so much so that potsherds have been designated as the "fossils of culture." Yet close attention is.

given to bone and metal objects, together with occasional preserved artifacts of wood, fiber, cloth, etc. The archeologist is also a specialist in the techniques of housing and burial. Thus we see that he has an abiding interest in material cultures and holds the key that unlocks the history of the past. The wealth of information now available on the Old Stone Age, the New Stone Age, and the early ages of metals is primarily a history of material culture. Our ideas of the social life and beliefs of the ancients are merely inferences based upon the character and relations of material artifacts, upon skeletons in graves, and upon other data gleaned from house sites.

However, though seeking extinct peoples, the archeologist articulates his data with those relating to living peoples, so that his time charts connect with written history; furthermore, he carefully scans the data of material culture collected from the living in a search for suggestions as to the use and significance of the different kinds of artifacts. It follows, then, that the complete history of research in material culture, when written, must give adequate space to archeology.

Finally, our museums of anthropology, industry, history, and art are storehouses for the conservation of artifacts where one may pass the works of man in review from the earliest time to the present. It may be confusing to think of the objects in an art museum as material, but, if one imagines an archeologist and an artist walking through a hall of sculpture, the former will consider the statuary as artifacts indicative of the cultures to which they belong; the latter, as examples of art, and he will judge them according to the esthetic standards of his own culture. Our stand in this chapter is with the archeologist.

The following two references are suggested as additional reading: Holmes (1919); MacCurdy (1924).

CLASSIFICATION CONCEPTS

At the outset it is well to note that material culture faces the problem of multiplicity in detail: Even the number of facts to be recorded for a single tribe is appalling. So our only hope lies in classification, and, while there is danger in insisting upon ultimate consistencies in such logical schemes, we cannot avoid their use. For our purpose a few categories may be set up:

1. Material culture objectives
2. Techniques
3. Special equipments
4. Products

If we visit a museum and pick up an artifact, the convenience of such concepts is evident. If the artifact be a loin cloth, its use is defined by reference to the objective, *clothing;* but its production results from certain procedures in the techniques of spinning and weaving, using some kind of mechanical equipment. We mention these obvious matters because the student of material culture may focus attention upon any one of these categories to the relative exclusion of the others. If the differences between these categories are ignored the results of such emphasis may lead to confusion. The third and fourth categories deal with artifacts, whereas the second is expressed in action or skills. The first is largely a classification of generalizations by the student but is based upon observation. The techniques may be more or less expressed in speech and so become non-material constructs; if writing is practiced they become in a sense material in the form of books, records, drawings, etc. It need not surprise one, then, that specialists in material culture take different attitudes toward the phenomena included. Some take the artifacts as they find them, study their form and construction, without much regard to their use or to the various processes and skills involved. Others may study in detail the mechanical or other principles involved in the production of artifacts, how the native learns to handle his materials and tools, and other data concerning his methods. Little or no attention may be given to the product or its use. Thus one may study housing as an objective and amass a body of detail without so much as showing the houses themselves. It is well for the reader of the literature to bear this in mind. Our point of view is that all these approaches are important and that in the end no one of them should be overemphasized.

For the sake of orientation further comment on these classificatory concepts seems in order. First, as to social objectives—the group strives for realization in many directions, such as:

feeding	gaming
housing	fighting
clothing	trading
transporting	disposing of the dead
decorating	healing the sick
worshiping	

There is no need for extending this list, since, if the reader desires completeness or a more detailed grouping, he can develop the subject further. So far as our experience with culture goes, no people are so primitive as to ignore the objectives listed above and many may even go farther afield. The difference between the primitive and civilized lies less here than under the categories to follow. No civilization yet devised has been able to transcend the homely needs expressed by these familiar terms. The food of civilized man, the processes of obtaining, preparing, and serving it, may stand in sharp contrast to primitive ways, but the objective is the same. It is when one fixes attention upon these objectives that all cultures seem fundamentally alike and glimpses of a basic pattern are manifest.

The second concept proposed is that of technique. To realize the foregoing objectives the culture group must foster and conserve special formulae and skills, or ways of doing things. As examples of such we list:

fire-making	stone-cutting	spinning
cooking	agriculture	weaving
tanning	domestication	painting
stone-chipping	ceramics	

Such a list can be extended, almost without end, for each designates a class rather than individual techniques. To begin with the first, there are many variants of each well-known method fot producing fire. The match is no less a technique than is an Australian firedrill, though the native is far ahead in individual control of the procedure since he can gather the necessary wood, fashion the drill, and produce fire within a reasonable time. We who use the match are subjected to a more complicated sequence of events before that convenience is available. Yet one may well question the value of such obvious distinctions. We cite them here because the behavior of man is such that these techniques are formulated in speech, which in turn guides the instruction leading to the learning of the procedure by the young and inexperienced. Such formulations are not strictly material, but are so intimately associated with artifacts that they are considered a part of material culture. In the literature of anthropology will be found long descriptions setting forth the movements, adjustments, controls, etc., that natives were observed using in the application of the techniques in question. While artifacts cannot be ignored entirely, attention can be focused upon the technique, and when one stands before a case in the museum he needs to be reminded that the artifact alone will not reveal the niceties of the technique.

We now turn to the artifact. This may be classified under a few main heads, if we have regard to the foregoing. It is a familiar saying that man is both a tool-user and a tool-maker. Most of the techniques he has devised require tools. Even among the very primitive, tools are needed to make other tools. A tool is an artifact, but not all artifacts are tools in the strict sense of the word. Thus a file is a tool with which a bone pendant may be made: Both are artifacts, but one is a tool. Suppose we consider spinning; the basic technique of spinning is the twisting of string from fiber or hair; to make string, fibers of suitable length and friction surface must be twisted upon each other. Such a result may be achieved without tools, as twisting in the fingers, rolling upon the thigh, etc., and with skill a fine quality of thread is produced. Again a tool may be introduced—the spindle; the treatment of the fiber is the same, except in so far as it involves the manipulation of the tool. Hence tools are to be conceived as special equipment for specific techniques.

Such distinctions should be kept in mind when one approaches the differentiation of tribal cultures. Thus most tribes use spindles, but the spindles may vary widely in their forms as well as in their method of use; for instance, some are allowed to twirl in suspension, others in a bowl or basket. Hence in recording spinning as part of a culture one must cover these minute points. Again there is something fundamental here, since the use of tools is nothing more or less than the mechanization of the production of goods. Occasionally in contemporary social and political discussions one hears the claim that mechanization is a new thing in the world; it is not. What may be new are the specific patterns of such mechanization. So we could equally well designate the above classification as special mechanical equipments for operating the standardized techniques to realize the objectives of culture.

Examples of tools and appliances are prominent in museum collections, as:

drills	knives
spindles	awls
looms	bows
scrapers	spears

To complete the classification we must take note of the products, as:

prepared food	clothing
fuel	leather
houses	pigments
cloth	ornaments
decorations	

In the main, these are the end-results of techniques and may constitute the final product, as a pair of shoes, or the prepared materials, such as leather, ready to be subjected to other techniques. Industry, as we conceive it, is something of a pyramiding process by which materials are transformed, united, or disintegrated by tools made with other tools, etc. It was not our intent that this classification should be made all-inclusive, nor that there should be no overlapping, but rather to fix attention upon the integrating nature of this sector of human behavior. What may appear as a complex technique, such as producing a pottery vessel from clay, is actually a sequence of several clusters of techniques, each composed of motor patterns and tool adjustments in a fixed order. Possibly it is the combination and permutation among so many elements that sets the stage for the variety and unending change in the material culture of man. Not all techniques need be equally mechanized to produce materials; for example, the cultivation of tobacco by some American Indian tribes called for a complicated technique but the most meager tools. Once produced and prepared, tobacco became an important material for use in many elaborate rituals, luxuriously equipped with other material appliances.

The predicament of the archeologist can now be sensed. He digs up artifacts, more or less complete, and usually restricted to the less perishable materials. These fall under the third and fourth heads in our classification, special equipments and products. Mostly these are tools or appliances of some sort, or ornaments, sculptures, painting, houses, etc. If an adequate conception of the culture is to be formulated, some conclusions must be formed as to objectives and techniques. If a bit of chipped stone seems to be a tool the archeologist wishes to know how it was used or to reconstruct the technique. This he may approximate by experiment, but still he cannot be certain. The only certainty lies in the artifact, its form and composition.

The Historical Framework

We usually think of archeology as contributing an historical framework for culture but often overlook the fact that this outline applies to material culture rather than to culture as a whole. The successive periods— paleolithic, neolithic, bronze, and iron—as applied to Western Europe are conspicuous achievements by the archeological method. By the detailed study of artifacts and their stratigraphic relations, these gross periods have been subdivided into a number of culture horizons. All this has been attained by an intensive study of stone and metal tools, for, while bone, ceramics, and art have contributed to the result, the backbone of the whole chronological structure rests upon tools. Throughout the paleolithic period, the material considered proper for tool-making was not merely stone, but preferably such stone as would fracture conchoidally, or chip. Even a simple outline of paleolithic prehistory is an interesting exposition of man's experiments in making tools by chipping stone. With the later neolithic period enters the specialization of shaping stones by abraiding, cutting, and grinding, but chipping still continued, as in the making of knives and projectile points. The first great change, however, lies in the introduction of ceramics. Still later copper and bronze begin to vie with stone as tool material, to be, in time, displaced by iron. The above is the accepted outline for culture prehistory in Europe and as such it is the story of material culture. In how far this will parallel man's history in other parts of the world remains to be seen, but the scheme seems to hold for the valley of the Nile, and here and there in North Africa and Western Asia there are a few finds which suggest a considerable area of the Old World as the cradleland of this succession of events in material culture.

Such, then, in brief is the history of material culture in its broadest outlines. Research in this field has consistently moved toward the solution of a few main problems. First, and above all, is the desire to know the place, order, and relative time at which important changes and innovations occurred. A second persistent demand is for knowledge of the manner in which such changes were brought about or facts of origin. The archeologist seems never to waver in his pursuit of the first of these objectives, whatever else he may do. Every student of material culture among the living, though often limiting his written statements to mere description, seems to feel the urge to concern himself with this problem, sooner or later venturing to assume distinctions between the older and later forms of the artifacts at hand. Neither may give much attention to questions of origin, but in the end each does develop something in the way of an origin theory. It would seem that the two problems are interdependent, because if we once recover the history of artifacts—their sequences and habitats—we can at least offer some explanation of the social and mental processes involved.

Burkitt (1925), Petrie (1910), and Harrison (1930, 1925) furnish interesting material in connection with this subject.

FIRE

A review of material culture, in general, is a part of our task, but to carry this through to reasonable completeness is impossible here. So we shall confine ourselves to selective comment in the hope that some problems and opportunities for new research may be suggested.

Two outstanding possessions of man are speech and fire. It is difficult to conceive of culture without both of these. Fire, in culture, is above all a technique or rather a group of specific methods, all of which must be learned. These offer the same scope for individual skills and efficiencies as do most similar social tasks. Occasionally one speculates as to what would remain if fire could be withdrawn from the place it seems to have held from the first. Its use is so continuously and intricately interwoven with most of the things we do that its elimination would threaten to tumble down the whole structure.

In historic time no people, however primitive, have been found ignorant of fire. True, there have been reports by casual observers that groups of wild natives without campfires had been sighted, but so far every tribe carefully observed has been found to be familiar with fire. To the archeologist the signs of a campfire or a hearth are never-failing evidences of man's presence.

Though neither true hearths nor campfires are reported among the remains of paleolithic man prior to the Mousterian period, there are evidences that man used fire long before that time. The famous site in China known as the home of Pekin Man reveals such use in early Pleistocene times; in England similar observations have been made for the Pre-Chellean period and even among remains claimed to date back to the Pliocene. Of course we know nothing of how these earliest men kindled fire or whether they even knew how to do it. Nature-made fire may have been accessible somewhere in their environment, thus offering a new supply once all the campfires were extinguished. On the other hand, certain suspicious lumps of pyrites in Magdalenian deposits suggest that a form of the strike-a-light was known at that time. Among historic peoples doubt has been expressed that the Tasmanians and the Andamanese knew how to make new fire because they were observed to depend upon embers from a live campfire. Naturally one doubts that a people of so late a date were completely dependent upon the continuity of the campfire.

Three concepts seem to have entered early into culture heritage—heat, light, and combustion. Each in its own way offered easy steps toward ever greater and greater control of certain environmental situations. The campfire and the hearth are still symbols in our culture and not infrequently social philosophers have professed to find in the mere clustering around the fire the well-spring to family and social evolution. Light was appreciated early, as evidenced by the use of torches and lamps in the old caves of Europe. Combustion was a technique for shaping wood, removing hair, feathers, etc. By controlled burning, trees could be felled and canoes fashioned from logs. Fire in itself may be continuous for an interval, but it cannot be hoarded and possessed like artifacts. It does mysteriously reside in fuels, which may become property, the need being to know how to start a fire and to possess the necessary tools.

Curiously enough, in this first try at descriptive material culture we are brought face to face with tools, or mechanization. So fire-making appliances are among the prized possessions of the museum curator and the discussion of these and the accompanying techniques forms a classic chapter in material culture. As a bird's-eye view, the following outline may serve:

Wood friction—(*a*) firedrills, hand, strap bow, and pump
(*b*) ploughs and saws
Strike-a-light—iron pyrites, flint and steel
Chemical—match
Compression—fire-piston
Electric—gas lighters, etc.

Perhaps the most ingenious device is the fire-piston found in Malaysia. This is a closed wooden tube with a plunger, a thrust of which generates enough heat to ignite tinder. As may be expected, the match and the electric spark are the fire tools most recent in origin. The origin of the fire-piston is obscure, but probably not ancient. The primitive forms are therefore wood friction and the strike-a-light, the most widely distributed being the simple hand-drill, possibly because the materials are to be found wherever firewood is available. Even so, the procedure is far from simple, as a little experimentation will show. Conserving fire must have been the easier procedure, and so those who record the ways of primitive men tell us of tricks by which fire may be carried long distances, as a smouldering coal in a horn, a slow-burning fuse, etc.

The mystery and power of fire did not escape even primitive man, as collections of folklore attest. In some cases the fire spirit is believed to reside in trees and kindling a fire merely releases it. A fire god is often given an honored place among other gods and perpetual fire finds its place in certain religious rituals. Even some pagan philosophers considered fire as one of the few elementary forms of existence. Such leads take us beyond the bounds of material culture but serve to emphasize the degree to which all cultures are founded upon material relations. That fire is of first importance is manifest, since it has held its position in culture from first to last. Even today, when we fancy ourselves far removed from primitive ways, fire plays an ever increasing rôle in our activities.

A favorite puzzle is how man came by fire in the first place. Though purely speculative, most can agree upon some points. Thus it is fairly certain that man knew and used fire before devising means of making it. Fires originate in nature even now. The boring of oil wells has revealed evidences of forest fires at a period when man could not have been responsible. It requires no stretch of the imagination to anticipate what humans would do in a setting where fires were frequent. The step from the first observations to the control of a campfire would be easy. In the meantime, experience with wood heating by friction could suggest to more than one the possibility of devising a fire-making tool of wood. A piece of pyrites chanced upon and struck, the resulting sparks would be recognized for what they were; sooner or later someone might be expected to think of making fire with them. Some speculators have assumed that the whole matter of making fire was imitation; that is, man stood by, saw the wind rub two trees together until fire was produced, or it may have been that when pyrites were struck some tinder was near, ignited, and blown into a flame by a timely breeze.   Such elaborate accidents are possibilities, but to people already acquainted with fire are not necessary explanations.   Far simpler suggestions seem adequate since it is the power of the human mind to think things out that produces artifacts and devises techniques; wanting such power, we doubt that accidents of this kind would lead to anything.   In short, there is no reason to doubt that all the known ways of making fire are only so many human inventions, like the match.

For further information on the subject of fire in material culture the reader is referred to Tylor (n.d.) and Hough (1890).

FOOD

Since food is indispensable to life perhaps we should have begun with it instead of with fire.   Yet we are concerned with specially learned techniques with respect to food rather than with its mere consumption.   As an animal, man might survive by seizing his food after the manner of the wild chimpanzee, but we give this subject a place in material culture for the very reason that man has devised many techniques and invented numerous devices having to do with the production, transportation, storage, and consumption of food.   Man is equipped with teeth appropriate to omnivorous existence and under necessity exercises little choice of food, as in parts of Australia, where the native black must eat everything he can lay hands upon—vegetable, bird, mammal, fish, snake, insect, and, on occasion, his own children—but, given a kinder environment, man exercises more discrimination.   An exclusively vegetable diet is about as rare as one in which meat only is consumed.   It is usual to consider food production as comprehended for the most part under gathering, hunting, fishing, domestication of animals, and agriculture.   We must also bear in mind that these terms represent clusters of techniques which produce not only food but products needed in the manufacture of many kinds of useful objects.   This is another situation in which it is advantageous to distinguish between the technique and the product.

Because food production is logically primary, it has been the fashion to designate cultures according to their dominating techniques, as food-gatherers, hunters, fishermen, herders, and farmers.   These are not wholly exclusive, for, while some are not farmers and others tame no animals, every people on occasion gather, hunt, and fish.   This may be why some authors make only three classes—hunters, herders, farmers—considering the first as distinct and inclusive of all who depend exclusively upon nature like predatory animals.   A favorite social philosophy has been that these respective types of feeding condition society and, consequently, culture.

Food-Gathering.   The term "food-gathering" is sometimes used to designate a type of culture.   However, it is legitimate to ask if any primitive people can be considered as gatherers of food rather than hunters.   To qualify for such a classification the mere gathering of food should be the major occupation and we cannot be sure that even the most primitive tribe known to modern history can so qualify. For example, the Tasmanians are considered one of the most backward peoples. Because of a tabu, they would not eat fish, but they gathered shellfish from the shore and used almost every available vegetable, small animal, snake, or insect. A considerable part of their time, especially that of the women, was given to the gathering of such miscellaneous foods. On the other hand, the men were industrious hunters of the kangaroo, the chief food animal in their habitat. The women were expert tree-climbers and used their skill in pursuit of the opossum and other small game. In other words, the Tasmanians did practice hunting at every opportunity. The Australian native likewise was disposed to gather all available foods, but also industriously pursued the kangaroo and other game. The Tierra del Fuegans are sometimes included in the same class because they gather shellfish and other small game, but when first discovered they were skilful fishermen and hunters. In the United States the so-called Digger Indians of Utah and the adjacent plateaus were looked upon as extremely primitive because they spent a large part of their time digging edible roots and on occasion ate grasshoppers and other insects. But here again we find that hunting was regarded as the desirable method of procuring food.

Almost the entire seacoasts of North and South America are dotted with shell-heaps formed by refuse from the primitive kitchen. Even in parts of the Old World many such heaps are found. It is sometimes assumed that these represent an old, very primitive culture at a time when human beings were mere gatherers of food, but excavation in such heaps usually reveals bones of deer and other large game, indicating that at no stage in this development was hunting unknown. We suppose that the true gathering type of food-getting is to be found among the chimpanzees and gorillas instead of among human beings. These great apes gather their food at random in their habitat, living chiefly upon vegetables and fruits. It is apparent from the foregoing that no human beings have followed exclusively this particular pattern for securing food. We conclude then that no human cultures are wholly dependent upon food-gathering and that wherever tribes have been observed as so engaged the restriction is temporary and the cause lies in the environment, for whenever mammals and birds are available hunting is the chief occupation.

It is significant to note, however, that for the most part the mere gathering of foodstuffs is regarded as woman's work. Further, every people, even the civilized, will when opportunity permits indulge in the gathering of simple food materials and in most cases women take at least an active part. One notes also that the mere gathering of food is an individual matter, each individual being self-directed, whereas the hunting of large game often takes on the form of teamwork.

For information on the subject the reader should consult Roth (1898), Horne and Aiston (1924), and Lothrop (1928).

Hunting. If we seek to characterize tribes according to hunting, a similar difficulty arises. The question is whether anywhere in the world can be located a tribe depending exclusively upon the hunt. If fishing is included, some of the Eskimo nearly qualify. For example, the Polar Eskimo find practically no vegetable food in their environment and so, with the exception of some fishing, live by hunting land and sea mammals. In the forests of Canada the caribou-hunting Indians also make little use of vegetable food. Thus it is possible to designate a number of primitive tribes who live chiefly by hunting and fishing; as additional examples the Tehuelches and Witoto in South America, the Chukchee, Koryak, and Yukaghir of Siberia, the Semang of the Malay Peninsula, the Bushman and the original Hottentot of Africa, etc., may be cited. The chief distinguishing feature is that none of these tribes engaged in agriculture, but it does not follow that all tribes who practice agriculture forego hunting.

Perhaps fishing should be included with hunting since the difference is largely one of habitat for the hunted. True fishing tribes are rare. Fishing is usually a seasonal occupation and rarely furnishes food for the entire year.

The special methods in hunting and fishing vary with the tribe and the species to be taken. Though some of these methods have wide geographical distributions, it usually happens that each tribe shows individuality in some particular. Practically always there is some mechanization and frequently ingenious appliances. Fishing seems to have changed less than hunting since all modern methods of fishing directly parallel the primitive; thus the use of hooks, spears, nets, weirs, traps, and poisons are to be found variously distributed among primitive peoples; further, hooks, spears, and nets have a respectable antiquity in the records of archeology. The use of explosives is modern and the chief exception. In the taking of mammals and birds there have been changes in the appliances, such as the use of firearms and steel traps, but otherwise the procedure is much the same. Snares, nets, spring-traps, deadfalls, and pits are still used; apparently all were invented by primitive man.

Mason (1900) urged the study of traps as a chapter in the history of human intelligent behavior. A trap is conceived of as a machine, a mechanization, a true invention. One might add that the stalking, surrounding, and tracking of game to be speared or shot is a performance in which man and animal match their very different patterns of behavior, one against the other.

Hunting shows us human life in the large: Nowhere do we see so clear a field for teamwork and organization as in the taking of big game. This does not imply that primitive man did not hunt alone, but such procedure as a "buffalo drive," involving the full man-power of the tribe under strict discipline, serves to illustrate the concept. Again, primitive war is an organized man-hunt.

Storage. Hoarding is a familiar phenomenon. Many living creatures do it on a large scale. Man, however, carries on with patterns all his own. The most conspicuous are the containers he constructs for both carriage and storage. Vessels of wood and other materials are a commonplace; even the crudest cultures possess something in this line. It has been stated that man is the only living creature to solve the problem of water storage. The canteen and the drinking-vessel have no animal parallels.

The storing of grains, beans, and hard seeds is a relatively easy matter, for if kept dry and safe from rodents and insects they will last for several years. The advantage here is obvious. The equipment for such storage consists of baskets, bags, boxes, pots, pits, bins, etc., all homely but ever present objects in material culture. The storing of animal, insect, and fresh vegetable foods was something of a problem to primitive man. Practically nothing of this kind was stored by the Tasmanian, yet such simple folk as the fishers of Siberia and Alaska stored fish in pits, while many of our Northwestern coastal tribes cured fish so successfully by drying that they could be kept for a long time. Where the climate was favorable meat was dried.

It is a commonplace to remark upon the failure of the savage to lay by food, yet we should not overlook the fact that most primitive cultures provide neither the stability of residence nor the mechanical devices for the protection of stored food. Even civilized man must wage continual war upon animals and insects and stand ready to fight his own kind. Possibly many primitive experimenters gave up in despair.

Cooking. Animals eat their food as they find it; theirs is a selective task. Man, on the other hand, subjects his food to more or less elaborate processing. These processes, with their multifarious appliances, bulk large in material culture. Cooking is a final preparatory process. Roasting, baking, and boiling are the chief forms of cooking, whether at a primitive campfire or on the range in an ultra-modern kitchen. All require some mechanization. Boiling is often regarded as the most complicated process, though without apparent reason except that those who have difficulty in imagining how it was discovered are inclined to overrate the inherent obstacles to its discovery. We see no difficulty, once man begins to use water containers around the campfire, but, in any case, the importance of boiling is not easily exaggerated. It is seen at its best among tribes who make pottery or who understand the use of copper or iron. Yet, by the simple device of dropping in hot stones, pots of wood, bark, basket materials, and skin will answer just as well. It is pertinent to ask if boiling is universal. Possibly not. There is doubt that the Tasmanian and some of the Australian tribes used the process, but this is about as far as one can go, for, though some tribes seemed to put little store upon it, they knew how to boil. On the other hand, many tribes boil most of their food; the pot is always on the fire.

Baking is an old process; even many gatherers of wild seeds make something resembling bread. Pulverizing and grinding are two basic process concepts in preparing the material for bread-making. Two novel forms of bread are made from the acorn and the manioc. The former was strongly developed in California, though also practiced by some of the Eastern Woodland Indians. The aboriginal California process of pulverizing and leaching acorns to remove the tannin and other poisonous ingredients ranks high among primitive techniques but is less novel than the grating of manioc and pressing out the poisonous juice with an ingenius basketry squeezer. The maize of the New World presented a simpler problem, since this cereal needs only to be pulverized, mixed with water, and baked; a novelty is the thin, paper-like bread of the Hopi Indians of Arizona. The two great cereals of the Old World are wheat and rice. The latter is usually boiled, but wheat, like maize, is ground to flour and baked. Somewhere, probably around the Mediterranean, yeast was discovered, giving a peculiar character to bread. Even the Jews seem to have acquired it relatively late.

The chief baking appliance was and still is in many parts of the world a flat stone; iron is a late substitute. The bake-oven was an Old World invention, unknown to the aborigines of the New World, though possibly older than the discovery of yeast.

The term "roasting" may cover all processes in which the food is subjected to the direct heat of the fire, as when a piece of meat is held over it. Such methods are practiced by all peoples, by preference or when suitable vessels are wanting. Many of the Plains Indians in the United States cooked meat by impaling it upon a stick over the fire, a process not very different from broiling a steak over a modern campfire. While it is justifiable to say that man declines raw flesh, we must not overlook the conventional character of all such matters. Once the concept prevails that all meat should be cooked, we may expect it to be brought to the fire, even though this is little more than a gesture. Some descriptions of Australian cooking indicate that the dead animal is little more than singed in the fire before being eaten. Further, the preparation and processing to which man subjects his food determine its taste. Once habituated to a taste, he insists upon having his food brought to that standard. Primitive peoples are even more resistant than are the civilized to changes from the accustomed taste.

DOMESTICATION AND HERDING

The occasional taming of animals and birds may be expected from the time man became man. His bias for experimentation and ability to reflect on observations suffice to explain what happened. The domestication of selected species as a continued process is what elevates taming to the level of material culture. The Old World seems to have been the center of animal taming; the conspicuous examples are the dog, horse, ass, ox, reindeer, pig, sheep, goat, elephant, camel, hen, goose, and duck. The New World added the turkey, guinea pig, and llama. In the Old World the bones of the dog and horse occur in archeological remains far back in prehistoric time, so it is not strange that little is known of the events leading up to the domestication of these animals.

A body of knowledge, formulated techniques, and beliefs are associated with each species and may vary from region to region. For one, the relation between the individual and his animals and their offspring is one of possession. The concept of taming goes hand in hand with possession and is a step toward a feeling of wealth and power. Hunting not only gave food but clothing and certain useful materials such as bone, horn, glue, and oil. Domestication added important new features in that some animals could perform work, as in transportation and agriculture. Even in hunting, the horse, dog, and elephant came to play important parts. (See Wilson, 1924; Allen, 1920.)

The so-called pastoral cultures have been elevated to a position of unusual importance in culture history. Apparently assuming that hunting was the primary form of existence, the guess was that such an interest in animals would lead to domestication and herding rather than to agriculture. The order of development thus proposed would be: hunters, herders, and farmers. However, serious doubt soon arose as to the reasonableness of this theory. For one thing, herding seems subject to an environmental control, since the industry operates best with ruminating animals naturally gregarious and adjusted to open grasslands. Further, herding was in the main an Old World development and as such was localized in the steppe countries. The chief Old World animals so domesticated were cattle, sheep, goats, horses, camels, and reindeer. All these animals seem to have inherited types of behavior suitable for herding. Goats and sheep fall in the same class and call for a somewhat different environment than that required for cattle or reindeer. The horse has a peculiar place in the history of Old World culture, chiefly as a transport animal. The ox and the reindeer served both as food and for transport. One peculiarity respecting the horse is its frequent use in controlling herds, especially cattle. Consideration could be given to a few other important animals, such as pigs, poultry, etc., but this would merely add further detail.

We began with the idea that the environment might be a deciding factor in herding. Thus the reindeer is found chiefly in regions unfavorable to other domestic animals and where agriculture is impossible. In recent years this type of herding has been introduced into Alaska and Northern Canada, where the industry is expected to grow into great economic importance. Reindeer products may thus be expected to hold a prominent place in the material culture of North America. The areas of the Old World in which herding has a respectable antiquity were more or less unfavorable to primitive agriculture. Another controlling factor may have been the tendency among men to specialize in food production, according to which, when once started on a line of development, other lines were inhibited. Herding for many reasons is not compatible with farming; one requires mobility and the other a sedentary life. Thus the difficulty of passing directly from herding to farming seems considerable, much greater than the transition from the simple gathering of vegetable food to planting. So it may well be that the hunting of certain wild cattle led to herding, and that the gathering of wild wheat led to the cultivation of this cereal. Herding and agriculture would thus have a more or less independent order of development. Once it became the practice to herd one animal or sow one grain, man would be stimulated to experiment with others.

Perhaps one of the most significant consequences of herding is that it presents an easy road to wealth. What data we have indicate that even among the most primitive herders the number of animals is not limited to actual needs. The Plains Indians of North and South America acquired the European horse early in the seventeenth century, in many cases before these tribes were seen by white men. Some of these first observers report that individual Indians often possessed herds of three hundred and more. Since the horse was rarely eaten, such numbers would be luxury, their possession being accompanied by high social position and power. Many African chiefs owned large herds of cattle, as was the case with sheep among the patriarchs of the Near East. Another important point may be that the management of such large herds calls for organization. As such herds increase, the chief of the family or band, as the case may be, must organize a disciplined team of workers. Some investigators have found a rather high correlation between certain forms of marriage and herding. However this may be, the usual tendency is for the man to own the herd and thus weaken the economic power and freedom of the woman. On the other hand, woman becomes less a beast of burden or a drudge and has more leisure. Among most primitive peoples, easy wealth for the man means more women, no matter what form of marriage may prevail.

One economic aspect of Old World herding deserves notice, namely, the use of milk. The time and place of origin for the discovery of milk as food cannot be determined. It is generally assumed that its use began with the people who possessed cattle, yet, strange to say, not all the cattle-raising tribes of the Old World used milk. Even in historic times there is a decided aversion to the use of milk in China, Korea, Japan, India, and the Malay countries. On the other hand, milking was common among the Tibetans, Mongols, Turks, Semites, and other Mediterranean peoples. Space forbids further consideration of the various interesting economic aspects of herding.

(See Herskovits, 1926; Laufer, 1917, 1914; Hahn, 1896; Hobhouse, Wheeler, and Ginsberg, 1914; and Forde, 1934.)

AGRICULTURE

The events that led primitive man to take up the planting and cultivating of useful plants remain a subject for speculation. Many theories have been proposed to account for this kind of behavior, but none of them can be fully justified by the information we possess. These beginnings were so early in prehistoric time that no record of them is obtainable. It is true that archeologists tell us when recognizable domestic grains and fiber appear in man's history, but these data give us no clue as to how he came to persist in his experiments and ultimately to develop one of the most important aspects of material culture. Some theorists propose that agriculture originated in arid regions where man first began to assist plants in their severe struggle with a harsh environment. Again others believe the place of origin must have been in a semi-tropical region where a minimum of attention and control would yield satisfactory results. While one of these theories may be as good as the other, it remains true that the data at hand suggest that the most ancient peoples practicing agriculture lived in semi-arid regions. This is noticeable not only in the Old World but also in the New. While the importance of agriculture is not easily overrated, it may not have been the sole cause for the development of great civilizations in Egypt and Western Asia since a complex of many causes may have contributed to this result.

As previously stated, all types of man show some preference for vegetable foods. Hence, as may be expected, a list of all the species eaten by man would be extensive and varied. On the other hand, students of the subject frequently point out that cultivated food plants fall into two or three main classes, as tubers, grains, and fruits. The great civilizations of the Old World seem to have specialized in grain—wheat, rye, barley, oats, rice, and millet. In the New World the barbaric civilizations of Mexico and South America were in the main supported by the cultivation of maize. It is interesting to note that there were originally three great cereal areas: rice in Southeastern Asia, wheat around the Mediterranean Sea, and maize in the New World. Since the growing of rye, barley, oats, and millet have striking similarities to the growing of wheat, in contrast to rice and maize, we may say that man has domesticated three fairly distinct regional types of plant life. Rice is in the main aquatic, wheat grows on the uplands, maize is somewhat adaptable but must be hand cultivated. It is not strange, therefore, that farming techniques for each are not easily transferable from one to the other. Maize cultivation is essentially with the hoe. Wheat, on the other hand, is sown broadcast and allowed to shift for itself. Rice is transplanted in wet ground but needs attending. In early times the Old World agriculturists introduced draft animals, chiefly the ox and the buffalo, to assist in preparing the soil and to some extent in harvesting and threshing the crop. Aboriginal maize culture was and still is essentially a hoe process, the modern cultivator invented by Europeans being merely a substitute for the hoe.

Efforts have been made to discover the wild plants from which those cultivated by man were derived. Since wild plants have restricted distribution, it was hoped that once the natural habitat of the parent was known, the same would be the probable place of origin for the domesticated plants. However, it has proved difficult to identify these ancestors, and the problem is further complicated by the tendency of man to carry domestic plants from one part of the world to the other. Thus in the Old World wheat was carried into all parts of Europe and to outlying districts in Asia—in fact, to all localities where it could be grown. Much the same thing seems to have happened in the New World since the cultivation of maize extended to the favorable parts of both North and South America. One important conclusion respecting the origin of domestic plants is that before 1492 no such plant seems to have been common to both the Old and the New Worlds.[2] This suggests that agriculture arose independently in two parts of the world. Whatever may be the case, it is clear that early migrants from one to the other did not carry domesticated plants, possibly because they were not agricultural peoples.

In our discussion of food-gathering, we referred to the large part women played in this activity. By some it is assumed that the beginnings of agriculture were in the experiences of the plant-gatherers and that in consequence woman was the inventor of agriculture. There is nothing improbable in this, but it is far from clear that all primitive agriculture was woman's work. It is noted that among many hunting peoples where agriculture plays only a minor part the tending of the crop usually falls to the woman. This is particularly true in forms of hoe culture, but, on the other hand, in many parts of the New World a considerable part of agricultural labor was performed by men. In many parts of the Old World woman seems to have taken only an incidental part in farming. In other words, the apportionment of labor between men and women does not in itself favor any theory as to the dominance of either sex in the original development of agriculture.

In an earlier section we remarked upon the distinction between the objectives, the techniques, and the mechanization of such material culture complexes. In agriculture a great deal can be done with simple tools. Thus a field may be cleared by burning, the earth loosened by a pointed stick, the seed planted by hand, weeding also by hand, and hoeing with a stick or bone. With no other equipment a good crop of maize might be harvested. Manioc, yams, taro, potatoes, etc., could be handled in the same way. A good hoe merely speeds the process. The Old World plow is a mechanization of the digging-stick and the hoe, as are the harrow and the modern cultivator. The displacement of human by animal power is another necessary part of this complex, as are certain methods of transportation. The grinding of grain reaches a mechanical status where the development of power by animals, wind, or water enables some inventive genius to displace human muscle, whence another mechanical achievement. Such is invention.

We cannot follow up all the details of even primitive ingenuity. For example, fertilizing. Somehow the value of wood ash was sensed by early farmers. In America maize was fertilized by fish, a widespread custom. Also the dung of animals and humans was employed, the ancient Aztec selling human dung in the market as do the modern Chinese. Some scholars have speculated upon how primitive man arrived at such correct guesses, but again why marvel, since man is man. It is the working of the human mind. Magic may have played a part, since it is recorded that certain peoples used the dung of the swift-running deer to make plants grow fast. It may well be that the concept of fertilizers was developed in advanced centers of agriculture, then spread to the less

---

[2]Claims have been made that the sweet potato is the exception (Dixon, 1932).

sophisticated, but, once the idea is fixed in folk-thought, the above assumption about deer dung would follow in due course. Some people would call it magic, others faulty logic.

HOUSING

Housing is one of the common traits of man. Biologically, it may be an outgrowth of nest-building, burrow construction, etc. There is, at least, nothing peculiarly human in the mere making of a shelter; the difference lies not in the objective as much as in the concept of what a house should be and the processes involved in its construction. Even from very early times the object in building a house was not merely to provide a place to sleep but, above all, a place for the fire. In cases where the fire is not actually in the house it is so situated as to bear a close relation to it. Which came first is probably a senseless question, but, casting an eye over the peoples of the world, we see the fire always present, even though the shelter may be merely a tree trunk or a stone. The campfire needs protection from the wind even more than man. The history of man's success in getting his fire into the house and the smoke out would in itself constitute a fascinating chapter in invention.

Even a general discussion of housing is out of the question. Such may naturally include all buildings, whether designed for dwellings or otherwise. Possibly it is in the use of houses that man breaks away from his biological inheritance. No animal seems to have built a temple or an office building, or any elaborate structure for the mere joy of possession. However, the dwelling seems to be the basic form of housing and so deserves our initial consideration.

The popular idea is that for a long time mankind lived in caves, assuming that these were the most satisfactory shelters provided by nature. While it is true that the remains of Stone Age man are associated with caves in Western Europe and a few adjoining areas, the facts are that these early men did not really live in caves but at their sheltering mouths. In the same class may fall rock-shelters and cliff-houses, all of which have defensive values. It has been assumed that early man took to such places of refuge for protection against predatory animals. Obviously, there was some advantage in such dwellings, but many primitive tribes have been observed living in the open without such protection. Further, many parts of the world seem not to have been the habitat of animals especially dangerous to man. Australia, for example, may never have possessed such a fauna. Even in the New World there were practically no animals that made a practice of hunting human beings. On the other hand, it must be recognized that man's greatest enemy was his own kind and that the protection needed was chiefly against raiding parties from other tribes. However this may be, the simplest type of house is to be found in Australia and Tasmania, consisting solely of a few stones or wooden slabs set on edge. The winds in that country are cold and bleak, blowing usually from one direction. Consequently, a simple windbreak would suffice to protect the campfire and give comfort to the native. In

Patagonia more elaborate windbreaks are used, reminding one of open tents. In this case the family sits under a skin cover with the campfire in front. In the forests of Canada a simple lean-to of brush is used in the same way. The defensive value of such houses would be small, but in their particular environments they afforded considerable comfort.

The conical house is a common type and the most portable. The term "tent" is used when the cover is of skin or fabric, otherwise it is known as a hut, wickiup, etc. Usually the foundation for this structure is a tripod of poles, either tied at the top or with interlocking forks. However, the number of poles in this foundation may vary, three or four being the usual number. The spaces may be filled in with other poles, producing a conical structure with a circular base. Finally, this may be covered with brush, grass, skins, or other materials. The best-known forms are the tipis of the Plains Indians, the original hogan of the Navaho, the summer tent of the Eskimo, etc. Probably somewhat of this type is the dome-shaped, bark-covered house of the Eastern Indians in North America and certain tribes in Africa. Instead of a tripod framework, these houses are supported by poles, bent to form a semicircle.

The so-called underground house, or, better, the pit house, has received more attention than it deserves. The known houses falling under this head vary from simple earth-covered houses to those completely subterranean. The common form is a pit, roofed over by a conical structure. In general, this form suggests development from a conical shelter and an excavation. Yet many pit houses are shallow, mere excavations of a foot or two. The outside walls and occasionally the roofs are banked with earth. Possibly the idea in the builder's mind is to increase the comfort of the interior, earth being the most accessible insulating material. Curiously enough, the distribution of such houses is continuous from Western Europe, across Siberia, and down into North America. While the types vary in this wide area, nevertheless certain close structural similarities are observed. For example, a certain kind of underground house with a long narrow entrance was used in Southwestern United States in prehistoric times but has surviving prototypes in various parts of the Rocky Mountain region, in Alaska, and in parts of Siberia. All this suggests that this general type of house was not an original primitive form but developed in due course after experience with other types of houses, and the idea spread from Asia to North America.

It might be assumed that the idea of a rectangular building was suggested by the corresponding log structure. However, the log cabin seems to be of recent origin in the world. In Lake Dwellings and other remains of early structures in Europe and around the Mediterranean Sea the walls of rectangular wooden houses were formed by placing the timbers vertically. In parts of North America boards were used. They also were set on end. At present the Navaho build a hogan of logs, laid horizontally as in a log cabin, but we are informed that this structure is of recent origin and probably suggested by European models. The log cabin of the American pioneer was brought from the Old World. There are certain relatively primitive houses in northern Asia built log-cabin fashion and this mode of construction is known in some parts of southeastern Asia, but with no suggestion of antiquity. This subject might well bear extended study. To us it would seem the line of least resistance to build a log structure, cabin fashion, but in this, as in other material appliances, our notions of the obvious are of doubtful justification. Most primitive rectangular houses seem to have been of stone or similar materials and developed chiefly in semi-arid countries. This may be an explanation for the common flat roof. In any case, more complex civilizations are accompanied by this type of rectangular flat-roofed housing.

HOUSING ACCESSORIES

Houses, like other appliances, have developed by accretions and the integration of separate inventions. The lighting problem was given an initial lift when transparent glass was discovered, apparently in the late Roman period, thus resulting in the glass window. Chronologically, the true window came late, the door and the smoke-hole supplying what light there was. Another important feature is the chimney. It may seem strange to us that the recognition of this simple device was so long delayed, but nowhere in prehistoric America does the idea seem to have been grasped. Even in medieval Europe most of the houses were heated by a central fire, the smoke escaping through a hole in the roof. The modern stove had to wait for a Franklin and the necessary experience with metals.

These are but a few of the many studies one could make of housing accessories, not to mention architectural devices, such as methods of dressing stone, the use of lime, cement, nails, etc. Again, the house is something resulting from labor, and so is conceived as the property of someone. Among some primitive peoples, such as the Indians of the Plains, the Pueblos of Arizona, etc., the house belonged to the woman, who did most of the construction and repair.

The reader is referred to Jochelson (1907), Morgan (1881), Waterman (1921), and Kroeber (1923, Chap. 10, p. 241) for additional material on this subject.

TRANSPORTATION

One consequence of accumulating an equipment for culture is that it must be transported, for, even if the abode is fixed, one must transport food products to the home. The inland Australian has neither beast of burden nor waterways. When camp is moved the required equipment is carried, consisting of one or two trough-like wooden dishes, a woven bag or two, a digging-stick, a spear or two, an *atlatl,* a shield, two or three throwing-sticks, and, of small tools, a firedrill and a stone knife. The men, women, and children gather these up in their arms and set out for a new camping place. Most of the load is carried by the women. The contrast between this migration of a human group and the wanderings of a band of chimpanzees is striking. The latter carry nothing except their young, and for the most part these are expected to hold on by their own strength; nor does the chimpanzee seem to choose a distant objective, move there, and use the place as a base of operations.

Transportation by man-power, or self-transportation, is at least biologically basic. No transport equipment is needed as long as the load can be carried in the hands or balanced on the head, but man is fond of mechanizing things, so even the Australian we have cited puts a cord around his waist into which he thrusts his clubs and *atlatls;* his woman makes a bag for carrying small articles and food, a container for other objects, etc. It is this mechanization of transportation which gives the topic a place in material culture, and a prominent place it is. Moving himself and his ever increasing baggage is one of the most important achievements of man, and the end is not yet.

Our task, then, is the study of transportation appliances. For these, various rough classifications have been proposed—for one, those on water, on land, and in the air. Perhaps snow and ice should have a separate heading. Mason was disposed to regard footwear, sandals, moccasins, shoes, snowshoes, and skis, as equipment for transportation. With us these have become so much a matter of dress and sport that we overlook their important original functions. The same author regarded the various devices for bundling the baby, as well as all kinds of handbags, packs, and carrying-baskets, as aids to transport. All these are important appliances and belong to the equipment of the human being as a beast of burden.

Among the more civilized the burden-bearer becomes a professional laborer, as in contemporary life the loader of ships and freight-cars. Those who visit the Congo and adjacent parts of Africa are familiar with long trains of carriers. The pre-Columbian civilizations, like the Aztec and Inca, transported most of their freight by such carriers; important persons and the disabled were carried in litters or sedan-chairs as in the Old World. We must ignore the details of all such appliances but may call attention to one peculiarity and its distribution. In Africa and some adjacent areas burdens are carried on the head. This procedure was practically non-existent in pre-Columbian America, where burdens were placed on the back and supported by a band across the forehead. This is a good illustration of the mutual exclusiveness of some material techniques.

If we turn now to transportation on water, we face one problem of early man. We are still uncertain as to man's inherent swimming powers. There is some evidence that infants swim automatically; yet if not put to test soon enough, and exercised, they must laboriously learn it. Most, but not all, native peoples swim. The Eskimo do not, though they go to sea in boats. On the other hand, the Tasmanians and the canoe Indians of Tierra del Fuego were swimmers, as are most inland peoples where streams are numerous. So swimming has been rationalized into a skilled performance and thus is not to be classed with walking. However, our problem is with boats. How these were invented cannot be definitely known. Dug-outs are found in neolithic village remains and so it is usually assumed that a floating log was the ancestor of the canoe. On the other hand, the raft may be fully as old. Granting that the dug-out is the original boat, it is not difficult to understand the integration of inventions and experiences leading to the plank-canoe, the bark-canoe, and the skin-covered boat. The point would soon be reached at which the size of the boat would be limited by the strength of materials, the sources of power, and the effectiveness of social organization. Ships, more ships, and bigger ships are still the lure.

The first application of power was probably by the paddle. Everywhere in the New World this was the method except among some of the Eskimo, who used a true oar. We do not know when the oar appeared in the Old World, but, once boats came to be ships, the discovery of such a device could not be long delayed. The galley-slave as an institution is an eloquent reminder of the part man-power played in navigation. The sail also may be old because simple forms of this device were used by many primitive people. We suppose that it is equally true to say that the sail made the ship and the ship made the sail. The elaboration of the two must have gone hand in hand. Steering developed from the paddle; Egyptian drawings show how the ancients adapted an oar to the purpose.

On land, man's problem was not only to increase his carrying-power but to find a means of transport for himself. The radical departure here was the harnessing of domestic animals. It is conceivable that the sled and the cart were invented first and drawn by men. If the dog was the first domesticated animal he may have been used as a pack-animal and eventually harnessed to a drag or a sled. The pack-dogs of the Indians of the Rocky Mountain country, the dog-travois of the Plains Indians, the sleds of the Eskimo and Siberians, and the dog-carts of Europe all suggest the possibility of such a development. Yet the invention of the cart was necessary to set off the whole gamut of development in traction. Much speculation has been recorded as to how the wheel was invented, but we are still none the wiser. Of one thing we can be sure—its application to transportation started something which still seems in its youth.

How lack of a cart concept may change the whole history of transportation can be seen in the course of culture in Peru; there the llama was used as a pack-animal, but the development got no further. Probably the cart came into use in open plains country among early Aryan peoples, the earliest known users. The use of carts in other environments would require some road construction, a somewhat different road than that needed for foot-men and domestic animals. Further, the road is an interlocking feature in this material culture complex. Good foot-roads were built by the Aztec, Maya, Inca, and others in the New World. Aqueducts were successfully designed by the Aztec to supply the capital city with drinking water. Stone bridges were provided and in the Andes suspension bridges were constructed of vines and ropes. All the ancient kingdoms of the Old World built roads. Wherever they occur, they are evidences of social discipline and organization of great territorial extent.

The modern history of land transportation is characterized by the use of power from steam, oil, and electricity. The horse, mule, and ox now play a minor rôle.

It is by developing transportation that man has overcome the regional limits to his culture. If he needs greater variety and quantity in the materials used by his culture adequate transport technique will supply them. It is such improvements in transportation that obscure the intimate relation between material culture and the regional geography of the habitat.

See Mason (1895) and Harrison (1925) for further details.

TEXTILES

All peoples known to history understood how to twist string and intertwine flexible twigs. Archeologists can assign antiquity to both processes. They seem so simple that they may well be among the oldest techniques, probably antedating fire. So far as we know, they have no strict analogies in animal behavior. Further, they are of great importance because they are the foundations of a vast material development—spinning and weaving in all their ramifications. The processes are simple: on the one hand, any fiber, flexible bands or rods with surfaces offering enough friction to give tensile strength; on the other, materials flexible enough to interlock, one passing over, the other under, etc. Even primitive man seems to have searched his environment for materials adaptable to these processes. He could and still can achieve a great variety of spinning and weaving with the fingers alone, but the tribal differences lie chiefly in the manner and degree of mechanization.[3]

CORDAGE

There were but four classes of fibers in general use: cotton, bast, wool, and silk. The latter may be considered separately since it is more specialized and restricted in its ancient distribution, apparently an invention of the Chinese and relatively late in man's history. Many kinds of cotton, bast, and wool were used both in the Old and the New World. Good spinning can be done with the bare hands; among some primitive tribes the final twist was given by rolling the fiber over the leg under the palm of the hand. Yet almost everywhere that such spinning was performed a spindle came into use. This was an efficient mechanization and prevailed from ancient times to the present. Europe added the distaff, a device for holding the fiber. Many simple mechanical devices were known for preparing the fiber and for carding. The spinning wheel was a further advance in mechanization.

However, the great revolution in spinning came with the application of power. The initial step was taken in 1764 in England and before the close of the century hand-spinning was no longer necessary.

Rope-making is an old art, even primitive people excelling therein.

[3]For a comprehensive view of textiles in all phases see Kissell (1918).

Hunting peoples frequently made thread and rope of sinew fibers. The Australian, lacking good fibers and wools, made cord of his wife's hair. Some of the Polynesians were rather put to it because about the only fiber in their environment was the coconut which is difficult to spin; the problem was solved by twisting the fiber and then braiding it, three-ply. Such great quantities of this braid were used in their culture that most of the spare time of the men was given to its preparation.

The uses of cord are many. All kinds of binding and lashing were dependent upon it. The net and the snare required well-made varieties. Cloth is wholly dependent upon spun threads, but even people who dressed in skins knew how to sew and so needed thread.

Our traditional cultural background conditions us to look upon spinning as a household art, or as woman's work, and not so long ago the distaff was the symbol of womanly virtue. In the world at large spinning was almost always woman's work, but here and there the man took a hand, as among the Pueblos of our Southwest, in Polynesia, and among the aboriginals of Australia. Everywhere it seems to have been looked upon as a filling-in occupation, to be taken up when lounging about the campfire or resting in the shade; the ideal was to accumulate lengths and lengths of string for future use. Even people who made little attempts to lay by food hoarded string.

WEAVING

The basic principle in this technique is the interlocking of sticks, leaves, and similar flexible materials. Some early observers of Indians in the Saskatchewan country say they often made a simple shelter by crawling into a thicket of reeds, cutting out the stalks over a small circular area, then bending over the standing reeds, interlocking them, and reinforcing the whole by weaving in part of the cut-off material. Such procedures may not be the initial steps in weaving, but they show how it could happen. A more advanced type of housing consists in erecting a row of posts and filling the spaces by passing branches of trees through them horizontally, as over, under, etc. Fish weirs are usually made in similar fashion.

BASKETRY AND MATTING

Among many primitive peoples the main textile development is in basketry and mats. Even in civilization these terms cover a wealth of artifact and function. Under another head we remarked upon the classification of basketry technique (p. 522). Some students object to saying that all baskets and mats are woven on the ground that sewing is a process somewhat apart from weaving. However, we are considering baskets and mats as a whole and so may recognize such classifications as woven and coiled (sewed). Certainly the structural concepts of the two have little in common; it is in materials and artifacts that a relation is obvious. That this is more than an academic matter is suggested by the observation that, though coil basketry has a more restricted distribution than woven, they usually occur together. Even the Tasmanians made baskets by both weaving and coiling.

Woven baskets vary greatly in appearance and form according to the character of the materials, the uses to which they are put, and the style of weave. The common weaves are checker (or straight) and close and open twine. Of these there are several varieties. A basket, however, is a structure enclosing a predetermined space so that special techniques are devised for the beginnings as well as for finishing of the edges, both of which go far in establishing tribal differences. As in all such matters, the styles and techniques are highly standardized in a given tribe, thus making it easy for the museum curator to identify a basket.

When flexible materials are used throughout, we have mats and bags, which sometimes differ from cloth merely in that untwisted materials are employed. The uses of mats are many, as for sitting upon, sleeping upon, for hangings, house covers, and sails.

CLOTH

The use of thread or yarn for the warp and woof produces fabrics known as cloth. Weaving proceeds chiefly in two dimensions or two directions at right angles. The flexible character of the materials calls for a rigid support afforded by the loom frame. Yet the simplest mechanization seems to be two sticks driven upright into the ground, holding a horizontal cord on which the warp threads are hung. Such devices are best known among the eastern Indians of the United States; the woof is inserted with the fingers and pushed upward by them or with a pointed instrument. The only limit to the quality of the cloth so produced lies in the skill of the operator; it may well equal that of a power-loom. One peculiarity of this weaving is that the fabric grows downward instead of upward as on a frame or in a true loom. That downward weaving was used in neolithic times is shown by certain drawings on pottery of that period. Weights were sometimes placed on the ends of the warps. The Greeks, Romans, old Scandinavians, and later Icelanders used more elaborate looms arranged on the same principle. These methods of downward weaving are sometimes listed as the one-bar loom method, weighted and unweighted.

On the two-bar loom, or complete frame, the tension of the warp is supplied by the frame. Primitive forms of this loom occur in North and South America and Africa. A more elaborate and complete form is used by the Navaho Indian of today. Another simple loom is one for belts and narrow strips of cloth, without a frame, the tension given by fastening one bar to the weaver and the other to a post. This form is widely distributed in the New World and in Asia.

Various devices (heddles) are known for parting the warp so that the woof thread (shuttle) can be passed the desired distance in one operation. These are employed in some form in even the simplest looms. The power-loom begins with a foot treadle to operate the heddles, leaving the hands free to throw the shuttle. Apparently this invention was made in China or India. In England, late in the eighteenth century, a mechanical device was added to operate the shuttle, after which the full mechanization of weaving resulted in due course.

We cannot make this review exhaustive and so pass over such techniques as netting, lace, etc., which are nonetheless widely and anciently distributed.

TEXTILE DESIGNS

It is often stated that weaving is the open road to art. Almost perfect rhythm or repetition results, and the closely parallel lines please the eye. In two-colored weaving elements a rhythmic pattern will appear automatically and with such a start the human mind can enter upon an unlimited variety in designing. It has been suggested that weaving stimulated counting and knowledge of numbers. Some primitive techniques call for a recognition of even and odd numbers and many design patterns require rhythmic counts, as 2, 4, 6, 2, 4, 6, etc. If, as assumed, woman was the chief weaver and basket-maker, she may have been a pioneer in applied arithmetic. In the matter of designs the geometric, rigid character of the weaving technique conditions the weaver to geometric forms, so it is possible that many such forms, even though carved and painted, originated in this way.

It is sometimes assumed that the mechanization of weaving added many new weaves. Strange to say, it did not; all the apparently intricate weaves of a Jacquard loom were known to ancient folk using the simplest of devices. Perhaps these ancients exhausted the practical geometrical possibilities in weaving.

Mason (1907) should be consulted by the reader who is interested in further details.

CLOTHING

The subject of dress has been a favorite field for speculation. It is, above all, a human characteristic. The evolutionary step from a state of natural nudity to costume has been and still is intriguing, but, as in other cases where direct observation fails, little has been achieved. We have deferred this discussion of clothing because the need seems less than for food, fire, shelter, and transport. Except in severe climates, man can live, and frequently has lived, without clothes. Further, there has been some confusion as to dress and clothing—one conceived as a mere custom, the other as a necessity. The former, to be logically consistent, must include everything done to the body by man. If a bit of mud is smeared on purposely, that would fall under this type of behavior. In its fundamentals, the difference between men and some anthropoids is far from clear cut because in captivity the latter hold things around the neck, try on shoes, etc. However, this is quite different from a group of such animals in nature devising and using such materials for adornment. Speech may play a major part in such human affairs. Another favorite subject is as to whether the first efforts at clothing were directed toward the sex organs. Speculation along all these lines we must forego here.

It seems a fair assumption that every human living since fire came into use practiced at least some form of bodily decoration and made a gesture toward clothing. Such customs begin with culture. Skins of animals and woven materials have played the chief rôle in primitive costume. Because of their function in travel, the feet have received special attention, resulting in a variety of footwear—a matter of great economic importance. The study of this subject alone will pay a good dividend.

The most common article of primitive clothing is some form of the robe or blanket. Many of our United States Indian tribes went about in winter wearing little more than a robe and moccasins. The anti-evolutionists may be right in insisting that clothing did not originate in the blanket which when tucked around the waist easily becomes a skirt, for the history of the invention is lost. On the other hand, no one can deny that the concept of the blanket as something to wear still survives as a part of civilized cultures. Space forbids further analysis of clothing and dress in its material, social, and esthetic aspects. The mode of life and the several tasks pursued by the individual lead to many variants such as work-aprons, water-proof garments, armor, etc. Headgear, even more than footwear, becomes greatly elaborated, with many social associations.

One important use for any form of apparel is as a means of identifying the individual according to his group. Mere facial and bodily form is not sufficient to place a savage in his group, nor is it always possible to know every member of one's band, but the most trifling decoration or detail of costume, if standardized throughout, will suffice. A mere glance will classify an individual as a homebody or a foreigner. The social and culture value of group differences in this respect is of the highest order. It is possibly the obvious practical value of the tribal mark that has conditioned the growth of customs in dress and ornamentation. Another line of speculation has had to do with shame—whether man is ashamed because he wears clothes or wears them because he is ashamed. The course of development here is far from settled.

The mere list of technological topics in world costumes is forbidding for such a brief paper. Certain distinctions are stimulating, if not otherwise significant. Thus the history of tailored clothing, or cutting the material to fit the body and conform to the pattern concepts in the mind of the garment-maker, forms an interesting subject. In the world at large, tailoring had a limited distribution before the mechanized looms of Europe sent out a flood of cloth, followed by ready-to-wear garments.

Tailored skin garments were confined to the arctic and subarctic parts of the earth. Most weavers did not cut their cloth but wove rectangular pieces, the folding and joining of which would make ponchos, pants, etc. Right-angled lines were universal, and the fit was little more than make-believe. Most hand-made cloth was of coarse thread, which tended to ravel when cut. We suspect, then, that the skin-clad people of the cold North were the first tailors.

Wissler (1922, pp. 60-65) furnishes information on this subject with respect to the American Indian.

CERAMICS

We come now to an invention which, though of remote origin, is believed to be later than fire, basketry, and certain other basic techniques. The controlling observations are that pottery does not appear in Europe until after paleolithic time and that in other parts of the world archeologists have brought to view early deposits with no pottery. In other words, pottery comes relatively late, as did domestication and agriculture. The classical theory is that baskets were first coated with mud to make them fire-proof. This is not necessarily true. The chances are good that vessels of sun-dried clay were used before fired pots and that the first experiences in working clay had some relation to house-building and other construction processes. In Southwestern United States, where archeologists have set up a kind of chronology, it is observed that sun-dried clay vessels with fiber temper were the first to appear. These could not be fired because the fiber would burn and crack the walls of the vessel; such tempering was suitable in adobe bricks and walls and probably developed in that association. When fired pottery appears, it is tempered with sand or similar materials.

Pottery and modeling in clay go hand in hand; at least both diverge from a common concept. No material man played and worked with was so plastic and so dependent upon him for details of form. Artistic excellence was achieved in spite of the stiff lines inherent in the structure of basketry, but in clay there were no such limitations. So it is not strange that utility is far from being the sole objective even among primitive potters. The development of form has been varied, but the greatest range appears in color and decorative design. So the intensive study of pottery is as much a task in art as in technology.

Again, pottery is almost indestructible, for, though the pot be easily broken, the sherds seem to live on for ever. One such sherd may be to an archeologist the key to the life of an extinct tribe. Thus the expert may see in the sherd not only the form of the vessel and the original materials but also how the vessel was modeled and the character of the firing.

To the geographically minded it may appear significant that some parts of the world never housed pottery-makers. Tasmania, most of Australia, and parts of the Arctic are believed to be such lands. There are here and there in the several continents localized areas where it has not been found, as certain islands in the Pacific, a few spots in the United States, a large part of Northwestern United States and most of Canada, the southern part of South America, etc. This means that pottery containers are not essential to a well-rounded culture, not even to cooking. Life today would be somewhat different if ceramics had never been invented, but none of our important basic activities would have failed to function.

The chief mechanization in pottery is found in the wheel and the kiln. The wheel is thought to have come into use in Eastern Asia about 4000 B. C. and to have found its way into Western Europe in the Iron Age. It was unknown in the aboriginal New World and among primitive people generally.

Guthe (1925), Bunzel (1929), and Mason (1907, Chap. 5) should be consulted for additional data.

METALS

We now turn to a subject usually given great historical importance. When savage and civilized met, one of the obvious contrasts was in cutting-tools—the sword, ax, and knife. Cutting-tools of stone, bone, shell, wood, etc., thus became the symbols for lowly cultures and in consequence the term "Stone Age" has been given somewhat greater significance than it deserves. Many historians have regarded the discovery of iron as the turning-point in the evolution of society. In any case, steel has played a large part in the development of modern material culture. Somewhere between iron and stone, stand copper and bronze.

The history of this metallic development is readily accessible, even in a good encyclopedia. The gross outline of the subject may be comprehended from the following statements. In the Old World the sequence of stone, copper, bronze, and iron was parallel to the order of development in the New World, except that there iron was missing; so the use of iron can be set down as originating in the Old World. As to other metals, the two hemispheres were about on a par. African natives are known to have worked iron for a long time and there is some reason to believe that they passed directly from stone to iron. Whether Negro peoples actually discovered iron is a debatable question, but the probabilities are that they got the necessary knowledge from other peoples or that the working of iron spread to them as it did eventually to all the peoples of the earth.

Peake (1927), MacCurdy (1924), and Gowland (1912, p. 235) treat of this subject.

TOOLS

So far in this discussion we have considered artifacts that were ends in themselves, as a shoe is the final end-product of a line of production. Now we meet with a large array of artifacts designed for use in the production of other artifacts. In this sense they are not ends in themselves. As someone has said, the animals grow tools, man makes them. Various classifications of tools have been proposed, the best-known one by Mortillet and Mason (see Mason, 1895, p. 34). The one we give is essentially the same.

CLASSIFICATION OF TOOLS
Cutting-tools
   a. Striking—ax, adze, chisel, gouge, etc.
   b. Bearing-down—knife, plane, shears

    c. Friction—saw
Smoothing-tools—scraper, rasp, file, grinder, etc.
Breaking-tools—hammer, club, pestle, metate, mill, etc.
Perforators—needle, pin, awl, punch, drill, pick, spear, etc.
Holders—tong, clamp, nail, wedge, etc.

The sole virtue in such a scheme is convenience. In their elementary forms all these tools are for the hand and hence conditioned by the things the hand can do. The control of movement and power are the two chief factors in these situations and go far to explain the directions of tool elaboration. With all mankind, in varying degrees, the bare hands and teeth have and may continue to perform a great deal of work similar to that done with tools, and to an imaginative person most primitive tools appear as extensions of such activities.

For early man, tools of stone, bone, and shell are best known because they are less destructible. This may give them an exaggerated importance, but it cannot be helped. Probably the best tool material readily accessible to primitive man was stone. Chert-like stone could be fractured to give the desired sharpness and so was exploited to the full. The quickest method to produce a tool was by fracturing such a stone. An Indian once told the writer that, though steel knives were used when he was born, he once lost his knife when out alone but got along very well by use of an improvised stone knife. He had never made one before but knew about them by tradition.

We see no need for any explanation of origin for stone tools other than that they were inventions. Each modification and improvement was arrived at in the same general way. As we have said before, a primitive tribe existed as a small self-contained group, so all essential tools were made by some members of the band from accessible materials. One of the first steps in undermining the organization of a tribe through contact with white culture is to substitute for their own, tools they cannot make.

One can best familiarize himself with stone tools by visiting a museum and acquiring some knowledge of the problems pertaining to them.

The handles of tools are no less interesting than the tools themselves. The practical thing is to insert a piece of cutting-material into a stick and thus make an ax. Were the whole of stone, it would be too heavy, but also too frail as the handle would break easily. Students of early Stone Age tools find no real evidence of hafting until about the Mousterian level. If this is correct, then hafting is a relatively later invention. Obviously power, speed, and range can be increased by hafting.

Though weapons are usually treated separately, they are tools in a sense, though rarely used to make other tools. Hunters kill game with about the same equipment used to kill men. The skills acquired in one may be readily adapted to the other. Food is usually secondary in the man-hunt, but the mere matter of killing is much the same; the savages know when to strike and how.

The machine tool is not wholly modern. The wheel and the pulley appear early in the Old World, as do various forms of treadles. Man-power, animal-power, wind, and water were harnessed to tools in some fashion in antiquity, all of which blazed the way for the modern automatic machine.

Holmes (1919) and MacCurdy (1924) should be consulted for further details.

THE GRAPHIC ARTS

Art may not be material, but a hard-and-fast line cannot well be drawn between the material and non-material. There are materials and tools necessary to all art. Writing, for example, must be considered in relation to materials, otherwise we omit a large section in our subject. The origin of writing is obscure because many methods and mediums may be employed to reach the same end. Yet pigments and tools must have been present even in the early stages. Writing and drawing may result from the same tools and materials. A picture and an inscription might be executed upon a rock by the same workman, using the same tools. The history of our alphabet is fairly well known, and others known to the modern world are not wholly mysterious.

In general, three forms of writing are known: pictographic representation, the representation of sounds suggested by pictures as occurring in the name of the object represented, and symbols for the phonetic elements in speech. All forms of writing become more or less arbitrary associations between specific sounds or words and standardized drawings. The chief social function of writing is obvious. The transporting of the message and its preservation as a record call for special materials as well as tools and techniques of execution.

Pigments appear in cave-paintings of the Old Stone Age. For the most part, these were natural, to be found by searching the environment. Lampblack was always accessible to fire-users. Apparently these colors were mixed with water and again with grease, but for a time no efforts were made to produce additional shades by mixing pigments. The brush is probably very old, since a serviceable one can be made by beating and fraying the end of a stick. The surviving Pueblo Indian potters of Arizona and New Mexico still prefer a brush of their own manufacture made by shredding the end of a yucca-leaf rib. Ink, as we know it, came from Eastern Asia, where it has a reasonable antiquity. The steel pen followed the quill in Western European history.

Any good reference book will give an outline of the history of writing and printing. Paper-making is an important feature of all material cultures among people who maintain forms of printing. In North America the annual production of newsprint paper alone exceeds three and one-half million tons. Yet paper may have originated apart from writing, as tapa in Polynesia and the paper used for votive offerings in ancient Mexico. It was the integrating of writing, block-printing, and paper that constituted the significant invention we speak of as printing.

PRIMITIVE ECONOMICS

The modern use of the term "economics" implies that the subject is concerned with the relations between men arising in activities associated with the satisfaction of material human needs. The definition we have offered for material culture, dealing as it does with all artifacts and materials used by man, would at least involve the fundamentals in economics. The same is true of human geography, a subject which professes to treat of man's adaptation to environment, active and passive, and which must, in a large way, deal with material cultures because it is the environment which furnishes the materials with which cultures operate. The student of living cultures usually attempts a complete analysis and so is not concerned with clear-cut distinctions within a culture. Contemporary opinion inclines to a kind of social gestalt theory conceiving culture as a functioning whole, or to the idea that the individuals living the culture are so closely integrated that even such a subject as pottery cannot be handled without some consideration being given to social factors. As stated at the outset, the emphasis may be placed upon the artifact, as it must in archeology, but when living peoples are studied one cannot stop here without losing much of significance in the data of the subject.

Perhaps the most conspicuous study in primitive economics is one of the Maori by Firth (1929). A perusal of this volume will show that material culture has a large place in the discussion, the difference being in the space given to the history of economic adjustments between the Maori and the encroaching European and the social consequences of the same. From this and other attempts to formulate the subject of primitive economics it appears that the accumulated data of material culture offer a promising field for research.

Malinowski (1922) and Hobhouse (1915) furnish more detailed treatment of this topic.

WORK

In modern society the term "labor" is usually restricted to individuals and activities immediately concerned with the production of goods. We choose a different term in the hope that some of the inevitable confusion may be avoided. The traditions of our own culture make it difficult to understand the primitive situation. The one inescapable condition is that all the objects making up material culture must be produced by work. In many cases the task is long and exacting. White people say that natives are lazy, but this merely means that they are not interested in the tasks sanctioned by white culture, for when engaged in their own traditional tasks they are industrious. Again work is purposeful activity and largely self-directed through learned skills, learned under social tuition.

Everywhere there is more or less organization of work and it is in such that the modern problems of labor arise. We have briefly sketched some of the tasks confronting the civilized and the primitive, giving particular attention to the techniques to be learned and the tool equipment recognized in the respective social situations. So it may be worth while to have a look at what primitive people do.

In temperate and sub-arctic zones such people follow a seasonal round, just as much standardized as other culture processes. One of the adjustments all peoples make is to the diurnal cycle, night and day; next to this, the cycle of the seasons. The Eskimo, because of their contrasting environment, are often cited as an illustration of an elaborate annual work cycle, a good account of which is given by Weyer (1932, pp. 79-97). Thus these people go in winter to the sea to hunt on the sea-ice and move inland in summer. The Indians of northern Canada move into the forests in winter and out upon the tundra in summer. Even in the bison country of northern United States, the rule was to camp in wooded hills in winter and roam the open plains in summer. With many peoples the year is a four-part cycle, the abode and work varying in each season.

In fairly constant climates such cycles are less conspicuous. Thus the Tasmanian was a constant wanderer, but the several tribal units seem to have followed a cycle which took them inland in summer and along the coast in winter, an adjustment to change in climate and available foods. In the interior of Australia the tribes roam or walk about within a more or less definite range. Many jungle peoples practice some agriculture and live in fixed villages. Their annual cycle is less accentuated. Agriculture in temperate climates and in areas where rains fall in a part of the year only is accompanied by a marked cycle in work even among the civilized; it is only in modern cities and factory communities that people work continuously at the same tasks. The vacation custom is probably an outgrowth of the cyclitic practice of rural life and the observance of rest days. One of the difficulties in adjusting native life to civilization is that the habitual annual cycle of the native clashes with that of the white.

Further, the native's cycle, like our own, is so integrated into his culture that there is no room for a new cycle. The clash of patterns here is a stern reality.

See Buxton (1924) and Powdermaker (1933, Chap. 6) for further information.

ORGANIZED LABOR

Comments upon the subject of work organization have been made in previous sections of this volume. In primitive settings the chief may call the tribal organization into function for a mass hunt, for fishing, or to prepare the fields for cultivation. Such mobilizations may, at times, include the whole population, as when certain North American Indians engaged in berry-picking, the Maori of New Zealand in gathering wild flax, etc. Children, women, and men were all at work on such occasions. Such wholesale mobilization is characteristic of a single self-contained camp or village rather than of a large political unit. When a number of villages are organized under a ruler more selective brigading appears.

In barbaric kingdoms public works are the result of forced labor, but little of this type appears under primitive conditions. Slavery seems to have had its origin in ancient times, some forms of it appearing among certain primitive groups. The origin of this institution seems to lie in war captives. Once a stranger is made captive, the tendency might well be to force upon him some of the most uninteresting and unpleasant kinds of necessary work. The division of work between the sexes may in part be forced by the men, but the social setting will largely determine what is allotted to each. Mason (1907) was disposed to regard woman as the real worker and so the chief contributor to culture. He rather overstated the case, but did call attention to the favorable situation of primitive woman. The fire and children narrowed the range of her activities; relatively speaking, she has been the home-body. Waiting at the campfire gave the successive periods of leisure necessary for weaving, pottery, etc., the exercise of any of the special skills known to her mothers and sisters, and the devising of new ones. There is reason to believe that woman did make many of the improvements that have made material culture what it is.

A considerable part of work may go to materials and their arrangement for ritualistic ceremonies. The relative amount of time given to such matters varies greatly. The Hopi Indians, for example, spend about half the year in ceremonies; another peculiarity of this tribe is that during their month which corresponds roughly to our December no work is performed, except necessary household routine. The Australian Aranda gather for several weeks at more or less fixed locations for ritualistic performances relating to their totems; thus this period of activity forms a sector in the annual cycle. The consideration of these aspects of the work problem will take us too far into ritualism to be compatible with the conventional limits to our subject.

The material compensation for work or for the work represented in property and artifacts is fundamental. Even with the very primitive, the giving of services outside the bounds of the immediate family calls for compensation, usually in food. On pages 523-524 we see how a Samoan boat-builder is paid. Ceremonies are usually looked upon as of public concern so that labor must be given, but even here it is customary for the few individuals taking the lead to receive food and presents. The fees of the primitive doctor and priest are in evidence everywhere. As someone has said, society seems to be founded upon obligations to pay. Incidentally, in primitive communities compensation in material things is given more often than not for services on a non-material level, as for magic, medical treatment, service in ceremonies, etc. Barter is merely giving goods for goods, but the services usually paid for are of a distinctively professional character.

MATERIAL CULTURE IN MODERN LIFE

In the preceding pages the emphasis has been upon long-time perspective in the growth of material cultures. If now we turn to a consideration of the place material culture holds in modern life the ramifications of the subject appear overwhelming. Most of the social sciences are concerned with special groups of problems within this field and especially with the adjustments everyone must make to a changing material culture. The adequate treatment of the subject involves a synthesis of many lines of research and experience, a task not to be attempted here. Further, we should inevitably fall into the snarled entanglements of materialism and other social philosophies.

Modern material culture manifests a tendency to rapid accumulation and a somewhat less rapid discarding of old artifacts and techniques. The latter has been aptly characterized as culture lag. Everyone seems to agree that accretion in material culture is now accelerated, but this may be over-emphasized, since history furnishes other examples of rapid change, such as the use of the horse, fire-arms, slave labor, standing armies, etc. Among examples on a primitive level are the extinction of the buffalo as a material crisis in Plains Indian culture, and in central Canada the sudden change of Indian economy in fur production, in New Zealand the wild-flax trade, etc., all of which called for immediate adjustments in many culture patterns. Yet there is reason to believe that the pace in modern material culture is not only swifter but that still greater acceleration is to come. The nature of invention is such that each advance makes an increasing number of combinations possible. Hence new and startling inventions may be looked for; new sources of power, strange synthetic artifacts, partial control of the weather and what-not are in the offing. That the other sectors of our culture must be adjusted to them is obvious. Since these material artifacts are the stern realities in our social environment, these rapidly accumulative changes are disconcerting. There are those who fear that the whole of culture may collapse under this strain, but a complete breakdown is unlikely because among the many competing national units some will be able to carry on.

The conditioning power of modern material culture is evident. It may be that some anthropologists are justified in assuming that among simple folk ritualistic, emotional, and esthetic patterns ride roughshod over material culture; we doubt it, but there can be no question as to what is happening in our own culture. Material culture is dominant. This is not to say that material culture is everything, but when yoked to its running-mate, biological well-being, its conditioning power is not only great but relentless. Nor are these new patterns in the affairs of men, since, from the days of cavemen to the present, in art, belief, and folklore is reflected deep concern for well-being and the production of goods. Public health and industry are the concepts now to the fore. The latter is comprehended in material culture, the former is by no means independent of material equipment. It appears that our material culture demands more and more of the individual so that the chief job in public health has been to offset the harsh demands of modern industry. It is now more important than ever that the individual be ready for work when the whistle sounds. Under primitive conditions it was the duty of the chief to see to it that the community functioned to the required efficiency level sanctioned by its culture; it was for the shaman or medicine man to keep the community healthful. When the chief failed, the shaman took a hand; if he failed, all was lost. The main outlines of this pattern still operate.

The diffusion of culture has been a favorite concept among historians and anthropologists. In initial group contacts material culture stands a good chance to lead because the mere exchange of presents may lead to trade, or exchanges of artifacts. History can cite several examples of world-wide diffusion, such as tobacco and fire-arms. Modern trade is largely dependent upon the diffusion of such material traits. Moreover, it is generally recognized that non-material traits follow trade. A people may conceivably take over the use of electricity for light, power, and communication without producing a single appliance or adding to the mechanization by the minutest of inventions; their material culture is now enlarged. This may or may not demand some change in the production of goods for exchange and a minimum of social adjustment. Yet how many such artifacts and techniques can be taken in without unduly straining the health and non-material culture of the group is an unanswered question, but sooner or later the non-material culture of the group concerned will experience pruning and enlargement.

Whatever may be the interpretation of modern life, we cannot escape recognition of the universal tendency to mechanize in a material way. A university may once have been a log, with a professor on one end and a student on the other, but not now. Apparatus, furniture, cameras, counting machines, elevators, furnaces, electric plants, etc., are the barest essentials. The stage and the church are almost equally equipped and even the home is a marvelous mechanical complex. Whatever may be the drives in modern life, the hope seems to be that material culture will see us through.

See Hankins (1928) and Ogburn (1922) for treatments of this phase of our subject.

Résumé

In this mere outline of material culture many important considerations have been ignored. We have noted that this phase of culture is by no means the exclusive province of anthropology since it rises to first place in contemporary social science. What we have sought is perspective in time sequence by regarding the material cultures of all ages and regions as continuous trains of events. The following comments may serve as a résumé.

1. It is a truism to say that material culture is accumulative, since all phases of culture are accumulations. This does not mean that nothing is ever lost, but that by a selective accumulation the material culture of the moment comes to be. Some of our culture equipment has outlived its usefulness but we still carry it along.

2. The evolution of tools and machines has sometimes been inferred from structural resemblances. This is the way in which the zoologist proceeds in such interpretations, as the evolution of the face from fish to

man, etc., but in that case it is assumed that certain biological factors control the outcome. In case of artifacts, it is human behavior that controls by breaking up wholes into parts and assembling the same in new ways. One may have some measure of success in identifying the parts of an artifact, but this would not of itself reveal the order in which the new complex was built up. Where historical documents are lacking, the evolution of artifacts may be revealed by archeology; but these failing, one must resort to analysis and logic. Yet the case is not entirely hopeless for few inventions start with zero.

3. The important behavioristic factor in the history of material culture is invention. As so used, the term stands for a pattern of culture change. Many attempts have been made to formulate an adequate definition of this pattern but without conspicuous success. Two recent writers have made a try at this but without carrying it to final conclusion, leaving much to be inferred. We refer to Ogburn (1922) and Hocart (1933).

Ogburn concerns himself chiefly with such questions as whether inventions are certain to follow when the social setting is favorable. There is evidence both for and against the idea, so it is still debatable. Hocart regards the great inventions as not linear in evolution but does not elaborate the idea. He seems to regard them as regional and erratic. The great field for invention in material culture is mechanization, and what we here speak of as invention is an integration of existing techniques and skills, for example, the steam-engine. Gas and electric spark gave the combustion engine—there were no new elements in this combination. That this is true of ancient invention seems probable though on a smaller scale. When we speak of the invention of agriculture we have in mind something like this: the ideas that seeds germinate in favorable soil, that plants compete with each other for space, that good seed reproduces itself in kind, that plants can be protected from animals and birds, that sun and rain are essential, etc.—ideas which are recognized as related in thought and integrated into a pattern. The lucky accident is not enough; it must be seen by a person who has in mind some problem to solve. It is this constant interlocking of techniques that results in the giant complex of modern material culture symbolized in the machine.

4. The timing of activities is the key to material life and mechanization. Even among the very primitive, programs for the day and the year are standardized; families may separate according to an agreed plan to meet again at a distant point. Of course it is a commonplace to say that all civilizations now run by the clock. Machines are timed and transportation conducted according to schedule. The general tendency has been to demand even greater precision in the regulation of daily routine with the result that one must ever keep an eye upon the wrist-watch. One of the greatest stumbling blocks to primitive peoples when "trying to go white" is this keeping time in minutes rather than in days.

5. The modern world professes to be conscious of standards of living which are conceived in terms of material culture. Housing, furniture, automobiles, food, clothing, are the terms in which standards are set.

Many may protest that this is too materialistic, but a review of current discussions will justify the weight given these objective parts of our culture. In all ages it seems that material culture sets a standard of well-being. There have been cultures in which a meal and a bit of cloth would suffice for charity, but not today; even gasoline is now a necessity.

The standard of living is qualitatively a statement of the material culture scheme for a people. Buck's monograph on Samoa gives a picture of the material equipment regarded as necessary for each family to function socially. A similar statement for our culture group would present the norm for the standard of living.

6. It is customary to differentiate and even rank peoples according to the variety and complexity of their material cultures. A list of the mechanical devices, processed materials, and other artifacts belonging to an Eskimo tribe stands in sharp contrast to a similar list for Middletown. One difference seems to lie in that, on the Eskimo level, the small self-contained groups cannot so specialize individual production as to maintain an equipment approaching the Middletown level, nor does such a town of itself produce all that it possesses. There is then a kind of reciprocal relation between the type of national organization and material culture.

7. Population density seems conditioned by material culture. To support fifty persons to the square mile requires quite a different economy from one under which there is a full square mile or more for each person. Hunters, gatherers of wild seeds, and herders need more land than do farmers, but even the latter have sharp limits if the type of political organization remains primitive. The extreme mechanization of industry calls for a wide-flung organization, regimentation, and a high level of discipline.

8. Deep-set technological and economic patterns are observable in material cultures. These patterns vary in distribution from local to continental range. For example, when maize was taken to Europe it was sown broadcast like wheat, and when wheat was given to certain Indian tribes they planted it in hills like maize. Much more intricate patterns are observable which serve to set off the East from the West and one country from another.

The question arises as to whether early sets in material culture condition future development. This is but another way of asking if the course of history is changed by specific events. Some of the gross distinctions between the Old and New World suggest that failure to make certain inventions may send cultures on divergent roads. Even in the Old World there are curious regional differences. Some believe that Old World civilization was built around a few basic complexes in material culture, as cereals for food, the cart, plow, and ox for work, the camel for trade, and the horse for war. Yet Eastern Asia diverged in this development by not using milk, spinning silk instead of wool, and raising rice instead of wheat. The New World tried to build up great civilizations around maize, without the wheel and draft animals. A good cereal (maize) it did have. There may be something to this idea in that once a line of development is started, innovations are inhibited.

9. The totality of man's history, when written, must be in terms of material culture. In the same way that the rocks and fossils give the outline of the earth's history, may we expect that the remains and marks of artifacts will give the sequential framework for culture.

SELECTED REFERENCES

ALLEN, G. M. 1920. Dogs of the American aborigines. *Bull. Mus. Comp. Zool.*, **63**, 431-517.

BOGORAS, W. 1904. The Chukchee—material culture. (*Mem. Amer. Mus. Nat. Hist.*, Vol. 11, Pt. 1.) New York & Leiden: Amer. Mus. Nat. Hist. Pp. 276.

BUCK, P. H. See Te Rangi Hiroa.

BUNZEL, R. L. 1929. The Pueblo potter: a study of creative imagination in primitive art. (*Columbia Univ. Contrib. Anthrop.*, Vol. 8.) New York: Columbia Univ. Press. Pp. xii+134.

BURKITT, M. C. 1925. Prehistory: a study of early cultures in Europe and the Mediterranean basin. (2nd ed.) Cambridge, England: Univ. Press. Pp. xxiii+438.

BUXTON, L. H. D. 1924. Primitive labour. London: Methuen. Pp. viii+272.

DIXON, R. B. 1932. The problem of the sweet potato in Polynesia. *Amer. Anthrop.*, **34**, 40-66.

FIRTH, R. 1929. Primitive economics of the New Zealand Maori. New York: Dutton. Pp. xxvi+505.

FORDE, C. D. 1934. Habitat, economy and society. London: Methuen. Pp. xiv +500.

GOWLAND, W. 1912. The metals in antiquity. *J. Roy. Anthrop. Instit. Great Britain & Ireland*, **52**, 236-287.

GUTHE, C. E. 1925. Pueblo pottery making: a study at the village of San Ildefonso. (*Phillips Acad., Dept. Archaeol., Papers of the Southwest Expedition*, No. 2.) New Haven, Conn.: Yale Univ. Press. Pp. x+89.

HAHN, E. 1896. Die Hausthiere und ihre Beziehungen zur Wirtschaft des Menschen. Leipzig: Duncker & Humbolt. Pp. x+581.

HANKINS, F. H. 1928. An introduction to the study of society. New York. Pp. xiii+760.

HARRISON, H. S. 1924; 1925. A handbook to the cases illustrating stages in the evolution of the domestic arts: Pt. I. Agriculture, the preparation of food, and fire-making. (2nd ed., 1925.) Pt. II. Basketry, pottery, spinning, and weaving, etc. (2nd ed., 1924.) (*Handbooks of the Horniman Museum and Library.*) London: London County Council. Pp. 44; 77.

————. 1925. A handbook to the cases illustrating simple means of travel and transport by land and water. (*Handbooks of the Horniman Museum and Library.*) London: London County Council. Pp. 71.

————. 1930. Opportunism and the factors of invention. *Amer. Anthrop.*, **32**, 106-125.

HERSKOVITS, M. J. 1926. The cattle complex in East Africa. *Amer. Anthrop.*, **28**, 230-272, 361-388, 494-528, 633-664.

HOBHOUSE, L. T., WHEELER, G. C., & GINSBERG, M. 1914. The material culture and social institutions of the simpler peoples. An essay in correlation. (*London School of Econ. & Pol. Sci., Ser. Stud. Econ. & Pol. Sci., Monog. Sociol.* No. 3.) London: Chapman & Hall. Pp. 299.

HOCART, A. M. 1933. The progress of man. London: Methuen. Pp. 332.

HOLMES, W. H. 1919. Handbook of aboriginal American antiquities: Pt. I. Introductory. The lithic industries. (*Bur. Amer. Ethnol. Bull.* 60.) Washington, D. C.: Govt. Print. Office. Pp. xvii+380.

HORNE, G., & AISTON, G. 1924. The savage life in Central Australia. London: Macmillan. Pp. xi+184.

HOUGH, W. 1890. The method of fire-making. *Rep. U. S. Nat. Mus. for 1888,* 395-409.

JENKS, A. E. 1900. The wild rice gatherers of the upper lakes: a study in American primitive economics. *19th Ann. Rep. Bur. Amer. Ethnol.,* Pt. 2, 1013-1137.

JOCHELSON, W. 1907. Past and present subterranean dwellings of the tribes of North Eastern Asia and North Western America. *Cong. int. des Américanistes, XVe Session, tenue à Quebec en 1906,* 115-128.

KISSELL, M. L. 1918. Yarn and cloth making: an economic study. New York: Macmillan. Pp. xxvii+252.

KROEBER, A. L. 1923. Anthropology. New York: Harcourt, Brace. Pp. xi+523.

LAUFER, B. 1914. Some fundamental ideas of Chinese culture. *J. Race Develop.,* 5, 160-174.

———. 1917. The reindeer and its domestication. *Mem. Amer. Anthrop. Asso.,* 4, 91-147.

LOTHROP, S. K. 1928. The Indians of. Tierra del Fuego. (*Mus. Amer. Indian, Contrib.,* Vol. 10.) New York: Heye Foundation. Pp. 244.

MACCURDY, G. G. 1924. Human origins: a manual of prehistory. Vol. I. The old stone age and the dawn of man and his arts. Vol. II. The new stone age and the ages of bronze and iron. New York: Appleton. Pp. xxxvii+440; xv+516.

MALINOWSKI, B. 1922. Argonauts of the western Pacific. London: Routledge; New York: Dutton. Pp. xxi+527.

MASON, O. T. 1895. The origins of invention: a study of industry among primitive peoples. London: Scott. Pp. 419.

———. 1896. Primitive travel and transportation. *Rep. U. S. Nat. Mus. for 1894,* 239-593.

———. 1900. Traps of the Amerinds: a study in psychology and invention. *Amer. Anthrop.,* 2, 657-675.

———. 1904. Aboriginal American basketry: studies in a textile art without machinery. *Rep. U. S. Nat. Mus. for 1902,* 171-548.

———. 1907. Woman's share in primitive culture. New York: Appleton. Pp. xiii+295. (See esp. Chap. 3.)

MERRILL, E. D. 1931. The phytogeography of cultivated plants in relation to assumed pre-Columbian Eurasian-American contacts. *Amer. Anthrop.,* 33, 375-382.

MORGAN, L. H. 1881. Houses and house-life of the American aborigines. (*Contrib. North Amer. Ethnol.,* Vol. 4.) Washington: Govt. Print. Office. Pp. xiv+281.

NORDENSKIÖLD, E. 1919. An ethno-geographical analysis of the material culture of two Indian tribes in the Gran Chaco. (*Comp. Ethnog. Stud.,* 1.) Goteborg. Pp. xi+293.

———. 1920. The changes in the material culture of two Indian tribes under the influence of new surroundings. (*Comp. Ethnog., Stud.,* 2) Goteborg. Pp. xi+293.

OGBURN, W. F. 1922. Social change with respect to culture and original nature. New York: Huebsch. Pp. viii+365.

PEAKE, H., & FLEURE, H. J. 1927-1933. The corridors of time: Vol. I. Apes and men. Vol. II. Hunters and artists. Vol. III. Peasants and potters. Vol. IV. Priests and kings. Vol. V. The steppe and the town. Vol. VI. The way of the sea. Vol. VII. Merchant venturers in bronze. Vol. VIII. The horse and the sword. Oxford: Clarendon Press. Pp. vi+138; vi+154; v+152; iv+208; 160; viii+160; vii+168; vii+152.

PETRIE, W. M. 1910. The arts and crafts in ancient Egypt. (2nd ed.) London.

PITT-RIVERS, A. LANE-FOX. 1906. The evolution of culture and other essays. Oxford: Clarendon Press. Pp. xx+232.

POWDERMAKER, H. 1933. Life in Lesu: the study of a Melanesian society in New Ireland. New York: Norton. Pp. 352.

ROTH, H. L. 1890. The aborigines of Tasmania. London: Kegan Paul. Pp. xxv+224+cx.

ROTH, W. E. 1924. An introductory study of the arts, crafts, and customs of the Guiana Indians. *38th Ann. Rep. Bur. Amer. Ethnol.*, 25-745.

TE RANGI HIROA (BUCK, P. H.) 1930. Samoan material culture. (*Bernice P. Bishop Mus. Bull. 75.*) Honolulu: Bernice P. Bishop Mus. Pp. 724.

TYLOR, E. B. (n.d.) Researches in the early history of mankind and the development of civilization. New York: Holt. [1878?] Pp. iv+388.

————. 1904. Anthropology: an introduction to the study of man and civilization. New York: Appleton. Pp. xv+448.

WATERMAN, T. T., et al. 1921. Native houses of western North America. (*Mus. Amer. Indian, Indian Notes & Monog.*, No. 11.) New York: Heye Foundation. Pp. 97.

WEYER, E. M., JR. 1932. The Eskimos: their environment and folkways. New Haven, Conn.: Yale Univ. Press. Pp. xvii+491.

WILSON, G. L. 1917. Agriculture of the Hidatsa Indians—an Indian interpretation. (*Stud. Soc. Sci.*, No. 9.) Minneapolis: Univ. Minn. Press. Pp. viii+129.

————. 1924. The horse and the dog in Hidatsa culture. (*Anthrop. Papers, Amer. Mus. Nat. Hist.*, Vol. 15, Pt. 2.) New York: Amer. Mus. Nat. Hist. Pp. 125-311.

WISSLER, C. 1922. The American Indian: an introduction to the anthropology of the New World. (2nd ed.) New York & London: Oxford Univ. Press. Pp. xxi+474.

PART V

ANALYSES OF SOME CORRELATES
OF SOCIAL PHENOMENA

CHAPTER 14

THE PHYSICAL ENVIRONMENT[1]

VICTOR E. SHELFORD

University of Illinois

I. INTRODUCTION

The discussion of the relations of man's psychic, social, and cultural peculiarities has usually involved the distant past and indirect evidence as to the character of the physical environment. Furthermore, considerations of the environmental relations, ecology, and taxonomy of man have *not* been developed in a manner paralleling that of plants and animals. Accordingly the plan and purpose of this section is to outline the relations of man in terms applied to animals and plants. It is believed that this will help to bring the relations of man to his physical environment within the scope of modern scientific measurement.

A first necessity is to consider the organization of the community of plants and animals of which he is a part. This community is the ebbing and flowing matrix in which all characteristics of both man and other animals have been developed.

Natural communities are composed of both plants and animals with more or less inseparable connections and obligate interdependencies. This may be illustrated by man's dependence upon domestic animals and cultivated plants and by the numerous interdependencies in natural communities. It is obvious that ecology cannot properly be divided into plant, animal, and human ecology but is in fact bioecology.

Bioecology has been concerned in a large part with the natural communities of plants and animals which dominated the face of the land before man destroyed them with his steel implements, steam and gasoline power, and high explosives. These original major biotic communities may in a rough way be classed as deciduous forest, grassland, coniferous forest, desert, tundra, etc. These natural communities are regarded as the best of climatic indicators. Little has been done relative to communities of cultivated areas.

II. MAN-DOMINATED COMMUNITIES AND THEIR FORERUNNERS

Some of the general principles of relations governing the original plant-dominated communities, their replacement by man-dominated ones, and the interactions within both may well be illustrated in the deciduous-forest area of North America.

This deciduous forest was dominated in the uplands by oaks, hickories,

---

[1]The writer is indebted to Professor E. T. Hiller for suggestions and citation of literature, to W. P. Flint and Dr. J. Howard Beard for information relative to the chinch bug and death rates.

maples, beech, cherry, and in the river bottoms by willows, sycamore, ash, elms, hackberry, and certain types of oaks. The forest was originally practically continuous. Travelers through it in the early history of the settlement of our country often remarked on its continuity and monotony. The principal animals of that period were those indicated in Figure 1, of which the deer, black bear, bobcat, gray fox, fox-squirrel, gray squirrel, and numerous birds such as the wild turkey, wood cock, blue jay, wood thrush, house wren, oven bird, screech owl, etc., were characteristic. There is also a large number of birds and mammals which normally inhabit the edges of woods such as border natural openings caused by erosion, landslides, rock outcrops, water course, fire scars, etc. Man in his primitive state made such clearings, and in the settlement of the grove-covered parklands of midwestern North America showed a similar relation by selecting settlement sites at the edges of woodlands.

The food relations of the true forest inhabitants are shown in Figure 1, where the various edible parts of the dominant trees and of shrubs and

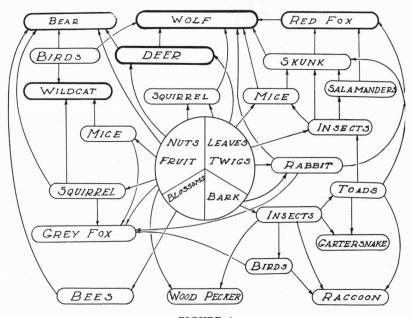

FIGURE 1

SHOWING THE FOOD NETWORK AND GENERAL INTERRELATIONS OF THE ANIMALS AND PLANTS OF THE ORIGINAL BIOTIC COMMUNITY OF THE DECIDUOUS FOREST OF NORTH AMERICA

The center, representing source of food supply, is made up of the leaves, fruits, etc., of oaks, maples, hickories, beeches, elms, etc., and other shrubbery and herbaceous undergrowth. Arrows point to the organism using all or a part of the organism from which they originate.

herbs are shown in the center as constituting the basic food supply of the community. All animals are dependent directly or indirectly upon the vegetation for their food. The animals of the community doubtless experienced fluctuations in food supply such as variation in the amount of acorns and mast produced from year to year as well as the amount and character of the more delicate herbaceous undergrowth. This was doubtless reflected in changes in the animal population but nothing is known of the character of these fluctuations under primeval conditions. The deer is known to increase to very considerable numbers but this is in areas where its predatory enemies such as the wolf, bear, and bobcat have been removed. Nothing is known of fluctuations in the community from definite records. All our experience with communities, however, suggests that such fluctuations occurred and were probably of considerable significance. It may furthermore be assumed that these fluctuations in numbers of individuals of constituent species were directly or indirectly attributable to shifts in the physical environment such as changes in rainfall, etc., from year to year or from cycle to cycle. This has been demonstrated over and over again for insects and the more rapidly reproducing lower mammals such as rabbits, mice, etc. Examining the food-network chart in Figure 1 we note that the deer feeds on twigs, nuts, and fruits. Deer occasionally eat some herbs but rarely grasses as grasses are not available in any great numbers in the original forests. The other mammals which feed upon these plant products are the rabbits, mice, squirrels, and to a partial extent the gray fox and the bear. There appears to be no evidence that these animals destroy enough of the products of the vegetation to influence greatly the general appearance of the forest or to exceed the ordinary fluctuations due to physical conditions. Previous to white settlement it may be assumed to have been a community of organisms sufficiently well adjusted to go forward without more than moderate fluctuations in the various constituents.

The dominants are those organisms which control the habitat. Man in his action through removing original vegetation and moving and disturbing soil passed from the rôle of important influent in the stone and bronze ages to dominant in the steel age. Man was not dominant until he began to use steel, remove the forest, and cultivate the land in such a manner as to keep out the trees which constitute the true dominants of all forest communities. He replaced these dominants by plants which he grows to provide food and animals which he cares for to provide food and clothing, and to act as beast of burden.

White settlement meant the destruction of the dominant trees of this original community. The accompanying decline in numbers of various animals dependent upon the forests followed their destruction. Figure 2 shows the decline in the deer, wild cat, wolf, and the gray fox. An increase in the deer accompanied the decline of its two principal enemies, the bobcat and the wolf, but this increase was short lived due to persecution by man. Decline and almost complete dropping-out of these animals

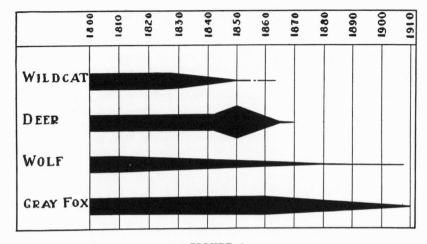

FIGURE 2

SHOWING THE DECLINE OF THREE SPECIES OF FOREST ANIMALS IN ILLINOIS AS
SETTLEMENT PROGRESSED

Man's competitors, the bobcat and wolf, suffered a more rapid decline than his
food-supplying species, the deer.

left a modified plant-animal community lacking these constituents in relatively small wooded tracts, and eventually certain species of trees such as
hickories and other trees whose wood was especially valuable for special
purposes were also removed.

Man's destruction of animals is a gradual one. He first traps the fur-
bearing animals and destroys those which he regards as dangerous to
himself and the game. The first animals to decrease in numbers are man's
competitors, the wolf and bobcat, which destroy game and domestic animals
which have been introduced. The process is continued until practically
all the large native animals are destroyed or crowded into positions of
inconspicuousness in the remnants of the original deciduous-forest community left in the wood lots.

We must next consider the cultural origin or source of immigration of
the white man who modified North America biologically, and also the
nature of those things which he brought in to replace the original vegetation and original animals which he destroyed. The group which settled the
deciduous forests of North America belonged almost entirely to central
western Europe, being English, Irish, Scotch, German, Dutch, and French.
These people brought with them the animals and plants which had been
domesticated and cultivated in Europe during several thousand years in
which nature was subjugated and land cultivation set up. The essential
features of their culture were therefore rather firmly established and were
introduced into North America almost in their entirety.

In addition to the white man's effects upon the native vegetation, he introduced various plants and animals, notably the cow, pig, sheep, horse, poultry, and domestic turkeys. The turkey was of Mexican origin and was taken to Europe and then to the colonies. The cow, which is regularly turned out to pasture, has aided materially in keeping down forest growth and helping blue grass and similar grasses, which are perhaps the most universally distributed plants associated with the white man. Native plants are replaced by wheat, oats, and garden plants of foreign origin. He also brought the apple, pear, grape, cherry, and currant for fruit. Insects of the original forest are replaced by crop pests from other climes. Notable among these are the corn borer, hessian fly, cabbage but-

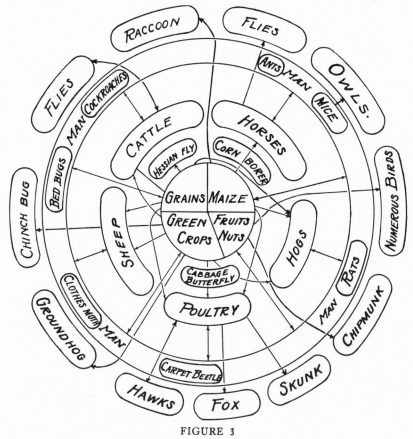

FIGURE 3

SHOWING THE TYPE OF DOMINANCE WHICH MAN EXERCISES

He forms a ring of control about his food- and clothing-supplying organisms. His introduced pests are shown within the circle of his influence. The native species which remain can operate only across his line of influence. Many of them are specially favored, however.

terfly, and numerous others which have a large influence on plants of a man-dominated community. Man's own habitations carry with them the cockroach, housefly, flea, bedbug, house mouse, black and Norway rats, etc.

The new dominance set up is of a different character and is illustrated in Figure 3, where the plants which form the basis of food supply and the animals which man controls are shown inside a ring which is designed to represent the dominance of man. All the relations of the inner group of subordinate plants and animals are controlled or influenced by man. The external biotic forces reach directly across man's influence so that a red fox, perchance, catches some poultry only when man's influence and protection breaks down. Therefore the taking of poultry by one of the native species has to cut across man's influence and takes place contrary to his dominant intent. Those organisms which persisted from the deciduous-forest condition and live along with man are commonly forest-edge animals and plants. Man himself is a forest-edge animal. He desired trees for shelter and frequently for building materials and shrubs of both the fruit-bearing or ornamental types. These, in general, characterize forest edges. Furthermore, as has already been stated, in the Illinois prairie the original white settlements were at the edges of woodlands, river-skirting forest, and groves.

The forest-edge animals which persisted with man are the skunk, raccoon, chipmunk, red fox, certain mice, and a very long list of birds. In fact, a vast majority of birds, small and large, avoid the interior of dense woods and congregate in the edges. These are the farm, garden, orchard, and park birds of which such as the cardinal, the robin, and a host of other very well-known species are examples. These are animals shown in Figure 3 as occurring outside the ring which is designed to represent

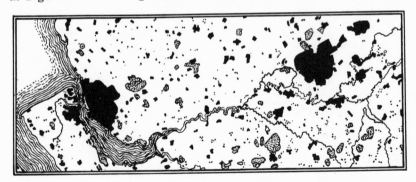

FIGURE 4

SHOWING THE ARRANGEMENT OF HUMAN POPULATION IN TWO LARGE CITIES WITH MANY SMALL VILLAGES (BLACK AREAS) AND SCATTERED FAMILY HABITATIONS (DOTS) IN BETWEEN THEM

The remnants of the original deciduous forest are seen as dotted areas. These are remnants of a community with food relations indicated in Figure 1.

man and his influence, and they operate upon the entire nexus inside the ring.

In their spatial relations, the remains of the deciduous-forest community and the man-dominated community form an intricate network in the early stages of settlement, but in the mature human community only small areas of the former occur. Perhaps the general relations would be best illustrated in Figure 4, which shows an area near Liverpool, England, but with maps available they could have been illustrated in the United States. The man-dominated community has practically supplanted the original-forest community. The former community comes after a time to cover all the better lands, especially the more level lands, while the rugged and hilly portions are sometimes still dominated by the original forest with a reduced population of influent animals. The dominance of man is accompanied by that of cattle and sheep as rural district co-dominants. The development of cities represents a mere intensification of man's dominance (see McKenzie, 1925). The native plants and animals are almost completely suppressed and the domestic ones very largely so. Only blue grass, a few weeds, and European cats and dogs persist. The omnipresent European mouse, rat, cockroach, and clothes moth are much more numerous than for the average of equal areas in agricultural districts. The less-frequent European bedbug occurs and marks the older buildings; its abundance indicates the state of society.

The cities are comparable in measure to some of the intensive aggregations of marine bivalves, such as the *Spisula subtruncata,* in which a single species practically suppresses the rest of the animals represented in the generalized community (Davis, 1922, 1925). These aggregations dominated by one species have been called "consociations." Hence a city is a consociation. These consociations often characterize communities dominated by plants as well as communities dominated by animals in the sea. For example, some areas of deciduous forest may be dominated by beech alone, although normally it is mixed with a considerable variety of other trees. This phenomenon of intensive grouping is therefore characteristic of communities of both plants and animals. The species occurring in the aggregation also occur scattered about mixed with the general population of a larger area, just as man is scattered about the country mixed with cows, sheep, horses, pigs, and a variety of cultivated plants. Human society viewed from this standpoint, therefore, presents no particularly new or special problems to the animal ecologist. The sociologist is interested in the study of the interrelations of families and individuals of this one dominant species and their study is comparable to Davis' attempt to interpret these intensive aggregations of bivalves on the Dogger Bank of the North Sea. These *Spisula* cities (Figure 5), if one pleases to call them such, are explained on the basis of physical conditions which lead to a failure of *Spisula* spat to be carried away. Many come to rest together in the same locality. These areas are as large as those occupied by some of our large cities, being from 600 to 700 square

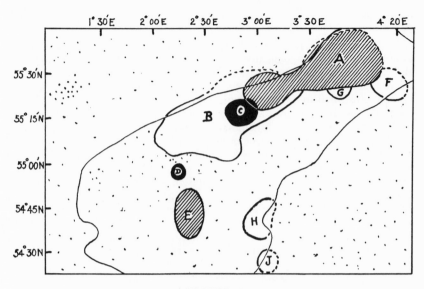

FIGURE 5

SHOWING THE DENSE AREAS OF THE BIVALVE MOLLUSK *Spisula subtruncata* ON DOGGER BANK IN THE NORTH SEA

The oldest areas are solid black; those of medium age, shaded; and the youngest, unshaded. The stippling of areas outside the patches is purely diagrammatic, each dot representing a large number of individuals, as Davis gives only frequency and not spacial relations; it represents the distribution of *Spisula* outside the aggregations.

(After Davis, 1923)

miles including from five hundred billion to five trillion specimens. The small size makes it possible for the population to be large and their social life is very simple if any social life could be said to exist other than that of forming these very dense patches. Davis finds that *Natica alderi* (another bivalve) also forms similar patches. The arrangement of man and of the marine mollusks is probably also similar to the arrangement of some of the high social mammals, particularly the prairie dog. Regarding the prairie dog in New Mexico, Bailey (1931) says, though they are irregularly distributed in colonies over the great plains area, they may be said to occupy practically all of it, although one colony may be many miles from another. Some of the colonies are extensive, occupying many square miles, while others are limited to a few acres or little groups of one dozen or even a half dozen animals. This statement could easily be applied to a distribution of human population where some cities and villages cover several square miles, others are limited to a few acres, and some to little groups of one-half dozen individuals in the scattered houses shown in Figure 4. Prairie dogs increased following the withdrawal of their natural enemies as human settlement increased materially. Dog towns frequently destroyed all the food supply within reach, when they are alleged to have moved the towns. Man has the advantage of controlling transportation which brings necessities into population centers. Likewise food for the large groups of marine animals is carried naturally and continuously in the water and there is no problem of transportation.

III. General Characteristics of Mankind and Their Origin with Reference to Physical Environment

Rigor of the Physical Environment

The rigors of physical environment which man developed have doubtless had a very profound influence upon those psychic and social qualities which modern scientific method is able to describe. Man cannot withstand the heat of the tropical sun or rigors of the temperate winters without protective covering or shelter. His large size renders it difficult for him to find protection among natural objects. On the other hand, small animals, foxes, rabbits, squirrels, mice, etc., which also require shelter, find it easily under dense low vegetation or in natural cavities. Man's relations to natural objects are similar to those of bears and wolves, which are of similar size. The population of large animals which require shelter is quite limited and often local especially in the cold season. Families can live only in protected places along ravines among fallen trees in dense woods as do the American wolves at the present time. From these homes primitive man may well have assembled in hunting groups to kill large game after the manner of wolves which return to the family den after the feast is over. Read (1920, Chaps. 1 and 2) has suggested this origin of man's social qualities. He assumes that the human type separated from the rest of the anthropoid stock through the adoption of life on the ground, the addition of flesh to a diet of fruit and green plants, and finally the adoption of hunting in packs. This was carried out with few or poor weapons, perhaps only rock fragments. Such hunting would be a necessity only when food from plant sources failed in a severe season.

The adoption of hunting large game in a climate with sharp dry season, or severe cold winter, is a necessity illustrated in the habits of the wolf which feeds on small mammals in summer and aggregates in packs to secure the large ungulates which feed on twigs, buds, or dry food in winter. Sigurd Olson (in press) has mapped the dens and wolf hunting packs in Superior National Forest and Quetico Park. The wolves appeared to have aggregated along lines near their dens and moved northward and back again along an elliptical course. The habits of the wolf and man were in the past very similar and even at present there is in general a better and more universal understanding between man and dogs than between man and any other wild or domestic animal. A fundamental social similarity is probably the reason.

The outstanding reason for the development of a social organization in men and wolves appears to be a rigorous season in which special ingenuity and cooperation, especially the latter, are necessary for continued existence. In securing a proper background for further discussion it is necessary to define the habitat relations of some animal species and of man in the form of a definite statement of fact on which suitable working hypotheses may be built.

Statements as to habitat relations common to a family or genus may usually be made when these groupings are well known. Certain characteristics commonly run through a whole group and may be defined as generic or family characteristics. Where family characteristics may be recognized, generic or subgeneric groups may have the general family habitat relations and, *in addition,* more specialized characteristics belonging to each generic group. These peculiarities of habitat relation are usually assumed to be in a large degree innate or hereditary and it is necessary to know these qualities very thoroughly both as regards the norm and the individual variations before inferences as to the effects of external conditions may be made.

Because the writer is very familiar with them, the tiger beetles (Cicindelidae) are selected for a formal statement such as may later be made relative to man.

The tiger beetles (Cicindelidae) are small forms with characteristic heavy covering of the beetle group and usually with strong wings and keen eyesight. The adults come forth in open spots commonly on bare ground in moderate temperatures, during midday in temperate regions and in early morning and evening in some very hot areas. The larvae of all live in cylindrical burrows. The head and first thoracic segment form a circular disk which just fits the burrow and the food is secured by snapping up insects that pass near at hand. There are several genera. The larvae of some of these, while retaining the characteristics outlined, have adopted a special mode of life in the very rainy tropics (tropical rain forest areas); the larvae make their burrows in the twigs of plants (one is a coffee pest) while the adults of some species move about tree trunks instead of on the ground. If we concentrate our attention on the genus Cicindela, which includes a large number of species, we find that there are various modifications of habit suited to the surrounding physical conditions—so that one·species may be distinguished from another on the basis of habits or culture, which means the place and manner of making the larval burrows, etc. This is fairly characteristic of each species but still quite flexible, undergoing modification from time to time and place to place in accord with physical conditions (Shelford, 1911).

The Hominidae are erect, ground-inhabiting omnivores of large size, without a protective hair covering, requiring protection and shelter from the sun and rigors of winter. They prefer the shrubbery margins of woodland or forest glades near a body of water or a spring. Wherever they have invaded the more open country they have selected thickets, groves, or stream-skirting forest for habitations. Their social life is characterized by some form of cooperation essential to preserve life through rigorous periods in the form of cold winters or dry seasons, etc. This cooperation often takes the form of cooperative hunting, community storage of food, etc. Several genera of Hominidae have doubtless become extinct. The one living genus *Homo* is represented by several species.[2] All retain the characters enumerated.

The white men of western Europe who settled in North America during the seventeenth century may be assumed to have lived for thousands of years in the deciduous forests of Europe and to have developed their habitat preference there. They failed for a long period to change the essential dominance of the forest trees; and their relations were similar to prairie-dog colonies on the North American grassland. With the development of steel, the forests were readily removed and a self-perpetuating dominance set up. While these men were thoroughly adapted to the physical climate and vegetation of their geographical habitat, their domi-

---

[2]It is now time to forget the superstition as to the brotherhood of man and the question as to which of the brothers is to be "saved" or enslaved. The brotherhood is generic, for if there is only one species of Homo in the world there is only one or two species of Canis (wolf) and eleven species of Cicindela (tiger beetles) in North America; sixteen species of wolves and coyotes falling into two subgeneric groups and about 100 species of Cicindela falling into eleven subgeneric groups are recognized. In the taxonomy of this large group species of tiger beetles, species differ in several essential characters such as gross bodily proportions, external ornamentation, character of pilosity and its arrangement, and color pattern; subspecies differ in two or three of the general characters, and varieties in only one or only in color. If species based on gross differences are recognized then we may recognize Linneus' four varieties of *Homo sapiens* as four species: we have *Homo europaeus, H. afer, H. asiaticus,* and *H. americanus.* In general, it is recognized that these groupings or other similar ones differ as do other clearly differentiated zoological species. They are not accepted as different species, however, for three reasons: (*a*) fertility of crosses between the species; (*b*) intergrades about the margins of the areas occupied by the different types which follow from cross fertility; and (*c*) the "psychic unity" of mankind. The last may be dismissed, there is a psychic unity in other genera as, for example, Canis, and it may as well be generic as specific; the generic view is essential for the making of comparison with other animals.

The bugaboo growing out of the usual infertility of the mule and certain features of animism have introduced a criterion into the taxonomy of the human race applied nowhere else in animal taxonomy. One needs only to quote O. Hertwig's *Lehrbuch der Zoologie* (first edition about 1888), using Kingsley's translation. Referring to the sterility of hybrids, he says:

> This is a rule, not a law. The mule (which only very rarely reproduces) and many other hybrids are indeed sterile, but there are not a few exceptions, although the number of experiments in reference to this point is very small. Hybrids of hares and rabbits have continued fruitful for generations; the same is true of hybrids obtained from the wild buck and the domesticated she-goat; from *Anser cygnoides* and *A. domesticus;* from *Salmo salvelinus* and *S. fontinalis; Cyprinus carpio* and *Carassius vulgaris; Bombyx cynthia* and *B. arrindia.*

The half century which has passed since Hertwig gathered his information has increased the number of crosses and also the number of fertile hybrids.

nance was the result of *culture*. The outset of culture dominance marked the beginning of human ecology in the strict sense as opposed to animal ecology or bioecology. In the case of plants and animals, dominance results from physiological superiority in meeting the fluctuations of the physical environment. To this must be added in a few cases superior size or other special qualities (as, for example, size in dominant trees). In the case of grasses and marine animals, dominance results from sheer physiological superiority. Among grasses this quality is manifest as superior water-getting properties accompanied by abundance due to successful reproduction in all the varying physical conditions. Abundance is perhaps the greatest factor in the dominance of the marine semi-motile organisms (see Figure 5), but abundance results from physiological superiority.

Using the criteria applied to plants and animals, the suitability of a climate for man must be judged by (*a*) his abundance as indicating innate physiological fitness for the physical conditions, and (*b*) the degree or intensity of his dominance. This is indicated in part by the uniformity of coverage of habitat area. The diversity of subdominant agricultural organisms which complete man's dominance indicates its stability and permanency. In the case of the deciduous-forest area, what is known as diversified farming is the usual practice. This is characterized by the cultivation of a maximum number of plants and animals, including those originally adapted to the climate, and, with them, a maximum number of acclimated types. The plants of the latter group require more care in the form of cultivation to stop competition with native plants for water, etc., while the animals require food and shelter. Notable among the animals requiring shelter is the domestic fowl.

In contrast to the condition found in the deciduous-forest area of North America, the grassland area, particularly its western two-thirds, appears comparatively unsuited to the white race. The population is small, averaging perhaps one-tenth to one-twentieth that of the deciduous-forest area. The number of plants and animals cultivated is greatly restricted; planted crops are limited to grain and corn, and drouth renders these uncertain. Grazing should have been the chief occupation over much of the area.

Dominance criteria for the most advantageous area for the western Europeans are not the same as those used by Huntington, still the area of dominance is included in his area of maximum energy. The west European's true dominance in North America is bounded roughly by a line connecting Minneapolis, Kansas City, Dallas, Montgomery, Raleigh, Portland (Me.), Ottawa, Grand Rapids, and Minneapolis. This area does not correspond at all well with Huntington's (1919; see map) distribution of energy. There are discrepancies in Europe also; dominance reaches to the east beyond Moscow. The Mediterranean peoples would, according to this view, be regarded as a different subspecies having dominated a different original biotic community characterized by broadleafed evergreen trees, the fallow deer and wild rabbit originally being important influents. The west European fits this climate fairly well also.

IV. THE PROBLEM OF THE INFLUENCE OF THE PHYSICAL ENVIRONMENT ON THE WHITE RACE

In order to discover effects of physical environment on social and psychic phenomena of the contemporary white man or to distinguish those factors which are likely to influence him, four things are necessary:

1. A knowledge of characteristic habitat relations and physical-factor responses which are common to all of the several species of mankind (genus *Homo*) must enable the investigator to distinguish general characters from those belonging to a particular subgroup. The generic peculiarities have already been pointed out, see page 577.

2. An analysis of his surrounding climate and the general character of his physical environment.

3. The selection of a section of human society, the characteristics of which are definitely known.

4. The limitation of the study to a culture which has been transplanted to *similar* and to *radically different* physical environments, while the parent society and its culture remain in the original environment under the essential physical conditions in which it developed its characteristic pecularities.

A. Settlement of North America—a Transplantation Experiment

In the seventeenth, eighteenth, and nineteenth centuries white men from the west central European deciduous forest established themselves in the deciduous forest of east central North America. This constitutes an example of transplantation to a similar set of conditions. Their invasion of the dry grassland in the last two decades of the nineteenth century should afford some hint of the effect of changed physical conditions. Such a combination affords, in effect, a check or control and two transplantations into different physical environments, the similar environment being understood as different in various minor details such as in the distribution of rainfall, etc. In such a quasi-experimental combination one may find correlations with various physical phenomena.

B. Physical Conditions in the Deciduous Forests of Europe and North America

The deciduous-forest climate is characterized by rain in all months, 24-60 inches (60-150 millimeters) being the usual mean annual rainfall. The lowest mean monthly temperatures are usually about freezing, the highest about 75° F. (23° C.). Snow occurs practically annually in essentially all the deciduous-forest areas and frost is a regular annual occurrence over the entire territory. In general the changes of temperature are slow. Leaf fall of deciduous trees produces considerable change within the original deciduous forest, lets in the sun and wind of the winter

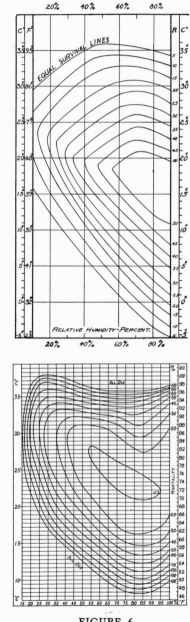

FIGURE 6

a. Temperature—relative-humidity—equal-survival lines for 55 persons out of 120 about to die, whose deaths are affected by weather. Survival ranges from 5-50 depending on conditions. Based upon Huntington's data. From Shelford's *Laboratory and Field Ecology.*

b. Equal-mortality lines for the codling-moth pupa under constant conditions.

months, likewise reduces the protection afforded by the forest-edge-like surrounding which man puts up about his habitations. Two differences between the deciduous-forest climate of Europe and North America are to be found in the distribution of rainfall and the lower summer temperatures. The tendency in North America is for rainfall to be greatest in the late winter and spring, whereas in European deciduous forests the tendency is for rainfall to be greatest in the fall and winter. The mean monthly temperature for the hottest months in the west European deciduous forests is usually 59-65° F. and in North America, 70-75° F. The west European rainfall is about 2 inches in the hottest month, and the North American about twice that amount.

The mean intensity of solar radiation is 15 per cent greater in the deciduous forest of North America than in Europe. The cloudiness is much greater in Europe and this, coupled with the effects of higher latitude, makes the greatest difference between the two areas one of solar radiation.

These are the changes of climatic conditions which the white man encountered when he left Europe and came to America, and they apparently may have some significant effects.

C. Direct Effect of the Physical Environment

1. *Temperature and Humidity.* In Huntington's studies of deaths of the white man, practically all of the western European stock which settled the deciduous-forest area of North America has shown that temperature and moisture conditions, under average day-to-night changes and variability from day to day, are markedly correlated with the number of deaths occurring. In the case of other animals, the writer (1927) constructed Figure 6b to show the mortality of codling-moth pupae under different temperature and humidity combinations. Percentage mortality is represented by the equal mortality lines. The curves are of the same type as those worked out by Huntington (1919) and roughly sketched by Pierce (1916). There is also a striking resemblance between these charts and charts of the rate of development of the codling-moth pupa (Shelford, 1927) and the various instars of the chinch bug (Shelford, 1931). This does not mean that sharp differences in the mortality of these organisms will occur so as to limit the number of individuals or that there is any relation between the rate of development and the economic importance of the insects cited. The data do, however, indicate an important law covering the effect of temperature and humidity in combination, but no inference can be drawn which gives the phenomena importance in social matters.

2. *Variability.* Another set of conditions which influence man in some respects is variability, which is understood to mean changes in temperature from day to day. Figure 7a (modified from Huntington, 1919) shows a survival of the 55 persons out of 120 likely to be affected by differences in temperature and moisture. The survivals decrease sharply

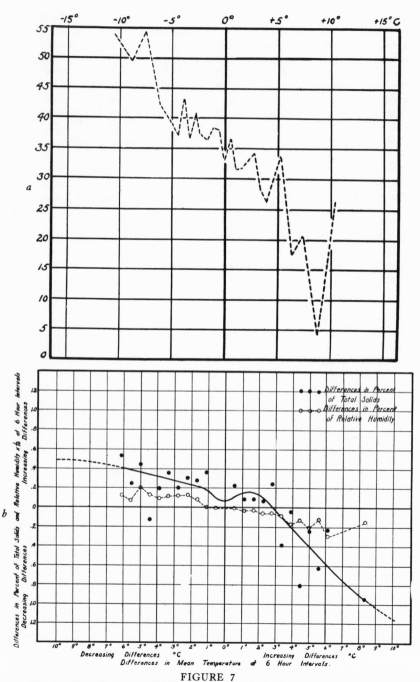

FIGURE 7

a. Showing the effect of variability on the survival of the 55 persons described for Figure 6a. Based upon Huntington's data. From Shelford's *Laboratory and Field Ecology.*

b. Showing the effect of variability on the quality of cow's milk.

with rise in temperature and increase sharply with downward changes in temperature from day to day. Thus if today was cooler than yesterday man was favorably stimulated. Huntington (1915) has also presented data showing greater student efficiency with falling temperatures and lesser efficiency with rising temperatures. The writer found that rising temperature increased the length of the codling-moth pupal stage while falling temperature shortened it. As a further test of this principle he persuaded Davidson (1927) to make a test of dairy-cow's milk under rising and falling temperatures, with milkings every six hours. The curve (Figure 7b) is very similar to those for deaths and student efficiency. No one could expect any important results from a phenomenon in which both effects are so evenly balanced. This response probably does not influence the number of moths emerging in any season, the total deaths, or total milk solids for a given year. The stimulating effect of variations in physical factors from hour to hour, from day to day, and from season to season has been so often demonstrated by experiment as to require little comment.

3. *Rainfall and Temperature.* The variations in infant mortality among west Europeans in Australia is correlated with rainfall. The effect of combinations of temperature and moisture as rain is indicated in Taylor's figure (Figure 8). If one follows the broken line on 20° C. to the right, which represents increased rainfall, the infant mortality is seen to increase through 7, 8, 9, and 10 per cent. Ten per cent falls on a little more than 50 mm. (2 in.) of rain per month, which represents the maximum deaths at that temperature. At greater rainfall the death rate declines rapidly up to 100 to 125 mm. (4 or 5 in.), when, on the whole, it changes less rapidly. Similar facts are brought out by following 15° C. through the increases in rainfall. If inferences may be made, we infer that in western Europe the summer months are quite unfavorable for infants, as the hottest month is between 59° and 63° F. (15°-17° C.) and the rainfall about 2 in. In North America the hottest months are between 70° and 75° F. (19°-24° C.) and the rainfall during these months is 4 and 5 in. Hence these months are, on the basis of the chart (Figure 8), as favorable as in the original home in Europe. From the graph the effect of conditions on the American plains (grassland) may be inferred. Here two inches of rain per month is quite usual and summer temperatures run high: a high infant mortality is to be expected.

Temperature and rainfall likewise apparently affect either man's vigor or the vigor of his bacterial parasites. This has not been brought out by direct studies, but Figure 9 shows the correlation between deaths in Chicago and St. Louis from 1840 to 1928 with estimated extension to 1934 and damage to grain crops by chinch bugs, which are known to be controlled largely by weather. Omitting exotic cholera the correlation between the chinch-bug damage and the deviation of the death rate from normal is rather striking down to about 1905. After that it is

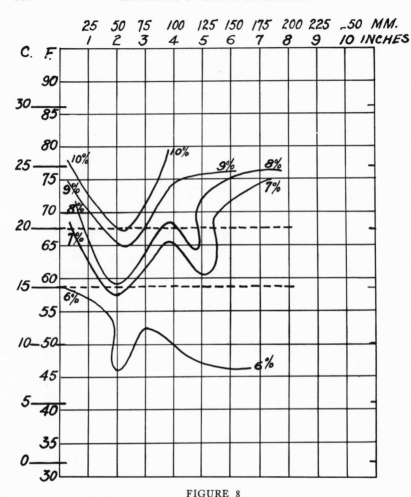

FIGURE 8

MEAN MONTHLY TEMPERATURE AND TOTAL MONTHLY RAINFALL CHART WITH
EQUAL INFANT-DEATH-RATE LINES SUPERPOSED
The dash lines are merely for reference (see text).
(After Taylor, 1927)

much less perfect, as cultural control of insect pests and diseases has
partially replaced weather control.

It may be assumed that it is the elimination of some of the human
diseases such as scarlet fever, typhoid, diphtheria, and other infectious
disorders, coupled with bug-control measures, that has lessened the earlier
intimate correlation between the death rate and chinch-bug damage to

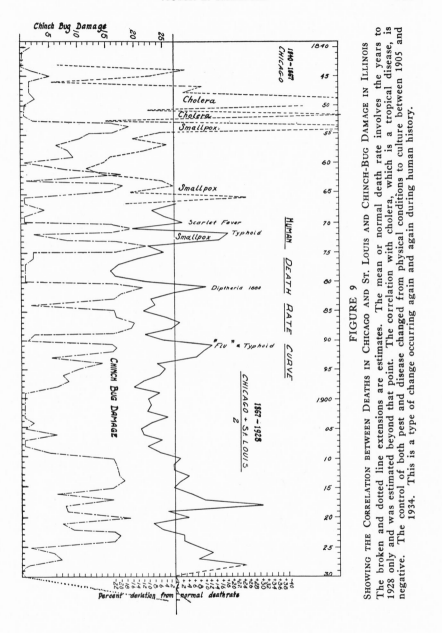

FIGURE 9

SHOWING THE CORRELATION BETWEEN DEATHS IN CHICAGO AND ST. LOUIS AND CHINCH-BUG DAMAGE IN ILLINOIS

The broken and dotted line extensions are estimates. The mean or normal death rate involves the years to 1928 only and was estimated beyond that point. The correlation with cholera, which is a tropical disease, is negative. The control of both pest and disease changed from physical conditions to culture between 1905 and 1934. This is a type of change occuring again and again during human history.

crops. The relations of the chinch bug to physical factors is quite well known. The most important condition favoring abundance may be expressed as an amount of rainfall in April sufficient to produce a good growth of the food plants, followed by a dry May and June. Figures 10-13 show the spring trend of climograph lines in years in which bugs did little or no damage and in which the damage was severe. Wet springs are detrimental to a large population of chinch bugs. It is generally understood that two favorable (i.e., dry) years are usually necessary to a large outbreak, but there are a very great many instances where the bugs were present in numbers which caused no damage in a given year but increased enormously and did severe damage in the following year. The relations of man to these combinations of temperature and rainfall has not been investigated but, by inference from the correlation with chinch-bug abundance, the type of spring weather which is favorable to the insect may be expected to be unfavorable to man or favorable to his bacterial parasites. The chinch bug influences a very small portion of man's diet, has no direct effect upon him, and carries no diseases to which he is susceptible. It is obvious that the relation of both organisms is to the conditions and not to each other.

Variation in the amount and distribution of rainfall considered in relation to temperature has shown stronger correlations with success and failure of domestic animals, insect pests, etc., than other factors studied. Using weather and the detailed records of the success of reproduction, etc., for sheep, especially in England, Johnson (1924) found convincing suggestions of important effects on sheep in different years and different localities. Steggerda (1929) found similar relations for domestic poultry. The characteristic results with the chinch bug, known and repeatedly verified since 1870, have merely been elaborated by the writer in Figures 10-13.

The codling moth of the apple was brought here from Europe and flourishes best in those years which are preceded by a heavy fall and winter rainfall and, in general, in the wetter years. The years of great outbreak have been preceded by wet autumns and winters, in other words, by a repetition of the usual yearly march of temperature and rainfall for western Europe (see Figures 12 and 13).

With the exception of the indirect relations between chinch-bug success and a high human death rate in Illinois, no exhaustive studies of man or the diseases which attack him have been made by the use of two-factor diagrams. However, implications from the chinch-bug studies are to the effect that low rainfall and high temperatures, especially spring drouth, are unfavorable for man.

The weather changes which have marked effects are those which appear in exaggerated form in the longer, most intensive (drouth) cycles. A series of smaller cycles of lesser intensity usually fall within them. The larger cycles are recognized in the field of economics as crop or business cycles.

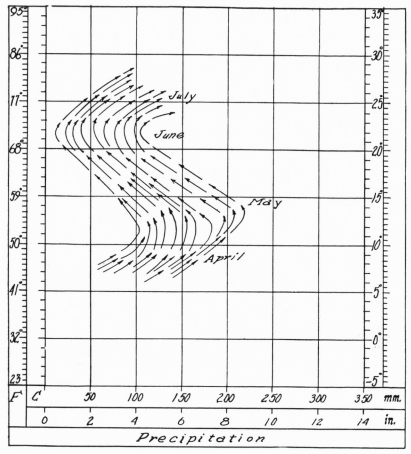

FIGURE 10

THE MARCH OF TEMPERATURE AND RAINFALL DURING THE SPRING MONTHS IN
YEARS WHICH ARE FAVORABLE TO CHINCH BUGS

D. Indirect Effects of the Physical Environment on the White Man

It is very difficult to separate indirect effects from the direct ones.
Separation has hardly been accomplished in the preceding sections. Probably the most potent indirect effects are through the quality of man's
food. Quantity of food was doubtless important when man had developed but little transportation, but quality can be important through
the amount of vitamin at any time. Diminished food supply is most
often the result of drouths during and following which men were in

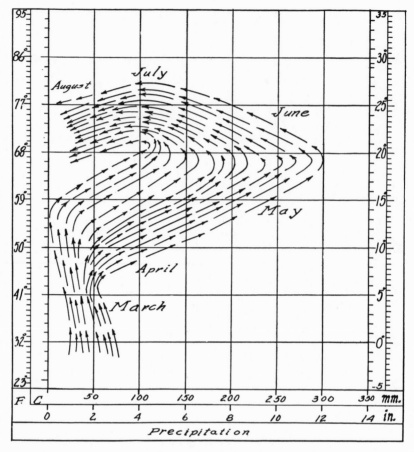

FIGURE 11

THE MARCH OF TEMPERATURE AND RAINFALL DURING THE SPRING MONTHS IN
YEARS WHICH ARE UNFAVORABLE TO CHINCH BUGS

the past forced to eat unusual things of inferior and perhaps unusual quality. This is, however, a field with few data.

E.   Transplantations to a Different Climate

Past the middle of the nineteenth century there was a migration of settlers from the eastern states into an area roughly bounded by a line connecting Calgary, Winnipeg, Fargo. Lincoln, Oklahoma City, Del Rio (Texas), Fort Stockton, Trinidad (Colorado), and Calgary. This represents the boundary of the great North American grassland exclusive of

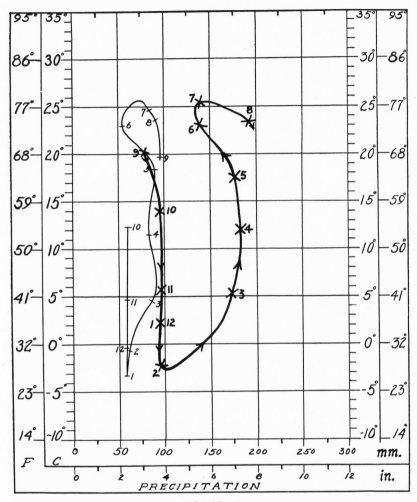

FIGURE 12

The light line represents the annual march of temperature and rainfall in years favorable to the chinch bug, a native American pest; the heavy line shows the march for a year unfavorable to the codling moth, a pest of European origin.

its numerous pseudopodium-like extensions, especially across the mountain passes to the west.

The inhabitants of the central part of this area came mainly from the eastern states. We may take Amarillo, Texas, Minot, North Dakota, Cheyenne, Wyoming, or Denver as examples of small areas of dense population which were transplanted from the deciduous-forest area.

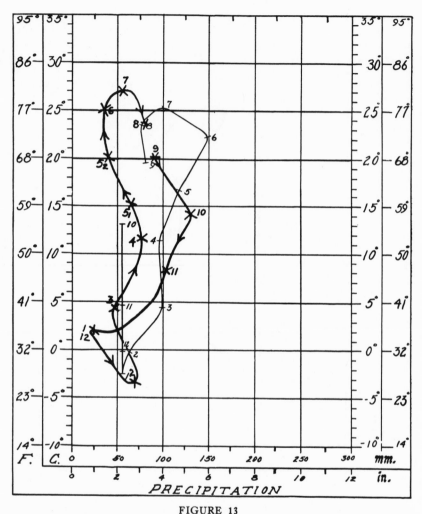

FIGURE 13

THE MARCH FOR A YEAR UNFAVORABLE TO CHINCH BUGS AND FAVORABLE TO THE
CODLING MOTH (HEAVY LINE)

On these unusually bleak plains one notes the first effort of man is to
build up a forest edge of trees and shrubbery. He sets, irrigates, and
waters poplars and various shrubs in an attempt to reproduce the forest
glade in which he originally lived. He has in this manner attracted many
animals to points much farther west than the longitude in which they
originally occurred.

Man is less able to stand the rigors of the great plains than he is those of the deciduous forest. He began his house building with the use of sod roofs and sod-sided dugouts, as lumber and other building materials had to be transported a long ways. He appears, however, to have retained most of his original characteristics and preferences for certain types of habitation, certain foods, etc. It is not possible to characterize the society of Denver and Amarillo as having any important differences from that of the deciduous forest of eastern North America. Man here retains and has tried to build up against large odds the original conditions under which he lived in Europe. Quite probably his average health is not quite as good on the plains as in the forest from which he came, but this is of little apparent significance. The scattered character of the settlements through these regions where only small populations can be supported might be expected to lead to somewhat different social relations. When one learns that young people come as much as fifty miles to a dance given in some small town where the music and general relations are essentially those of similar gatherings in the deciduous forest, one is at a lost to use such material to demonstrate any marked effects of this decidedly different physical environment. So far as casual observation can show the transplantation merely indicates the persistent and uniform character of man's habitat preferences and cultural methods.

Man's dominance on the plains is much less complete than in the deciduous forest. If we may judge from his 1934 experience he plows up the prairie sod, very frequently to his own essential destruction as a resident. His success over all but the most humid portions may be dependent upon a very intelligent use of the cow as a grazing co-dominant permitted to operate only to a point under which the more hardy grasses are favored at the expense of the weaker ones. It is not possible for him with his deciduous-forest culture to destroy all flesh-eating animals as this presents an increase of forage-eating rodents incompatible with success. Only those breeds of cattle that can stand severe conditions and pick a living where food is scanty can be utilized.

V. Discussion

The materials in this section have presented man's relations in the same terms as animals and plants are treated in community and other ecological studies. The relations of various animals to physical conditions have been elaborated to bring out similarities between certain responses of men and other animals. The conclusions which one may draw from these and other facts are as follows:

Man's relations to physical factors as regards vigor, health, and death are similar to the relations of other animals. Primitive man received the full impact of the climate and weather. As he developed, one by one the physical factor controls of the comfort, health, and disease of man and his domesticated and cultivated associates have been displaced by cultural controls; extremes of temperature by housing, cold by the building of fires; heat by air conditioning apparatus; disease by vaccines and sanitation; insect pests by poison and crop management, until only a little of the original relation remains to be discovered (see Goldenweiser, 1916; Thomas, 1927; Sorokin, 1928; Hiller, 1933).

All the species of mankind have certain common characteristics as regards relations to the physical environment. The men of the European deciduous forests possess these general characteristics and some more specific ones related to the climate and other physical conditions of the forest in which they originated. These properties have persisted through the rather brief period of a few hundred years under other conditions. The studies of domestic animals, especially of sheep and poultry, have shown physiological characters in full accord with the physical climate of their habitats in the wild state after thousands of years of domestication.

Does culture change more rapidly? "Sometimes not" is the answer from observation of the use of domestic animals and cultivated plants by west Europeans. The invasion of new areas by this white civilization has carried with it all the old favorites. These include both domesticated and cultivated species from the west European deciduous forest and others borrowed from other peoples during thousands of years of trading. Few or no animals have been domesticated by modern man. All the apparent opportunities afforded in southern Africa and North America have led to few or no attempts. His domestication period is long since displaced by selective breeding. Innumerable unrecorded transportations of cultivated forms to all parts of the globe doubtless mark the path of an unparalleled conservatism in these regards. Domestic fowls received from India through a long series of barters were introduced into England and cultivated 2000 years before America was settled. These and the turkey borrowed from the Aztecs were introduced into America instead of domesticating the native turkey.

In the early stages of his development each group of men (following the inference from innumerable other animals) used the material available in his habitat for shelter building, food, domestication, etc. One by one the materials and associated organisms in the habitat of primitive man which he orginally found useful were displaced by cultural products or activities: the communal hunt by domestication of animals, skins by woven fabrics, gourds by pottery, stone by bronze and finally steel, wood by steel, wild fruits and grains by cultivated ones. Trade in these objects carried on with other groups of men early broke down the inter-specific barrier to marriage. It thus led to crossing between human species and subspecies, and to the use of materials secured in barter. Finally migration has led to separation from favorite materials. The use of these in preference to others near at hand coupled with a striking conservatism has led to very peculiar relations to materials for shelter and protection from the physical environment, etc.

To further our knowledge of man's relation to physical factors three or more fields are open:

1. Study of primitive men and of mammals with social organization.

2. Careful comparison of transplanted people with the parent stock.

3. Rigorous study of weather and human activity and characteristics to determine correlations which in some cases may be checked by experiments on other mammals.

For the illumination of the primitive, studies of the social organization of wolves along the lines of Read's (1920) hypothesis might prove to be very interesting and probably significant. Unfortunately, man's interests were, under primitive cultural conditions, and still are so nearly identical with those of the pack-forming wolf as regards game animals that the canine has been nearly exterminated. It also is probably true that in working on the characters of the northern people studies of tropical lowland anthropoids will not be significant. They are too largely vegetarians and are so well adapted to the conditions in which they live as to require only the simplest cultural development. Possible material for comparison with the white man may be available in the more rigorous climate of high mountains in the tropics. Primitive people suitable for such study hardly exist.

Relative to contemporary society, the question as to whether comparisons of groups of similar original quality who have transplanted themselves to different conditions can succeed remains to be answered when someone has the temerity to undertake such investigation. Detailed study of similar men may possibly reveal definite qualities which may be correlated with large changes in physical conditions and in the general character of biological environment of man such as the difference between deciduous forest and dry grassland. To discover these differences very definite tests of men themselves will have to be set up and applied with the greatest care. One has little chance of pointing them out from mere contact with the two environments. The grassland and deciduous-forest environments were sufficiently different to make a change of practically all the dominant or influent species of plants and animals, evident as one passed from one to the other under original conditions.

The field of study of weather and climate in relation to the activities of contemporary society and the individuals which constitute it is open and permits of some degree of comparative experimentation on other species which are members of the man-dominated community. At the present time this field claims few serious workers and innumerable critics. Some of the former have undertaken analyses as regards man, the amount of labor in which is almost prohibitive. They have doubtless implied or caused others to imply too great importance to the correlations observed. The critics have often not understood the results and made erroneous comparisons and denials. It must be borne in mind that the study of the relations of man or other animals to the variable physical conditions of nature, through weather records, is an essential background for successful experimentation and analysis. It is only in the last few years that experiments which aimed to have any relation to the variable physical conditions of nature were devised.[3] Methods of analyzing weather conditions in relation to biological phenomena are likewise new. To find relations of human deaths to variability paralleled by milk quantity in another mammal and by rate of development in a moth is but one encouraging tiny brick in a gigantic wall. It can be removed only by the repetition of the same analyses and experiments and the doing of new ones, giving negative results. The world expects in 20 years the equivalent of what medicine has produced in 2000 years.

The fact that students of human ecology fall in two groups, viz., those who study large units in their geographic surroundings and those who study details of small social groups in the hope that the small groupings may be built together into larger ones, should not be permitted to hinder studies in this complex field. It must be recognized that man is very poor material to use for such investigation and no other organism can easily be substituted. His culture is often modified more by those tabus which have grown up out of his fears of death or physical injury, his shyness, and fear of loss of property or privilege, etc., than by the physical environment. These tabus have been crystallized and accentuated by certain of the pack or tribe leaders who could retain and increase their power over the others of the group and thereby increase their own advantage. At first it was perhaps illustrated by tabus about eating portions of the game caught in community hunts and is finally illustrated by modern advertisements of cures for halitosis.

Man-dominated communities are not in the proper field of the writer because the dominance is brought about by cultural activities rather than physiological superiority. In the field of animal ecology he has, however, chosen the geographical or large-unit viewpoint because the entire community possesses potentialities and properties not possessed by the smaller units taken separately.

---

[3]Physiological experiments have most commonly been concerned with the function of internal parts. Experiments even when concerned with the organism as a whole have nearly always been conducted under constant conditions in imitation of the successful sciences of physics and chemistry. The conservative way in which these constant temperatures have been followed is characteristic of the social-psychological makeup of man. Until investigators realize that the physical factors of the environment are always changing, and have a better knowledge of the manner in which animals live through these changes, progress will be slow.

The writer's experiments set up on the codling moth in 1917 were one of the early attempts, possibly the first, to simulate the natural day to night change in temperature, moisture, and light in an idealized way. These experiments demonstrated the retarding effect of constant temperatures and bridged the gap between the natural changes in physical conditions and the constant temperature experiments.

Bibliography

BAILEY, V. 1931. Mammals of New Mexico. *U. S. Dept. Agric. Biol. Survey, North Amer. Fauna,* No. 53. Pp. 412.

DAVIDSON, F. A. 1927. Relation of taurine cattle to climate. *Econ. Geog.,* **3**, 466-485.

DAVIS, F. M. 1923. Quantitative studies of the fauna of the sea bottom: I. Preliminary investigation of the Dogger Bank. *Min. Agric. & Fish., Fisheries Investigations,* Ser. 2, **6**, 1-54.

————. 1925. Quantitative studies of the fauna of the sea bottom: II. Results of investigations in the Southern North Sea. *Min. Agric. & Fish., Fisheries Investigations,* Ser. 2, **8**, 1-50.

GOLDENWEISER, A. A. 1916. Culture and environment. *Amer. J. Sociol.,* **31**, 628-633.

HILLER, E. T. 1933. Principles of sociology. New York: Harper. Pp. xix+ 661. (See esp. Chap. 15.)

HUNTINGTON, E. 1915. Civilization and climate. New Haven, Conn.: Yale Univ. Press. Pp. xii+333.

————. 1919. World power and evolution. New Haven, Conn.: Yale Univ. Press. Pp. 287.

JOHNSON, E. L. 1924. Relation of sheep to climate. *J. Agric. Res.,* **29**, 491-500.

MCKENZIE, R. D. 1925. The ecological approach to the study of the human community. Chap. 3 in *The city,* by R. E. Park and E. W. Burgess. Chicago: Univ. Chicago Press. Pp. 63-79.

OLSON, S. F. 1932. The life history of the timber wolf and the coyote. Thesis, Univ. Ill. Library.

PIERCE, W. D. 1916. A new interpretation of the relationships of temperature and humidity to insect development. *J. Agric. Res.,* **5**, 1183-1191.

READ, C. 1920. The origin of man and his superstitions. Cambridge, England: Univ. Press. Pp. 250.

SHELFORD, V. E. 1911. Physiological animal geography. *J. Morphol.,* **22**, 551-618.

————. 1929. Laboratory and field ecology. Baltimore: Williams & Wilkins. Pp. xii+608. (See esp. Chaps. 2, 3, 11, and 15.)

————. 1930. Phenology and one of its modern descendants. *Quar. Rev. Biol.,* **5**, 217-226.

————. 1931a. An experimental and observational study of the chinch bug in relation to climate and weather. *Bull. Ill. N. H. Survey,* **19**, 487-547.

————. 1931b. Some concepts of bioecology. *Ecology,* **12**, 455-467.

————. 1932. The basic principles of the classification of communities and the use of terms. *Ecology,* **13**, 105-120.

SOROKIN, P. 1928. Contemporary sociological theories. New York: Harper. Pp. 808.

STEGGERDA, M. 1929. Relations of domestic fowls to climate. *Ecology,* **10**, 337-342.

TAYLOR, G. 1927. Environment and race. London: Oxford Univ. Press. Pp. 369.

THOMAS, F. 1925. The environmental basis of society. New York: Century. Pp. vii+336.